Some Aspects of
INTERNAL IRRADIATION

Some Aspects of
INTERNAL
IRRADIATION

Proceedings of a Symposium held at
The Homestead, Heber, Utah, 8-11 May 1961

Edited by

THOMAS F. DOUGHERTY

WEBSTER S. S. JEE

CHARLES W. MAYS

BETSY J. STOVER

University of Utah College of Medicine.
Salt Lake City, Utah, U.S.A.

SYMPOSIUM PUBLICATIONS DIVISION

P E R G A M O N   P R E S S

NEW YORK · OXFORD · LONDON · PARIS

1962

96662

574.19
D732

PERGAMON PRESS INC.
122 East 55th Street, New York, 22 N. Y.

PERGAMON PRESS LTD.
Headington Hill Hall, Oxford
4 & 5 Fitzroy Square, London W.1

GAUTHIER-VILLARS
55 Quai des Grands-Augustins, Paris 6

PERGAMON PRESS G.m.b.H.
Kaiserstrasse 75, Frankfurt am Main

Copyright © 1962
Pergamon Press Ltd.

Library of Congress Card Number 62-19279

Printed in Poland to the order of PWN—Polish Scientific Publishers
by the Scientific-Technical Printing House (DRP), Warsaw

PREFACE

MOST of the symposia on effects of irradiation have been concerned primarily with the effects of external radiation, particularly X-irradiation. There are few reviews concerning the pathological changes induced by internal irradiation. The papers presented in this volume are a written record of a symposium, *Some Aspects of Internal Irradiation,* which was held at Heber, Utah, May 8–11, 1961.

The aim of this symposium was to bring together some of the individuals who have been interested for a long period of time in the pathological effects of internal emitters. The participants presented original data and took the opportunity to discuss the interrelationships of several aspects of the unique problems of internally deposited radionuclides. This discussion has been edited by both the discussants and the editors.

Certain of the invited participants presented material which aimed at the fundamental mechanisms by which irradiation might induce malignancy. Two indirect mechanisms were considered. One was concerned with the influence of irradiation on endocrine-mediated carcinogenesis and the other was the interrelationship between radiation and viral carcinogenesis.

One of the basic differences between external and internal irradiation is the duration of the radiation and the range of the particles emitted. Internally deposited radionuclides may have low penetrating radiation, as in the case of alpha particles, but, due to the biological circumstances involved, may expose tissue for a long period due to the long half-life of the radionuclide. Each, then, of the internally deposited radionuclides has its peculiar radiation and metabolic characteristics (absorption, fate and excretion) as an element in a given biological system. Therefore, the radiation dose delivered cannot be considered as a purely physical problem, but the particular biological system must also be considered. As a corollary to this unique situation, the pathological effects of such internal deposition depend, again, on the location of the radionuclide. This, in turn, is dependent upon the mechanisms by which the element is metabolized. It is impossible to determine dose/response relationship of internally deposited radionuclides without considering the unique biological circumstances which occur in their metabolism. The rates at which internally deposited radionuclides are excreted may change with variations in the internal environment. These variations may occur as a result of adaptation to the external environment. Therefore, dose/response relationships for any particular end point measured may change, due to the imposition of a variety of stressful circumstances.

In addition to the problems of metabolism and of dosimetry, a variety of pathological endpoints are considered. A dose/response relationship is observed for many hematological and biochemical alterations, bone pathology, alterations in the central nervous system and eyes, and also to the general overall change in rate of the aging process. It should be noted in relation to these endpoints that a lethal dose is actually due to the sum of several different pathological events which lead to death. This is different for radiation from the concept of toxicity where it applies to a single unique effect, e.g. a toxin or chemical poison. Dose response should be related, then, to the extent of a particular pathological event rather than to lethality in general. This emphasizes the fact that pathological changes vary in degree of severity and reversibility and each is related to a localized dose in the case of internal emitters.

Finally, some indirect mechanisms by which pathological changes of a wide variety may be induced are also discussed by several authors. For example, the production of indirect pathological changes could occur through the alteration in the minute vasculature of various organs and tissues. Therefore, a variety of radiation effects may be manifested through this indirect mechanism. The possibility that spontaneous fracturing, due to some internally deposited radionuclides such as radium, may be due to loss of bone vasculature is also considered by one of the authors. An indirect effect on certain pathological changes may also be related to the importance of the role played by radiation in altering hormonal balance. This altered hormonal balance may influence carcinogenesis and also a variety of other biochemical, hematological and structural changes in tissues and organs.

Those of us in the Radiobiology Division of the Department of Anatomy, University of Utah College of Medicine, wish particularly to thank all the participants for their scientific contributions, and I wish to thank the senior staff of the Radiobiology Division who not only presented their work, but also played an important part in the organization of the symposium. In addition, we wish to thank those who helped plan the symposium, particularly Mrs. Anne Clarke, who was the executive secretary of the symposium and editorial board. Charlotte Emmons, Garth Westenskow and David Taysum are due thanks for recording the discussion and the individual papers. Secretarial help was provided by Jo Anne Clayton, Mary Lou Horsley, and Rodney L. Jones. Finally, the editors deserve the thanks of all participants for reviewing the manuscripts as well as the discussion. The chairmen of the various sessions at the symposium were vital to the success of the symposium and their contribution is recognized by all. Finally, we wish to acknowledge the aid of the Office of Special Services of the Atomic Energy Commission for financial support of the symposium.

THOMAS F. DOUGHERTY

Heber, Utah

CONTENTS

PART I

EFFECTS OF INTERNAL IRRADIATION IN THE DOG

PART II

SOME BIOLOGICAL EFFECTS OF IRRADIATION

PART III

SOME ASPECTS OF Sr^{90} TOXICITY

PART IV

DOSIMETRY OF INTERNALLY DEPOSITED RADIONUCLIDES

PART V

THOROTRAST IN MAN

LIST OF PARTICIPANTS

ALLEN C. ANDERSEN Research Radiopathologist, Lecturer in Pathology and Principal Investigator for AEC Projects, School of Veterinary Medicine, University of California, Davis, California.

JAMES S. ARNOLD Pathologist and Co-director of Laboratories, Providence Hospital, Portland, Oregon.

DAVID R. ATHERTON Research Associate, Division of Radiobiology, University of Utah College of Medicine, Salt Lake City, Utah.

RENATO BASERGA Assistant Professor of Pathology, Department of Pathology, Northwestern University School of Medicine, Chicago 11, Illinois.

ROBERT C. BAXTER Senior Technical Associate in Radiation Biology, Department of Radiation Biology, University of Rochester, Rochester, New York.

DAVID L. BERLINER Associate Research Professor of Anatomy, Department of Anatomy, University of Utah College of Medicine, Salt Lake City 12, Utah.

MARTHA L. BERLINER Research Instructor in Anatomy, Department of Anatomy, University of Utah College of Medicine, Salt Lake City 12, Utah.

ROLF G. BJORNERSTEDT Research Associate, Department of Radiation Biology, University of Rochester, Rochester, New York.

HENRY A. BLAIR Professor of Physiology, Director, Department of Radiation Biology, University of Rochester, Rochester, New York.

LARRY W. BLAKE Research Assistant, Division of Radiobiology, Department of Anatomy, University of Utah College of Medicine, Salt Lake City 12, Utah.

LEO BUSTAD Manager, Experimental Animal Farm, Biology Laboratory, Hanford Laboratories, General Electric Company, Richland, Washington.

KENNETH R. BRIZZEE Associate Professor of Anatomy, Department of Anatomy, University of Utah College of Medicine, Salt Lake City 12, Utah.

GEORGE W. CASARETT Associate Professor of Radiation Biology, Chief, Radiation Pathology Section, Department of Radiation Biology, University of Rochester, Rochester 20, New York.

M. SUSAN CHESTERS   Research Assistant, Department of Medical Physics, The University of Leeds, The General Infirmary, Leeds 1, England.

WILLIAM R. CHRISTENSEN   Professor and Head, Department of Radiology, University of Utah College of Medicine, Salt Lake City 12, Utah.

WILLIAM J. CLARKE   Senior Scientist, Biological Laboratory, Hanford Laboratories, General Electric Company, Richland, Washington.

WALTER D. CLAUS   Special Assistant of Director, Division of Biology and Medicine, U. S. Atomic Energy Commission, Washington 25, D. C.

TERENCE H. COCHRAN   Pathologist, Co-director of Laboratories, Providence Hospital, Portland, Oregon.

HAROLD D. COPP   Professor of Physiology and Head, Department of Physiology, University of British Columbia, Vancouver 8, Canada.

NORMAN L. DOCKUM   Biology Scientist, Biological Analyses, Biological Laboratory, Hanford Laboratories, General Electric Company, Richland, Washington.

JEAN H. DOUGHERTY   Head, Hematology Section, Research Instructor in Pathology, Division of Radiobiology, Department of Anatomy, University of Utah College of Medicine, Salt Lake City 12, Utah.

THOMAS F. DOUGHERTY   Professor of Anatomy and Head, Department of Anatomy; Director, Division of Radiobiology, University of Utah College of Medicine, Salt Lake City 12, Utah.

ROBERT A. DUDLEY   First Officer, Division of Isotopes, International Atomic Energy Agency, Kaerntnerring, Vienna 1, Austria.

PATRICIA W. DURBIN   Lecturer in Medical Physics, Division of Biology and Medicine, Lawrence Radiation Laboratory, University of California, Berkeley 4, California.

JAMES A. ENGLISH   Professor of Oral Biology; Dean, School of Dentistry, University of Buffalo, Buffalo 14, New York.

F. GAYNOR EVANS   Professor of Anatomy, Department of Anatomy, University of Michigan, Ann Arbor, Michigan.

ROBLEY D. EVANS   Professor of Physics, Department of Physics, Massachusetts Institute of Technology, Cambridge 39, Massachusetts.

MOGENS FABER   Professor, University of Copenhagen, Director, Finsenlaboratoriet, Strandboulevard 49, Copenhagen, Denmark.

MIRIAM P. FINKEL   Associate Biologist, Division of Biology and Medicine, Argonne National Laboratory, 9700 South Cass Avenue, Argonne, Illinois.

JACOB FURTH   Professor of Pathology, Department of Pathology, Director of Laboratories, Francis Delafield Hospital, New York 32, New York.

MARVIN GOLDMAN   Associate Research Radiobiologist, School of Veterinary Medicine, University of California, Davis, California.

HAROLD GOLDTHORPE   Head, Biochemistry Section, Division of Radiobiology, Professor of Biochemistry, University of Utah College of Medicine, Salt Lake City 12, Utah.

WANDA M. HAMMER   Research Assistant, Division of Radiobiology, Department of Anatomy, University of Utah College of Medicine, Salt Lake City 12, Utah.

ROBERT J. HASTERLIK   Professor of Medicine, Associate Director, Argonne Cancer Research Hospital, 950 East 59th Street, Chicago 37, Illinois,

JOHN B. HURSH   Professor of Radiation Biology, Assistant Chief, Division of Radiology and Biophysics, University of Rochester, Rochester. New York.

LYLE A. JACOBS   Research Assistant, Department of Anatomy, University of Utah College of Medicine, Salt Lake City, Utah.

WEBSTER S. S. JEE   Head, Bone Section, Division of Radiobiology, Assistant Professor of Anatomy, University of Utah College of Medicine, Salt Lake City 12, Utah.

JAY B. JENSEN   Research Assistant, Division of Radiobiology, Department of Anatomy, University of Utah College of Medicine, Salt Lake City 12, Utah.

HORTON A. JOHNSON   Assistant Professor of Pathology, Department of Pathology, University of Utah College of Medicine, Salt Lake City 12, Utah.

HARDIN B. JONES   Professor of Medical Physics and Physiology, Donner Laboratories, University of California, Berkeley 4, California.

HENRY S. KAPLAN   Professor of Radiology and Executive, Department of Radiology, Stanford University School of Medicine, Palo Alto, California.

NORMAN F. KEMBER   Lecturer, Department of Medical Physics, Royal Free Hospital School of Medicine, 8, Hunter Street, London, W. C. 1. England.

XENIA KHARETCHKO   Research Instructor, Department of Anatomy, University of Utah College of Medicine, Salt Lake City 12, Utah.

HARRY A. KORNBERG   Manager, Biological Laboratory, Hanford Laboratories, General Electric Company, Richland, Washington.

LEONARD F. LAMERTON   Professor of Biophysics Applied to Medicine, Institute of Cancer Research, Royal Cancer Hospital, Department of Physics, Downs Branch, Clifton Avenue, Belmont, near Sutton, Surrey, England.

SAMUEL LESHER   Associate Biologist, Division of Biological Sciences, Argonne National Laboratories, 9700 South Cass Avenue, Argonne, Illinois.

HENRY F. LUCAS   Associate Chemist, Division of Radiological Physics, Argonne National Laboratory, 9700 South Cass Avenue, Argonne, Illinois.

LEONIDAS D. MARINELLI   Associate Director, Division of Radiological Physics, Argonne National Laboratory, 9700 South Cass Avenue, Argonne, Illinois.

CHARLES W. MAYS   Head, Physics Section, Division of Radiobiology, Department of Anatomy, University of Utah College of Medicine, Salt Lake City 12, Utah.

ROGER O. MCCLELLAN   Scientist, Experimental Animal Farm, Biological Laboratories, General Electric Company, Richland, Washington.

JAMES R. MCKENNEY   Biological Scientist, Experimental Animal Farm, Biological Laboratory, Hanford Laboratory, General Electric Company, Richland, Washington.

RENON S. MICAL   Research Assistant, Division of Radiobiology, University of Utah College of Medicine, Salt Lake City 12, Utah.

ROBIN H. MOLE   Deputy Director, Medical Research Council, Radiobiological Research Unit, Harwell, Didcot, Berks, England.

KARL Z. MORGAN   Director, Division of Health Physics, Oak Ridge National Laboratory, Oak Ridge, Tennessee.

BETTY JANE MULRYAN   Technical Assistant in Radiation Biology, Department of Radiation Biology, University of Rochester, Rochester, New York.

PIERRE F. NIZZA   Dr. Veterinary Medicine, French AEC, Sharp B. P. No. 6, Foutenay aux Roses, France.

WILLIAM P. NORRIS   Associate Biologist, Division of Biology of Medical Research, Argonne National Laboratory, 9700 South Cass Avenue, Argonne, Illinois.

THEODORE T. O'DELL, JR. Associate Biologist, Biology Division, Oak Ridge National Laboratories, Oak Ridge, Tennessee.

MAUREEN OWEN Physicist, Medical Research Council, Bone-Seeking Isotopes Research Unit, The Churchill Hospital, Headington, Oxford, England.

WILLIAM W. PARMLEY Division of Radiobiology, Department of Anatomy, University of Utah College of Medicine, Salt Lake City 12, Utah.

ROBERT D. RAY Professor of Orthopedics, Head, Department of Orthopedic Surgery, University of Illinois, Chicago, Illinois.

CARL E. REHFELD Associate Veterinarian, Division of Biological and Medical Research, Argonne National Laboratory, 9700 South Cass Avenue, Argonne, Illinois.

ROBERT E. ROWLAND Associate Physicist, Division of Radiological Physics, Argonne National Laboratory, 9700 South Cass Avenue, Argonne, Illinois.

MARTIN A. RUSHTON Professor of Dental Medicine and Head, Department of Dental Medicine, Guy's Hospital, London, S. E. 1, England.

GOTTLIEB L. SCHNEEBELI Research Associate, Department of Anatomy, University of Utah College of Medicine, Salt Lake City 12, Utah.

CARLISLE C. SMITH Assistant Professor of Radiology, Department of Radiology, University of Utah College of Medicine, Salt Lake City 12, Utah.

WALTER S. SNYDER Assistant Director, Division of Health Physics, Oak Ridge National Laboratory, Oak Ridge, Tennessee.

F. W. SPIERS Professor and Head of Department of Medical Physics, The University of Leeds, The General Infirmary, Leeds 1, England.

BETSY J. STOVER Head, Chemistry Section, Associate Research Professor in Chemistry, Division of Radiobiology, University of Utah College of Medicine, Salt Lake City 12, Utah.

GLENN N. TAYLOR Head, Clinic Section, Division of Radiobiology, Department of Anatomy, University of Utah College of Medicine, Salt Lake City 12, Utah

DAVID TAYSUM Research Associate, Division of Radiobiology, Department of Anatomy, University of Utah College of Medicine, Salt Lake City 12, Utah.

LAWRENCE W. TUTTLE Associate Professor of Radiation Biology, Department of Radiation Biology, Research Associate in Radiology, University of Rochester, Rochester, New York.

JANET A. TWENTE   Research Associate, Division of Radiobiology, University of Utah College of Medicine, Salt Lake City 12, Utah.

BURTON E. VAUGHAN   Assistant Branch Head of Biophysics, U. S. Naval Radiation Defense Laboratory, San Francisco, California.

JANET VAUGHAN   Director, Medical Research Council, Bone-Seeking Isotopes Research Unit, Churchill Hospital, Oxford, England.

SHIELDS WARREN   Professor of Pathology, Harvard Medical School, Cancer Research Institute, New England Deaconess Hospital, 194 Pilgrim Road, Boston 15, Massachusetts.

PIERRE WENGER   Professor and Director, Institut du Radium de Geneve, Geneva, Switzerland.

K. YOKORU   Research Associate, Department of Pathology, Francis Delafield Hospital, Columbia University, 99 Ft. Washington Avenue, New York 32, New York.

PART I

EFFECTS OF INTERNAL IRRADIATION IN THE DOG

STUDY OF THE LONG TERM BIOLOGICAL EFFECTS OF INTERNAL IRRADIATION IN ADULT BEAGLES

T. F. DOUGHERTY

Radiobiology Division of the Department of Anatomy,
University of Utah College of Medicine,
Salt Lake City, Utah

THE basic program of the Radiobiology Division of the Department of Anatomy, University of Utah, is a comparative study of the biological effects in adult beagles of the internal irradiation resulting from five different radionuclides. They are Ra^{226}, Pu^{239}, Ra^{228}, Th^{228}, and Sr^{90}. Dr. T. F. Dougherty has been director of the laboratory since 1955. He succeeded Dr. J. Z. Bowers who was the first director (1950–55). Present and past members of the senior staff and their areas of responsibility are listed below:

Section	Head
Administration	T. F. Dougherty
Biochemistry	H. C. Goldthorpe
Bone and Autoradiography	W. S. S. Jee
Chemistry	B. J. Stover
Clinic	G. N. Taylor
Hematology	J. H. Dougherty
Neuroanatomy	K. R. Brizzee
Pathology	H. A. Johnson
Physics	C. W. Mays
Radiology	W. R. Christensen

Former section heads who have contributed much to the program are the following:

Bone	J. S. Arnold
Business Manager	C. N. Stover, Jr.
Clinic	R. C. Bay
Clinic	C. E. Rehfeld
Pathology	T. H. Cochran
Physics	M. A. Van Dilla

The initial plans, made in 1949–50, were to compare the effects of Pu^{239} and Ra^{226} in dogs. The reason was that utilization of Pu^{239} as a source of nuclear energy was proceeding rapidly, and plutonium production was becoming an important industry. Because of prior experience with radium

3

poisoning, the potential of plutonium as an industrial hazard was recognized during the early years of plutonium production. Consequently,
studies were done to determine relative toxicities of Pu^{239} and Ra^{226} in
mice, rabbits, and rats. This information, in conjunction with the knowledge of the effect of Ra^{226} in humans and the observed differences in human and rodent metabolism of the two radionuclides and their decay
products, was used to establish the tolerance value of 0.04 μc Pu^{239} as
compared with 0.1 μc for Ra^{226}; i.e. in terms of μc, plutonium was considered 2.5 times as damaging to human beings.

The original experiment was [designed ⌐mainly ⌐by] A. M. Brues,
R. D. Evans, W. L. Langham, J. Z. Bowers, W. D. Claus and E. Brandt,
and utilizes the beagle which has a longer lifespan and a skeleton more
like that of a human than a rodent. At that time, the ambiguous role of
Ra^{228} ($MsTh_1$) and Th^{228} (RdTh) in the interpretation of human radium
poisoning data was reconsidered, and these two radionuclides were included in our comparative study. Later, Sr^{90} was added when it attracted
world-wide attention as an environmental hazard.

The experimental plan as it now exists is given in Table 1. There we
have given the injected $\mu c/kg$ for the six or seven dose levels of each of
the five radionuclides, and the numbers of dogs to be injected at each
dose level. Note that all of our planned Ra^{226}, Pu^{239}, and Sr^{90} dogs have
been injected, but that some of the Ra^{228} and Th^{228} dogs have not yet
been injected. We have also tabulated, in each of these categories, the
number of dead dogs. Each dog receives a single intravenous injection
at about 18 months of age. At this age the epiphyses of all bones are fused
except those of the ribs. They are usually injected in a group of six or
seven, one at each dose level of a given radionuclide plus one control.
The large number of dogs to be maintained over many years and the rather
small size of the laboratory have made it necessary to introduce the dogs
into the experiment over a long period of time. The first six dogs were
injected December 1, 1952, and we anticipate that the injection plan given
in Table 1 will be completed in a few years. In general, the Ra^{226} and Pu^{239}
dogs were injected earliest, and the Sr^{90} dogs later than most of the others.
The Ra^{228} and Th^{228} injections are being spread over the greatest period
of time. Our general clinical policy is to provide the dogs with the best
possible medical care, with the one exception that, if the treatment would
interfere with one of the important endpoints of the study, then it is not
carried out.

The dose levels are related to the human m.p.l. for Ra^{226} and each has
a code number. The five dose levels designated by integers are those

TABLE 1

Summary of Basic Experiment as of March 31, 1961

A. All planned Ra^{226}, Pu^{239} and Sr^{90} dogs have been injected

Dose level code No.	Ra^{226}			Pu^{239}			Sr^{90}		
	Inj. (μc/kg)	No. of dogs		Inj. (μc/kg)	No. of dogs		Inj. (μc/kg)	No. of dogs	
		inj.	dead		inj.	dead		inj.	dead
5	10	10	10	2·8	9	9	100	12	1
4	3·2	12	11	0·90	12	12	32	12	0
3	1·1	12	9	0·30	12	12	11	12	0
2	0·34	12	0	0·096	12	7	3·4	12	0
1·7	0·17	12	1	0·048	12	0	1·7	12	0
1	0·057	12	1	0·016	12	0	0·57	12	0
0	0·000	12	2	0·000	12	1	0·00	12	0

B. Some of the planned Ra^{228}(MsTh$_1$) and Th^{228}(RdTh) dogs have not yet been injected

Dose level code No.	Ra^{228}				Th^{228}			
	Inj. (μc/kg)	No. of dogs			Inj. (μc/kg)	No. of dogs		
		planned	inj.	dead		planned	inj.	dead
5	10	7	7	7	2·8	2	2	2
4	3·2	7	7	7	0·90	4	4	4
3	1·1	12	9	5	0·30	12	7	4
2	0·34	12	9	3	0·096	12	7	4
1·7	0·17	12	8	0	—	—	–	–
1·5	—	—	–	–	0·032	12	7	1
1	0·057	12	9	0	0·016	12	7	0
0·5	0·019	6	2	0	0·0051	12	7	1
0·2	—	—	–	–	0·0017	8	3	0
0	0·000	12	9	0	0·0000	12	7	0

C. Numbers of dogs planned, injected and dead by nuclide

Nuclide	Planned	Fraction injected	Fraction dead
Ra^{226}	82	82/82 = 1·00	33/82 = 0·40
Pu^{239}	81	81/81 = 1·00	41/81 = 0·51
Ra^{228}	80	60/80 = 0·75	22/80 = 0·28
Th^{228}	86	51/86 = 0·59	16/86 = 0·19
Sr^{90}	84	84/84 = 1·00	1/84 = 0·01
All	413	358/413 = 0·87	113/413 = 0·27

Dogs which were either lost accidently or deemed unfit and which were later replaced have not been included.

specified at the early meetings of the consultants, and those designated by non-integers have been added by the laboratory staff. Since these dose levels were originally specified as "retained" doses, the actual injected doses are 4 times the desired "retained" doses of Ra^{226}, Ra^{228} ($MsTh_1$), and Sr^{90}, and 1·11 times the desired "retained" doses of Pu^{239} and Th^{228} (RdTh).*

The desired "retained" $\mu c/kg$ are the same for all the radionuclides except Sr^{90}, in which case they are greater by a factor of 10. Dose level 1 is the basis of the scheme, and it is 10 times the maximum permissible Ra^{226} activity/kg in man. Level 1 is $10 \times \dfrac{0 \cdot 1 \; \mu c \; Ra^{226}}{70 \; kg \; man} = 0 \cdot 0143 \; \mu c/kg$.

All other dose levels are simple multiples of level 1 as shown on the following list:

Level 0·2 is 1/9 of level 1
Level 0·5 is 1/3 of level 1
Level 1·5 is 2 times level 1
Level 1·7 is 3 times level 1
Level 2 is 6 times level 1
Level 3 is 18 times level 1
Level 4 is 54 times level 1
Level 5 is 162 times level 1

The numbering system for the dogs has been built around the injection program and serves as a code to describe each dog's place in the experiment. The first letter tells the sex (M, male; F, female). M or F is followed by a number which denotes chronological order of groups. Next comes a code letter for the radionuclide (R for Ra^{226}, P for Pu^{239}, M for Ra^{228}, T for Th^{228}, and S for Sr^{90}). The final number is the dose level number as defined above and with 0 meaning control.

Examples: M1R5 is a male animal in the first radium group at the highest dose level.

---

*Since radioactive decay and excretion occur continuously, the term "retained" dose is obviously meaningless unless the time after injection is specified. Our present measurements indicate that:

average Ra^{226} retention = 0·25 after 330 days
average Pu^{239} retention = 0·90 after 6 days
average Ra^{228} retention = 0·25 after 235 days
average Th^{228} retention = 0·90 after 6 days
average Sr^{90} retention = 0·25 after 150 days

STUDIES OF THE RETENTION AND DISTRIBUTION OF Ra^{226}, Pu^{239}, Ra^{228}, (MsTh$_1$), Th^{228}, (RdTh), AND Sr^{90} IN ADULT BEAGLES

BETSY J. STOVER, D. R. ATHERTON and C. W. MAYS

Radiobiology Division, Department of Anatomy,
University of Utah College of Medicine,
Salt Lake City, Utah

INTRODUCTION

CONCURRENTLY with the awareness of the need for a comparison of biological effects of Pu^{239} and Ra^{226} in an animal more like man than a rodent is, which subsequently led to the establishment of this laboratory, came recognition of the dearth of accurate data on the retention and distribution of these radionuclides. Without this information it was difficult indeed to make meaningful comparisons of observed biological effects. Accordingly, a strong program to study retention and distribution of the several radionuclides of our study was established very early in the history of this laboratory. In this paper we attempt to summarize the most generally applicable results of a decade's work. The inspiration for these lengthy (and at times tedious) studies is the belief that there exist relationships between the onset and/or development of biological effects and functions of radiation dose rate and time. We anticipate a high degree of empiricism in our analyses of these relationships, but we remember that empirical correlations are often the springboard to theoretical explanation.

The retention and distribution measurements are primarily oriented to ultimate expression as radiation dose rates, and we herewith define "average radiation dose rate" $\equiv$ rate of energy dissipation per gram of tissue. Radiation dose rate will be employed in this meaning throughout this paper, and we have elected to use rads per day as the unit (1 rad = 100 erg/g tissue). We do recognize the limitations of using average radiation dose rates in face of the overwhelming evidence of the nonuniformity of the irradiation in these animals, which is discussed extensively in the following paper. One of our future objectives is the determination of the distribution of the magnitudes of the dose rates and its relationship to the average rate.

Determination of the average radiation dose rates requires knowledge of three kinds: the nuclear properties of the radionuclides, their chemical or extranuclear properties, and the biological system into which the

7

radionuclide is introduced, which in this study is the young adult beagle.

The nuclear properties of the five radionuclides and their decay products, when pertinent, are summarized in Table 1. [1,2] Ra^{226} has a long half-period, and for purposes of our study it decays at a constant rate. Ra^{226} emits an alpha particle to become Rn^{222} which is also an alpha emitter of 3·82 days half-period, and it is followed by several shorter-lived nuclides

TABLE 1

Nuclear Data

Radionuclide	Half-period	Average energy per disintegration (in MeV)			
		Recoil	Alpha	Beta	Gamma
Pu^{239}	24,300 y	0·09	5·14	—	—
Ra^{226}	1,622 y	0·09	4·77	—	0·01
Rn^{222}	3·82 day	0·10	5·49	—	—
Po^{218}	3·05 min	0·11	6·00	—	—
Pb^{214}	26·8 min	—	—	0·24	0·28
Bi^{214}	19·8 min	—	—	0·59	1·60
Po^{014}	$1·64 \times 10^{-4}$ sec	0·15	7·68	—	—
Pb^{210}	19·4 y	—	—	0·01	0·04
Bi^{910}	5·0 day	—	—	0·31	—
Po^{210}	138·4 day	0·10	5·30	—	—
Ra^{228}	5·8 y	—	—	0·01	—
Ac^{228}	6·13 hr	—	—	0·41	0·96
Th^{228}	1·91 y	0·10	5·40	—	0·02
Ra^{224}	3·64 day	0·10	5·67	—	0·01
Tn^{220}	51·5 sec	0·12	6·28	—	—
Po^{216}	0·158 sec	0·13	6·77	—	—
Pb^{212}	10·64 hr	—	—	0·12	0·19
Bi^{212}	60·5 min	0·04	2·04	0·40	0·70
Po^{212}, Tl^{208}	$3·04 \times 10^{-7}$ sec, 3·1 min	0·11	5·80	0·19	1·16
Sr^{90}	27·8 y	—	—	0·20	—
Y^{90}	64·2 hr	—	—	0·93	—

The branched decay of Bi^{212} is as follows:

$$63·8\% \ Bi^{212} \xrightarrow[1·04 \ \gamma]{0·62 \ \beta} Po^{212} \xrightarrow[0·00 \ \gamma]{8·78 \ \alpha} Pb^{208}$$

$$36·2\% \ Bi^{212} \xrightarrow[0·04 \ \gamma]{6·05 \ \alpha} Tl^{208} \xrightarrow[3·40 \ \gamma]{0·56 \ \beta} Pb^{208}$$

leading to Pb^{210} with a 19·4 y half-period. Thus to gain meaningful information on radiation dose rates from Ra^{226}, we must not only document the retention and distribution of the parent nuclide, but we must know where Rn^{222} and the subsequent shorter half-period decay products undergo decay. Also we must determine what happens to Pb^{210} and its decay products, although this is of lesser importance. With respect to decay products, Pu^{239} is the simplest of our five radionuclides in that it decays to U^{235} which has a very long half-period. Thus we need only consider Pu^{239}.

We recognized very early that Ra^{228} would be the most complicated one of the five because of its decay products. Although we have done a great deal of work to date on Ra^{228}, we report very little of it in this paper. The reason is that studies by Mays et al. at this laboratory[2] have shown that the value 6·7 y for the Ra^{228} half-period is in error and that the value actually should be about 5·8 y. Consequently, the work we have done requires considerable revision before it attains a comparable degree of meaningfulness. We should also note that, in contrast with Ra^{226} and Pu^{239}, the half-period of Ra^{228} is short enough so that decrease by physical decay must be considered in the dose rate determination. Ra^{228} decays by beta emission, and there follow five alpha and three beta transitions, all of shorter half-period, before a stable nuclide is reached. The first and longest-lived of the alpha emitters is Th^{228}, and it is also one of the five radionuclides which we inject. Thus we are doing two studies of the thorium (4n) decay series, one beginning at Ra^{228} and one at Th^{228}. Since the Th^{228} half-period is just 1·9 y, there will be a significant decrease in its radiation dose rates as a consequence of radioactive decay. In contrast, the radiation dose rate resulting from Ra^{228} will increase over the first several years as a consequence of the buildup of Th^{228}, and then it will decrease. Important decay products in this series which must be measured are Ra^{224}, Tn^{220}, Pb^{212}, and Bi^{212}. The fifth nuclide in our study is Sr^{90} which decays by beta emission to Y^{90} which is also a beta emitter. The half-period of Sr^{90} is 27·8 y and thus radioactive decay will have some effect on the change of radiation dose rate with time.

In considering the chemical properties of these radionuclides we note that Sr^{90} and the three radium isotopes are alkaline earths and physiological analogues of calcium. Since the strontium ion is more nearly the size of the calcium ion, we can anticipate greater similarity between strontium and calcium than between radium and calcium. The alkaline earths exhibit just one valence state in aqueous solution and it is the divalent state. The other two parent nuclides, Th^{228} and Pu^{239}, are isotopes of actinide elements. Thorium, the first member of the actinide series, binds its first 5f electron fairly loosely so that the tetravalent state is the only stable one in aqueous solution. Plutonium presents quite a different problem. It is unique among the 103 known elements in that it has four valence states, all of which can co-exist in significant amounts in aqueous solution. The major portion of the Pu^{239} given the beagles is in the +4 state. In general, the small size and the many orbitals available for bonding of tetravalent thorium and plutonium result in formation of complex ions and molecules. In sufficient quantity, both elements are insoluble at physiological pH and form a variety of insoluble phosphates. At that pH both undergo extensive hydrolysis and both will form oxygen-linked polymers. The thorium polymer is more labile than that of plutonium.[3] Plutonium is the smaller of the two tetravalent ions, which, in general, results in greater stability of plutonium complexes.

Some general aspects of the chemistry of some of the decay products are as follows. Rn^{222} and Tn^{220} are isotopes of the inert gas radon, and they form no strong chemical bonds. Yttrium and actinium are trivalent in aqueous solution, in sufficient amounts they are insoluble at physiological pH, they form insoluble phosphate compounds, and in general, have a greater tendency to form complex ions than the divalent cations of the alkaline earth family but a lesser tendency than thorium and plutonium. The +3 yttrium ion is very nearly the same size as the +2 calcium ion. Lead exhibits both divalent and tetravalent states with the divalent occuring more frequently in aqueous solution. Since it is a transition element, its chemical properties differ from those of the alkaline earths. Bismuth also is multivalent, but the +3 state is the important one in aqueous solution. It is a member of Group V of the periodic table, while actinium and yttrium are members of Group III; thus +3 bismuth differs chemically from +3 yttrium and actinium. For example, there is a greater tendency for bismuth to hydrolyze.

MATERIALS AND METHODS

Young adult beagles (14 to 20 months of age with but few exceptions) are given a single intravenous injection of a predetermined amount of one of the five radionuclides. Approximately 9 ml of a solution of the radionuclide in a citric acid, sodium citrate buffer (pH = 3·5 and 0·08 m in total citrate) are injected. The choice of a citrate buffer as an injection vehicle is a consequence of the unique chemistry of plutonium, which is discussed above. To obtain a solution suitable for intravenous injection in which Pu^{239} is primarily tetravalent, we have employed a procedure in which the final step is complexing with citrate.[4] Merely for consistency all the radionuclides have been administered in the same diluting fluid. A separate solution is prepared for each dog and a duplicate dose is measured. It is called the injection standard. The dogs are confined in metabolism cages one to two weeks prior to and three weeks following injection, and then they are returned to their outdoor runs. They are brought back to the cages as needed. Interim excreta collections are made over a period of four days. The methods of radiochemical analysis and *in vivo* measurement which we have employed are now widely used. The reader who desires details should consult references. [4, 5, 6, 7, 8, 9, 10, 11]

RESULTS

In the following paragraphs we compare the biological behavior in adult beagles of the five radionuclides following a single intravenous injection.[4,7,8,11] The comparisons will be made for the first 1000 days following injection. In Fig. 1 the concentrations in plasma during

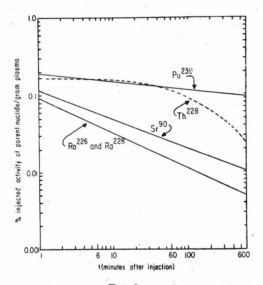

FIG. 1.

The decrease in plasma concentration of Ra^{226}, Ra^{228}, Pu^{239}, Th^{228}, and Sr^{90} during the first ten hours following a single intravenous injection.

the first ten hours after injection are shown. The results for Ra^{226} and Ra^{228} are not essentially different, and the radium concentrations are seen to be lower during the interval 1 min to 10 hr than those of the other three. The rate at which the Sr^{90} concentration decreases is almost the same as that of the radium isotopes but the concentration is consistently higher.

The three alkaline earths decrease by about a factor of 20 during this interval. The concentrations of Pu^{239} and Th^{228} are higher and decrease more slowly. During the first hour after injection these two curves essentially coincide; then, Th^{228} decreases more rapidly than does Pu^{239}, which decreases only by a factor of two over this period. At ten hours the Th^{228} concentration has decreased to about 1/4 that of Pu^{239}, and it is then about twice as high as the Sr^{90} value at that time.

Further comparisons of the plasma concentration of the radionuclide are made in Table 2, which gives the values at 100 and 1000 days after injection.[4,7,8,11] The radium isotopes continue in lowest concentration, and Sr^{90}, while higher, still decreases at about the same rate. They decrease by a factor of about 17 over the interval, while Pu^{239} plasma concentration remains comparatively high and it decreases by only a factor of two during the entire interval. At 100 days the Th^{228} concentration is about 1/10 that of Pu^{239}, and during the interval decreases by about 1/3 biologically and by a similar amount by radioactive decay so that the effective decrease is about a factor of 9. We note that at 1000 days decay factors must also be included for Ra^{228} and Sr^{90}.

TABLE 2

Concentration in Plasma

(Fraction of injected nuclide/g plasma) $\times$ 10^6

Nuclide	$t = 100$ days	$t = 1000$ days
Ra^{226}	0·087	0·0050
Ra^{228}	0·087 $e^{-\lambda t} = 0·085$	0·0050 $e^{-\lambda t} = 0·0036$
Sr^{90}	0·16	0·0089 $e^{-\lambda t} = 0·0087$
Pu^{239}	1·9	0·97
Th^{228}	0·20 $e^{-\lambda t} = 0·18$	0·062 $e^{-\lambda t} = 0·023$

In Fig. 2 we compare the retention by beagles of the five radionuclides.[4,7,10,11] Both biological fractional retention and the effective fractional retention, in which the decay factor is included, have been plotted. The Pu^{239} and Th^{228} fractional retentions were derived from excretion studies, Ra^{226} fractional retention was determined by whole-body gamma-ray counting and radon exhalation, and that of Sr^{90} was determined by whole-body bremsstrahlung counting. The decrease in Pu^{239} retention is really very slight from 20 to 1000 days, since it drops from about 88 to 75 per cent in that period. The biological fractional retention of Th^{228} almost exactly parallels that of Pu^{239}. However, the short half-period of Th^{228} makes a very marked difference in the effective retention of the two. Fractional retention of Ra^{226} is considerably lower than that of Pu^{239}, and Ra^{228} retention differs because of radioactive decay. The fractional retention of Sr^{90} decreases at the same rate as that of Ra^{226}, but it is lower.

In addition to the *in vivo* determination of Ra^{226} and Sr^{90} retention, the urinary and fecal excretion of these two nuclides has also been studied. Thus we can relate retention and blood level. In Table 3 renal clearance

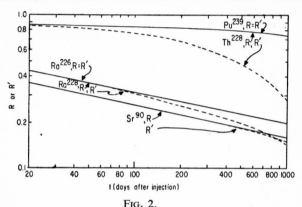

FIG. 2.

Biological fractional retention (R) and fractional retention $(R' = Re^{-\lambda t})$.

numbers for the five nuclides in units of g plasma per day are given, as well as the fecal to urinary excretion ratio.[4,7,8,11] With these two numbers the total clearance of the particular radionuclide can be calculated. The beagle kidneys excrete radium most effectively since they can clear 1700 g plasma per day. The value for Sr^{90} of about 1200 is a little lower, but is twice as high as that for Th^{228}. Pu^{239} excretion by the beagle kidney is ghastly inefficient; Pu^{239} has to make the circuit many, many times before the kidney will throw it away. The fecal to urinary excretion ratio for Ra^{226} is roughly equal to 2·5. The value for Pu^{239} initially is about 2·1 and decreases to about unity at 1000 days. The ratio for Th^{228} is roughly the mirror image of that for Pu^{239}. Initially urinary excretion predominates to give a ratio of 0·25 which gradually increases to about unity at 1000 days. Our

TABLE 3

Efficiency of Excretion

Nuclide	Ra^{226,228}	Pu^{239}	Th^{228}	Sr^{90}
Renal clearance (g plasma/day)	1700	40	600	1200
Fecal to urinary excretion ratio				
for first 22 days	2·5	2·1	0·25	1·4
for $t \sim$ 1000 days	2·5	1	1	1

data for Sr^{90}, soon after injection, give a value of 1·4, while later values are about unity.

Deposition of the alkaline earth nuclides in soft tissues is low. Approximately 1 per cent of the injected Ra^{226}, Ra^{228} and Sr^{90} is retained in soft tissues for a significant period of time. In the case of Pu^{239}, liver deposition is very important. The average initial fractional deposition is 28 per cent and the rate of decrease is slow. In our dogs the injected Pu^{239} divides itself between skeleton and the liver in roughly the proportions of the weight of the skeleton and liver, and deposition in both sites decreases very slowly. Consequently, the average dose rate to liver is about the same as that to the skeleton during the first three years.[4] Although the skeleton is the major site of deposition for Th^{228}, there is significant deposition in the kidneys and in the reticulo-endothelial system.[11] During the first few years after injection, the soft tissue deposition is depleted more rapidly than is the skeletal deposition.

TABLE 4

Concentrations of Radionuclides in Eyes and Plasma

Nuclide	Dog	Days since injection	Eye weight (g)	% Injected nuclide / g eye	% Injected nuclide / g plasma
Ra^{226}	T16R5	12	5·2	$3·7\times10^{-3}$	$1·2\times10^{-4}$
	M1R5	908	5	$3·0\times10^{-5}$	$7·6\times10^{-7}$
	F8R5	968	5·8	$2·5\times10^{-5}$	$1·0\times10^{-6}$
	F6R5	1015	5·5	$1·2\times10^{-6}$	$9·0\times10^{-7}$
	T1R5	1074	6·0	$5·4\times10^{-6}$	$3·9\times10^{-7}$
	M4R5	1091	4·7	$3·0\times10^{-5}$	$4·2\times10^{-7}$
	M5R5	1220	5·3	$9·7\times10^{-6}$	$5·9\times10^{-7}$
	M7R5	1288	4·8	$1·5\times10^{-5}$	$5·2\times10^{-7}$
	T2R5	1368	5·7	$1·3\times10^{-5}$	$5·8\times10^{-7}$
Pu^{239}	T18P5	217	8·1	$3·7\times10^{-4}$	$1·4\times10^{-4}$
	F6P5	1194	5·1	$2·8\times10^{-4}$	—
	M12P4	1462	5·8	$2·3\times10^{-4}$	$2·0\times10^{-5}$
	F2P4	1556	5·9	$3·4\times10^{-4}$	$7·5\times10^{-5}$
	M1P4	1724	5·1	$5·0\times10^{-4}$	$6·1\times10^{-5}$
Th^{228}	T6T4	651	5·6	$5·8\times10^{-4}$	$5·9\times10^{-6}$
	M2T2	1234	5·9	$6·3\times10^{-4}$	$1·2\times10^{-5}$
	M1T2	1282	5·6	$6·1\times10^{-4}$	$5·9\times10^{-6}$
Sr^{90}	T13S4(R)	8	6·0	$2·2\times10^{-4}$	$2·0\times10^{-4}$
	T13S4(L)	8	6·1	$3·0\times10^{-4}$	$2·0\times10^{-4}$
	F1S5	960	5·6	$4·9\times10^{-6}$	$3·4\times10^{-6}$

TABLE 5

Radionuclide Concentration in Parts of Eyes

Dog	Part	Weight (g)	% Injected nuclide / g eye $\times 10^4$
M4R5	Iris	0·049	1·4
	Retina	0·878	0·33
	Choroid and posterior sclera	1·044	0·81
	Lens and cornea	0·718	0·27
	Vitreous	2·038	0·02
M5R5	Iris	0·053	1·6
	Retina and choroid	0·305	1·1
	Posterior sclera and residual eye	1·57	0·05
	Lens and cornea	0·822	*
	Vitreous	2·52	*
M7R5	Iris	0·046	1·5
	Choroid and retina	0·481	0·97
	Posterior sclera and residual eye	1·290	0·13
	Lens and cornea	0·857	*
	Vitreous	2·139	0·01
M12P4	Cornea	0·170	*
	Iris	0·050	12·
	Lens	0·509	*
	Vitreous	1·417	*
	Dorsal choroid and retina	0·418	12·
	Dorsal sclera	0·373	4·0
	Ventral choroid and retina	0·431	10·
	Ventral sclera	0·255	6·7
T13S4	Cornea	0·153	2·
	Iris	0·056	43·
	Lens	0·540	*
	Vitreous	1·839	1·1
	Dorsal choroid and retina	0·723	11·
	Dorsal sclera	0·487	3·1
	Ventral choroid and retina	0·349	10·
	Ventral sclera	0·225	3·

* Less than limit of detection.

Since some interesting eye changes have occurred in the dogs,[12] we have measured the concentration of Ra^{226}, Pu^{239}, Th^{228} and Sr^{90} in eyes at long times after injection, and the results are given in Table 4. The concentrations of Ra^{226}, Pu^{239}, and Th^{228} in eyes are greater than the plasma concentrations, while that of Sr^{90} is about the same. Further measurements made on dissected eyes show that the radionuclides are principally deposited in pigmented areas of the eyes. These data appear in Table 5.

Now that we have considered total retention and soft tissue deposition, we next compare the fractional skeletal retention. In Fig. 3 the biological and effective fractional skeletal retentions are compared.[4,7,10,11] The curves for Ra^{226}, Ra^{228} and Sr^{90} are essentially the same as the curves for

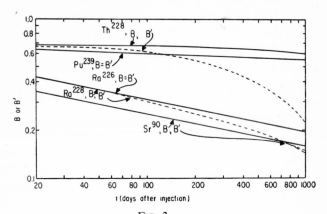

FIG. 3.

Biological fractional skeletal retention (B) and fractional skeletal retention
$(B' = B^{-\lambda t})$.

these nuclides in Fig. 2. This, of course, is a result of the fact that most of the radionuclide is deposited in the skeleton. The biological fractional retention of Th^{228} in the skeleton is a little higher than that of Pu^{239}, and it decreases very slowly. The total biological fractional retention of these two nuclides is essentially the same but there is a difference in skeletal and soft tissue distribution. While this difference is fairly small, the actual skeletal retentions of Pu^{239} and Th^{228} differ greatly because of radioactive decay.

Next we consider the retention and distribution of those decay products whose half-period is such that we must study their metabolism. In this sense, the most important Ra^{226} decay product is its daughter, Rn^{222}, and a thorough study has shown that the Rn^{222} which is retained is essentially all in the skeleton and that its retention is roughly 0·045 μc $Rn^{222}/\mu c$ Ra^{226} injected.[13] We also have made some preliminary studies on the retention and distribution of Pb^{210} formed ultimately from the decay of Rn^{222}.[14] Our data indicate that a large fraction of Pb^{210} and its important alpha-emitting decay product, Po^{210}, are retained in the skeleton.

The nuclide Ra^{228} presents the most complicated decay product problems to solve, and especially important is Th^{228}, the longest lived one. For several reasons, the most important of which is the redetermination of the Ra^{228} half-period, we will sidestep the important question of migration of Th^{228} formed *in vivo*. We will say only that we have some evidence that a very small part of the Th^{228} moves from the site at which it was formed and deposits elsewhere in the animal. When Th^{228} is the injected nuclide, we have considerably more information to report.[9,15,16] We have studied the decay products, Ra^{224}, Tn^{220}, Pb^{212} and, to a lesser extent, Bi^{212}. Most of the Ra^{224} formed in the dog is formed in the skeleton, and a small fraction of this leaves the skeleton. Some is excreted, some deposits in soft tissues, and some redeposits in the skeleton. The result is that in the skeleton the activity of Ra^{224} is less than that of Th^{228}, while in the liver, the blood, and the excreta, the reverse is true. The fraction of Ra^{224} which undergoes migration decreases with time. A fraction of the Tn^{220} formed in the dog also leaves its site of formation. Some reaches the lungs and is exhaled, while some of it decays in the blood and forms Pb^{212}. Again the fraction of Tn^{220} which migrates decreases with time. The effect of the decreasing migration of these two nuclides with time is that it approximately counterbalances the biological decrease in Th^{228} skeletal retention. As a consequence, the decrease in average skeletal dose rate is essentially at the rate of radioactivity decay of Th^{228}, except soon after injection.

Limited studies done sometime ago at this laboratory showed that the Sr^{90} daughter, Y^{90}, undergoes little or no (equal to or less than 5 per cent) migration.[17]

We are now equipped to compare average radiation dose rates to the skeleton of dogs injected with Ra^{226}, Pu^{239}, Th^{228}, and Sr^{90}. In Fig. 4 are plotted the average radiation dose rates to the skeletons if 1 μc/kg of Ra^{226}, Pu^{239}, Th^{228} or Sr^{90} is injected. By comparing these on the basis of equal injected amounts, we accentuate the differences which result from the nuclear and chemical characteristics of these nuclides. Th^{228} with its many decay products, of which five are alpha emitters, greatly overwhelms the others when compared on this basis. It decreases very rapidly and after the first year the decrease is mainly given by radioactive decay. The dose rate for Pu^{239} shows a slight initial decrease followed by a very slow rate of decrease. The Ra^{226} curve shows a rapid initial decrease followed by a slower rate of decrease. Although the disintegration energies of Ra^{226} and its decay products are considerably greater than that of Pu^{239}, the radiation dose to the skeleton from equal injected amounts is greater for Pu^{239} because Ra^{226} and Rn^{222} are not retained as well. Since the beta energies of Sr^{90}

and Y[90] are much lower than alpha energies, the Sr[90] dose rate curve lurks down among the tic marks of Fig. 4. The shape of this curve is similar to that of Ra[226]. The fact that it is so much lower than the others should give a graphic illustration of the reason we give ten times as many μc of Sr[90] to our dogs as we give Ra[226]. Although we do not include quantitative data on Ra[228], it is appropriate to indicate that the shape of the dose rate

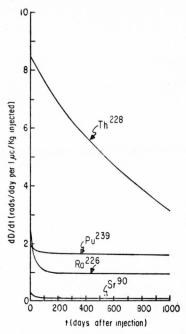

Fig. 4.
Average radiation dose rate to the skeleton when 1 μc/kg is injected.

curve is very different from those of the other four nuclides, which all show an initial decrease. The curve for Ra[228] shows an initial increase, while the decay product Th[228] is building up, and then after a few years it also decreases. The equations for the total retention, skeletal retention, and average dose rate curves of Figs. 2, 3, 4 have been compiled in Table 6, which includes partinent references.

DISCUSSION

The biological behavior of the nuclides Ra[226], Sr[90], Pu[239], and Th[228] reflects the similarities and dissimilarities of the four chemical elements represented. In these studies we have had the opportunity to compare four elements under roughly comparable conditions. The animals are the same

TABLE 6

Empirical Equations for Retention, Skeletal Retention, and Skeletal Dose Rate for 20 to 1000 Days after Injection[a]

Parent nuclide	Decay products	Total fractional retention	Fractional skeletal retention	Average dose rate to skeleton from parent and decay products (rad/day)	References
Ra^{226}		$R = 0.79t^{-0.20}$	$B \simeq R$	$dD/dt = I(2.0t^{-0.20} + 0.46)$	7,18
	Rn^{222}	$R = 0.045$	$B \simeq R$		13,18
Pu^{239}		$R = 0.90 - 0.0043t^{0.52}$	$B = 0.72t^{-0.04}$	$dD/dt = I\ 1.9t^{-0.04}$	4,18
Ra^{228}		$R' = 0.79t^{0.20}e^{-\lambda t}$	$B' \simeq R'$	(see reference 18)	7,18
Th^{228}		$R' = (0.19e^{-0.0011t} + 0.69)e^{-\lambda t}$	$B' \simeq 0.65e^{-\lambda t}$	$dD/dt = I\ 8.5e^{-\lambda t}$	11,18
	Ra^{224}		$B' = 0.53e^{-\lambda t}$		16,18
	Tn^{220} and its decay products		$B' \simeq 0.45e^{-\lambda t}$		9,18,19
Sr^{90}		$R' = 0.68t^{-0.21}e^{-\lambda t}$	$B' \simeq R'$	$dD/dt = I\ 0.30t^{-0.21}e^{-\lambda t}$	10,18
	Y^{90}	$R' \simeq 0.68t^{-0.21}e^{-\lambda t}$	$B' \simeq R'$		17,18

[a] For each decay chain, λ is the decay constant of the parent nuclide; $I = \mu c/\text{kg}$ injected.

2*

breed, approximately the same age at injection, and live in approximately the same environment. In addition, the administration of the radionuclide is nearly the same for all of the dogs, and they all receive comparable diets and clinical care. Thus, while biological factors are not actually held constant, we do have the advantage in these studies that there is a great deal of consistency in the biological factors. Under these conditions the biological behavior of the two alkaline earth radionuclides was found to differ markedly from that of the two actinide element radionuclides, and while differences between members of the pairs also were measured, they were found to be much less marked. This is consistent with the chemical characteristics of these four elements. Ra^{226} and Sr^{90}, for which the calcium in the body serves as a non-isotopic carrier and which are in general more soluble at physiological pH than the other two elements, have been found to leave the blood very rapidly, which is characteristic of the rapid ionic diffusion. They are diluted in the body fluids and deposited in bone quickly and with a comparatively high degree of reversibility, since there is initially a sufficient return from the bone to the blood that about half of the injected nuclide is excreted during the first week following injection. In contrast, the two actinide element radionuclides, for which there appears to be no physiological carrier metal ion and which are generally less soluble, tend to hydrolyze and form complexes with a great variety of anions and molecules, leave the blood much more slowly. In the blood they are almost completely in a non-diffusible form, which lacks the lability of the alkaline earth plasma protein complexes. Gradually these nuclides deposit in the skeleton and soft tissues when the local conditions favor the forming of an even more stable complex or compound than existed in the blood. This deposition shows a much greater irreversibility since only about 10 per cent is excreted during the first week following injection.

In comparing Ra^{226} and Sr^{90} the similarities in distribution and the rates at which retention, excretion, and plasma concentration decrease are more striking than the small differences observed. While plasma concentrations and retentions of the two decrease at the same rate, the retention of Ra^{226} is higher while the plasma concentration of Sr^{90} is higher. Recognizing the importance of age on alkaline earth metabolism, the difference in retention has been examined to see if it merely reflects a small difference in the age of the animals at injection. From the results of an extensive study at this laboratory on the effect of age on Sr^{85} retention by the beagle, it has been found that the difference does not arise because of age.[20] It more likely represents a real consequence of the chemical differences between strontium and radium. It was also thought that the higher Sr^{90} plasma concentrations might result to considerable extent from a greater binding of Sr^{90} by plasma protein. However, preliminary studies at this laboratory indicate that the difference is not sufficient to account for a difference of a factor of two in plasma concentration. Ra^{226} is excreted more efficiently by both the beagle kidney and beagle gut. The difference is almost a factor of two. The plasma is cleared of Ra^{226} about 13·5 times per day while the value for Sr^{90} is about 6·5. Thus, while Ra^{226} is excreted more efficiently, the lower plasma concentration leads to a higher retention. The extent of the exchange from bone to blood must then be the critical factor in the higher retention of Ra^{226}, and leads to the generalization that Ra^{226} in bone salt is less soluble than is Sr^{90}. These differences, we believe, reflect the chemical differences between radium and strontium. The similar time dependence of both retention and plasma concentration suggest that the principal factor affecting these rates is a biological factor, and that it probably reflects the time scale of overall skeletal metabolism (exchange and remodelling) in the dogs. Thus, when two chemically similar elements are studied in very similar biological systems, the similarities observed result from the biological system and the small differences reflect the chemical differences of the two elements. This illustrates that a non-isotopic tracer can give a good description of a biological system but not necessarily a precise one.

The biological behavior of the pair of actinide element radionuclides also shows striking similarities and dissimilarities. The picture in this case is less clear because of the absence of even a non-isotopic metal ion carrier, plus the generally greater insolubility of these two elements at physiological pH. During the first hour, the major part of either Pu^{239} or Th^{228} injected remains in the blood in indiffusible form, presumably as protein complexes or perhaps as colloidal aggregates resulting from the great tendency toward hydrolysis. The earlier drop in Th^{228} concentration most likely results from the fact that the stability constants for these unknown complexes are smaller than comparable ones for Pu^{239}. This is consistent with the larger size of the tetravalent thorium ion compared with the tetravalent plutonium ion, and also is consistent with the observed greater lability of thorium in its oxygen polymers than that of plutonium in plutonium oxygen polymers. The early predominant urinary excretion and the much greater renal clearance value for Th^{228} are also consistent with the general chemical difference between Th^{228} and Pu^{239}. With this pair of nuclides, we have the interesting result that the greatly differing plasma concentrations and excretion efficiencies result in essentially the same fractional biological retention. Thus while excretion of Pu^{239} is considerably less efficient, more of it is present in the blood to be excreted, and the effect of the lesser efficiency is overcome. The differences in soft tissue distribution may also reflect the probably greater stability of the Pu^{239} complexes. Speculation is somewhat difficult since we do not know whether the transfer, say of Pu^{239} from a blood protein molecule to a parenchymal or reticuloendothelial cell in the liver, involves the transfer of a plutonium ion from one complexing molecule to another or whether a larger entity, i.e. of colloidal size, moves from the blood to the liver site. However, the more diffuse deposition in soft tissues of Th^{228} may, if the transfer is an ion transfer, reflect the greater lability of the thorium complexes in the blood.

The decrease in skeletal retention of Th^{228} is a little slower than that of Pu^{239}. Thus we have the interesting observation that in these two pairs of chemically similar nuclides, the larger members of the pairs, Th^{228} and Ra^{226}, are released from the skeletal tissue less effectively than are the smaller members, Pu^{239} and Sr^{90}.

Two factors limit our ability to compare the results obtained for Pu^{239} and Th^{228}. First, is that, for equal activities injected, the number of plutonium atoms is about 100 times the number of thorium atoms administered.[11,21] This is important since a greater concentration of atoms would lead to greater tendency for hydrolysis and thus, the formation of colloidal hydrolysis products. The second limitation we must consider is the multiplicity of valence states of plutonium. It has been frequently suggested that the oxidation reduction systems of the body will keep plutonium in the tetravalent state. However, there is no unequivocal evidence to support this speculation, and it is possible that plutonium in the animal is not all tetravalent, while thorium is.

In the comparison of biological effects of internal irradiation, there is considerable variance in opinion as to the basis upon which the comparisons should be made. In the studies reported herein, we have emphasized the importance of the nuclear and extranuclear characteristics, as well as the biological organism being studied, on the retention, distribution, and finally the average skeletal dose rate. Also the role of decay products is extremely important in many cases and this has been emphasized in our studies. Fig. 4 emphasizes the diversity of average skeletal dose rates to our dogs which would result if 1 μc/kg of each of the nuclides were injected. The integrals of these curves, i.e. the cumulative average radiation doses, also exhibit disparity when compared in this manner. Although determination of average dose rate curves has been a major goal, we do not claim this to be the solution to the problem. It merely provides us with the tools we need in order to examine the problem on an equal energy rate basis unconfused by differences in retention, RBE for alphas and betas, non-

uniformity factors, etc. Also, it is likely that the correlation between biological effects and dose rate and time will differ according to the effect
being observed, because of the intrinsic differences in the different biological
systems of the animal. Furthermore, we would be remiss if we did not
recognize that an additional needed tool for our study of the effects of
internal irradiation is the relationship of the average radiation dose
rate to the distribution of localized dose rates.

An important limitation of the equations summarized in Table 6 is that
more of the higher dose level dogs have been studied than lower dose level
dogs, so that the results are more descriptive of the biological behavior
of the nuclides at the higher dose levels. When using these results, we must
remember that they may not be too accurate for the lower dose level dogs.
The serial sacrifice information was limited to the higher dose levels, and
now we have just enough information about differences in retention and
distribution in lower dose levels to realize that the effect may well be important as early as 1000 days. For example, the amount of Pu^{239} in the skeleton
of P2 dogs with bone tumors at long times after injection, is less than would
be anticipated by the equation of Table 6, but we do not have the requisite
information at shorter time intervals to be able to calculate equations
for each dose level.

Again in reference to Table 6, it is extremely important to call attention
to the fact that the mathematical descriptions we have used for our data are
strictly empirical. They imply no mechanism; they are highly dependent
upon the times at which we have chosen to make our measurements; there
is no theoretical basis for the choice between exponentials and power
functions. We have usually used power functions since it has been possible
to describe the data with fewer arbitrary parameters in this way. The
exception is Th^{228}, and we have described most of these measurements
by a sum of exponentials. This was done mainly as a matter of convenience,
for the short half-period of Th^{228} requires consideration of decay very soon
after injection. If fractional biological retention data are described by a sum
of exponentials, it greatly expedites integrating the derived dose rates to
obtain cumulative radiation doses. In summary, the equations of Table 6
are useful as interpolation formulae for the higher dose levels, but they
are not valid as extrapolation formulae.

SUMMARY

The biological behavior of Ra^{226}, Pu^{239}, Th^{228} and Sr^{90} in young adult
beagles for the first 1000 days following a single intravenous injection has
been studied. Plasma concentration, excretion, fractional retention, distri-

bution, metabolic fate of the decay products, if any, and the average radia-. tion dose rate to the skeleton have been determined. The results are considered in terms of the nuclear and chemical characteristics of the radionuclides and the biological organism. The results for the pair of alkaline earth radionuclides are, in general, similar with interesting small differences, and this pair differs markedly from the pair of actinide element radionuclides, which in turn show some interesting similarities and dissimilarities. The combined effect of nuclear and chemical properties and the biological organism result in markedly different average radiation dose rates to the skeleton when compared on the basis of equal injected activities. These empirical relations are presented herein as useful interpolation formulae to describe a specific case.

REFERENCES

1. D. STROMINGER, J. M. HOLLANDER and G. T. SEABORG, Table of isotopes, *Rev. Mod. Phys.* **30**, 585–904 (1958).
2. C. W. MAYS, D. R. ATHERTON, F. W. BRUENGER, B. J. STOVER, W. M. HAMMER and W. W. PARMLEY, Determination of the half-period of Ra^{228} (mesothorium) *Research in Radiobiology*, COO-222, 27–48 (September 30, 1960).
3. JOSEPH J. KATZ and GLENN T. SEABORG, *The Chemistry of the Actinide Elements*, Wiley, New York (1957).
4. B. J. STOVER, D. R. ATHERTON and N. KELLER, Metabolism of Pu^{239} in adult beagle dogs, *Rad. Res.* **10**, 130–147 (1959).
5. M. A. VAN DILLA, R. L. SCHUCH and E. C. ANDERSON, K-9: A large 4π gamma-ray detector, *Nucleonics* **12**, No. 9, 22–27 (1954).
6. M. A. VAN DILLA and D. H. TAYSUM, Scintillation counter for assay of radon gas, *Nucleonics* **13**, No. 2, 68–69 (1955).
7. M. A. VAN DILLA, B. J. STOVER, R. L. FLOYD, D. R. ATHERTON and D. H. TAYSUM, Radium (Ra^{226}) and radon (Em^{222}) metabolism in dogs, *Rad. Res.* **8**, 417–437 (1958).
8. B. J. STOVER and D. R. ATHERTON, Metabolism of Sr^{90} in adult beagle dogs, *Proc. Soc. Exp. Biol. Med.* **99**, 201–205 (1958).
9. C. W. MAYS, R. HALDIN and M. A. VAN DILLA, Thoron exhalation in radiothorium-burdened beagles, *Rad. Res.* **9**, 438–444 (1958).
10. C. W. MAYS, D. H. TAYSUM, W. FISHER and B. W. GLAD, Bremsstrahlung counting of Sr^{90} injected dogs, *Health Physics* **1**, 282–287 (1958).
11. B. J. STOVER, D. R. ATHERTON, N. KELLER and D. S. BUSTER, Metabolism of the Th^{228} decay series in adult beagle dogs, I. Th^{228}(RdTh), *Rad. Res.* **12**, 657–671 (1960).
12. G. N. TAYLOR, C. E. REHFELD, G. SCHNEEBELI and H. JOHNSON, Eye changes induced by internal irradiation (this vol. p. 163).
13. C. W. MAYS, M. A. VAN DILLA, R. L. FLOYD and J. S. ARNOLD, Radon retention in radium-injected beagles, *Rad. Res.* **8**, 480–489 (1958).
14. D. R. ATHERTON and B. J. STOVER, Measurement of Pb^{210} in bone of dogs injected with Ra^{226}, Radiobiology Laboratory, University of Utah, COO-218, 85–92 (March 1959).

15. M. A. VAN DILLA, B. J. STOVER and J. S. ARNOLD, On the retention and translo-
[cation of Ra^{224} (ThX) in dogs, *Am. J. Roentgenol.* 77, 503–510 (1957).

16. B. J. STOVER, D. R. ATHERTON and D. S. BUSTER, Distribution of the decay products, Ra^{224} and Pb^{212}, in dogs injected with the nuclide, Th^{228} (Abstract), *Rad. Res.* 12, 476 (1960).

17. J. S. ARNOLD, B. J. STOVER and M. A. VAN DILLA, Failure of Y^{90} to escape from skeletally-fixed Sr^{90}, *Proc. Soc. Exp. Biol. Med.* 90, 260–263 (1955).

18. C. W. MAYS, B. J. STOVER, B. W. GLAD and D. R. ATHERTON, Skeletal dosimetry in Utah beagles, Radiobiology Laboratory Annual Progress Report, COO-218, 121–145 (March 31, 1959).

19. B. J. STOVER, Pb^{212} (ThB) tracer studies in adult beagle dogs, *Proc. Soc. Exp. Biol. Med.* 100, 269–272 (1959).

20. B. W. GLAD, C. W. MAYS and W. FISHER, Strontium studies in beagles, *Rad. Res.* 12, 672–681 (1960).

21. B. J. STOVER, F. W. BRUENGER and D. R. ATHERTON, Chemical determination of thorium in our Th^{228} (RdTh) stock solutions, *Research in Radiobiology*, COO-220, 211–214 (March 31, 1960).

RELATIONSHIP OF MICRODISTRIBUTION OF ALPHA PARTICLES TO DAMAGE*

W. S. S. JEE, J. S. ARNOLD,† T. H. COCHRAN,†
J. A. TWENTE‡ and R. S. MICAL

*Division of Radiobiology, Department of Anatomy, University of Utah College
of Medicine, Salt Lake City, Utah*

INTRODUCTION

FOR many decades it has been known that internally deposited radioactive substances used in the self-luminous dial painting industry caused pathological bone changes and neoplasia. Subsequent discovery of plutonium created a need for knowledge of its relative toxicity. This led to the intensive study in Utah of the radionuclides in self-luminous dial paint and plutonium in adult beagles.

The present report summarizes some of our studies by autoradiography of the distribution of plutonium, radium, mesothorium and radiothorium; the relationship of distribution to damage and the consideration of dose parameters in relating dose to damage.

MATERIALS AND METHODS

The materials used in this report are from a project to study the histological changes and incidence of tumors over a wide range of radiation doses in adult beagles at the University of Utah Radiobiology Laboratory.[1]

Many autoradiographic techniques were utilized to describe the pattern of gross and microscopic localizations of radionuclides and to analyze quantitative autoradiograms for local dose measurements. Detailed autoradiograms were used principally to observe translocation of radionuclides and the relationship of microdistribution of isotope to damage.[2,3,4] Contact autoradiograms on Eastman Kodak's NTB plates and Ilford film were used for the gross distribution and quantitative autoradiographic studies, respectively.[5]

The determination of local dose was made by scanning of quantitative autoradiograms with a microdensitometer and direct track counting. These

---

* Supported by the U.S.A.E.C.

† Present address: Department of Pathology, Providence Hospital, Portland, Oregon.

‡ Present address: Department of Experimental Biology, University of Utah.

procedures have been reported earlier and some of the results will be used in this report.[6]

Histological studies were performed on Zenker-formol fixed, demineralized, celloidin embedded, and hematoxylin and eosin stained sections.[7]

EXPERIMENTAL OBSERVATIONS

The pattern of distribution of Th^{228} and Pu^{239} in bone is similar.[8,9,10] The initial deposits are on mineralized bone surfaces (periosteal, endosteal, resorption cavities, forming osteons, Volkmann and haversian canals and vascular channels; Figs. 1, 2, 3, 4, 7) and in the reticuloendothelial system. They differ only in that a significant fraction of Pu^{239} deposits in the liver[12] and a small amount of Th^{228} is in the kidney and blood vessels.[13] Bone remodelling alters the initial surface deposits by bone resorption and apposition (Fig. 10). This process results in the concentration of activities in osteoclasts, macrophages, and a low level volume deposit of isotope (radium-like deposit) in post injection bone[9,10,11] (Figs. 10 and 11). The lower amount of activity in post injection bone is determined by the rate of bone apposition and the concentration of radionuclide in the plasma (Figs. 5 and 6). Continual remodelling results in an increased volume of bone receiving alpha irradiation (Figs. 5, 6 and 11).

The short range alpha particle probably kills any osteocytes within its trajectory. For example, there is a loss of osteocytes within the range of the surface deposits of isotopes in dogs receiving high doses of plutonium and radiothorium (Fig. 8). This high dose inhibits any shift in the location of the radionuclide and produces peritrabecular fibrosis[11] (Fig. 9). Shifts in sites of plutonium deposition can be detected without autoradiography. The locations of empty lacunae in trabecular bone coincide with sites of plutonium deposition (Fig. 12).

Recent studies have demonstrated that irradiation injury to the vascular system in bone results in bone necrosis and abnormal bone remodelling.[10,11,14,15] The location of most of the terminal blood vessels supplying bone is within the range of alpha particles deposited on bone surfaces (Figs. 3, 4, 5 and 6). All vascular channels in the compacta and the vessels in apposition to trabeculae in the spongiosa are receiving alpha irradiation.[11]

The formidable problem of calculating meaningful measurements of local doses is evident from the analyses of quantitative autoradiograms in dogs receiving 3·0 $\mu c/kg$ of plutonium. Difficulties arise from variation in dose within different sites in a bone and at identical sites in individual

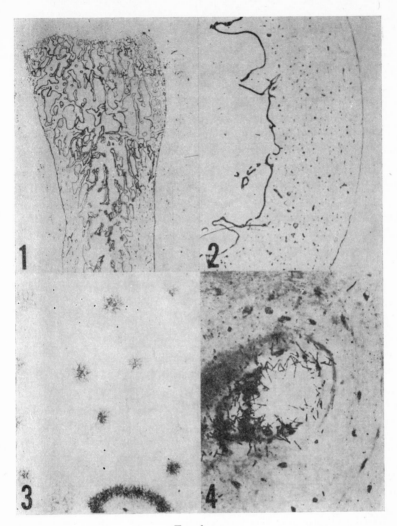

FIG. 1.
Bone surface deposits of Pu^{239} and subsequent low level volume deposits in post injection bone. Contact autoradiogram of distal radius ($\times 1\frac{1}{2}$).

FIG. 2.
Differential Pu^{239} deposits in periosteal, endosteal, and haversian canal surfaces in cortical bone. Contact autoradiogram ($\times 4$).

FIG. 3.
Differential deposits of plutonium in haversian canals and surfaces of forming osteones. Contact autoradiogram ($\times 110$).

FIG. 4.
Surface deposits of Pu^{239} in canal of forming osteone. Detailed autoradiogram ($\times 200$).

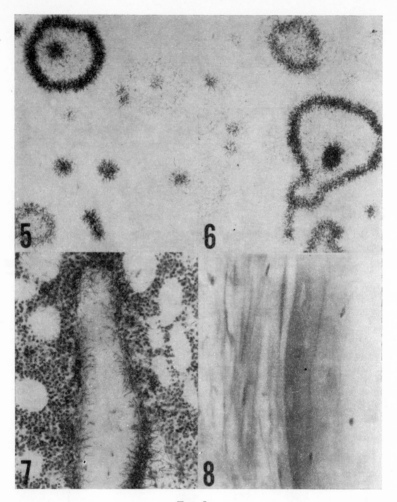

FIG. 5.

Differential uptake of Pu^{239} on surfaces of six haversian canals and three osteones with volume deposits. Note intense annular and punctate deposits on surfaces of the forming osteone and existing haversian canals at time of injection. Contact autoradiogram ($\times$110).

FIG. 6.

Compacta four years post injection with increased volume of bone and severe non-uniformity of Pu^{239}. Contact autoradiogram ($\times$110).

FIG. 7.

Initial bone surface deposit of Pu^{239} on trabecula. Detailed autoradiogram ($\times$125).

FIG. 8.

Empty lacunae (loss of osteocytes) near edge of trabecula. Note adjacent peritrabecular fibrosis. H & E stained celloidin section ($\times$320).

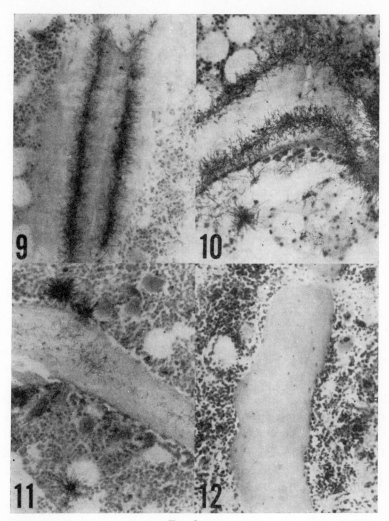

FIG. 9.
A predominant bone surface deposit in high level dogs having received Pu^{239} for
three years. Note peritrabecular fibrosis. Detailed autoradiogram ($\times 125$).

FIG. 10.
Active apposition of post injection bone with low volume deposits of Pu^{239}. Note
alpha tracks originating from macrophages in marrow cavity. Detailed autoradiogram ($\times 125$).

FIG. 11.
Low volume deposits of Pu^{239} throughout the trabecula (resembles radium deposition) and punctate areas of activity in macrophages. Detailed autoradiogram
($\times 125$).

FIG. 12.
Non-uniform distribution of empty lacunae in trabecula of a P3 dog. The areas
lacking osteocytes coincide with location of Pu^{239}. H & E stained celloidin section
($\times 125$).

bones, change in patterns of dose with time, and in the dose parameters to be considered when relating dose to damage.

Variations in local dose exist due to the differential uptake of isotopes. There are different concentrations of radionuclides in various microscopic sites (trabecular vs. haversian canal surfaces; Figs, 1, 2, 3, 5 and 6) and from bone to bone (humeral vs. metatarsal spongiosa; Table 1).[16,17] The pattern of dose rates changes with time after injection due to bone remodelling. Initially 96 per cent of the plutonium in the lumbar vertebral bodies is located on trabecular bone surfaces, which is reduced to 67 per cent at 1500 days. The remaining plutonium is located in osteoclasts, macrophages, reticular cells, post injection bone, osteons and periosteal bone surfaces.[18] The average local dose rate* to soft tissue lining bone surfaces is 40 rad/day during the first month and 30 rad/day at one year after injection. In the areas where the initial surface deposits are buried by post injection bone, the average dose rate to surface cells is only 1·5 rad/day[18,19,20]. The changing patterns of local dose differ with various injected dose levels in that the concentration of radionuclide can alter the rates of remodelling[10] (Figs. 9, 10 and 11).

Coinciding with the changes in local dose is a change in the volume of cells at risk with time. Initially in the thoracic vertebral body spongiosa only 22 of the marrow and 45 per cent of the trabecular bone is within the range of the alpha particles located on bone surfaces.[16] Subsequent bone remodelling increases the volume of cells at risk by the redistribution of a larger portion of activity throughout the bone and marrow (Figs. 7 and 11). In the dogs forming peritrabecular fibrosis, the volume is reduced (Fig. 9).

The time elapsed from the acquisition of radionuclide to appearance of damage should be considered in relating local dose to damage. It is known that different doses will elicit a different time in appearance of damage (Table 1). Therefore, calculations of cumulative local dose should involve the time in which the damage appears. However, the lack of serially sacrificed animals in the Utah study leaves no alternative but to calculate cumulative dose for the entire burden time of the dogs.

As much as 20–25% of the retained dose of plutonium is located in the liver. The average dose rate to the liver is essentially equal to the average skeletal dose rate.[12] The initial deposition is found uniformly deposited in both hepatic and Kupffer cells (Figs. 14 and 16). Late term effects result in regenerative liver nodules appearing as multiple, spherical, pink nodules

---

* Distance at which dose rate is equal to average dose rate over a range (35·4μ) is 12·5μ.[19]

TABLE 1

Sequence of Histopathological Events at Different Sites of Spongiosa after Approximately 3·0 μc/kg Plutonium[a]

Sites	% Dose $10^{10}\mu^2$ trab. surface	Lost marrow cells (days)	Bone resorption (days)	Peritrab. fibrosis (days)	Lost peripheral osteocytes (days)	Regenerated marrow cells (days)	Lost 50% Osteocytes (days)
Prox. Hum. Metaphyses	0·610	7	15	28	28	92	1200
Lumbar Vertebral Body	0·535 0·479	7	28	92	92	210	406
Rib	0·411	7	92	92	92	210	406
Radial Metaphyses	0·0679 0·0934	none[b]	210	210[c]	210	777[e]	1200[e]
Metatarsal Metaphyses	0·0637	none[b]	777	210[d]	777	none	none

[a] Excerpts from article in preparation.[17]
[b] Fatty marrow exists throughout life span.
[c] Spotty distribution.
[d] Spotty and thin.
[e] Bone marrow cells are normally not found at this site.

3

34 W. S. S. JEE *et al.*

several centimeters in diameter (Fig. 13). Histologically these regenerated hepatic cells are above average size and show a decreased glycogen content.[21] Contact and detailed autoradiograms show little activity in the nodules while elsewhere there are intense plutonium localizations in periportal areas in contrast to the initial uniform deposition throughout the liver[22] (Figs. 14, 15, 16 and 17).

Ra^{226} and Ra^{228} (mesothorium) deposit in high concentration in rapidly calcifying bone matrix beneath osteoblastic surfaces ("hotspots") and throughout the pre-existing old bone in areas of lighter, more uniform concentration ("diffuse components"; Figs. 18, 19, 20, 21, 22 and 23). Bone formed after injection is diffusely labelled (Figs. 24 and 25) and the amount of radium deposited is proportional to the concentration in the plasma at the time of bone apposition. In both cortical and trabecular bones some hotspots are buried and removed by normal or pathological remodelling*[8,10,23] (Figs. 19, 21, 23, 24 and 25).

Although all existing bones are labelled with radium, the non-uniformity of this isotope is quite severe. The hotspots contain about 57 times as much activity per unit bone mass as the diffuse distribution. Osteocytes located within the range of intense hotspots are killed (Fig. 26). Therefore in these areas the concentration of radium has dissipated its energy in bone mineral. However, in the remaining bone containing the diffuse component, the osteocytes are not affected (Fig. 27). Again the critical deposition site is on bone surfaces as exemplified by the appearance of peritrabecular fibrosis in areas of hotspots and diffuse radium deposits in dogs receiving 10 μc/kg of radium (Figs. 23 and 24). The fibrosis adjacent to the hotspots is slightly deficient in amount of tissue, suggesting that the concentration of radium in hotspots is too great to allow for formation of scar tissue (Fig. 23).

The significance of the hotspots gains prominence in injected dose levels less than 0·3 μc/kg of Ra^{226}. Lowering the amount of radium injected into the dog will result in local dose of hotspots equal to that of diffuse component in dogs receiving high dose levels (10 μc/kg), where the diffuse concentration is known to produce bone tumors. When such a situation occurs, the volume of cells at risk from hotspots will be small in comparison to the volume of cells at risk involved with the diffuse component of high doses.

Localization of radium intermediate in concentration to hotspots and the diffuse component are found about haversian canals. This is observable grossly in autoradiograms of cortical bone from tibial compacta in dogs sacrificed at 16 days and four years post injection (Figs. 18 and 19). Due

* Another mode by which radium diminishes in bone is by long term exchange.[26

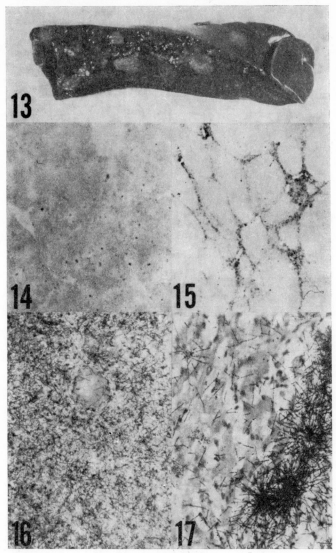

FIG. 13.
Slice of liver from a dog injected with 0·1 μc/kg of Pu^{239}. Note the large regenerative nodules ($\times 13$).

FIG. 14.
Initial uniform deposition of Pu^{239} in liver. Most of the black spots are artifacts. Contact autoradiogram ($\times 2$).

FIG. 15.
Non-uniform deposits of Pu^{239} four years post injection due to destruction and regeneration of hepatic cells. Contact autoradiogram ($\times 2$).

FIG. 16.
Initial uniform Pu^{239} deposits in liver. Detailed autoradiogram ($\times 125$).

FIG. 17.
Low level deposits in regenerated liver cells and intense concentration of Pu^{239} in periportal area from same liver as Fig. 15 ($\times 250$).

36 W. S. S. JEE *et al.*

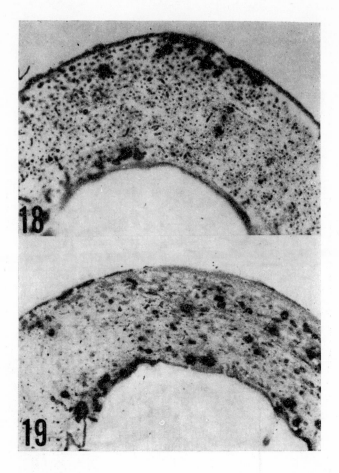

FIG. 18.

Pattern of radium deposits in compact bone after 16 days post injection. Note non-uniformity with large and small hotspots corresponding to areas of forming osteones and vascular channels (principally haversian canals). Contact autoradiogram (×4).

FIG. 19.

Pattern of radium deposits in compact bone after four years. Note persisting intense concentration in osteones and vascular channels, more noticeable diffuse component than Fig. 18, lack of activity in many areas due to loss of bone tissue and diffuse deposits in the marrow due to endosteal bone proliferation. Contact autoradiogram (×4).

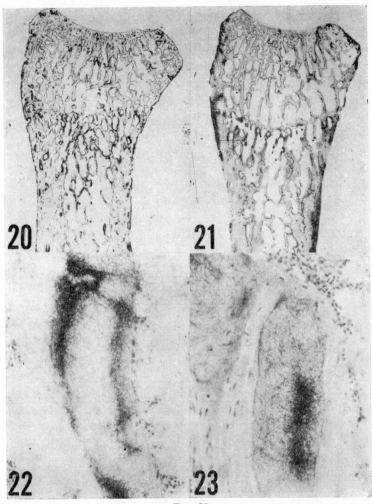

FIG. 20.
Gross distribution of radium in distal radius 16 days post injection. Hotspots are
located on bone surfaces. Contact autoradiogram ($\times 1\frac{1}{2}$).

FIG. 21.
Gross distribution after four years. Note burying of hotspots and more prominent
diffuse component than in Fig. 20 although they both had identical exposure time
to film. Contact autoradiogram ($\times 1\frac{1}{2}$).

FIG. 22.
Initial deposition of hotspot and diffuse component on trabecula. Note hotspot
beneath osteoblasts and osteoid layer on right border of trabecula. Detailed
autoradiogram ($\times 125$).

FIG. 23.
Buried hotspot in trabecula from dog injected with 10 μc/kg of radium. Intense
concentration of diffusely deposited radium has stopped bone remodelling and
induced peritrabecular fibrosis. Note lack of cellularity in fibrosis in region adjacent
to hotspot. Detailed autoradiogram ($\times 125$).

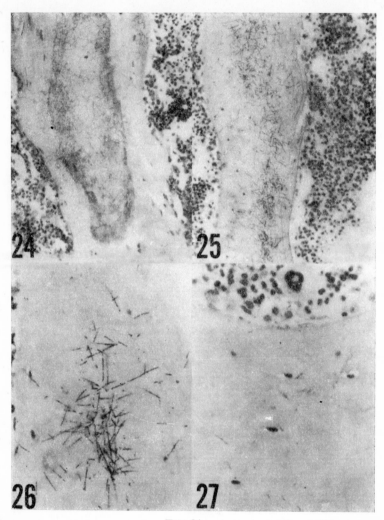

FIG. 24.
Pathologically remodelled trabecula with peritrabecular fibrosis in 5-level radium
dog. Note lack of hotspots and osteocytes, besides irregular basophilic staining
of the trabecular border. Detailed autoradiogram (×125).

FIG. 25.
Irregular distribution of radium in Rl. 7 dog. Detailed autoradiogram (×125).

FIG. 26.
Lack of osteocytes in volume of bone containing hotspot. Detailed autoradiogram
(×320).

FIG. 27.
Viable osteocytes in bone containing diffuse component in same trabecula as Fig.
26. Detailed autoradiogram (×320).

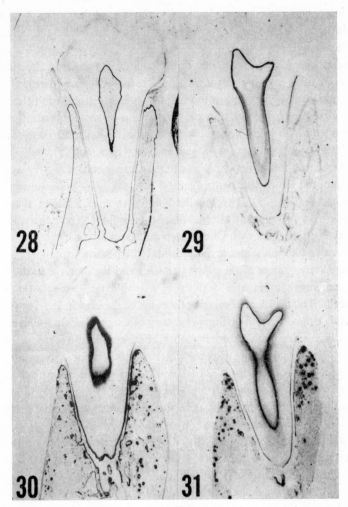

FIG. 28.
Pattern of Pu^{239} deposits in tooth and adjacent mandible 1 day post injection.
Contact autoradiogram ($\times$2).

FIG. 29.
Additi on of non-uniform volume deposit of Pu^{239} in post injection dentine within
the pulp cavity after 2 years post injection. Contact autoradiogram ($\times$2).

FIG. 30.
Pattern of Ra^{226} deposits in tooth and mandible 16 days post i njection. Contact
autoradiogram ($\times$2).

FIG. 31.
Pattern of mesothorium (Ra^{228}) deposits in tooth and mandible. Contact autoradiogram ($\times$2).

to the importance of vascular damage[15] these local dose rates from radium and plutonium deposits are being re-evaluated in relation to damage in haversian canals.*

The deposition pattern of four radionuclides in teeth is quite similar.[24] In general, there is a high concentration on newly formed dentinal surfaces of the pulp chamber and an intermediate concentration lining the vascular channels of the apical portion of the root, a lower concentration in the cementum and alveolar bone enveloping the periodontal membrane, and a much lower concentration in the enamel (Figs. 28, 30 and 31). Quite unlike bone, the initial deposition pattern persists except for the apposition of dentine and cementum with age and alteration by pathological resorption of teeth (Fig. 29). The localized deposition in teeth of these radionuclides correlates well with the sites of histopathological responses. However, teeth have very few sites which can respond to an adverse external stimulus. The vascular channels in the periodontal membrane are the only vessels which are within range of the alpha particles and the damage to the vascular supply can result in bizarre activity of osteoblastic, osteoclastic, odontoblastic cells. The problem of relating dose to the damage in teeth is quite difficult at this time due to the colony's history of excessive dental disease which apparently results from external rather than hereditary factors. The chief condition is periodontal disease which results from the accumulation of tartar, a consequence of a soft diet which does not encourage sufficient dental exercise.[25] This periodontal disease tends to mask the effects of the radioisotopes as one diminishes the dose. Changes induced by high concentration of radionuclide have been discussed in detail elsewhere.[24]

The acute chronic effects and distribution patterns of these radionuclides in soft tissues have been reported elsewhere.[13,21,22] Only a few chronic pathological effects of radiothorium and accompanying autoradiographic studies will be reviewed again to show there is an awareness of radionuclides in soft tissues. Generalized vascular changes, nephrosclerosis and regenerative liver nodules occur in high level radiothorium dogs (4 and 5 levels). These regenerative nodules in liver are identical to changes induced by plutonium. Detailed autoradiograms show the radiothorium restricted in the reticuloendothelial cells (Fig. 34) in contrast to the initial uniform deposition of plutonium. Radiothorium is also distributed diffusely throughout the kidney with hotspots in the renal papillae and at sites of vascular occlusions (arterioles and glomeruli; Fig. 33). Some of the renal changes include peripheral glomerulosclerosis, sclerotic arteries, and degeneration and regeneration of tubular epithelium.[13]

---

* Work in progress involving the bone and physics groups.

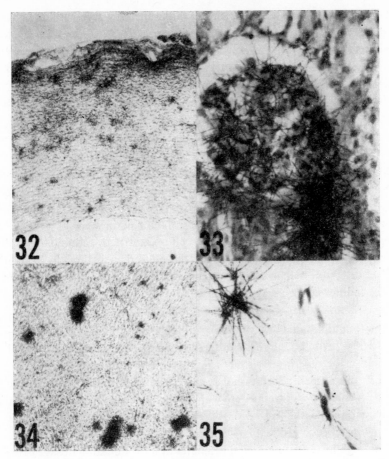

FIG. 32.
Concentration of alpha particles from R^{228} within the aortic media.
Detailed autoradiogram ($\times$ 32).

FIG. 33.
Concentration of radiothorium in renal papilla. Detailed autoradiogram ($\times$ 450).

FIG. 34.
Punctate deposits of radiothorium in reticulo-endothelial cells of the liver. Detailed
autoradiogram ($\times$ 70).

FIG. 35.
Burst of alpha tracks (radiothorium) from a macrophage and a few alpha tracts
originating from the fixed macrophages of a capillary in the bone marrow cavity.
Detailed autoradiogram ($\times$ 450).

Concentrations of alpha particles of radiothorium occur within the aortic media (Fig. 32). Aortic lesions are evident grossly as fine wrinkling of the subintimal surface. Histologically there is thickening and a patchy loss of elastic tissue in the outer half of the media. The inner media shows fragmentation of the elastica and the spreading of part of the smooth muscle by pools of basophilic ground substance.[21] These changes are not noticeable as the doses are lowered.

DISCUSSION

Many changes in mineralized and soft tissues can be explained by the non-uniform distribution of the alpha emitters in the body. Intense concentrations of plutonium in the liver induce liver pathology. The alpha particles located in bone kill osteocytes, induce peritrabecular fibrosis and alter the circulation.[15] It takes less plutonium than radium to produce the above changes because most of the plutonium is directly irradiating critical cells* (vessels in haversian canals and endosteal cells), while much of the radium energy is dissipated in bone mineral.

In spite of considerable differences in the pattern of irradiation to bones by the four radionuclides, the morphological patterns of damage are quite similar.[10,23] This is due to the altered circulation resulting from the direct irradiation of blood vessels.[15] The subsequent abnormal remodelling of bone in this altered circulation may or may not be dependent on the continuous presence of radionuclides in the skeleton. Therefore, when relating dose to damage the entire time between acquisition of radionuclide to death must be considered.

Although historically the first estimates of local radiation dosage distribution of alpha emitters was done in 1951,[27] there is very little published data available to enable one to thoroughly understand the relationship of dose to damage. All studies of alpha emitters have been restricted to terminal radium patients.[28,29] The work on mice by Marshall and Finkel shows promise.[30]

There will be a long delay before sufficient local dose measurements from quantitative autoradiography will be available to critically determine relative toxicities. The complexities of the problem have been reviewed in detail by Lamerton.[31] There is no agreement as to which dose parameter to choose. Nor is there a complete understanding of the complex reactions of bone receiving irradiation. The late term effects of various bone-seeking radionuclides have been described at the histological level, but the sequence

---

* Refers to cells believed to be principally influencing bone remodelling.

of changes is incomplete. More work is needed on different radionuclides and dose levels in order to fill the gaps in our knowledge.

In the meantime, the only practical thing to do is to use the available cumulative dose absorbed by the skeleton (average skeletal dose) determined by the comprehensive studies of the chemistry and physics groups of the Radiobiology Laboratory.[19] Attempts have been made to quantitate changes from late term effects of bone-seeking radionuclides but these studies are handicapped by the lack of serially sacrificed animals or animals sacrificed at common intervals. Therefore, at present all pathology resulting from the late term effects of bone-seeking radionuclides has been related to cumulative dose absorbed by the skeleton.[1] Meanwhile, autoradiographic studies should contribute to the explanation of how different radionuclides behave in the body and eventually provide some useful local dose measurements.

ACKNOWLEDGEMENT

I would like to express my gratitude to the numerous members of the laboratory who made this study possible. A special thanks to Julian Maack for helping to prepare the numerous photographs and to Professor T. F. Dougherty, the Director, for his constant support of our studies.

REFERENCES

1. T. F. DOUGHERTY, *Research in Radiobiology*, Univ. of Utah College of Medicine COO-223, 1–30 (1961).
2. J. S. ARNOLD and W. S. S. JEE, Embedding and sectioning undecalcified bone and its application to radioautography, *Stain Technol.* 29, 225–239 (1954).
3. L. A. WOODRUFF and W. P. NORRIS, Sectioning of undecalcified bone with special reference to radioautographic applications, *Stain Technol.* 30, 179–188 (1955).
4. J. S. ARNOLD, An improved technique for liquid emulsion autoradiography, *Proc. Soc. Exp. Biol. Med.* 85, 113–116 (1954).
5. J. A. TWENTE and W. S. S. JEE, Determination of Pu^{239} content of bone tissue: A comparison of radiochemical, track counting and photoelectric density technique, *Health Physics* (in press).
6. J. A. TWENTE, J. S. ARNOLD, C. W. MAYS, D. H. TAYSUM and W. S. S. JEE, Supplement B, Localized dosimetry in bone, I. Instrumentation, Annual Progress Report Radiobiology Laboratory, Univ. of Utah College of Medicine COO-215, 98–101 (1958).
7. W. S. S. JEE and J. S. ARNOLD, India ink-gelatin vascular injection of skeletal tissues, *Stain Technol.* 35, 59–65 (1959).
8. J. S. ARNOLD, Second Annual Conference on Plutonium, Radium and Mesothorium, Radiobiology Laboratory, Univ. of Utah College of Medicine, 4–17 (1954).
9. J. S. ARNOLD and W. S. S. JEE, Bone growth and osteoclastic activity as indicated by radioautographic distribution of Pu^{239}, *Am. J. Anat.* 101, 367–417 (1957).

10. J. S. ARNOLD and W. S. S. JEE, Autoradiography in localization and radiation dosage of Ra²²⁶ and Pu²³⁹ in bones of dogs, *Lab. Invest.* **8**, 194–204 (1959).

11. W. S. S. JEE and J. S. ARNOLD, The toxicity of plutonium deposited in skeletal tissues of beagles. I. The relation of the distribution of plutonium to the sequence of histopathologic bone changes, *Lab. Invest.* **10**, 797–825 (1961).

12. B. J. STOVER, Metabolism of radioactive isotopes which deposit mainly in the skeleton, *Health Physics* **1**, 373–378 (1959).

13. T. H. COCHRAN, J. S. ARNOLD and W. S. S. JEE, Nephritis induced by Th²²⁸ citrate in dogs, *Fed. Proc.* **16**, 354 (1957).

14. W. S. S. JEE, J. S. ARNOLD and T. H. COCHRAN, Skeletal changes induced by chronic doses of plutonium, radium, mesothorium and radiothorium, *Anat. Rec.* **130**, 420 (1958).

15. W. S. S. JEE and J. S. ARNOLD, Effects of internally deposited radioisotopes upon blood vessels of cortical bones, *Proc. Soc. Exp. Biol. Med.* **105**, 351–356 (1960).

16. J. A. TWENTE, E. G. BUTLER, O. FREUDENBERGER and W. S. S. JEE, Localized plutonium dosimetry in bone, Annual Progress Report, Radiobiology Laboratory, Univ. of Utah College of Medicine, COO-218, 190–206 (1959).

17. J. A. TWENTE, An evaluation of radiochemical and microdensitometric dose measurement in bone and their relationship to damage (in preparation).

18. J. A. TWENTE, E. G. BUTLER and W. S. S. JEE, The localized distribution of Pu²³⁹ in the lumbar vertebral centra of 5-level dogs. *Research in Radiobiology*, Univ. of Utah College of Medicine, COO-220, 168–196 (1960).

19. C. W. MAYS, Determination of localized alpha dose. I. With particular emphasis on plutonium, Semi-annual Progress Report, Radiobiology Laboratory, Univ. of Utah College of Medicine, COO–217, 161–180 (1958).

20. C. W. MAYS, Determination of localized dose. II. From alpha-emitters buried in mineralized bone, *Research in Radiobiology*, Univ. of Utah College of Medicine, COO-220, 200–207 (1960).

21. T. H. COCHRAN, Histopathological findings, Annual Progress Report, Radiobiology Laboratory, Univ. of Utah College of Medicine, AECU-3522, 73–85 (1957).

22. W. S. S. JEE, T. H. COCHRAN and R. MICAL, Microscopic distribution of plutonium-239 and thorium-228 in beagles, *Research in Radiobiology*, Univ. of Utah College of Medicine, COO-220, 144–148 (1960).

23. W. S. S. JEE, J. S. ARNOLD, R. S. MICAL, B. BIRD, O. FREUDENBERGER and M. LOWE, Bone: Histopathologic and autoradiographic studies, Annual Progress Report, Radiobiology Laboratory, Univ. of Utah College of Medicine, COO-215, 74–97 (1958).

24. W. S. S. JEE and J. S. ARNOLD, Radioisotopes in the teeth of dogs. I. The distribution of plutonium, radium, radiothorium, mesothorium and strontium and the sequence of histopathologic changes in teeth containing plutonium, *Arch. Oral Biol.* **2**, 215–238 (1960).

25. C. E. REHFELD and F. H. SORENSON, Environmental and radiation effects on the dental health of beagles, *Research in Radiobiology*, Univ. of Utah College of Medicine, COO-220, 43–72 (1960).

26. R. E. ROWLAND, The deposition and the removal of radium in bone by a long term exchange process, *Clinical Orthopaedics* **17**, 146–153 (1960).

27. F. E. HOECKER and P. G. ROOFE, Studies of radium in human bone, *Radiology*, **56**, 89–98 (1951).

28. M. HINDMARSH and J. VAUGHAN, The distribution of radium in certain bones from a man exposed to radium for thirty-four years, *Brit. J. Radiol.*, Suppl. **7**, 71–80 (1957).
29. R. E. ROWLAND and J. H. MARSHALL, Radium in human bone: The dose to microscopic volumes of bone, *Radiation Research* **11**, 299–313 (1959).
30. J. H. MARSHALL and M. P. FINKEL, Comparison of microdosimetry and tumor production for Ca^{45}, Sr^{90} and Ra^{226} in mice, International Atomic Energy Report on Oxford Conference on relation of radiation damage to radiation dose in bone, Oxford, England, April (1960).
31. L. F. LAMERTON, Considerations of radiation damage in relation to bone damage, *Radioisotopes in the Biosphere*, ed. Caldecott & Snyder, Univ. of Minnesota Center for Continuation Study of the General Extension Division, 382–400 (1960).

INCIDENCE OF BONE CANCER IN INTERNALLY IRRADIATED DOGS*

Thomas F. Dougherty

*Division of Radiobiology, Department of Anatomy,
University of Utah College of Medicine,
Salt Lake City, Utah*

INTRODUCTION

The primary aim of the project at the University of Utah is to compare the toxicity of certain internally-deposited radionuclides. These are: radium (Ra^{226}), plutonium (Pu^{239}), mesothorium (Ra^{228}), radiothorium (Th^{228}) and strontium 90 (Sr^{90}). Many different endpoints for the action of these toxic substances are being studied. These include the induction of subtle biochemical changes, hematological changes and differences in metabolism of these radionuclides. Several pathological events which are induced include the production of cancer, fracturing and acceleration of ageing.

Although it is evident that all of these radionuclides may produce different pathological changes, they all have in common the fact that they deposit in bone. Consequently, among the various types of cancer produced by these radionuclides, bone cancer appears to be induced most frequently. It should be made clear, however, that cancer of various types of soft tissues is also induced and this carcinogenic activity is also being studied. However, since the carcinogenic action of these radionuclides has not been notable with respect to large numbers of soft tissue cancers thus far, attention is paid here primarily to bone tumors. As an accompaniment of this research on carcinogenic dose response, investigations are in progress which include the overall body metabolism of the radionuclides with particular emphasis on their metabolism by skeletal tissue. The total amount of radionuclide in bone at various times following its administration is determined. Thus, the rate of excretion and the amount of radionuclide retained by skeletal tissue is ascertained. In addition, methods have been designed using autoradiography and microradiography to investigate the intimate histological complex metabolism of the radionuclides by skeletal tissue which is influenced by the growth and remodelling of bone during the growing, maturing and ageing periods of life.

* This work has been supported by the AEC—Contract No. AT(11-1)–119.

47

This interim summary should not be taken to be a final report concerning the incidence of osteosarcomas in the radionuclide-treated dogs and of course is not conclusive with respect to the carcinogenic dose-response relationship. It is a preliminary statement in which the interrelationships of days since injection of the radionuclide, the time of death from osteosarcoma or other causes, and the absorbed dose to the skeleton in rads will be presented.

MATERIALS AND METHODS

The design of the experiment is given in detail elsewhere.[1] There are about 12 dogs for each of the different dose levels of radionuclide. The dogs are injected after the closure of most of the epiphyses with the exception of the rib cage. The radionuclide is given intravenously in one injection. The first dogs were injected in 1952, but the entire injection schedule is still incomplete. There are three groups for mesothorium and five groups for radiothorium still to be injected. The reasons for the delay in fulfilling the planned injection schedule for Ra^{228} and Th^{228} were: (1) limitation on space in kennels created by maintenance of a sufficient breeding colony in order to produce dogs for the experiment at a desirable rate and housing of beagles for 16–17 months until they are of similar skeletal maturity; (2) introduction of Sr^{90} groups into the experiment in 1955; (3) placing priority to complete injection of Ra^{226}, Pu^{239} and Sr^{90}; and (4) addition of lower injection doses of Th^{228} and Ra^{228} due to the fact that the original top two dose levels for these radionuclides were too toxic. Therefore, kennel space was available for these animals to be injected only upon turnover in the animals resulting from the occurrence of tumors or lethal toxic effects.

The amount of radiation absorbed by each animal which developed a clinically recognized cancer was computed from retention equations experimentally determined for these beagles.[2] The average amount of radiation absorbed by the skeleton with the standard deviation of the sample (Table 1) was calculated for each injection level.

RESULTS

The number of living dogs, the number of dogs dying with osteosarcomas and other causes: the days since injection to death and the average absorbed skeletal radiation dose in rads with the standard deviation of the sample are tabulated by injection levels (Table 1). In general, osteosarcoma has been the major cause of death in this experiment. In many injection levels the incidence of death from this cancer is 100%. The earliest

TABLE 1

Incidence of Osteosarcomas in Utah Beagles as of 31 March 1961

Injection level	Living dogs	Deaths		Osteosarcoma dogs*	
		others	osteosarcomas	days inj. to death	rads to skeleton
R5	—	1	9	1110±200	12360±2110
R4	1	1	11	1590±190	5280±1050
R3	3	1	8	2140±370	2420± 530
R2	12	1	—		
R1·7	11	2	—		
R1	11	1	—		
R0	10	2	—		
P5	—	2	7	1480±310	6470±1590
P4	—	—	·12	1320±180	1790± 240
P3	—	—	12	1650±220	720± 110
P2	5	2	5	2360±570	330± 90
P1·7	13	1	—		
P1	13	1	—		
P0	11	1	—		
M5†	—	3	1	790	10900
M4	—	1	4	1120± 90	5310±490
M3	4	—	2	1300±160	2340±340
M2	6	0	—		
M1·7	5	—	—		
M1	6	—	—		
M0·5	2	—	—		
M0	6	—	—		
T5	—	2	—		
T4	—	2	2	740±130	3860±660
T3	3	—	4	800±180	1360±210
T2	3	1	4	1320±150	570± 20
T1·5	6	1	—		
T1	7	—	—		
T0·5	6	1	—		
T0·2	3	—	—		
T0	7	—	—		
S5	11	2	1	960	7860
S4	12	—	—		
S3	12	—	—		
S2	12	—	—		
S1·7	12	—	—		
S1	12	—	—		
S0	12	—	—		

* Averages and standard deviations are given to the nearest 10 days.

† This tabulation does not include dogs of the first 3 MsTh groups due to the high RdTh contamination in their injection solutions.

4

Th^{228} bone cancer occurred much sooner than with all other radionuclides (740±130 days). Bone cancer occurred later (time after injection) at the lower injection levels for all radionuclides. At approximately the same time of death the skeletal dose in rads absorbed differed among these various radionuclides. This is due to individual peculiarities in their biologic and physiochemical behavior.

The amounts of radionuclide injected were high enough so that the animals died before developing osteosarcomas.

The total rads to the skeleton at the time of death from osteosarcomas are quite similar for the 4-level dogs for all the isotopes with the exception of plutonium (Fig. 1). The rads absorbed by the skeleton for the P5 level

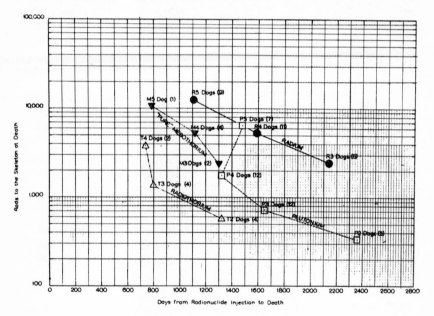

FIG. 1.

Mean skeletal dose in beagles dying with osteosarcomas. The average for each group is plotted and the number of dogs with osteosarcomas is shown in parentheses. More data, especially from the lower injection levels, will be forthcoming in future years.

are similar in amount to that absorbed by skeletons of the other 4-level groups. In spite of this, there are differences in elapsed time (the time of injection to time of death) from the tumors induced by the different isotopes. For example, there is almost twice as much elapsed time between T4 (740±130 days) and P5 (1480±310 days) levels. A comparison of the

P4 and P5 dogs to the T4 animals is emphasized because plutonium and radiothorium deposit in bone quite similarly, i. e., on bone surfaces.[3] The tumors, however, which arose in the T4 dogs were quite atypical as compared to those which occurred in plutonium-bearing animals. The two T4 radiothorium bone tumors occurred in the shafts of long bones (Figs. 2 & 3), whereas plutonium tumors are more ubiquitously distributed in spongy bone.

There is very little difference in elapsed time from injection to death between the T4 (740±310 days) and T3 (800±180 days) levels. The incidence of tumors at T3 (4 tumors out of 4 dead dogs) was greater than that for the T4 level group (2 tumors out of 4 dead dogs), although they occurred within the same period of time as those of the T4 animals. Moreover, there was about 3 times as much radiation absorbed by the skeletons of the T4 animals. The T3 animals had tumors occurring in spongy bone as compared to the shaft tumors of the T4 animals. At the T2 level, 4 out of 5 dead dogs had osteosarcomas. The total days to death are markedly greater for T2 dogs as compared to T4 and T3 level animals. The accumu-

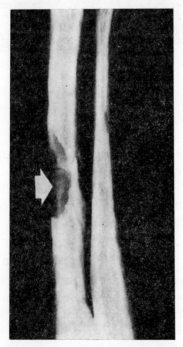

Fig. 2.

Post–mortem X-ray of radius and ulna from T-4 animal. The arrow points to a large osteolytic zone in mid-diaphysis of the radius (×2).

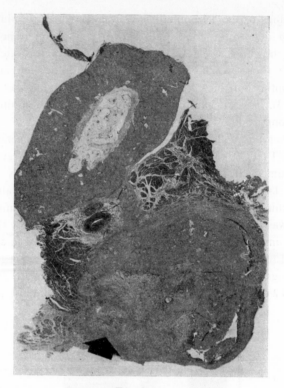

Fig. 3.

The celloidin section at the level of the arrow in Fig. 2 proved to be an osteogenic sarcoma histologically ($\times 17$).

lated dose to the skeleton, however, was approximately half that present for the T3 level. In comparison to plutonium, the T2 level animals develop tumors at about the same time as the P4 level, although the radiation dose (rads to the skeleton) was about 3 times greater for the P4 (1790 ± 240 rads) group as that for the T2 group (570 ± 20).

The T1.5 animals have survived as long as those of the P3 and P2 levels and no tumors have as yet occurred in this group.

There were seven tumors out of nine animals at 1480 ± 310 days in the P5 group. These osteosarcomas were not all evident grossly. Four were diagnosed microscopically.[4] If we relied entirely on microscopic evidence of tumors in this group, less than 50% of the P5 animals would be included in this category. The microscopically detected tumors in the P5 group were not the cause of death but were present in the animal which succumbed to other effects of plutonium.

The P4 animals survived fewer days from injection time to death (1320±
180 days) as compared to the P5 animals (1480±310 days). The amount
of radiation absorbed by the P4 group during this period of time was considerably less although 12 animals out of 12 animals (100%) developed
osteosarcomas. Also 100% (12 out of 12) died from osteosarcomas at the
P3 level. The actual length of time for the P3 level as compared to the
P4 and P5 levels is not very much greater (1650±220 days), but the amount
of radiation absorbed is still far less than the P5 level and less than the
P4 level (720±110 rads).

Five animals out of seven developed osteosarcomas at the P2 level
at 2360±570 days absorbing 330±90 rads. These animals had survived
longer from the time of injection than any of the others which had developed
osteosarcomas. Two deaths occurred from other than osteosarcomas.
One of these was a squamous cell carcinoma of the left frontal sinus, while
the other was from a respiratory injection.

In examining the accumulated dose time relationship from P4 to P2,
it is obvious that the larger the dose the shorter the lifespan due to cancer
death. On the other hand, it appears evident that over a longer period
of time the plutonium is highly carcinogenic. It is of some interest to ascertain whether the P1 level will produce tumors.

Mesothorium is biologically handled identically to Ra^{226}, being an
isotope of radium. Practically all of the radiation, on the other hand, is
derived from radiothorium and its daughter products.[2] Mesothorium
is a unique radionuclide. In general, it is interesting to note that it is intermediate in toxicity between radium and radiothorium (Fig. 1).

More rads are required at each carcinogenic dose level down to the
R3 level for radium to produce cancer than the other radionuclides. One
reason for this is that much of the expenditure of energy of radium is
through inert, inorganic material of bone rather than concentrating at
areas affecting cellular metabolism.[5] In other words, a smaller fraction
of the total radium energy is spent per unit cell than for the other radionuclides.

Among the Sr^{90} treated animals 3 have lived longer than 960 days without
signs of tumor formation. Two non-cancer deaths occurred—one at 35
days from toxemia and another at 250 days from hernia.

DISCUSSION

It should be remembered that the radionuclides which are administered
not only cause tumors but induce other pathological changes which, from
a lethal standpoint, are as important as the production of cancer. For

example, the dogs are also studied from the aspect of endocrine imbalance which might be related to both malignancy and accelerated ageing. Great emphasis is placed upon the changes which occur in clinical, biochemical, hematological and histopathological effects of the radionuclides as compared to the same alterations as they occur sequentially in non-treated ageing dogs.

There are tumors other than osteosarcomas which have occurred in the treated and non-treated populations. We have had several mammary carcinomas but these do not seem to be related to the action of any radionuclide.[6] There is essentially no difference between their occurrence in the control and treated populations. This will be the subject of a special report soon.

Leukemia, which was assumed to be a problem of some importance since this disease may be induced in mice by external and internal radiation, has not turned out thus far to be a cancer which is induced with any frequency. Two typical lymphomas in the ageing control population in the colony have occurred. It is therefore evident that this stock of beagles is susceptible to acquiring this disease. One lymphoma occurred in a 1·7 Ra level animal. However, it occurred 557 days after the administration of the isotope and there is reason to believe that this dog was abnormal hematologically at the time of administration of the radionuclide. It therefore seems unlikely that this questionable lymphoma was induced by radium.

A squamous cell carcinoma of the left frontal (paranasal) sinus occurred in a 2-level plutonium dog. This is of some importance since it has become evident in the radium dial painters that this is a site of cancer formation.[7]

Different species of animals could react to identical amounts of radiation in different ways due to intrinsic differences in their physiological composition. For example, one would expect that the spectrum of carcinogenic action of radiation might be as varied as the different susceptibilities of various species to the lethal effects of radiation. Besides these intrinsic differences, one has differences in longevity. It was obvious from the data reported here and other previous reports, that there are two important factors: one is that if the radiation dose is too large, tumors will not appear due to shortened lifespan because the lethal effects will occur from other causes; and two, if the dosage is too small, it is possible that a tumor may be produced with a sufficient exposure interval and this interval may exceed the lifespan of the particular animals being used for experimentation. Therefore, it is essential that comparisons be made among animals of the same species under highly similar circumstances of maintenance. etc.

Another variable which influences carcinogenesis is the plan of the experiment itself. For example, the chemical form and portal of entry of the radionuclide may play a very important role in relation to the site of deposition, the manner by which it is bound in a particular area, the capacity to move about in the blood stream and redeposit in other sites, etc. There are differences in absorption from lung alveolar surfaces as compared to intravenous administration or gastro-enterological entry.[8]

The age of the animal is extremely important. This is particularly true with respect to the production of cancers of bone, because the differences in rates of growth of osseous and dental tissues as well as rate of remodelling and cessation of bone growth would all influence the site of localization and concentration of the radionuclide. Recently formed bone has great avidity for alkaline earth radionuclide.[3]

These variables have been taken into account in the structure of the experiment at the University of Utah. As much as possible, the animals have come from the same breeding stocks, and maintained within the same kennels. Their immunization, dietary history, and general clinical status including hematological and ordinary biochemical evaluations have been on record for each dog since the time the dog was born. The animals are placed among the experimental group approximately at the same time. It is hoped that the general state of clinical health among the dogs will remain as it is now for a long enough period of time to have quite an even distribution in age between the treated and the control groups with the anticipation that some of the lower doses of radionuclides may not produce tumors until senility.

If one assumes that there is a uniform distribution of the radionuclide throughout the entire skeleton and if there is a threshhold dose for a particular amount of radiation to produce a sarcoma, one would have to give sufficient radionuclide so that when it is evenly distributed the amount of radioactivity would produce a tumor at all points. If, on the other hand, there is a non-uniform distribution so that at certain points an amount of radioactivity could accumulate in sufficient quantity to induce a tumor, then, as long as this requirement is met — a tumor could be produced even with much smaller doses than if there were an even distribution. There is no definite knowledge concerning solution to these two possibilities as yet. We do not even know at present whether there is a local threshhold amount of radioactivity required before a cancer can be produced. Another complicating factor is that there may be indirect effects of radiation which, by altering physiological mechanisms (e. g. altered circulation,[9] hormonal imbalance[10]) may be required to allow the carcinogenic effects of focal radiation.

Previous experiments concerning the induction of bone tumors by internally deposited radionuclides were designed mainly to elucidate the radionuclide/cancer dose-response relationship. In this experiment the average absorbed skeletal dose in rads is used as a basis for comparison of the dose response relationship of radionuclides. Other endpoints in relation to dose, of course, are being sought. However, it should be remembered that each of these radionuclides undergoes a metabolic fate and excretion which is relatively unique. Therefore, in addition to the study of the radionuclide in relation to carcinogenesis, the metabolism, fate and excretion of these radioisotopes must also be studied in order that one can ascertain the absorbed dose. This knowledge is of great value to evaluate other endpoints of pathological change. Further, there is the possibility that if one understands the rate of metabolism and excretion of various radionuclides, it might be possible to treat individuals in such a way as to enhance the rate of excretion and thus eliminate sufficient radionuclide to inhibit or delay the production of certain pathological changes.

This is not the place to argue whether or not there is a threshold carcinogenic dose. However, for practical purposes of experimental design and interpretation of pathological effects of radiation in the human population one must assume that there is a threshold. It will be noted from the data given here that no tumors have yet occurred at the 1-level dose of any of the radionuclides. Only with two radionuclides (plutonium and radiothorium) have tumors occurred at the 2-level. Now, if there were no threshold it would be expected that all of the animals would eventually get tumors because focal volumes of deposition are present even with the lower doses. It is possible that if the animals at the very lowest dose would live long enough, they might acquire cancers from the radionuclides. If the life span is too short for this to occur, this imposes a limitation on carcinogenesis which is in actuality a threshold. Therefore, within the limits of life of any species, lifespan may establish an effective threshold phenomenon. It appears that the dosage range was quite well selected in the present experiment with the possible exception of plutonium, radiothorium and mesothorium. The most important question of when or if osteosarcomas will occur in the lower injection levels is still unanswered. Only time will provide the answer.

REFERENCES

1. T. F. DOUGHERTY, Study of the Long Term Biological Effects of Internal Irradiation in Adult Beagles. This vol. p. 3.
2. C. W. MAYS, B. J. STOVER, B. W. GLAD and D. R. ATHERTON, Skeletal dosimetry in Utah beagles, Annual Progress Report, Radiobiology Laboratory, University of Utah, COO-218, 121–145 (1959).
3. J. S. ARNOLD, Second Annual Conference on plutonium, Radium and Mesothorium. Compiled and edited by C. N. STOVER, Jr., Radiobiology Laboratory, University of Utah College of Medicine, pp. 4–18 (1954).
4. W. S. S. JEE, Personal communication.
5. W. S. S. JEE and J. S. ARNOLD, The toxicity of plutonium deposited in skeletal tissues of beagles. I. The relation of the distribution of plutonium to the sequence of the histopathologic bone changes, *Lab. Invest.* **10**, 797–825 (1961).
6. G. N. TAYLOR, H. A. JOHNSON, C. E. REHFELD and W. FISHER, Soft tissue tumor incidence in beagles with long term internal radionuclide burdens, *Research in Radiobiology*. University of Utah, COO-222, 49–52 (1960).
7. J. C. AUB, R. D. EVANS, L. H. HEMPELMANN and H. S. MARTLAND, The late effects of internally-deposited radioactive materials in man, *Medicine*, **31**, 221–329 (1952).
8. W. H. LANGHAM, Radioisotope absorption and methods of elimination: Relative significance of portals of entry. *Radioisotopes in the Biosphere*. Edited by R. S. CALDECOTT and L. A. SYNDEV. University of Minnesota Center of Continuation Study of the General Extension Division, Minneapolis, 489–512 (1960).
9. W. S. S. JEE and J. S. ARNOLD, The effect of internally deposited radioisotopes upon the blood vessels of cortical bone, *Proc. Soc. Exp. Biol. Med.* **105**, 351–356 (1960).
10. J. FURTH, Radiation neoplasia and endocrine systems, In *Radiation Biology and Cancer*, Univ. of Texas Press, 7–25 (1959).

DISCUSSION

CHAIRMAN JEE: These three papers, and a number to follow, describe aspects of the main experiment of the Radiobiology Division of the Department of Anatomy at the University of Utah. I would like to remind you that we have a very difficult task, and that we are dealing with five radionuclides. We are very conscientious and are trying to fulfill the original proposal before we do anything we want to do. We do this in spite of the fact that it would probably be much more rewarding with respect to publications to pursue some of the interesting ancillary problems. In fact, we are handicapped in describing the overall picture because we have been limited in the number of animals available for serial sacrifice studies. Dr. Dougherty will open the discussion.

T. F. DOUGHERTY: It has just occurred to me that there is a very simple answer to a question I am frequently asked. Many people ask, "Why do you use dogs on that project?" My answer is, what other animal would you use for bone-seekers?

Another thing that occurred to me is that, as I have heard the speakers, both from abroad and at home, there is a considerable amount of affinity between the human bone-seeker and the elemental bone-seeker. The enthusiasm with which they seek is absolutely fantastic.

I have talked about the bone tumors which have occurred in our beagles. This was a difficult task, because I had to represent the whole group. Since there are many active participants in this program, we feel that this is the first instance of communistic cancer, because these tumors belong to all of us.

EVANS: There are a few remarks that I think should be made about the interplay of these results with those of the studies in humans. Let me point out a few things wherein this project has already helped a great deal in understanding radium and mesothorium and also plutonium in the human.

The first of these relates to the relative toxicity of mesothorium and radium in the human, which came to light so strongly again in 1950 at the time the design of this experiment was being made. It does turn out that, rad for rad, radiothorium and mesothorium appear more damaging than radium. However, this factor, alone, does not explain the magnitude of the effect we thought we saw in people. Another factor is the finding of Dr. Mays that the half-period of mesothorium is not 6·7 years but about 5·7 years. This has an enormous implication. It at least doubles the radiation dose from mesothorium and its daughters in the humans who were exposed twenty-five or thirty years ago. In fact, Louis Hempelmann made a clinical discovery of the error of the half-period of mesothorium in his review of these cases in the early 1950's. (J. C. AUB, R. D. EVANS, L. H. HEMPELMANN and H. S. MARTLAND, *Medicine* **31**, 221, 1952).

Because of the kidney damage in the radiothorium dogs, we have measured kidney function in all of the human radium cases. We have found no damage yet. The eye effects observed in the dog are not expected in the human because the human does not have the tapetum lucidum, so we have not examined the human eyes.

The limitations of this experiment should also be mentioned. As Dr. Jee has already commented, more animals for serial sacrifice are needed in the design of experiments of this kind. A serious limitation in the application of the results of these studies to the problems of industrial exposures is that each dog receives his radionuclide by a single intravenous injection. Other routes of administration such as inhalation of plutonium and chronic ingestion of strontium are being designed into other experiments at other laboratories.

The importance of comparing the toxicity of two radionuclides at a number of dose levels rather than just one is well illustrated by Dr. Jee's results on the variation in deposition and remodelling at different dose levels. This is consistent with the expectation that the ratio of toxicity, for example, of plutonium to radium in the dog, would probably be a function of dose level among other things. Thus, the ladder of doses is well justified and should be included in the design of future similar experiments.

Dr. Dougherty also pointed out that the incidence of leukemia was either very low or zero in these studies. The same holds for the human radium cases. Thus, we can agree that it is not an important endpoint in either of these studies. Additional similarities are the prominence of osteogenic sarcomas and spontaneous fractures. Osteoporosis is the first thing we see. The carcinomas of the paranasal sinus we do see.

I do think it is remarkable, in connection with Dr. Mole's philosophical remark yesterday, that, in what could be thought of as two parallel and independent experiments, the observations at the Argonne Laboratory and at M.I.T. on about the same total number of people, there is almost the same incidence (not counting duplications), about eight carcinomas and about twenty-four sarcomas. I think the Argonne count is nearly the same. So, it is very nice to parallel those two lines of human data with all that is going on here.

Finally, I think that Dr. Dougherty's slide, summarizing the bone tumors in the dogs, emphasizes the complexity of trying to evaluate quantitatively what we have innocently called the ratio of toxicity of plutonium to radium, for example. With what parameters are we going to associate it in a two-dimensional graph of this sort? At once one goes to three dimensions and visualizes in his mind's eye a third coordinate coming out here with per cent tumor incidence, and soon one will want four dimensions and more, I am sure. So, there are going to be enormous complexities, and the interpretations must be made slowly and carefully. It is going to be a difficult job even to determine this ratio, and the ratio of effectiveness in toxicity is going to vary with the dose and other parameters.

MOLE: I have several questions for Dr. Stover. First, you found a very high level of circulating plasma plutonium.

STOVER: Yes, it is high relative to the plasma concentration of the other nuclides at comparable times.

MOLE: Plutonium is also found in macrophages. Could the higher level of plutonium in the plasma result from a few circulating macrophages containing a relatively large amount of plutonium?

STOVER: I do not think this is the case, for we centrifuge out the cells and measure the concentration in the supernatant plasma. Further, I think that our results would be less consistent than they are, if a large part of the plutonium measured came from macrophages. If the plutonium were in a few cells, there would be a much greater variability between samples than if it were in the plasma. I will ask our hematologist if she sees many macrophages in the blood.

J. H. DOUGHERTY: We practically never see macrophages in the blood.

MOLE: When you say that there is about 1% of the injected Ra^{226} in soft tissue, do you take precautions to remove sesamoid bones, calcified bronchial rings and such from soft tissue?

STOVER: Yes. Our measurements of Ra^{226} in soft tissue are fairly limited. We sample liver, spleen, and kidneys routinely, and eyes occasionally. In a few cases we have combined the remaining soft tissues and measured them with a whole-body counter. We have detailed results on Ra^{226} for soft tissues for one dog which was sacrificed at 24 hours. The principal non-skeletal site was the liver, which contained about 6% of the injected Ra^{226}. Other tissues were much lower in Ra^{226} content, except the gut and contents which was high since the dog was sacrificed so soon after injection. These limited data again illustrate our need for more serial sacrifice dogs.

MOLE: In the dog, the fecal/urinary excretion ratio for Ra^{226} is 2·5, while in man it is much greater, perhaps a 1000 or so.

STOVER: The value for man is probably between 10 and 100.

MOLE: If there are relative quantitative differences in the way the material is excreted by the kidney and through the intestine, then you cannot expect the same retention function in different species. Is this something you would agree with?

STOVER: Obviously there are differences between species, especially in kidneys. I have read somewhere that the dog can be fed large quantities of salt water and excrete the salt in amounts which we could not. Apparently dog kidneys can do things that our kidneys cannot. This certainly must be a factor in retention.

CHAIRMAN JEE: I would like to comment on an example of difference in localized dose pattern and similarity in effect. Regenerative nodules appear in the livers of both plutonium and radiothorium dogs. Yet the distribution of Pu^{239} and Th^{228} in the liver cells is different. (See Figs. 14–17 and 34, W. S. S. Jee, "Relationship of micro-distribution of alpha particles to damage," this book.)

Pu ^{239} deposits uniformly in the liver (hepatic cells and reticuloendothelial cells). We believe that the hepatic cells are killed and replaced with larger cells, and the concentration in the periportal areas and the reticuloendothelial system gradually becomes greater than that in the hepatic cell. In contrast, Th^{228} in the liver is essentially all in the reticuloendothelial cells. Yet, in both cases we see the same regenerative nodules.

STOVER: Dr. Jee's autoradiograms show the deposition patterns of Pu^{239} and Th^{228} in the liver and illustrate the radiation dose rate patterns from these two nuclides. However, this is only part of the story for Th^{228}. Some of the Ra^{224} that is formed in the living dog leaves the bone and goes to the liver, so that in the liver the activity of Ra^{224} is greater than the activity of Th^{228}. While in the bone, the activity of Ra^{224} is less than the activity of Th^{228}. The answer we lack is the microscopic location of Ra^{224} in the liver, and, until we do have this information, we do not know the radiation dose pattern for livers of radiothorium dogs.

Still another factor in the radiation dose pattern of the liver arises from the fact that Pb^{212} which is attached to red blood cells, is found in the liver in activities equal to or greater than that of Ra^{224} and hence, greater than that of Th^{228}.

The pattern of irradiation in the living animal can be determined by measuring the activities of the Th^{228}, Ra^{224}, and Pb^{212}, and by making a series of autoradiograms on samples from the same liver at appropriate times. Dr. Jee and I hope to collaborate on this problem when the material and time are available.

HASTERLIK: Are the liver cells destroyed, and do you have clinical evidence of liver damage in these dogs?

CHAIRMAN JEE: Yes, the liver cells are destroyed in the plutonium dogs. We do not have sufficient material to show this in the case of the radiothorium dogs, but our material shows that the end result, regenerative nodules, is the same in both cases. My evidence is all histological since I am not a clinician. Dr. T. H. Cochran, a pathologist, looked at these early slides and reported that there was a necrosis of cells (Annual Progress Report, Radiobiology Laboratory, AECU-3522, p. 73, March 1957). Dr. Johnson, have you looked at those slides?

JOHNSON: No, I have not seen those. From the material I have seen it is just an assumption that these are regenerative nodules resulting from liver cell damage. They could be adenomas.

RADIOGRAPHIC CHANGES IN INTERNALLY IRRADIATED DOGS*

WILLIAM R. CHRISTENSEN, CARLISLE C. SMITH, CARL E. REHFELD
AND GLENN N. TAYLOR

Department of Radiology
University of Utah College of Medicine
Salt Lake City, Utah

SHORTLY after the initial realization of the damaging effects of radium and mesothorium ingestion, it became apparent that these radionuclides produced marked changes in skeletal structures and that these changes could be demonstrated radiographically.[1,2,3,4] With further experience it was proved that radiological alterations in the skeleton constituted the earliest evidence of physiological damage and that their extent and severity were roughly proportional to the total body burden of radioactive material.[1,5,6] Several articles describing these changes have appeared in the literature. The most detailed and accurate of these investigations was published in 1952.[5] The authors stressed the following radiological abnormalities:

1. Coarsening of trabeculae—most apparent in alveolar crests, ends of long bones and metacarpals, metatarsals and phalanges.
2. Areas of rarefaction—found in skull and ends of long bones.
3. Areas of increased density—2-3 mm in diameter in ends of long bones.
4. Increased calcification (lead line type) seen in patients of young age.
5. Destruction and collapse of weight bearing portions of long bones and vertebrae.
6. Resorption of teeth—mainly dentine portion of root, but sometimes also the crown.
7. Necrosis of mandible and maxilla.
8. Pathological fractures.
9. Malignancy-osteogenic sarcoma, fibrosarcoma and epidermoid carcinoma.

Unfortunately, these results cannot be equated to exact body burdens of known radionuclides. The problems of exact determination of body burden are well known. Furthermore, the exact composition of the radio-

* This work has been supported by the U.S. Atomic Energy Commission.

active materials ingested by the individual has been essentially unknown in each instance. Contamination with varying amounts of radiothorium and mesothorium was probable in most of the cases. Nevertheless, studies of this kind were the justification and major indication for a serious and continuous radiological evaluation of all experimental animals carried in the Utah AEC project.

The original experimental plan called for a complete skeletal survey at six-month intervals throughout the life of both poisoned and control animals.

The following films have been obtained on all animals at six-month intervals:

1. AP skull.
2. Lateral skull.
3. Posterior occlusal-mandible.
4. & 5. Anterior oblique occlusals-maxilla.
6. AP pelvis and lumbar spine.
7. Lateral pelvis and lumbar spine.
8. AP hind legs (single film).
9. & 10. Lateral of each hind limb.
11. & 12. AP of each forelimb.
13. AP thorax and dorsal spine.
14. Lateral thorax and dorsal spine.
15. Magnification view distal forelimb.

As is apparent, these 15 exposures have been so selected that AP and lateral views of almost all skeletal structures have been obtained. The only exceptions have been the forelimbs.

Unfortunately, a survey of this kind entails an unavoidable total body radiation exposure. Whereas it would have been desirable to limit radiation to those emanations arising from the retained radionuclides, the radiographic studies were considered essential. The total body dose delivered in the course of this routine study has amounted to 0·7 roentgens. In certain of the low level animals every other series has been limited in an effort to minimize total body exposure. No adverse effects of the radiological exposures have become apparent in any animal and no variation in the response of the low level group has been observed as a result of the lower exposure. In view of the fact that the routine radiological examinations involve an exposure of only 1·4 roentgens/year, it appears unlikely that a significant effect would be detectable.

As of this date many of the experimental animals have been followed for a period of eight years. A majority, especially those at higher dosage levels, have become definitive in that death has occurred as a result of radiation injury. However, in considering the results to be presented, it must be realized that all animals have not reached an endpoint and that experimental results are still accumulating. Further definitive information regarding low level animals can certainly be expected.

Since substantially no information was available concerning the possible skeletal effects of radium, mesothorium, plutonium and radiothorium in dogs, no preconceived pattern has been used in the radiological studies. As a matter of fact, virtually nothing is known of the normally expected ageing changes in dogs. Because of this, this study has been approached as an area of total ignorance and information collected with no serious preconceptions. Over the period of years recurring groups of pathological changes have been observed in the poisoned animals. These have not been duplicated in control animals of the same age. As a consequence, a clear-cut group of diagnostic criteria have been established as evidence of radio-nuclide injury. These changes may be summarized as follows:

1. Structural changes in the mandible.
2. Destructive changes in the teeth.
3. Pathological fractures—with and without healing.
4. Distortion of cortex of long bones.
5. Disturbance of metaphyseal trabeculation.
6. Osteolytic rarefaction.
7. Rib end demarcation.
8. Aseptic necrosis.
9. Tumor formation.

A striking similarity to the changes described by Aub *et al.* in human beings with radium and mesothorium toxicity will be noted.[5]

Before proceeding to a summary of the radiological data, it is probably desirable to consider each of these changes and to provide a more detailed description of the pathological sequence. As a background to this, however, please direct your attention to Figs. 1 and 2. These are magnified reproductions of an occlusal film of the mandible and the distal portion of the foreleg of a mature adult beagle. The appearances are typical of the normal animal. In the case of the mandible, note that the lamina dura and perio-dontal membrane are distinctly apparent and well defined. The trabeculae of the interalveolar crests are sharply outlined and form a definite, separate, roughly horizontal pattern. No zones of osteolytic rarefaction are present. The teeth are intact and show no evidence of caries. The forelimb, likewise, is a striking example of normal anatomy. The cortices of the radius and

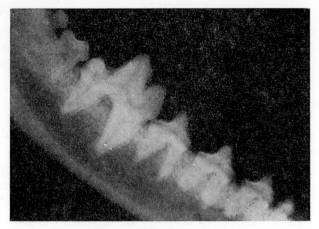

FIG. 1.

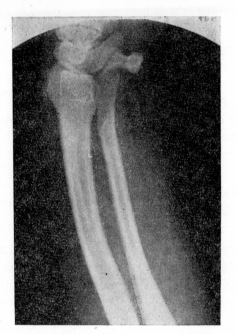

FIG. 2.

ulna are clearly outlined, smooth, and uniform in width. The medullary canal is clearly apparent. The metaphyseal trabeculae are distinct and regular in distribution. It is suggested that these figures be carefully studied as normal background for the pathological changes which will now be described in some detail.

1. *Structural changes in the mandible.* With very few exceptions alterations in the mandible have been the earliest detectable and most consistently visualized evidences of injury from alpha emitting radionuclides. The first change, Fig. 3, has appeared as a loss of the clean definition between the lamina dura and periodontal membrane. Later, Fig. 4, this

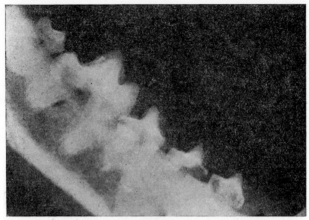

FIG. 3.

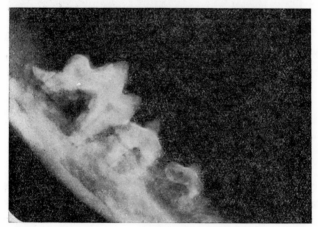

FIG. 4.

initial loss of sharp detail progresses to a total erasure of these structures through invasion of the mandibular trabeculae. Essentially simultaneously, the trabeculae, themselves, lose their distinct quality and sharp definition and become sclerotic. This sclerosis and obliteration of detail ultimately progress to complete incorporation of the root structures of the teeth into dense amorphous interalveolar crests. These changes are often complicated in later stages by the appearance of small zones of osteolytic rarefaction throughout the mandible. Aseptic necrosis of the mandible has been seen only in the very advanced stages of toxicity and at highest levels of dosage.

2. Destructive changes in the teeth. As a general rule, changes in the teeth have been detected relatively late and only in animals with a relatively high body burden. The changes begin at the gingival margin and progress either superiorly or inferiorly as irregular resorption. The root or crown eventually disappears.

3. Pathological fractures (Figs. 5 & 6). These are the most obvious evidence of significant skeletal damage. Since no fractures have occurred in control animals, any fracture has been considered evidence of pathological change. These injuries have occurred most commonly in ribs and the spinous processes of the dorsal vertebrae. However, virtually all bony structures have been involved at one time or another, even the bones. The pelvic and pectoral girdles.

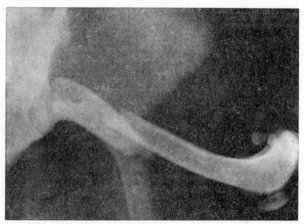

FIG. 5.

Some question may be raised as to the propriety of terming these pathological fractures in view of the fact that no gross abnormality may be apparent in the bones at the time of fracture. However, since they do not appear in normals, the term is probably justified.

Considerable attention has been given to the healing reaction of these fractures. Many have shown no body bridging and gone on to unequivocal false joint formation. The majority, essentially all those in low level animals, have healed quite satisfactorily, so well in fact that no residual evidence of the original fracture can be detected.

4. Distortion of the cortices of the long bones (Fig. 7). In general, this has been a toxic manifestation restricted to higher level animals, 3, 4, 5.

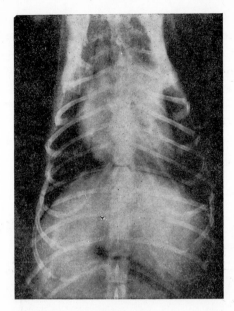

FIG. 6.

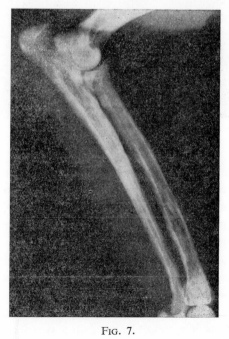

FIG. 7.

It has taken the form of rather gross, poorly defined zones of cortical overgrowth which extend inward and encroach upon the medullary canal or irregular thinning of the cortex. Both of these may result in irregularity of the external outline of the cortex, but gross configuration of bone structures is hardly affected. The same bony structures may be affected by both thinning and thickening. However, as a general rule one or the other of these processes predominates.

   5. *Disturbance of metaphyseal trabeculation* (Fig. 8). The sharp definition and orderly quality of metaphyseal trabeculation have been previously described. In contrast, the appearance of Fig. 8 is distinctly different. The clarity of individual bone septations has disappeared and an overall increase

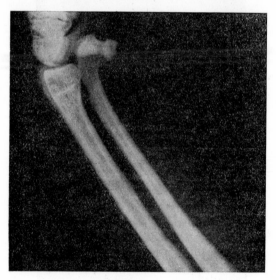

FIG. 8.

in density has occurred. The total number of individual trabeculae has been reduced and their orderly arrangement is no longer apparent. These changes have not been present in even the most aged controls. Whereas they have been most common in instances of high level toxicity, they have occurred with moderate frequency in 2 level animals.

   6. *Osteolytic rarefaction* (Fig. 9). Small, 2–5 mm, zones of osteolytic rarefaction have been a fairly common finding in all 4 and 5 level animals. Their number at lower levels has been small. Characteristically, they have occurred in random distribution throughout both long and flat bones and have been present in zones of trabeculation as well as in dense cortical

bone. Their margins are poorly defined and show no evidence of bony reaction.

7. *Rib end demarcation* (Fig. 10). This change has occurred only in the higher level animals. The essential feature is a fairly well defined, transverse zone of increased density at or near the distal end of the rib near the costochondral junction. In those instances where the zone of increased density is not at the costochondral junction, the segment of the rib distal (only

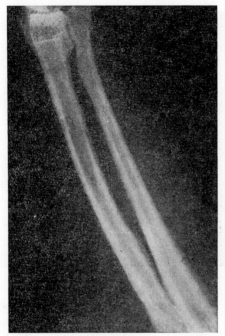

FIG. 9.

about 1 cm in length) is relatively radiolucent and deficient in trabeculation. These changes are presumably due to a disturbance of growth induced by the radioactive material. It occurs in the rib end because this is still an actively growing bony structure at the time of injection, i.e. with unfused epiphyses. The zone of increased density is not a deposition of radionuclide, but merely excessive bone formation and, in this respect, is similar to the so-called lead line.

8. *Aseptic necrosis.* This has been a relatively rare finding in these animals. Destructive changes in and about joint surfaces accompanied by zones of increased density have been observed in the vertebral column and the knees and hips, but not with sufficient regularity to be considered an important feature of the toxic syndrome in these animals.

9. Tumor formation (Figs. 11 and 12). As might be expected, osteogenic sarcomata have been the most dramatic evidence of radionuclide injury. The appearance and growth of these lesions have been readily detected on the routine films of the animals. The radiological appearance in no way differs from that seen in humans or other experimental animals. There is nothing typical of a radiation-induced osteogenic sarcoma. Whereas a majority have appeared in bones which are already the site of obvious

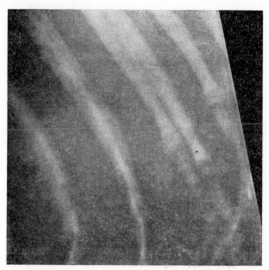

FIG. 10.

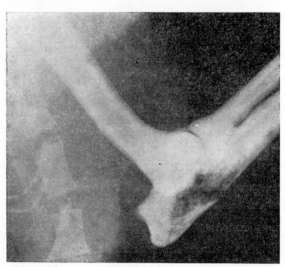

FIG. 11.

radiation injury, some have developed in skeletal structures which were quite normal radiographically and in animals who demonstrated no other signs of radiation damage to skeletal structures. In early stages, the tumors have commonly appeared as small zones of osteolytic rarefaction and, as such, have been difficult to differentiate from other non-malignant zones of rarefaction. The nature of the tumors has varied from predominantly osteolytic to markedly osteogenic. Primary location, rate of growth and tendency to metastasize have varied widely. The total number producing metastases, however, has been relatively small. Multiple tumors arising simultaneously at different sites in the same animal have not been uncommon. Even under these circumstances, the characteristics of individual tumors have been extremely variable.

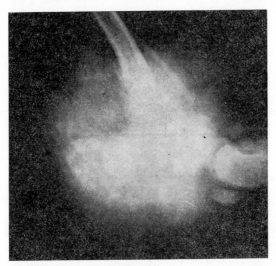

FIG. 12.

In Table 1 an attempt is made to summarize the development and incidence of the radiological findings described above. All figures represent very rough averages with no attempt, as yet, to establish statistical significance.

One immediately notes that 1 level animals have not been included. Clear-cut and unequivocal evidence of radiological damage has not yet been detected at this toxicity level.

It is quite apparent that the earliest changes have occurred in the highest level animals. Some have appeared within six months. The severity of the lesions also has followed this same general trend. However, the individual response within a toxic group has shown considerable variation, both

TABLE 1

Summary—Bone Changes

	Level	Onset (Years)	Fractures		Rib end	Tumors
			(No.)	(healing)		
Radium	2	4.5	+	excel.	0	0
	3	2.0	+	excel.	0	++++
	4	2.0	++	fair	+	+++
	5	1.5	++++	fair	+++	+++
Plutonium	2	5.0	+	excel.	0	++++
	3	3.5	+	excel.	+	++++
	4	2.0	+	excel.	++	++++
	5	1.0	+++	poor	++	++
Mesothorium	2	3.0	+	good	0	+
	3	2.0	++	fair	+	++
	4	1.5	+++	poor	0	+++
	5	1.0	++++	poor	++	+
Radiothorium	2	3.0	+	fair	0	++++
	3	1.5	+	fair	++	+++
	4	0.75	++++	poor	+++	+

as to time of appearance and extent of pathological damage. The individual variation in response is most striking.

Radiothorium and mesothorium appear to produce pathological changes somewhat more rapidly than plutonium and radium.

As has been mentioned previously, the earliest sign of radiation injury has usually appeared in the form of changes in the mandible. This is true of all the nuclides studied. No incidence figures have been presented for the other classes of radiological damage, namely tooth changes, cortical irregularity, distortion of metaphyseal trabeculation and osteolytic rarefaction. These changes have been rare in all 2 level animals; they occur only at high levels of toxicity. There has been no striking variation in their incidence from nuclide to nuclide. As a matter of fact, it is our present impression that the specific nuclide in any single toxic animal could not be predicted on the basis of the radiological evidence. Despite differences in site of distribution and emission characteristics the gross pathological changes in the skeletal structures are in no way distinctive.

As a general rule the incidence of fractures has increased with increasing levels of toxicity and become very high in the 5 level groups. Healing has been quite satisfactory at lower levels and become increasingly poor with higher body burdens. Mesothorium deserves special mention in this respect. The relative rate of fracture injury is high and the success of repair is low.

Rib end demarcation is an inconstant manifestation of injury occurring at high level dosage in all toxicity groups. It is probably more dependent upon age at the time of injection than any other single factor.

The overall features of tumor formation have been presented in detail elsewhere and their radiological characteristics have already been discussed. It might be desirable, however, to stress certain points which might appear superficially to represent inconsistencies in the data. Tumor incidence at high levels of toxicity is low. This is merely a manifestation of the fact that general radiation injury has killed the animal before tumor formation has occurred. The data further suggest that the definitive endpoint for all 2 and 3 level animals will be tumor formation. This is already clearly apparent in the case of plutonium and radiothorium.

What are the fundamental processes involved in this bizarre spectrum of skeletal changes? Tumor formation clearly stands apart. This is a response to long-standing radiation damage. The exact nature and mechanism of the malignant change is unknown at this point. There is little to be gained by further speculation. The remaining changes fit into rather definite response patterns, involving both destructive and productive changes. Pathological fractures, cortical thinning, osteolytic rarefaction, erosion of joint surfaces and resorption of teeth might all be considered to be evidence of destructive effects of radiation. Moreover, an intact blood supply would be required for many of these manifestations to appear. Certainly, significant areas of bone resorption cannot occur in the absence of functioning vascular structures.

How does one account, however, for responses which are productive in nature. Gross areas of cortical thickening of such severity as to encroach upon the medullary canal, increase in density and thickness of trabeculation of metaphyses and interalveolar crests, zones of increased density in bony structures involved with aseptic necrosis, and loss of differentiation between lamina dura and periodontal membrane all involve an element of productive reaction. Certainly it would be difficult to explain these reactions on the basis of destruction of osteoblasts or other living elements of bone substance.

It appears most likely that this irregular overgrowth of bone is a regenerative response following vascular injury. Zones of increased density have been shown to occur as a healing response in femoral heads whose blood supply has been compromised by fractures of the femoral neck. The reactive increase in density develops with the regrowth of the new blood supply.[7]

Although one must await additional experimental data, present histological evidence indicates that significant vascular damage occurs in the radionuclide poisoned animals.[8] If this is accepted as a significant feature of the pathologic process, one might then logically conclude that attempted regrowth and repair might be accompanied by bizarre reactive bone changes.

Both loss of bone substance and reactive bone overgrowth could be expected to follow vascular injury which was succeeded by total necrosis and resorption or varying degrees of damage succeeded by restoration of blood supply and subsequent bizarre bone regrowth.

There would hardly appear to be any other logical explanation for this bizarre combination of osteolytic resorption and irregular overgrowth.

In the final analysis the following general conclusions appear justified:

1. Gross skeletal changes constitute consistent and reproducible responses to body burdens of radium, mesothorium, plutonium and radiothorium.

2. On the basis of 5 years exposure the lowest body burden at which changes can be consistently detected is 2 level. No clear cut or obvious changes have yet been detected in the 1 level animals.

3. There is no specificity or rigid consistency in the skeletal changes produced. In any single instance of these heavy nuclide toxicities it would be impossible, on the basis of our experience, to confidently identify the exact nature of the inciting agent.

4. As a general rule, changes appearing in the mandible, amorphous sclerosis of interalveolar crests and loss of differentiation between lamina dura and periodontal membrane, are the earliest and most common manifestation of radionuclide intoxication.

5. The skeletal changes described have often occurred as isolated and localized findings. They are not usually generalized. The presence of a single finding has not necessarily meant that the entire spectrum of changes would be present.

6. Pathological fractures and tumors may occur in osseous structures whose gross radiological appearance is entirely within normal limits.

7. Whereas there are some differences in the skeletal changes described in cases of human radium and mesothorium toxicity from those seen in the beagles, the overall similarity is quite striking.

ACKNOWLEDGMENTS

The authors wish to acknowledge with thanks the able technical assistance of N. B. Nebeker in these experiments.

REFERENCES

1. T. BLUM, Osteomyelitis of the Mandible and Maxilla, *J. Am. Dent. Assoc.* **11**, 802–805 (1924).
2. W. B. CASTLE, K. R. DRINKER and C. K. DRINKER, Necroses of the Jaw in Workers Employed in Applying Luminous Paint Containing Radium, *J. Ind. Hyg* **7**, 371–382 (1925).
3. F. L. HOFFMAN, Radium (Mesothorium) Necrosis, *J.A.M.A.* **85**, 961–965 (1925).
4. H. S. MARTLAND, P., CONLON and J. P. KNEF, Some Unrecognized Dangers in the Use and Handling of Radioactive Substances, *J.A.M.A.* **85**, 1769–1776 (1925).
5. J. C. AUB, R. D. EVANS, L. H. HEMPELMANN and H. S. MARTLAND, Late Effects of Internally Deposited Radioactive Materials in Man, *Medicine* **31**, 221–329 (1952).
6. W. B. LOONEY, Initial Medical and Industrial Use of Radioactive Materials, *Am. J. Roentg.* **72**, 838–848 (1954).
7. S. S. COLEMAN and C. L. COMPERE, Femoral Neck Fractures: Pathogenesis of Avascular Necrosis, nonunion and Late Degenerative Changes, *Clin. Orth.* **20**, 247–265 (1961).
8. M. A. BLOOM nd W. BLOOM, Late Effects of Radium and Plutonium on Bone. *Arch. Path.* **47**, 494 (1949).

SOME HEMATOLOGICAL RESPONSES TO INTERNAL IRRADIATION IN THE BEAGLE

Jean H. Dougherty

*Department of Pathology and
Division of Radiobiology, Department of Anatomy,
University of Utah College of Medicine,
Salt Lake City, Utah*

INTRODUCTION

SINCE the hematopoietic system is known to be a sensitive target organ for internally deposited radionuclides, the hematological changes are being followed as one of the biological endpoints in the irradiated beagles at the University of Utah. One of the aims of this program is to compare the toxicity of Pu^{239}, Ra^{226}, Ra^{228}, Th^{228} and Sr^{90} to the hematopoietic system. At the present time this comparison is based on changes noted at comparable dose levels (P5 compared to R5, P4 to R4, etc.). These dose levels, however, are not exactly comparable as far as actual radiation dose to the animal although they were chosen so that the retained amounts of radioactivity are closely related.[1] Eventually, it is hoped to relate the hematological changes to average total radiation dose and/or dose rate to the skeleton since with present methods dose rate cannot be precisely determined to the bone marrow itself due to non-uniform dose delivery to this organ.

The early blood cell changes in dogs given the three highest amounts of plutonium and radium have been previously reported for the first year following injection of these radionuclides.[2] The present report summarizes the chronic hematological changes in animals receiving the intermediate and higher dose levels of all five radionuclides for as long a period as there are significant numbers of dogs on experiment. The findings at lower dose levels where changes are minimal or not apparent will be reported later. Since these animals will be followed throughout their lifespan, considerable data will eventually be collected on changes in the blood picture with ageing and the effect of low levels of irradiation on this process.

METHODS

Details of the injection plan and other data such as relation of dose levels, etc., are given in another section of this book[1] so that only hematological methods will be discussed below.

All hematological measurements are made from a 5 ml sample of oxalated blood drawn from the external jugular vein of the dog with the exception that non-oxalated blood from the syringe is used to prepare the blood films. All bleedings are done at approximately the same time in the morning prior to feeding. The hematological values determined are the volume of packed red cells (VPRC) using a Wintrobe hematocrit tube, sedimentation rate (uncorrected value at one hour), red cell count, hemoglobin (oxyhemoglobin method), reticulocyte count, cellular indices, white cell count, direct eosinophil and platelet count and differential cell count (400 cells counted). The techniques used are well standardized hematological procedures. All blood counts are made in duplicate by two observers, and if the results are not within accepted limits of accuracy for the particular method, additional counts are made.

The frequency of the post-injection determinations varies with the dose of the radionuclide which the dog receives. Three control counts are made on all dogs during the month prior to injection at approximately weekly intervals. After injection, high level dogs (4 and 5 level) are studied once a month close to the anniversary date of their injection, intermediate level dogs (3 level) every three months and lower dose levels (2 level and below) and controls (0 level) every three or six months. Ageing colony controls are examined at yearly intervals. Counts have been made on several dogs during the first week and then weekly during the first month after injection to determine when the earliest hematologic changes occur. Additional counts are also made if there is a change in the dog's clinical condition or if an unusual hematologic value is noted. A determination is also made shortly before euthanasia.

Bone marrow smears from several sites are routinely obtained at autopsy. These smears are stained similarly to blood smears and 500 to 1000 cells are differentially counted by two or more observers. The qualitative marrow findings obtained will be used to supplement and clarify quantitative findings in bone marrow sections.

RESULTS

The results are summarized in graphs giving mean values of volume of packed red cells (VPRC), sedimentation rate, platelets (for high level dogs only), polymorphonuclear neutrophils (pmns) and lymphocytes at monthly or three monthly intervals after injection. Since all dogs were not entered into the experiment at one time and, thus, environmental effects could enter into the results, the injected dogs for each radionuclide are related to their own control group (PO, RO, TO, MO, SO on the graphs). In levels where all dogs have died the graphs were terminated when only one dog remained alive. Not all groups of dogs have been on experiment for the entire period of the graphs so that more dogs enter into the mean values at the earlier points. Lack of space precludes graphing of all cell types. It is felt that the VPRC is the most accurate determination for red cells. Total leukocyte counts are not given as they mainly reflect changes in pmns and lymphocytes. Statistical determinations are being made and will be presented later.

Ra^{226} (*Radium*)

The hematological responses of dogs on the three higher dose levels of Ra^{226} for a period of sixty months are summarized in Fig. 1.

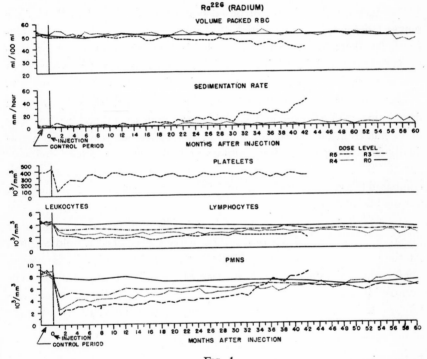

FIG. 1.

Hematological response of dogs injected with 0·0 (RO), 1·1 (R3), 3·2 (R4) and 10·0 (R5) μc/kg of Ra^{226} for sixty months.

The greatest early change is in the number of polymorphonuclear neutrophils (pmns). The 5 level dogs show a drop in pmns which begins about one week after injection and becomes maximal at two to three weeks (mean of about 400 cells/mm³) with a slight recovery at one month to a mean of 1500 cells/mm³. There is a steady gradual rise in these cells over the next thirty-two months and then a steeper rise to normal or above normal values as the dogs become terminal. The 4 level dogs show a drop in pmns to a mean value of 1600 cells/mm³ at two weeks followed by a rise to 2400 cells at one month and then a slow rise until they reach low normal values approximately $2\frac{1}{2}$ y after injection. The 3 level dogs show a drop in pmns to 2900 cells at three weeks and then a gradual return to low normal values over the next two years. The blood platelets follow the same pattern as the pmns with minimal values during the first month after injection and then a gradual return to low normal values by the sixth month. The normal mean and standard deviation of platelets for non-injected dogs of the colony is $350,000 \pm 70,000$/mm³.

The magnitude of change of blood lymphocytes is less than that of the pmns. However, after the initial decrease in these cells there is less tendency for them to return to normal levels. There is a sustained lymphopenia in both 4 and 5 level dogs. A minimal change is seen in 3 level animals which is probably not significant beyond eighteen months after injection.

The red cells are less affected than the white cells. There is no acute drop in mean VPRC even in 5 level dogs although several had brief periods of anemia from the first to the ninth month. After one year there is a gradually developing anemia in these dogs and all except one 5 level dog were anemic at the time of sacrifice. The mean pre-sacrifice VPRC was 37·0 as compared to a pre-injection mean of 50·0. The anemias were normochromic, normocytic in type.

The 4 level dogs show no change in red cells until fifty-six months after injection, when one of the two surviving dogs developed a mild anemia. At time of sacrifice the mean VPRC value of 4 level dogs was normal (49·0 compared to a pre-injection mean of 50·5). No decrease in red cells occurred in 3 level dogs over the sixty month period studied. The sedimentation rate in the 4 and 5 level dogs closely follows the VPRC in a reverse fashion.

Pu²³⁹ (*Plutonium*)

Fig. 2 summarizes the hematological changes observed following administration of the three highest dose levels of Pu²³⁹ over a period of fifty-four months.

In the 5 level dogs there is a fall in pmns to a minimal mean value of 470 cells/mm³ at three weeks and a slight rise to 780 cells/mm³ at one month. As with radium there is a terminal rise in pmns of the 5 level dogs which is not seen at lower levels. There is also a terminal increase of non-segmented pmns (stab and metamyelocytes) in 5 level dogs. The pmns of 4 level dogs do not fall as low initially but there is a similar degree of neutropenia to that seen in 5 level dogs from the tenth to the twenty-sixth month. Three level dogs have a pmn level of between 4000–5000 cells/mm^3 for the period reported.

The platelets of 5 level dogs show a quick recovery after falling to below 100,000/mm^3 at one month, and low normal values persist for the remainder of the experiment. At sacrifice, three of the nine 5 level dogs had a severe thrombocytopenia and one had a moderate increase in platelets.

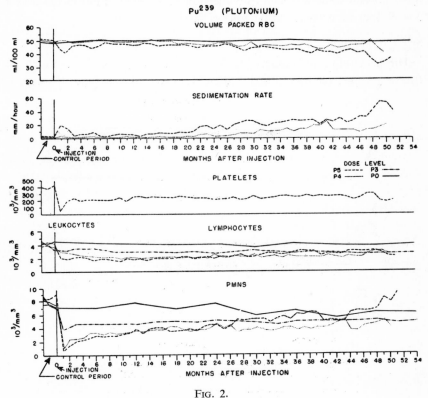

FIG. 2.

Hematological response of dogs injected with 0.0 (P0), 0.30 (P3), 0.90 (P4) and 2.8 (P5) μc/kg of Pu^{239} for fifty-four months.

The lymphocytes fall during the first month and achieve their lowest values by the end of the first year in both 4 and 5 level plutonium dogs. The degree of lymphopenia is similar for 4 and 5 level dogs. Three level dogs show a slight drop in lymphocytes after injection and these cells remain low during the fifty-four month period.

A brief period of anemia occurs between two and six months in all 5 level dogs. Low normal values are maintained until a further drop is noted at twenty-six months which becomes progressive until all animals are dead. The terminal anemia is more severe in the plutonium dogs (mean VPRC 29·0) than in radium dogs and is also normocytic, normochromic in type. Three of the dogs had a severe terminal anemia (VPRC below 25·0). The 4 level dogs did not develop an early transient anemia but VPRC values gradually fall beginning in the second year. At time of sacrifice the mean value was 44·3 (pre-injection mean 49·5). Four of the twelve 3 level dogs were anemic at the time of sacrifice.

Sr⁹⁰ (*Strontium*)

The hematological responses to Sr^{90} are shown in Fig. 3. Although all twelve groups have been injected, these dogs were inserted into the experi-

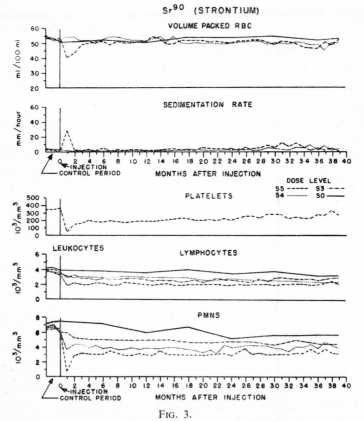

Fig. 3.

Hematological response of dogs injected with 0·0 (S0), 11 (S3), 32 (S4) and 100 (S5) $\mu c/kg$ of Sr^{90} for thirty-nine months.

mental plan more recently than dogs receiving the other radionuclides. The graph was terminated at thirty-nine months as only three groups have been on experiment for this length of time.

The pmns of 5 level dogs fall to very low levels at two weeks with values below 500 cells/mm³. At one month the mean count is still below 1000 cells. At two months there is a rise to 3000 cells and they remain at this level for the period reported. There is a decrease in pmns in 4 level dogs to values of around 4000 cells. A less definite effect is found in 3 level dogs which maintain about 5000 pmns which is in the low normal range.

A sustained decrease in lymphocytes is seen in 5 level dogs with a drop to one-half of normal values at one month. Three and 4 level dogs show a very gradual decline with the counts running around 3000 cells after injection. There seems to be no dose difference between 3 and 4 level dogs and this lymphocyte depression is very minimal.

The platelets of 5 level dogs fall to values between 10,000 and 40,000/mm³ at two weeks to one month. There is a rise at two to four months where they plateau at 200,000/mm³. Several of these dogs maintain values around 100,000/mm³ for many months.

As with plutonium there is an acute drop in red cells and a rise in sedimentation rate at one month in 5 level dogs with a return to normal values at three months. The values remain normal for the remaining period reported. The 4 level dogs have essentially normal red cell values for the thirty-six months.

Th²²⁸ (*Radiothorium*)

The responses of five groups of dogs which have been injected with Th²²⁸ (radiothorium) are given in Fig. 4. The graph was discontinued at thirty-nine months since only three groups of dogs have been on the experiment this long. The highest dose is 4 level instead of 5 level since only two groups were injected at the 5 level.

The pmns of 4 level dogs fall to a few hundred cells per mm³ during the first month. At one month they are still below 1000 cells (800 cells). There is a very slight rise thereafter and the cells plateau between 1000 and 2000 cells. The 3 level dogs show a drop in pmns to 2000 cells at one month and have only slightly higher values (around 3000 cells) after four months. The 2 and 1·5 level dogs were included since they show a definite but less marked drop in pmns.

The 4 level dogs show a drop in lymphocytes at one month to slightly below 2000 cells/mm³ with no subsequent tendency to recover. There is a slight drop in lymphocytes in 3 level dogs but by twelve months the values are back within the normal range.

The platelets in the 4 level dogs fall to extremely low values at one month (mean of 25,000/mm³). There is a gradual recovery until by six months they are again in the low normal range. A further fall in platelets is found as the dogs become terminal.

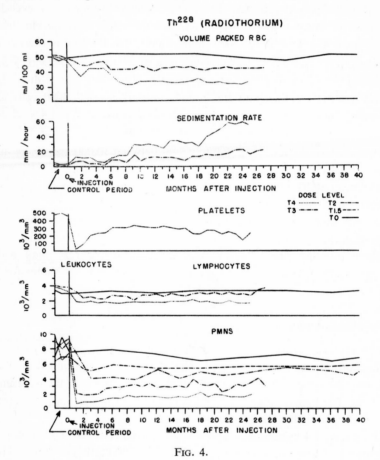

FIG. 4.

Hematological response of dogs injected with 0·0 (T0), 0·032 (T1.5), 0·096 (T2), 0·30 (T3) and 0·90 (T4) μc/kg of Th²²⁸ for thirty-nine months.

An early drop in the volume of packed red cells is found in both 3 and 4 level dogs with a slight recovery in the next two or three months. There is another fall beginning at seven months to even lower levels (values around 30·0 in 4 level and 40·0 in 3 level dogs) with no further tendency toward recovery. The sedimentation rate shows a progressive rise after eight months in both 3 and 4 level dogs.

Ra[228] (*Mesothorium*)

The hematological responses to Ra[228] (mesothorium) are presented in Fig. 5. There are only four groups of dogs injected thus far and only three groups have been on experiment for thirty-nine months.

The pmns show a different pattern of response from the other four radio-nuclides. These cells begin to fall at one month but do not attain minimal values until much later. The pmns of dogs on the 5 level dose decline to a mean value of 2200 cells/mm³ at thirteen months and values of this magnitude persist until the dogs are dead. The pmns of 4 level dogs also

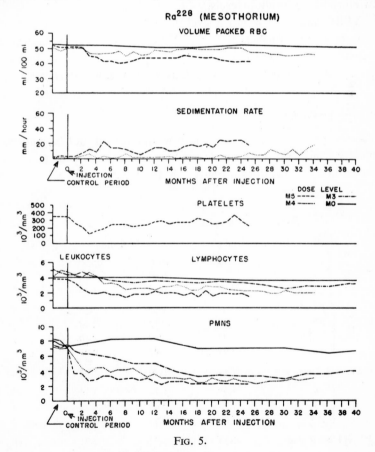

FIG. 5.

Hematological response of dogs injected with 0·0 (M0), 1·1 (M3), 3·2 (M4) and 10·0 (M5) μc/kg of Ra[228] for thirty-nine months.

reach this level at eighteen months and show only a slight recovery. The 3 level dogs drop to 3000 pmns by eighteen months and begin to show a slight rise by the thirty-first month.

The lymphocytes of 5 level dogs begin to fall by the second month and values of 1500–2000 cells/mm^3 are reached by the third month. This degree of lymphopenia is maintained thereafter. Four level dogs do not show a decrease in lymphocytes until the fifth month after injection and minimal values of around 2500 cells are reached by the eighth month and then remain at this level until the graph is terminated. Three level dogs develop a questionably significant drop in lymphocytes by thirty months.

The platelets of high level dogs fall to approximately 140,000/mm^3 by the third month and then rise to 250,000 by the sixth month and then slowly return to pre-injection levels.

The VPRC values of 4 and 5 level dogs fall by the third month. The 5 level dogs show a further decline of VPRC to 40·0 by six months and they remain anemic thereafter. The VPRC of the 4 level dogs returns to normal by fifteen months and only falls slightly again during the third year.

Bone Marrow Studies

A detailed presentation of bone marrow findings will not be made here. Preliminary results on bone marrow differential counts from mid femurs of injected and control dogs are given in Table 1.*

TABLE 1

Bone Marrow Analysis of M/E Ratio

		M/E average	95% Limits		No. of animals
			lower	upper	
I Controls		0.98	0.83	1·16	7
II	P5	2·44	1·68	3·53	6
	R5	1·67	1·12	2.48	9
	M5	1.93	0·69	5.40	5
	T4	3.94	1.92	8.08	4
All high level dogs		2·19	1·70	2.82	24
III	P4	1·95	1·14	3.34	7
	P3	1·28	0·43	3.84	4
	R4	2.08	0.74	5.81	7
P4, P3, R4 combined		1·82	1·22	2.71	18

*The data were compiled and analyzed by Dr. Lowell A. Woodbury.

The ratio of the percentage of developing myeloid cells to erythroid cells (M/E ratio) was determined for intermediate and higher dose level dogs and averages obtained for each radionuclide except strontium. The animals were divided into the following groups for analysis: I, controls; II, high level injected dogs (P5, R5, M5, T4); III, intermediate level (P4, P3, R4). Because the M/E values are ratios, all calculations were made using the logarithms of the ratios. The final tabulated values represent the antilogs of the calculations. Because of the use of logarithms, the averages obtained in this fashion will not necessarily check with the averages obtained in the ordinary fashion.

The general conclusions are as follows. There seems to be no overall general relationship between the length of time on experiment and the value of the M/E ratio. However, a series of test 5 level plutonium dogs autopsied at intervals up to two years showed a dose-time relationship.

The averages of the ratios of the dogs in group II are not significantly different from each other, that is, no difference in effect can be shown among the various radionuclides. The same conclusion applies to the different radionuclides or levels in the group III dogs. However, the average values of M/E for the control, II and III groups all show significant differences. In general, an effect of dose level was shown on the M/E ratio but no effect of radionuclide was demonstrated.

DISCUSSION AND SUMMARY

The great majority of the studies on the effects of bone-seeking radionuclides on the hematopoietic system have been on smaller species and after injection of much larger doses of radionuclides than those given here. There have been several reviews recently comparing internal versus external radiation effects on blood cells.[3,4,5] Studies on smaller species will be only briefly mentioned since a considerable difference in effect between rodents and rabbits as compared to dogs or monkeys might be expected due to differences in bone mass, pattern of bone growth, lifespan of the animals, etc.

After Ra^{226} administration no hematological changes were noted in rats, mice or rabbits at 0·01 $\mu c/g$ whereas a depression of both red and white cells was seen in mice and rats in doses between 0·02 and 0·03 $\mu c/g$ and leukocyte reduction at 0·1 $\mu c/g$ in rabbits but no anemia.[6] No hematological alterations were noted in 300 days in mice, rabbits and rats after administration of 0·0003 and 0·0006 $\mu c/g$ of Pu^{239} whereas a minimal to moderate depression of leukocytes and platelets was noted in these species within 100 days after 0·003 $\mu c/g$ and an anemia in rats and mice but not in rabbits at this dose.[6]. A leukopenia lasting 200 days after injection of 4.6 μc/kg of Pu^{239} into beagle pups and adult mongrels has been reported.[7]

There have been several studies in which hematological changes were found after Sr^{90} administration. When given to 6–8-week-old rabbits in doses of 500 to 1000 μc/kg, an anemia, leukopenia and thrombocytopenia appeared in sixteen days lasting to 219 days.[8] Changes in hematopoiesis as evidenced by femur marrow changes have been reported in rats at 100–500 μc/kg.[9] Dogs given 150 μc/kg of Sr^{90} showed marked hematological effects.[10] Also, lethal doses to monkeys of 500–2000 μc/kg resulted in leukopenia and thrombocytopenia in five days and an anemia appeared after ten days.[11]

We have found hematological changes in doses far lower than reported for mice, rats or rabbits. There are no reports of studies in larger species of animals using comparable doses to those used here.

A comparison of the effects of these five radionuclides as to initial effect and recovery rate of blood cells indicates that radiothorium is the most toxic. This is to be expected due to its pattern of radioactive decay. An attempt was made to relate hematological changes to average radiation dose to the skeleton in rad/day and total average rads at periods of from one to four years. The highest dose level was selected. The data in Table 2 were obtained from retention and distribution studies presented in another section of this book.[12]

It is apparent that factors other than total radiation dose or dose rate enter into changes in hematopoiesis, i. e. factors such as metabolism of

TABLE 2

*Average Radiation Dose to Skeleton**

t (y)	Average dose rates (rad/day)					Average dose (rad)				
	10·4μc Ra^{226}/kg	2·88μc Pu^{239}/kg	9·95μc Ra^{228}/kg	0·888μc Th^{228}/kg	99·4μc Sr^{90}/kg	Ra^{226}	Pu^{239}	Ra^{228}	Th^{228}	Sr^{90}
1	11·1	4·4	14·2	5·6	8·0	4630	1670	3580	1930	3900
2	10·3	4·3	19·6	3·9	6·8	8640	3250	9650	3900	6600
3	9·9	4·2	38·3	2·5	6·0	12200	4790	16900	5000	9500
4	9·6	4·1	36·5	1·7	5·6	15700	6320	24400	5800	10900

*The average dose calculations are based on uniform dissipation of the energy in the skeleton. Weight of skeleton is taken as 10 per cent of the dog's weight at injection.

the radionuclide, its location in bone and amount in soft tissues, etc. Although Pu^{239} and Th^{228} have the lowest dose in rads per day and total dose, they have more effect on blood cells. This may be due to their location on bone surfaces which results in more direct irradiation of marrow, and they also may cause greater changes in blood supply to marrow, etc. The buildup in dose rate for Ra^{228} as contrasted to the other radionuclides is reflected in the slower decline and recovery of the blood cells.

In general, there is a dose response effect on blood cells for all radionuclides. This is particularly true for the pmn response where the greatest initial effect is found. No early increase in these cells was noted at two or four days, although this has been reported for other species. A depression of pmns is seen after injection of the three highest doses of all the radionuclides and even after lower doses for some (Pu, RdTh). It is interesting to note that dogs with a marked degree of neutropenia for several years show no increased evidence of infection. Also it should be emphasized that there is some degree of recovery of pmns even in lethal doses.

There is a lymphopenia in all high level dogs with some decrease also in 4 level and even in 3 level dogs. The fact that these cells show little tendency toward recovery in contrast to the granular leukocytes suggests an indirect mechanism of action. This is also borne out by the fact that there is very little or no activity present in lymphatic tissues after the first twenty-four hours following injection. It has been suggested that the reduction in lymphocytes may be related to altered adrenocortical function in high level dogs.[13]

Although a decrease in red cells and a reduced red cell volume[14] has been seen with all the radionuclides, the pattern of change and dose level where changes are found differ among them. Radiothorium produces the most sustained red cell depression although there is slight recovery after the initial drop even in the higher levels. Both high level plutonium and strontium dogs have a transient anemia during the first few months after injection with subsequent recovery to normal levels. The plutonium dogs again develop a progressive anemia after two years as the dogs become terminal. No early period of anemia is found in 5 level radium dogs although they also become anemic before death. An anemia is found occasionally in 4 level dogs but not in 3 level dogs thus far with the exception of radiothorium and a few plutonium dogs. The mechanism of this anemia has been investigated using Cr^{57} tagging of red cells and no clear-cut effect on red cell survival was found although slight damage to red cells was suggested by the fact that survivals for many of the anemic irradiated dogs fell into the low normal range.[15]

In conclusion, it should again be emphasized that these are interim results which are presented here and more meaningful comparisons and conclusions can only be drawn when the experiment has been completed and data from other aspects of the project are related to the hematology program.

REFERENCES

1. T. F. DOUGHERTY, Study of the long term biological effects of internal irradiation in adult beagles. This vol., p. 3.
2. J. H. DOUGHERTY, J. Z. BOWERS, R. C. BAY and P. KEYANONDA, Comparison of hematologic effects of internally deposited radium and plutonium in dogs, *Radiology* **65**, 253–59 (1955).
3. A. HALLAENDER, *Radiation Biology I*, Part 2, McGraw-Hill, New York, 1029–1090 (1954).
4. M. ERRERA and A. FORSSBERG, *Mechanism in Radiobiology*, II, Academic Press, New York and London, 108–121 (1960).
5. L. O. JACOBSON, E. K. MARKS and F. LORENZ, The hematological effects of ionizing radiation, *Radiology* **52**, 371–395 (1949).
6. L. O. JACOBSON and E. L. SIMMONS, Studies of the metabolism and toxic action of injected radium. Part II, The hematological effects of parenterally administered radium. A comparison of plutonium and radium effects, USAEC report AECD-2372 (1946).
7. E. PAINTER, E. RUSSELL, C. L. PROSSER, M. N. SWIFT, W. KISIELESKI and G. SACHER, Clinical physiology of dogs injected with plutonium, AECD-2042 (1946).
8. M. OWEN, H. A. SISSIONS and J. VAUGHAN, The effect of a single injection of high dose of Sr^{90} (500–1000 $\mu c/kg$) in rabbits, *Brit. J. Cancer* **11**, 229–248 (1957).
9. W. A. D. ANDERSON, G. E. ZANDER and J. F. KUZMA, A study of toxic doses of Sr^{90} in the adult rat, *A.M.A. Arch of Path.* **62**, 433–440 (1956).
10. M. P. FINKEL and A. M. BRUES, Sequelae of radiostrontium administration to dogs, *Rad. Res.* **3**, 224–5 (1955).
11. G. M. EDINGTON, A. H. WARD, J. M. JUDD and R. H. MOLE, The acute lethal effects in monkeys of radiostrontium, *J. Pathol. and Bacteriol.* **71**, 277–293 (1956).
12. B. J. STOVER, D. R. ATHERTON and C. W. MAYS, Studies of the retention and distribution of Ra^{226}, Pu^{239}, Ra^{228}(MsTh), Th^{228} (RdTh) and Sr^{90} in adult beagles, This vol., p. 7.
13. D. L. BERLINER, M. L. BERLINER and T. F. DOUGHERTY, The effects of chronic irradiation by internally deposited radionuclides on corticosteroid biosynthesis, This vol., p. 179.
14. J. E. PARKINSON and J. H. DOUGHERTY, Effect of internal emitters on red cells and plasma volumes of beagle dogs, *Proc. Soc.* **97**, 722–725 (1958).
15. J. E. PARKINSON, The effect of internal emitters on red cell survival in beagle dogs, *Rad. Res.* **10**, 63–66 (1959).

DISCUSSION

MOLE: I would like to ask if any studies of bone marrow sections have been made and whether this myeloid-erythroid ratio changes as you get farther away from the bone surface.

J. H. DOUGHERTY: We have examined some bone marrow sections. The cellular composition near bony surfaces does not seem to differ markedly from areas of active hematopoiesis in the shaft. However, it is not possible to obtain M/E ratios on bone marrow sections and it is quite possible that some differences exist. In a small series of serially sacrificed "test-run" 5 level plutonium dogs we have found lower M/E ratios in bone marrow smears of flat bones (rib and sternum) than in long bones (femur and humerus).

T. F. DOUGHERTY: A point made by Dr. Jean Dougherty that was skipped over a bit is that there is regenerative capacity of marrow at a time when there is a marked anemia or a leukopenia in the dogs. Unfortunately, leukophoresis cannot be performed on these chronic toxicity animals, so one cannot get at bone marrow regeneration studies in this way. However, the point that she made is that the marrow can respond to intercurrent infections.

HISTOPATHOLOGICAL ENDPOINTS IN COMPACT BONES RECEIVING ALPHA IRRADIATION*

W. S. S. JEE

*Department of Anatomy, University of Utah College of Medicine,
Salt Lake City, Utah*

INTRODUCTION

THE following observations are part of a larger study of the comparative toxicities of radium (Ra^{226}), plutonium (Pu^{239}), mesothorium (Ra^{228}) and radiothorium (Th^{228}) in beagles. One of the chief aims of the project is to provide a quantitation of histological changes in bone induced by a wide range of radiation doses.

The present report will summarize our progress in quantitative histopathological studies of tibial compacta with and without radionuclides. These observations along with the critical analyses of the changes in trabecular bone constitute our program on quantitation of histopathological changes in bone as a consequence of long term effects of bone-seeking alpha emitters. Although our fiindings on the tibial compacta are based upon autopsied beagles containing relatively large quantities of radionuclides and succumbing to osteogenic sarcomas, it is hoped that these findings will shed some light on the selection of endpoints in the skeleton which will be useful in evaluating the injurious effects of smaller quantities of bone-seeking radionuclides.

MATERIALS AND METHODS

Transverse sections of the tibial diaphyses from 15 controls and 46 beagles given radionuclides were surveyed (Table 1). The 46 dogs represent R5, R4, R3, P5, P4, P3, P2, T4, T2, T1·5 T0·5, M5, M4, M3—14 nuclide dose level combinations. A complete breakdown of these experimental animals and details of the chronic toxicity experiment can be found elsewhere.[1] Briefly, young adult beagles of mixed sexes between 14 and 20 months were given a single intravenous injection of one of the principally alpha emitting bone-seeking radionuclides (Pu^{239}, Ra^{226}, Ra^{228}, and Th^{228}). These dogs were permitted to live until moribund when they were anesthetized with sodium pentothal and exsanguinated. The entire skeleton was

*Supported by U.S.A.E.C. and a (equipment) grant from the American Cancer Society Institutional Grant No. IN-30A.

TABLE 1

Changes in Compacta of Tibiae in Beagles Containing Radionuclides

Radionuclide	No. of specimens	Inj. dose (μc/kg)	Average accumulated rads	Average days post injection	Percentage				
					Open vascular channels	Viable osteocytes	Resorption units	Canal plugs	Canal plugs blocked channels
Controls	25		0	1089–3896(a)	84.0	85.9	5.9	1.2	9.41
226Ra-5	10	10.0	11,617	1033	37.4	29.3	19.5	6.3	9.93
226Ra-4	9	3.0	5560	1774	42.6	37.1	13.8	9.0	6.37
226Ra-3	4	1.0	2462	2143	52.9	71.3	6.4	7.6	6.19
239Pu-5	4	2.7	6335	1385	31.6	26.5	18.1	9.5	7.20
239Pu-4	4	0.9	1645	1178	48.0	45.8	10.1	6.4	8.12
239Pu-3	8	0.3	760	1711	44.9	43.1	9.0	6.2	8.87
239Pu-2	6	0.09	336	2277	—	—	—	4.5	—
228Th-4	6	0.9	3910	755	14.4	10.9	15.8	7.6	11.26
228Th-2	4	0.09	575	1336	44.2	38.0	11.9	4.3	12.97
228Th-1.5	1	0.03	220	1921	—	—	—	8.6	—
228Th-0.5	1	0.005	40	1976	—	—	—	2.9	—
228Ra-5(3)	4	10.0	9965	730	19.6	8.9	16.2	8.3	9.68
228Ra-4(3)	2	3.0	3940	896	24.5	22.5	10.7	7.9	9.55
228Ra-3(3)	1	1.0	1820	1185	42.1	56.1	10.2	1.7	34.05

(a) Age range at post-mortem of 15 animals. — No determination performed to date.   (3) μc Th^{229}/μc Ra^{228}=0.06.

TABLE 1 (Cont'd.)

Changes in Compacta of Tibiae in Beagles Containing Radionuclides

Radionuclide	No. of specimens	Inj. dose (μc/kg)	Average accumulated rads	Average days post injection	Percentage				
					Forming osteon	Abnormal osteon	Hypomin. osteon	Hypo. & enlarged canal	Porosity
Controls	25		0	1089–3896[a]	3·5	0	6·2	1·0	4·2
226Ra-5	10	10·0	11,617	1033	10·3	4·9	11·8	9·6	14·6
226Ra-4	9	3·0	5560	1774	9·9	3·6	15·4	11·0	12·1
226Ra-3	4	1·0	2462	2143	6·5	2·8	17·9	10·8	9·6
239Pu-5	4	2·7	6335	1385	14·5	3·9	12·4	10·4	17·1
239Pu-4	4	0·9	1645	1178	10·2	1·2	15·3	7·5	11·1
239Pu-3	8	0·3	760	1711	6·7	1·6	16·8	4·1	5·3
239Pu-2	6	0·09	336	2277	—	0	10·9	4·9	5·6
228Th-4	6	0·9	3910	755	9·1	2·8	1·7	3·9	13·6
228Th-2	4	0·09	575	1336	12·2	1·5	9·0	3·6	7·6
228Th-1·5	1	0·03	220	1921	—	0	11·0	5·0	5·9
228Th-0·5	1	0·005	40	1976	—	0	5·4	1·0	4·4
228Ra-5[3]	4	10·0	9965	730	9·0	4·2	—	—	—
228Ra-4[3]	2	3·0	3940	896	9·1	3·1	—	—	—
228Ra-3[3]	1	1·0	1820	1185	10·1	1·6	—	—	—

[a] Age range at post-mortem of 15 animals. — No determination performed to date. [3] μc Th^{228}/μc Ra^{228}=·006.

thoroughly studied. In this report only the studies involving the tibial diaphysis will be reviewed.

Altered circulation in the tibia was measured by the introduction of a vascular injection mass (India ink, 1 part: 14% solution of calfskin gelatin, 1 part) into the femoral artery of a disarticulated hindlimb. After disarticulating and defleshing the tibia, the mid-diaphysis was sawed into three adjacent 2 cm long specimens. The middle segment was fixed in absolute acetone for microradiography, while the proximal and distal segments were fixed in Zenker-formol and demineralized for hematoxylin and eosin stained celloidin sections. The descriptions of structural changes and technical procedures used have been described in detail elsewhere.[2,3]

Detailed analyses of distal and proximal tibial mid-diaphyses from hematoxylin and eosin stained celloidin sections provided the following information (Figs. 5, 6, 7, and 8):

1. Per cent of patent vascular channels. This was determined by counting the number of vascular channels filled with India ink.

2. Per cent of viable osteocytes.

3. Per cent of resorption units. A resorption unit is a cavity with a diameter equal to an average sized osteone. Also the number, size and content of the resorption cavities were recorded.

4. Per cent of canal plugs. Most were partial plugs and only a few were complete plugs.

5. Per cent of forming osteones. These osteones had osteoblasts lining the surface of the cavity.

6. Per cent of abnormal osteones. Generally these osteones were structurally abnormal in shape, due to the orientation of osteocytes and lamellae and often contained basophilic staining tissue.

   Detailed analyses of the microradiographs of tibial mid-diaphyses provided the following information (Figs. 1, 2, 3, 4, 9, 10, 11 and 12):

1. The per cent of hypomineralized osteones. In the process of bone formation, osteoid tissue calcifies rapidly to over half of its eventual full mineralization. Further mineralization takes many months.[4] These hypomineralized (low density) osteones were used as an indication of recently formed bone[5] or as an indication of some mechanism by which internally deposited radionuclides inhibit the osteones from achieving full mineralization.

2. Per cent of hypomineralized osteones with enlarged canals. These structures were interpreted as an indication of an increased remodelling

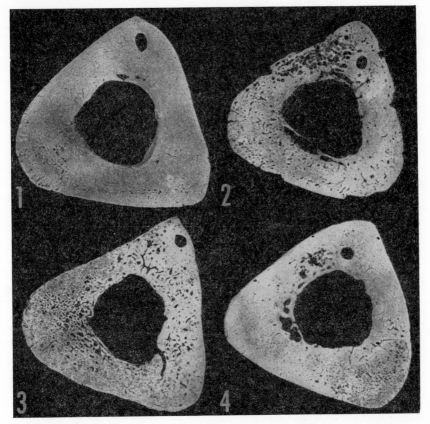

FIG. 1.

Seven-year-old control.

FIG. 2.

Extreme damage due to radium. Note periosteal and endosteal resorption.

FIG. 3.

Relatively more diffuse distribution of cavities.

FIG. 4.

Localized damage in two regions.
Microradiographs of tibial diaphyses ($\times 2\frac{1}{2}$).

7*

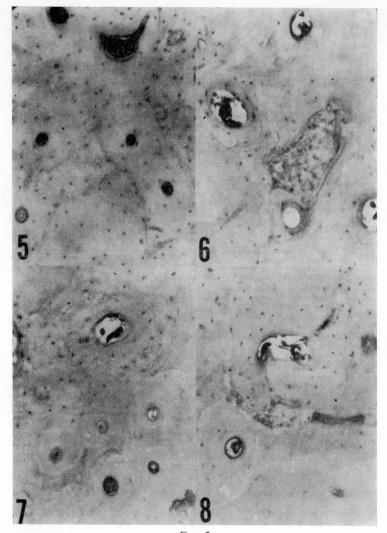

FIG. 5.

Control. Note plugged canal.

FIG. 6.

Note abnormal osteone and forming osteone.

FIG. 7.

Note relationship of India ink to viable osteocytes.

FIG. 8.

Note huge osteone adjacent to region of dead bone.
Areas from hematoxylin and eosin stained celloidin sections ($\times$75).

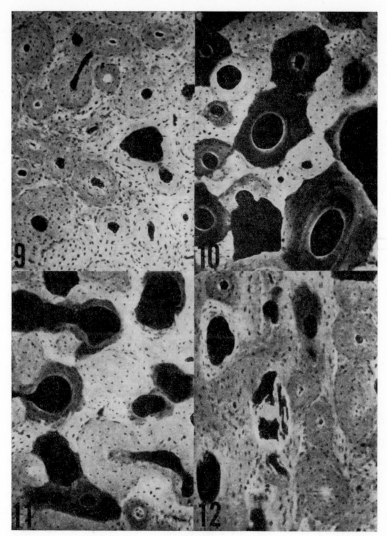

FIG. 9.

Control with resorption cavity and canal plug.

FIG. 10.

Large hypomineralized osteones with and without enlarged canals.

FIG. 11.

Many resorption cavities and canal plugs.

FIG. 12.

Hypermineralized tissues (white) in abnormal osteone with enlarged canal.
Areas from microradiographs ($\times 50$).

rate (forming osteones) or as endpoints of pathological remodelling with the persistence of the enlarged canals resulting from cessation of appositional bone growth.

3. Per cent abnormal osteones.

4. Per cent canal plugs. Both the abnormal osteones and canal plug counts supplemented the counts from celloidin sections.

5. Per cent porosity. This includes an analysis of the loss of bone from the endosteal, periosteal and core (interstitial lamellae, haversian bone and vascular channels) regions of the compactum. Measurements were made by cutting out and weighing areas of missing bone from an enlarged photograph ($\times 52$) of the microradiograms.

The histopathological endpoints described above were unevenly distributed in tibial compacta containing radionuclides (Figs. 2, 3, and 4). Therefore, entire cross sections were analyzed. Three cross sections of the tibial diaphysis from each dog containing approximately 6000 osteones were surveyed.

The table and histograms summarizing the findings have included the average accumulated skeletal dose in rads and the elapsed time from the acquisition of radionuclide to death. The dose values were obtained from the report of Mays et al.[6] in which the calculations assumed a uniform distribution of radionuclides in mineralized tissues.

RESULTS

I. Observation on Control Animals

There was very little spread in the measurements of 15 control beagles, whose ages range from 1089 to 3896 days. This holds true for the determination of patent vascular channels involving the vascular injection technique which is well documented by the excellent agreement between the numbers of viable osteocytes, and labelled vascular channels. An earlier paper from this laboratory shows that there is an excellent correlation between patent vascular channels and viable osteocytes.[3]

In the control group not all the vascular channels are patent (84%) nor are all the osteocytes alive (85·9%). There is a ratio of canal plugs to blocked channels of 1:9. It is assumed that this ratio is reliable and that vascular channels in the compactum are branched and, therefore, any upstream vascular plug could block many channels downstream.

All the remaining observations indicate that the turnover rate (remodelling) of the compactum is low and constant in the age range between 3 and 10 years. The averages of these measurements are: 5·9% resorption units,

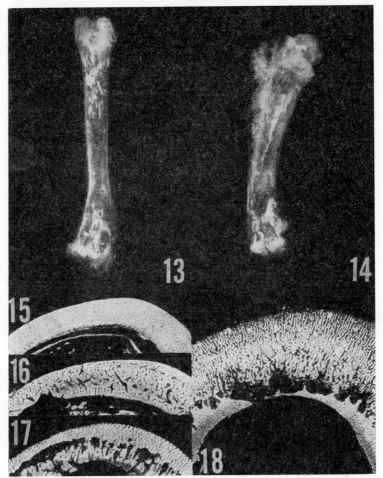

FIG. 13.
Control rabbit femur with micropaque filled vessels ($\times \frac{1}{3}$).

FIG. 14.
Structurally distorted femur with micropaque after partial plugging of nutrient
artery. Contralateral femur of Fig. 13 ($\times \frac{1}{3}$).

Microradiographs of compact bone ($\times 4$).

FIG. 15.
Control to Fig. 18.

FIG. 16.
Increased porosity after treatment.

FIG. 17.
Massive resorption after treatment.

FIG. 18.
Massive periosteal bone proliferation.

3·5% forming osteones, 6·2% hypomineralized osteones, 1·0% hypomineralized osteones with enlarged canals and 4·2% porosity. Most of the osteones are fully closed and have achieved full mineralization except for 6·2% of the hypomineralized osteones. The porosity of 4·2% of the compactum is due to the presence of haversian canals and resorption cavities. Resorption cavities are the result of the process of cavitation in existing bone and replacement with a new secondary osteone. Resorption of the periosteal or endosteal bone surfaces is slight. Resorption cavities present in the core of the compactum are randomly distributed and never exceed three times the diameter of an average osteone. The cavities usually contain loose connective tissue, osteoblasts and/or osteoclasts.

II. Compacta Containing Radionuclides

The histograms of the tibial compacta containing radionuclides show the following common effects (Figures 19, 20, 21 and 22):

1. The quantity and type of histopathologic changes in the compacta are dose dependent. This holds true for all nine endpoints analyzed.

2. Elapsed time between the acquisition of the radionuclide and death is of utmost importance. Increased burden time (lifespan with radionuclide) increases the opportunity to express damage because this increases the volume of the bone remodelled as a function of time. For instance, two groups of animals containing plutonium showed nearly identical damage, although the absorbed radiation doses differed by a factor of two. The P3 dogs survived 1711 days post injection and received 760 rads and the P4 dogs survived 1178 days post injection and received 1645 rads. The P3 dogs receiving the lower dose survived some 600 days longer after the acquisition of the radionuclide than those receiving the higher dose.

3. There appears to be a threshold dose for the formation of abnormal osteones. The threshold exists for both the radiothorium and plutonium series. However, this observation may be premature since there are many animals in the T0·5, T1·5, P2 and lower injected doses in all four radionuclide groups still alive.

4. There is a marked loss of bone as measured by resorption units and total porosity in beagles with high dose levels of radionuclides. Sites of the missing bone include the endosteal, periosteal and core regions. In the core, the phenomenon of clumping of resorption cavities is quite common (Figs. 2, 3, and 4). In the lower dose animals the diminution of bone is restricted to the appearance of resorption cavities not more than three times the diameter of an average osteone within the core of the compacta

(Fig. 4). A few of the animals containing radionuclides exhibit porosities well within the normal values.

5. There is a marked increase in the number of both hypomineralized osteones with enlarged canals, and completed hypomineralized osteones. In compacta containing large amounts of radionuclide, the osteones containing large canals are incomplete and lack bone forming cells. The presence of the radionuclide has inhibited the completion of osteones both in architecture and mineralization.

6. There is an increased exaggeration of the relationship between canal plugs and blocked vascular channels. The ratio of canal plugs to blocked channels is as high as 1:35 compared to 1:9 for the controls.

7. A comparison of the relative effectiveness of all four radionuclides was made using calculations of radiation dose which assumes uniform distribution throughout the skeleton. The bone surface depositors (radiothorium and plutonium) are much more effective rad for rad. Radiothorium was more damaging than plutonium which may be due to its longer range alpha particles and its rapidly decaying daughter products.

III. Peculiarities of Compacta Containing Radium (Fig. 19)

Compacta containing radium shows a large variety and quantity of histopathological alterations. There is marked inhibition of bone formation and conversely a stimulation of bone resorption which results in an increased porosity of the bone. All three groups of animals absorbing different doses and having different burden times of the radionuclide show similar patterns of stimulated bone resorption. All areas of the compacta in the R5 group are involved (contrary to the controls). Approximately 40% of the total porosity is from the periosteal and endosteal surfaces. A few cases in both the 4 and 5 level radium animals exhibit an abnormal proliferation of periosteal and endosteal bone. The endosteal proliferation generally fills the entire marrow cavity while the periosteal proliferation often accounts for the addition of 50% more bone.

The appearance of resorption cavities in the 4 and 5 level animals is unique in that there are cavities as large as 30 times the diameter of an osteone. Three and six tenths per cent of the resorption cavities are at least four times the diameter of an average osteone. Not only are these cavities large, but they usually appear in clumps confined to one or two quadrants of the compacta, while the remaining bone appears less affected (Figs. 2, 3, and 4). The contents of these cavities consist of loose or dense connective tissue (fibrosis) with the absence of osteoblasts and osteoclasts. Frequently, they contain bone marrow cells and red blood corpuscles.

The presence of radium produces many hypomineralized osteones with enlarged canals. Not only do these hypomineralized osteones with enlarged canals appear in large numbers, but they are usually much larger than the average sized osteones in diameter (Fig. 10).

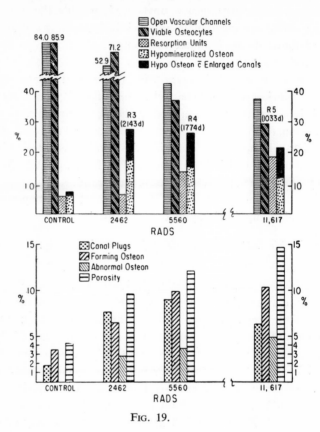

FIG. 19.

IV. Peculiarities of Compacta Containing Plutonium (Fig. 20)

There is no doubt that in the four groups of animals containing plutonium and having absorbed radiation doses ranging from 336 to 6335 rads that the compacta are affected with what appears to be an increased rate of bone remodelling, altered circulation and loss of viability.

Compacta containing plutonium exhibits all the abnormal structures seen in the compacta containing radium. This radionuclide produces an environment much less efficient for massive bone resorption and equal in the production of hypomineralized osteones. Bone resorption is found throughout the compacta. In the dogs studied to date, the resorption cavities in the core of the compacta are much smaller in size than those analyzed from the compacta containing radium (Fig. 11). Only 1% of the resorption cavities are more than four times the diameter of an average sized osteone. In one specimen the osteone was found to have a diameter 25 times that of an average osteone. All of the remaining osteones have diameters three times that of an average osteone and the contents of these cavities are similar to those observed in the compacta with radium.

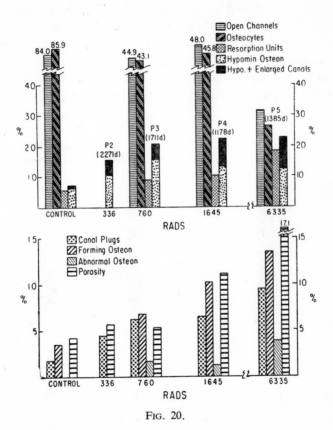

FIG. 20.

V. *Peculiarities of Compacta Containing Radiothorium* (Fig. 21)

Studies of the compacta containing radiothorium are incomplete. However, extreme changes are induced by the 4 level radiothorium animals in a comparatively short span of time (755 days). These compacta exhibit a reduction in the number of patent vascular channels (14·4%) and in the number of viable osteocytes (10·9%). The drastic reduction in circulation appears to have inhibited the formation of many of the histopathological alterations. Depression of bone remodelling is reflected in the few hypo-mineralized structures observed; however, the total bone porosity is greatly increased and must have occurred soon after the acquisition of the radio-nuclide and before the massive reduction in circulation. A loss of bone is observed scattered throughout the compactum. The bone resorbed from the periosteal and endosteal surfaces represents 40% of the porosity. Earlier observation found that the entire metatarsal compactum of a 4 level radiothorium dog at autopsy was lacking in functional vascular channels and that the blood flow was restricted to their periosteal and the endosteal surfaces of the compactum.[3] Hence, the massive absorption was limited to these particular areas. Four per cent of the resorption cavities were larger than three times the diameter of an average osteone and one cavity was 25 times the diameter of an average osteone.

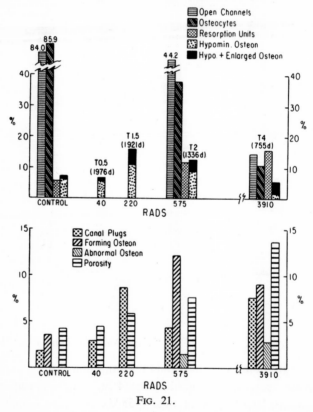

FIG. 21.

Processing of the celloidin sections in the T1·5 and T0·5 animals has not been completed. It would be premature to discuss the scanty measurements available at this time.

VI. *Peculiarities of Compacta Containing Mesothorium* (Fig. 22)

The specimens in this category are limited to an analysis of celloidin sections. These animals did not receive pure mesothorium but a ratio of μc Th^{228} to Ra^{228} equal to 0·006. There is no doubt that mesothorium is very effective in depressing the remodelling of compacta, and reducing numbers of patent vascular channels and viable osteocytes in a short span of time. The extreme reduction in these two endpoints and the high ratio of canal plugs to blocked vascular channels indicates that vascular channels supplying the compacta in the marrow spaces have been affected.

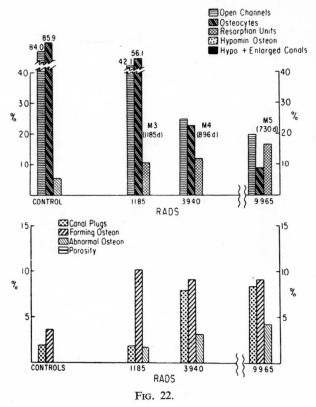

FIG. 22.

DISCUSSION

The analyses of damage to the tibial compacta represent only a portion of our program to quantitate histopathological changes in bone as a consequence of long term effects of bone-seeking alpha emitters. Surveys of trabecular bone damage are to be completed. These changes are more difficult to detect, but are of greater importance in that bone tumors arise principally from these areas. Histological parameters for the analyses of trabecular bone changes in dogs with various radionuclides and radiation doses have been defined. These include the descriptions of early and late term changes of trabecular bone,[7,8] and a recent attempt at quantitation of these changes in dogs injected with 2·8 μc/kg of plutonium.[9]

All the structural changes observed in dog bones have been reported for normal and radium-bearing human beings.[5,10,11,12,13] In normal human compacta, large cavities are found in the endosteal region (osteoporosis) and the canal plugs are located very close to the periosteum[5] while these same structures are found throughout the compactum in radium-bearing humans[14] and radionuclide-bearing beagles. Rowland reports a 40 per cent incidence of canal plugs in an individual who painted watch dials for a two-month period at age 15 and died at age 47 with an osteogenic sarcoma.[14] The highest concentration detected in our studies was 9·5 per cent in beagles, but this animals only survived five years with the radionuclides compared to 32 years for the watch dial painter.

From this investigation it may be concluded that the functional and structural changes in compacta subjected to continuous internal irradiation appear to be dose dependent. High radiation doses alter the circulation, produce bone necrosis and bizarre osteones, stimulate bone resorption and inhibit bone formation. In general, the altered environment in these bones appears to have accelerated bone remodelling or inhibited hypo-mineralized osteones from achieving full mineralization. These pathological entities appear to result from the animal's attempt at adaptive reaction to the adverse environmental change in the circulation.

Bone necrosis and reactive changes are not the exclusive responses of internally deposited alpha irradiation. Drugs, trauma and operative proce-dures (cortisone, fractures, ligation of periosteal and nutrient vessels, etc.) result in endosteal and periosteal bone formation and medullization of the cortex (gross enlargement of haversian canals).[15,16,17,18]

Experiments in this laboratory used the injection of a particulate suspen-sion to produce partial ischemia similar to that caused by internal irra-diation. Infarcts were produced by intra-arterial injection of dextran sul-fate and charcoal into the nutrient arteries of the femurs from two month old rabbits, while the contralateral limb served as control (Figs. 13 and 14). Reactive changes included stunted growth and increased porosity at two weeks (Fig. 16); massive bone resorption (Fig. 17) and endosteal bone growth at one month; and a bizarre proliferation of periosteal bone at three months (Fig. 18). The contralateral limb from the same rabbit after three months appeared normal (Fig. 15).

The ratio of canal plugs to non-functional vascular channels of 1:9 in controls increased to as high as 1:35 in chronic toxicity animals. This ratio (1:35) implies that radiothorium and mesothorium must have inflicted damage on the main vascular channels in the marrow cavity which leads to the compacta. These vessels in the marrow cavity are the main supply lines to the cortical bone.[18] In our histological examination of the vascular injection studies of the spongiosa we observed a loss and diminution of functional vessels in the marrow cavities of bones containing high doses of radiothorium and mesothorium. The cavities are occupied by intense fibrosis, hemorrhage and loss of vascularity.[19]

The main pitfalls in the attempt to quantitate histopathological changes are the tedium of the techniques, the unchallenged sensitivity of the endpoints for damage and the incorrect assumption that the damage observed in a cross section of tibia will be a representative change of the skeleton. Microscopic survey involves analysis of some 6000 osteones per tibia per animal. At present the dogs succumbing to bone tumors have readily detectable histological damage, but no radiologically detectable damage. However, in the near future the surviving crop of beagles with lower radiation doses may not have histologically detectable tissue damage in the skeleton and yet bone tumors will occur. This is contrary to observation that tumors appear to arise from areas of gross tissue damage where high doses were used, which inevitably produced gross damage.[11,20,21] It is obvious that a single alpha particle can produce damage, but the event may go undetected due to the transient, reparable and localized nature of the damage. Another important factor is that the trauma of ageing, may mask many minute alterations induced by the radionuclides. However, at present the decision regarding their sensitivity must be deferred.

SUMMARY

1. Tibial diaphyses from 15 controls and 46 beagles given a single intravenous injection of one of the bone-seeking radionuclides (Pu^{239}, Ra^{226}, Ra^{228} or Th^{228}) were analyzed for patent vascular channels, viable osteocytes bone resorption, canal plugs, forming osteones, abnormal osteones, hypomineralized osteones, hypomineralized osteones with enlarged canals and porosity.

2. The results indicated that turnover rate of the compacta of dogs between three and ten years old was slow and constant.

3. Structural changes in compacta containing internally deposited alpha emitters appeared to be dose dependent. High radiation doses altered the circulation, produced bone necrosis and bizarre osteones, stimulated bone

resorption and inhibited bone formation. The increased accumulations of these structures indicated a more rapid turnover rate for the radionuclide-bearing dogs when compared to controls.

4. The ratio of canal plugs to blocked vascular channels in damaged campacta was as high as 1:35 as compared to 1:9 for controls. The high ratio (1:35) was due to damage to main arterial channels supplying cortical bone in the marrow cavities.

5. Time played an important role in that many of the changes were cumulative. Two groups of dogs show nearly identical damage, although the radiation doses and burden times of radionuclides were 1711 days, 760 rads and 1178 days, 1645 rads, respectively.

6. The circulation factor was mainly responsible for the altered remodelling. The response of compact bone to partial ischemia was massive resorption and endosteal and periosteal bone proliferation resembling changes induced by internally deposited radionuclides in bone.

ACKNOWLEDGEMENTS

I would like to express my gratitude to my former colleague, Dr. James S. Arnold, for a very stimulating discussion in the embryonic years of this project which led to these studies; to Loring Beals, Patrick Nolan, Renata Tegge, Renon Mical and Constance Bell for their technical assistance and to Professor T. F. Dougherty, Director of the Division of Radiobiology, Department of Anatomy, for his constant support of our studies. Also I must thank Walter Stevens and Julian Maack for their help in preparation of the manuscript.

REFERENCES

1. T. F. DOUGHERTY, Research in Radiobiology, Annual Progress Report, Radiobiology Laboratory, College of Medicine, University of Utah, COO-223 (1961).
2. W. S. S. JEE and J. S. ARNOLD, India ink-gelatin vascular injection of skeletal tissues, *Stain Technol.* **35**, 59–65 (1960).
3. W. S. S. JEE and J. S. ARNOLD, The effect of internally deposited radioisotopes upon the blood vessels of cortical bone, *Proc. Soc. Exp. Biol. Med.* **105**, 351–356 (1960).
4. R. AMPRIMO, Raporti fra processi di recostruzione e distribuzione dei minerali nella ossa. I. Ricerche eseqiute col metodo di studio dell' assorbmento dei raggi Roentgen, *Z. Zellforsch.* **37**, 144–239 (1952).
5. J. JOWSEY, Age changes in human bone, *Clinical Orthopaedics* **17**, 210–218 (1960).
6. C. W. MAYS, B. J. STOVER, B. W. GLAD and D. R. ATHERTON, Skeletal dosimetry in Utah beagles, Annual Progress Report, Radiobiology Laboratory, University of Utah, COO-218, 121–139 (1959).

7. W. S. S. JEE, J. S. ARNOLD and T. H. COCHRAN, Skeletal changes induced by chronic doses of plutonium, radium, mesothorium and radiothorium, *Anat. Rev.* **130**, 420 (1958).

8. W. S. S. JEE and J. S. ARNOLD, The toxicity of plutonium deposited in skeletal tissues of beagles. I. The relation of the distribution of plutonium to the sequence of histopathological bone changes, *Lab. Invest.* **10**, 797–825 (1961).

9. J. TWENTE, W. S. S. JEE, B. J. STOVER and D. R. ATHERTON, An evaluation of radiochemical and microdensitometric dose measurements in bone and their relationship to damage (In preparation).

10. W. B. LOONEY, Late effects (twenty-five and forty years) of early medical and industrial use of radioactive material. Their relation to the more accurate establishment of maximum permissible amounts of radioactive elements in the body, Part I, *J. Bone and Joint Surg.* **37A**, 1169–1187 (1955).

11. H. LISCO, Bone as a critical organ for the deposition of radioactive material, In *Bone Structure and Metabolism*, Little-Brown & Co., Boston, 272–283 (1956).

12. R. E. ROWLAND, J. H. MARSHALL and J. JOWSEY, Radium in human bone: The microradiographic appearance, *Rad. Res.* **10**, 323–334 (1959).

13. R. E. ROWLAND and J. H. MARSHALL, Radium in human bone: The dose in microscopic volumes of bone, *Rad. Res.* **11**, 299–313 (1959).

14. R. E. ROWLAND, Plugged haversian canals in a radium case, Radiological Physics Division Semiannual report, ANL-6199, 36–43 (1960).

15. H. A. SISSIONS, The osteoporosis of Cushing's syndrome, *J. Bone and Joint Surg.* **38B**, 418–433 (1956).

16. E. STOREY, The effect of intermittent cortisone administration in the rabbit, *J. Bone and Joint Surg.* **40B**, 103–114 (1958).

17. J. TRUETA, Regeneration of bone and cartilage, Proc. of XV Congrès de la Societé Internationale de Chirurgie, Lisbone, 1–11 (1953).

18. M. BROOKES, Sequelae of experimental partial ischaemia of long bones of the rabbit, *J. Anat.* **94**, 552–561 (1960).

19. W. S. S. JEE, J. S. ARNOLD, R. S. MICAL, B. BIRD, O. FREUDENBERGER and M. LOWE, Bone: Histopathologic and autoradiographic studies, Annual Progress Report, University of Utah, Radiobiology Laboratory, COO-215, 74–97 (1958).

20. M. HELLER, *Histopathology of irradiation*, NNES Series, McGraw-Hill, New York, 70–161 (1948).

21. W. S. S. JEE, J. S. ARNOLD and T. H. COCHRAN, On the genesis of osteogenic sarcoma in dogs, *Anat. Rev.* **127**, 423–424 (1957).

DISCUSSION

LAMERTON: Mr. Chairman, I think we all regard with great admiration the essay on quantitative histology that Dr. Jee showed to us today, because one knows how extremely difficult it is to do this sort of thing, what superb technique is required, and what patience.

A point I would like to make is that interesting as is the comparison of the various alpha emitters on the basis of these various quantitative criteria, even more interesting would be the comparison of the alpha emitters with the beta emitters. If it were possible for these same criteria to be employed in a strontium-bearing animal we might find something extremely interesting about the comparative response to alpha and beta radiation.

JEE: That is an excellent point. I am looking forward to tackling the comparison of the effects of alpha and beta emitters, although the bulk of the reports and my own observations indicate that there are very few common endpoints of damage between alpha and beta irradiation to skeletal tissue.

MOLE: I would like to ask two questions of Webster Jee. The first one is this: In the animals with mesothorium and radiothorium and no apparent blood supply in the bone, or very little, whereabouts is the vascular damage? You can see it in the haversian systems, but how far upstream can you find vascular damage? Does the nutrient artery get damaged? Where does it first start to happen?

The second question is the one I asked yesterday: What is the underlying basis for that bony overgrowth which Dr. Christensen's radiograph showed and which is on a different scale magnitude from the things you showed us today?

JEE: Bony overgrowths have been reported in the literature years ago. Professor Trueta has a list of the reprints which show that by cutting down the vascular supply, the bone responds with overgrowths. So, I believe it is triggered by the vascular environment.

MOLE: What is the largest artery that shows damage histologically?

JEE: The nutrient artery never shows it. Most of it is restricted to capillaries. The distribution of damaged vessels is not too uniform.

MOLE: I am asking about blood vessels. Do you get thrombosis filling up the lumen? Do you get intimal proliferation? What happens?

JEE: Most of it looks like thrombosis. There is some pericapillary fibrosis too, which is very difficult to quantitate in that is also occurs in the normals.

SPIERS: I have only a very small comment in relation to Dr. Mole's question. I don't think he would expect to see damage in canals more than a certain size, and certainly not in the nutrient artery. I think probably some of the bigger haversian canals the arteries will get through.

MOLE: That is true if you are thinking only in terms of direct damage; but if you think of indirect effects you might have things happening quite unexpectedly. That is partly what I was asking about.

SPIERS: I thought this was one of the causes of an indirect effect—that you block something and got an effect further on. The picture would be quite different with strontium.

JEE: We think most of it is direct, but some of the indirect mechanisms have been postulated in a recent publication with Jim Arnold (*Proc. Soc. Exp. Biol. Med.* **105**, 351, 1960).

DOUGHERTY: Once again we should think about the fact that plugging of small vessels occurs in several different ways, and that we can have both direct and indirect effects of irradiation here.

Bud Andersen has pointed out that with relatively large doses we get an increase in plugging of vessels with a mucopolysaccharide.

I would like to call your attention to one of the slides that Dr. Jee showed, in which he used dextran sulfate. I am an expert on dextran sulfate. He didn't tell me he was going to use dextran sulfate, but I will tell him what he did. I published on dextran sulfate and the alterations in blood vessels in 1950.

There are a whole host of polysaccharides, particularly the sulfated polysaccharides, both synthetic and naturally occurring, constituents of ground substance and constituents of the ground substance of bone, which plug vessels, and dextran sulfate is a very good one among the synthetics. We forget that there is a very nice paper by a British pharmacologist by the name of Woolton, who has shown this for a group of naturally occurring polysaccharides, particularly those occurring in cartilage, particularly chondroitin sulfate C. We also forget that Huper, for example, who now is doing industrial health work in the Public Health Service, several years ago demonstrated the production of vascular plugging by using carboxymethyl cellulose.

All these essentially act the same way. What we have shown essentially is that the endothelial cell can take up this material and deposit it and hold it within its cytoplasm, and this is one way. Another way is minute thromboses which occur.

Then I would like to call to your attention the fact that Dr. Casarett here has made a point of this in natural ageing, and that is that you have arterial and capillary fibrosis.

I personally think that all of these go together, that you do two things with radiation— that you set off a whole host of events. First, you can have immediate damage from radiation to the endothelial cell which then can cause a secondary proliferation at that site. But this isn't necessary, because once you damage an organism at all you increase (for some unknown reason at the present time) the mucopolysaccharides in the blood. You can do this, incidentally, with growth hormone if you choose the proper animal, the diabetic one. It has been demonstrated you can kill a 600 lb sow with vascular plugging by injecting 40 mg of growth hormone within 24 hours.

These are all things which could be indirect effects of the radiation. I am not saying that all effects of radiation are indirect; I think they are both. So, once you start a process it is a continuing one.

I think this is a very important lead, and it should be pushed very much in the whole radiation field, because I don't think it is only in the case of bone but I think it is in the case of many other things, too. Incidentally, you can do it by just giving daily administrations of histamine.

ROWLAND: I would like to make one comment to underline what Professor Dougherty has told us. I want to applaud Webster for initiating these studies and asking the question: What causes this plugging, other than radiation?

In 1934 Drs. Jaffe and Pomeranz (*Arch. Surg.* **29**, 566, 1934) wrote a paper in which he described the appearance of histological sections cut from the compacta of the long bones of humans who had been for many years subject to chronic vascular insufficiency. In this paper he states: "Pink staining haversian plugs are present."

With this as a clue, we have searched and found a few cases where we were able to get bone samples from amputations, usually as a result of gangrene of the extremity following atherosclerotic conditions. We found in some of them bone that microradiographically was indistinguishable from radium cases containing hypermineralized plugs, hypermineralized osteons, large areas of resorption and hypermineralized lacunae. Here, the only insult we were aware of was the lack of vascularity.

DOUGHERTY: May I just mention one word. We didn't mention amino nitrile.

You duplicate everything that you see with radium with amino nitrile.

VAUGHAN: I had occasion to go through all the literature of cases of radium poisoning, and one of the striking things that is described and that is commented on by those who have done post mortems on human cases, or who have studied their experimental material carefully (and I hope Dr. Robley Evans will substantiate what I say), is the amount of damage to blood vessels unrelated to bone.

Apparently atheromatous changes are considered by some of those who have done post-mortems characteristic of radium poisoning. It has never been put on a proper statistical basis. However, one of the outstanding features when I came to list the sort of pathological picture that one found in both human cases of radium poisoning and of experimental material was the frequent comment on rather gross lesions in the big vessels, suggesting that this was something quite different from radiation from the vessel lying within the bone.

I think this is something that we should just remember, and not assume the damage to the vessel that occurs in radium poisoning, and which we see by these remarkable changes within the bone, is dependent on the radiation dose received from the bone-seeking isotopes. There may be some other cause.

THE EFFECT OF AGEING AND INTERNAL EMITTERS ON BLOOD CHEMISTRY

HAROLD C. GOLDTHORPE

Dept. Biological Chemistry and Radiobiology Division,
Dept. of Anatomy, University of Utah College of Medicine
Salt Lake City, Utah

INTRODUCTION

THE purpose of this study was to determine the effect of injected radio-nuclides upon the blood chemistry of beagle dogs and with the eventual goal of correlating it with pathological changes found at autopsy.

In addition to the toxic effect program, we are carrying out the same bio-chemical studies on a colony of normal dogs throughout their lifespan; consequently, we are obtaining a unique record of normal blood chemistry values on approximately one hundred dogs. The irradiated dogs can then be compared to the normal ageing control dogs of about the same age.[1]

The study consists of periodic determination of the chemical constituents of the blood. Some twelve constituents are being followed. The injected dogs receive a pre-injection analysis, followed by post-injection analyses at one, two and six month intervals and yearly thereafter. Finally a terminal analysis is done.

Changes in Beagle Blood Chemistry with Age

With regard to the figures, the mean values for the serum constituents of the normal ageing controls for the whole colony are given with plus and minus the standard deviation. The number of analyses locating the points are given. The number of dogs studied up to and including seven years is considerably larger than for dogs eight years or older. Additional studies on older dogs may change these mean values.[1,2]

Serum calcium[3,4,5,6] and serum inorganic phosphate[7,8] values are summarized in Fig. 1. At 0·5 year of age the calcium value is below the normal mean and rises above it at one year of age. It stays fairly constant until after the sixth year and then appears to enter into a steady decline, remaining within the normal range, however.

At 0·5 year of age inorganic phosphates are 6 mg per 100 ml serum and at one year have dropped to the colony mean. Between 2 and 6 years of age we find the value slightly below the normal mean; from then on, there appears to be a slight increase above the mean.

Total serum proteins[9,10,11] of normal control dogs at 0·5 year of age are below the normal mean, with 5·2 g/100 ml, but by 1 year have almost reached the normal mean value as shown in Fig. 2. This is reached at 2·4 years and continues to show a slight rise in value to 6·5 g/100 ml at 7 years, then appears to remain constant.

Serum albumin and globulins are also shown in Fig. 2. There is a gradual increase as noted above in total serum protein values to about four years of

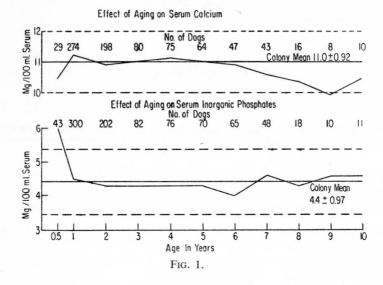

FIG. 1.

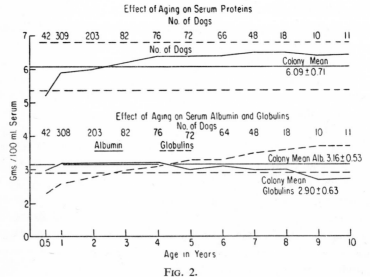

FIG. 2.

age; thereafter, remaining constant the rest of the lifespan. This increase is shown to be due to the gradual increase in serum globulins throughout life together with a gradual decrease in serum albumin at least up to and including 10 years of age. The serum albumin increases from 0·5 to 1 year of age, remains constant in value to 4 years of age, followed by a gradual decline. The serum globulin value also starts out at 0·5 year of age at a lower than normal value (2·3 g) but starts immediately to show increased values and reaches 3·7 g at 10 years. At about 4·3 years there is a reversal in the albumin/globulin ratio.

The serum alkaline phosphatase[7,8,12] is seen in Fig. 3 to remain nearly constant in value. A slight decline from 4 to 9 years of age is apparent.

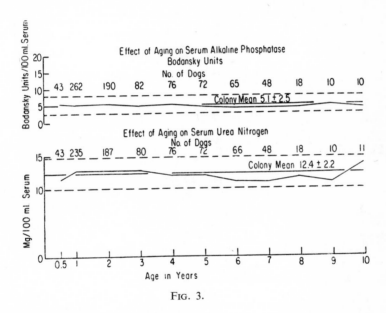

FIG. 3.

There is a slight increase in urea nitrogen[13,14] after 0·5 year of age to 1 year, also shown in Fig. 3. From 1 year to 3 years of age it remains constant. Following this period to the ninth year of age there seems to be a gradual decline in value. Whether the increase shown at 10 years (11 dogs) is significant remains to be shown.

Chlorides[15] and carbon dioxide capacity[16,17,18] are summarized in Fig. 4. The chlorides appear on the whole to show a slight decline with the exception of two fluctuations, one at 3 years and the other at 6 years of age. No explanation is attempted as there are enough analyses to make the points stable.

Carbon dioxide capacity starts out at 0·5 years of age on the low side of normal. It starts immediately to climb until 3 years of age and then is following by a decline until the 7th year is reached. The increase shown in the 8th and 9th years is not understood. The overall picture is of a slight increase in age.

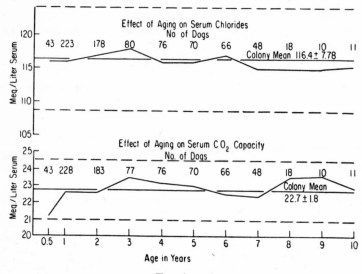

FIG. 4.

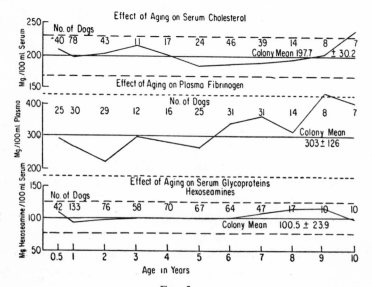

FIG. 5.

Cholesterol,[19,20] fibrinogen,[21] and total glycoprotein as hexoseamines[22] are summarized in Fig. 5. Serum cholesterol values fluctuate slightly from 0·5 to 9 years of age. The mean of the 7 values at 10 years is higher than the colony mean. Fibrinogen values fluctuate and seem to show a gradual increase throughout 0·5 to 10 years. The effect of age on glycoprotein values has been reported previously.[23] Serum glycoproteins show a drop in values after 0·5 years of age to 1 year of age. From then on the value remains fairly constant up to 6 years of age, followed by a slight rise in values to the 9th year.

Terminal Blood Chemistry of Internally Irradiated Beagles

The results are summarized in a series of bar graphs shown in Figs. 6 through 17. The bars show the mean obtained by averaging the terminal values for all the dogs of the same dose level of a given radionuclide. The

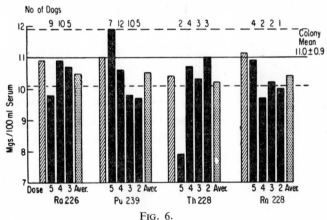

FIG. 6.

Terminal values for serum calcium.

final bar in each group is made up from the terminal values of the various dose levels. The number of analyses done to obtain the mean for each bar is shown in the upper part of the graph above the corresponding bar. It is to be noted that there are more results for Ra[226] and Pu[239] than for Th[228] and Ra[228]. The dose level is given as 5, 4, 3, and 2. The shading given the bars has the following meaning:

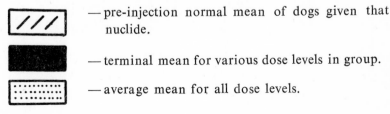

— pre-injection normal mean of dogs given that nuclide.

— terminal mean for various dose levels in group.

— average mean for all dose levels.

The colony mean with its standard deviation is also shown.

Interpretation of these results in terms of the amount and kind of irradiation the dogs received is exceedingly difficult. A major difficulty is that the terminal blood values may be profoundly influenced by the condition of the dog at this time. For example, the two 5 level Th[228] dogs died at 97 and 212 days after injection. Both were anemic and one was in kidney failure. The 5 level Pu[239] dogs suffered fractures, liver disorders, anemia, skeletal degeneration, and bone tumors. The 5 level Ra[226] dogs had fractures and bone tumors. The 5 level Ra[228] and 4 level Th[228] dogs had renal damage, fractures, and bone tumors. One must even exercise discretion on results from lower dose levels. For example, the two 2 level Ra[228] dogs died of pneumonia and hepatitis.

Many of the dogs, however, did have the common factor that they died with bone tumors. This group includes most of the following dose levels of the four radionuclides: 3 and 4 level Ra[226]; 2, 3 and 4 level Pu[239]; 2 and 3 level Th[228]; and 3 and 4 level Ra[228] dogs. Thus, we will limit our comments on the terminal blood values to this rather large group of dogs. In Fig. 6, we see a lowering in the terminal serum calcium value in the Pu[239] dogs and it appears that the decrease becomes greater as the dose level decreases. As shown in Fig. 7, there is a terminal increase in serum inorganic phosphate values for 2, 3 and 4 level Pu[239] dogs. The most striking change seen in serum inorganic phosphate, in the group of dogs we are considering, is the very high values noted for the 2 level Th[228] dogs.

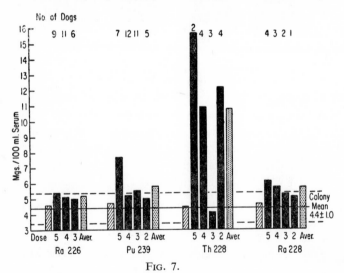

FIG. 7.

Terminal values for serum inorganic phosphates.

There is no great effect on total serum proteins apparent in Fig. 8, with the possible exception that the 2 level Pu^{239} values may be increased. In Figs. 9 and 10, we see the albumin and globulins separately. There is a slight decrease in the albumins for the 2 and 3 level Th^{228} dogs, which leads to an early reversal of the albumin-globulin ratio. Serum globulins are increased in the 2 level Pu^{239} dogs, and it is thus that the increase in globulins shows up in the increase in total serum proteins for this group of dogs.

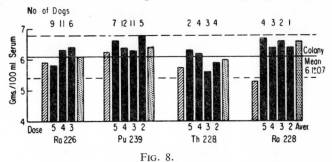

FIG. 8.

Terminal values for total serum proteins.

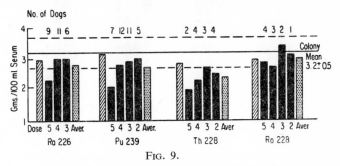

FIG. 9.

Terminal values for serum albumin.

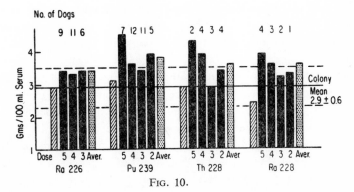

FIG. 10.

Terminal values for serum globulins.

There are many interesting changes shown in Fig. 11, which summarizes the terminal values for serum alkaline phosphatase. Both the 3 and 4 level Ra[226] dogs show increased values. The values for the 2, 3 and 4 level Pu[239] dogs are also increased and present the possibility of an interesting dose level effect, for the 4 level increase in greater than that of the 3 level which in turn is greater than that of the 2 level. Increases are also shown for the 2 and 3 level Th[228] dogs and the 3 and 4 level Ra[228] dogs. However, for both these nuclides it is the lower of the two dose levels where the greater increase is observed.

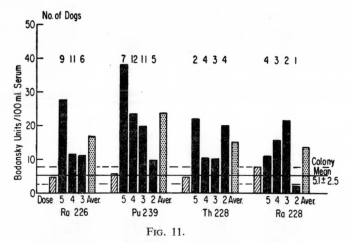

FIG. 11.

Terminal values for serum alkaline phosphatase.

Figs. 12, 13 and 14 summarize the terminal values for serum urea nitrogen, serum chlorides, and serum CO_2 capacity respectively. The most interesting effect on serum urea nitrogen is seen for the Pu[239] dogs. There appears to be a decrease, and it is greatest in the 4 level and least in the 2 level. Again, we have a suggestion of a dose level effect. There are no striking changes in either serum chlorides or serum CO_2 capacity for the groups of dogs we are considering.

Serum cholesterol values are presented in Fig. 15, and there are two interesting increases shown. They are in the 3 level Pu[239] group and the 2 level Th[228] group. A number of the groups we are considering show an increase in terminal values for fibrinogen, as is seen in Fig. 16. Both the 3 and 4 level Ra[226] values are up. with the 4 level increase being greater than that of the 3 level. Two, 3 and 4 level Pu[239] average values are high with the 3 level showing the greatest elevation. The 3 level Ra[228] group also shows an increase in fibrinogen.

Terminal values for serum glycoproteins, as hexoseamines, are summarized in Fig. 17. Again, we see some increases in the average values. Both the 3 and 4 level Ra^{226} values are up. There is a slight increase 2, 3 and 4 level Pu^{239} values and an increase in the 4 level Ra^{228} values.

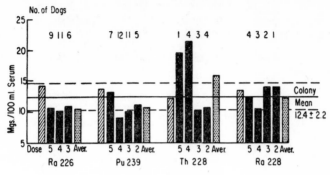

FIG. 12.

Terminal values for serum urea nitrogen.

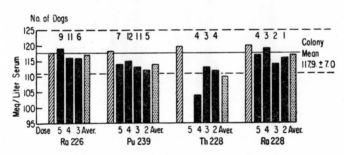

FIG. 13.

Terminal values for serum chlorides.

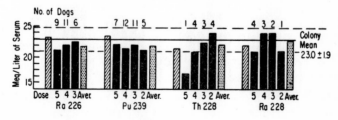

FIG. 14.

Terminal values for serum CO_2 capacity.

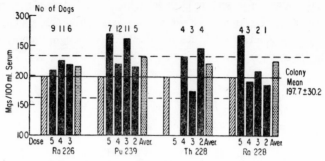

FIG. 15.

Terminal values for serum cholesterol.

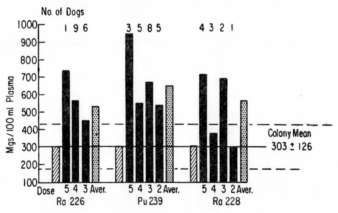

FIG. 16.

Terminal values for fibrinogen.

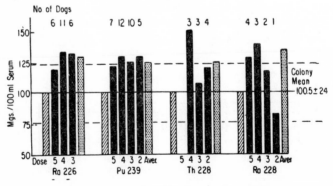

FIG. 17.

Terminal values for serum glycoproteins as hexoseamines.

DISCUSSION

There are few, if any, studies of this kind and extent with which our results can be compared. This opportunity to study serum constituents of a given group of dogs over a large portion of their lifespan is probably unique. Likewise, there is no other group of this size given these radionuclides which has been available for study. There are a few comparisons, however, which can be made with external irradiation.

The ageing studies have shown an interesting change in the serum proteins, namely, a reversal in the albumin-globulin ratio which occurs at about 4·3 years. In the internal irradiated dogs the same change in the relative amounts of albumin and globulin has been observed to occur a little sooner. For Ra^{226} the reversal occurs at about 2·4 years after injection which is at an age of about 3·7 years, and for plutonium it is observed at 1·4 years after injection or when the dog is about 3 years old.[1] It is interesting that a similar effect has also been shown in animals following X-irradiation.[24,25]

Of the many serum constituents studied, the most striking change is seen in the concentration of the enzyme alkaline phosphatase in the serum. The main values of almost all the groups showed a considerable elevation of values above the colony mean. This is of great interest, since most of the dogs studied suffered bone tumors and/or fractures and general skeletal degeneration.

Acute radiation disease, induced by external irradiation, has been observed to lower the alkaline reserve of the blood in a dose dependent manner.[26] Our mean values for CO_2 capacity showed little, if any, effect in the dogs which had received internal irradiation. This is not surprising, however, in view of the fact that most of these dogs lived a number of years after injection, while the external irradiation effects were observed in acute studies.

There appears to be an interesting relationship between serum glycoproteins and the incidence of bone tumors. An average value for dogs dying with bone tumors has been found to be 134 mg/100 ml serum. In contrast, the average value for another group of dogs which did not have bone tumors was found to be 102 mg/100 ml.[27] Finally, it is of interest to note that high values for fibrinogen and alkaline phosphatase have been recorded in dogs that died of high doses of X-irradiation; lower doses did not produce significant results.[28]

SUMMARY

In the normal ageing controls inorganic phosphates, total proteins, globulins, fibrinogen and glycoproteins all appear to have a slight increase in value throughout life. Calcium, serum albumin, urea, chlorides and carbon dioxide capacity tend to show a slight decline throughout life. Alkaline phosphatase tends to remain fairly constant throughout life. Cholesterol appears to decrease in value in early life and at about mid-life starts to climb to above normal values.

Terminal values for the various serum constituents in dogs which had been injected with one of several amounts of Ra^{226}, Pu^{239}, Th^{228}, or Ra^{228} have been summarized. The mean of each dose level of each of the radio-nuclides has been presented. These mean values are shown in comparison with the normal beagle colony mean. Special emphasis has been given those groups in which a large number of the dogs had bone tumors at the time the measurements were made. The most striking change was the elevation of the mean values of alkaline phosphatase for almost all the groups in which bone tumor incidence is high. Pu^{239} dogs showed a slight decrease in calcium with a slight increase of inorganic phosphates. The latter change appeared in some of the Th^{228} dogs also. An interesting finding in the study of the serum proteins is an advancement in time of the normal reversal of the albumin-globulin ratio. Pu^{239} dogs with bone tumors showed a slight decrease in serum urea nitrogen. Some increase in cholesterol values was noted. Both fibrinogen and serum glycoproteins showed an increase in the case of most of the groups of dogs with bone tumors.

REFERENCES

1. H. C. GOLDTHORPE and T. F. DOUGHERTY, A comparison of the effects of aging and internal irradiation, *Proc. Fifth Intern. Congress of Gerontology*, San Francisco, August, 1960 (in press).
2. H. C. GOLDTHORPE and S. BENNETT, Semi annual Progress Report, Radiobiology Laboratory, Univ. of Utah College of Medicine, COO-217, 96 (1958).
3. K. SALOMAN, BEVERLY W. GABRIO and G. F. SMITH, A precision method for the quantitative determination of calcium in blood plasma, *Arch. Biochem.* **11**, 433 (1946).
4. H. D. APPLETON, MARCIA WEST, MARY MANDEL and A. SALA, The rapid determination of calcium in biologic material, *Clin. Chem.* **5**, 36 (1959).
5. H. V. MALMSTRADT and T. P. HADJUOANNOU, Automatic titration of calcium or magnesium in blood serum, *Clin. Chem.* **5**, 50 (1959).
6. M. BETT and G. P. FRASER, A rapid micro-method for determining serum calcium, *Clin. Chem. Acta* **4**, 346 (1959).
7. C. H. FISKE and Y. SUBBAROW, The colorimetric determination of phosphorus, *J. Biol. Chem.* **66**, 375 (1925).
8. G. GOMORI, A modification of the colorimetric phosphorus determination for use with the photoelectric colorimeter, *J. Lab. & Clin. Med.* **27**, 955 (1941).
9. G. R. KINGSLEY, The determination of serum total protein albumin and globulin by the biruet reaction, *J. Biol. Chem.* **131**, 197 (1939).

10. John G. REINHOLD, Total protein, albumin and globulin, in *Standard Methods of Clinical Chemistry*, Academic Press, New York Vol. **1**, 88 (1953).

11. J. W. WEICHSELBAUM, An accurate and rapid method for the determination of protein in small amounts of blood serum and plasma, *Am. J. Clin. Path. Techn. Sec.* **16**, 40 (1946).

12. G. Y. SINOWARA, L. M. SHINOWARA and LOIS M. JONES, The estimation of serum inorganic phosphate and "acid and alkaline" phosphatase activity, *J. Biol. Chem.* **142**, 921 (1942).

13. A. A. ORMSBY, A direct colorimetric method for the determination of urea in blood and urine, *J. Biol. Chem.* **146**, 595 (1942).

14. H. S. FREEDMAN, Modification of the determination of urea by the diacetyl monoxime method, *Anal. Chem.* **25**, 662 (1953).

15. O. SCHALES and SELMA SCHALES, A simple and accurate method for the determination of chloride in biological fluids, *J. Biol. Chem.* **140**, 879 (1941).

16. D. D. VAN SLYKE and C. E. CULLEN, The bicarbonate concentration of the blood plasma, its significance and its determination as a measure of acidosis, *J. Biol. Chem.* **30**, 316–347 (1917).

17. D. D. VAN SLYKE and W. C. STUDIE, The determination of the gases of the blood, *J. Biol. Chem.* **49**, 1 (1921).

18. D. D. VAN SLYKE and J. M. NEILL, The determination of gases in blood and other solutions by vacuum extraction and manometric measurement, *J. Biol. Chem.* **61**, 523 (1924).

19. A. ZLATLIS, B. ZAK and A. BOYLE, A new method for the direct determination of serum cholesterol, *J. Lab. Clin. Med.* **41**, 486 (1953).

20. B. ZAK, Simple rapid microtechnic for serum total cholesterol, *Am. J. Clin. Path.* **27**, 583 (1957).

21. H. C. GOLDTHORPE, Unpublished procedure.

22. R. J. WINZLER, Determination of serum glycoproteins, *Methods of Biochemistry*, Ed. D. GLUCK, p. 279 (1955).

23. H. C. GOLDTHORPE and S. BENNETT, *Semiannual Progress Report*, Radiobiology Laboratory, Univ. of Utah College of Medicine AECU-3583, 69 (1957).

24. I. C. SCHEKARACHI and T. MAKINODAN, Electrophoretic analysis of sera from mice protected from lethal X-irradiation, *Intern. J. Rad. Biol.* **2**, 353 (1960).

25. CHARLES A. LEONE, N. R. HARTNETT, R. CRIST, CAROLEE MC BETH, Paper electrophoretic analysis of serums from irradiated rhesus monkey, *Rad. Res.* **10**, 357 (1959).

26. B. S. BABASHEV, Blood alkaline reserve in acute radiation disease, *Chem. Abstracts* **54**, 2, 1635c (1960).

27. H. C. GOLDTHORPE, S. BENNETT and R. A. OLSON, *Annual Progress Report*, Radiobiology Laboratory, Univ. of Utah, College of Medicine, AECU-3522, 131 (1957).

28. KATHRYN F. FINK, Blood chemistry study in dogs exposed to chronic X-radiation, *Biological Effects of External Radiation XI-2*, McGraw-Hill, New York 339 (1954).

29. H. C. GOLDTHORPE and S. BENNETT, *Semiannual Progress Report*, Radiobiology Laboratory, Univ. of Utah College of Medicine, COO-217, 96 (1958).

FRACTURE INCIDENCE IN BEAGLES RECEIVING SINGLE INJECTIONS OF RADIUM OR PLUTONIUM*

C. E. Rehfeld,† B. J. Stover, G. N. Taylor, and C. W Mays

*Division of Radiobiology, Department of Anatomy,
University of Utah College of Medicine,
Salt Lake City, Utah*

THERE is ample evidence that fractures will occur spontaneously in man when sufficient amounts of certain radionuclides are [retained in bone.[1,2,3,4,5,6] In the majority of the cases (man) cited the femur is affected and in many instances there is evidence of partial to complete repair.

Radium administered to rabbits[7,8] has caused fractures to occur. Similar results were observed in one study with rats.[9] In another study with rats it was observed that no amount of precaution would prevent fracturing of the long bones when the animals were handled.[10]

Plutonium deposition in the skeletons of beagles resulted in spontaneous fracturing[11] and similar effects were noted with radiothorium shortly thereafter.[12] A tabulation and comparison of fracture incidence in dogs given radium, plutonium, radiothorium and mesothorium was inconclusive due to the preliminary nature of the reports.[13,14] Fractures have also been reported in dogs given strontium.[15,16]

The dose-rate effect of Ra^{226} and Pu^{239} for the induction of fractures can be previewed with the aid of data collected at the University of Utah since 1952. These data were taken from a study still in progress. Fractures occurring in dogs injected with these radionuclides have appeared in large numbers in certain individuals and have involved the skeleton generally. This phenomenon can be considered an end-point together with tumor formation, blood changes and alterations in values obtained from biochemical studies.

The data have yielded information regarding radiation dosage at the time of the first fracture and one good area of comparison, the incidence of rib fractures produced by these two radionuclides under discussion. The differences in the effects of Ra^{226} and Pu^{239} are shown by variations in occurrence of long bone and irregular bone fractures and the nature of the rib fractures.

* The technical assistance of Ned Nebeker and Dawn Buster is gratefully acknowledged.

† Now at the Division of Biology and Medical Research, Argonne National Laboratory, Argonne, Illinois.

131

9*

Purebred beagles born and raised in the laboratory were the only animals used in this investigation. The beagles selected for this purpose were young adults which proved to be healthy according to information gained through physical, hematological, biochemical and radiological examinations. Including 12 dogs which served as controls in each of the groups, 82 were assigned to the Ra^{226} study and 81 similarly for Pu^{239}.[17] In addition to the 24 control dogs in these two groups, another 75 dogs in companion studies provided supportive control material.

After each dog was given a known quantity of either radionuclide by intravenous injection, a complete radiographic record was made of the skeleton at sufficiently frequent intervals so that any gross bone changes could be tabulated chronologically. Fractures occurred in certain animals and frequently they appeared to have healed. Whether or not these fractured bones had undergone successful repair soon became a point of interest.

If there was an interruption in the trabecular pattern of any bone in a transverse or oblique plane, it was concluded that a fracture had occurred. In the large majority of instances there was little need for such a definition; however, a counter definition served to determine whether or not a bone had healed. It is acknowledged that errors in interpretations of the repair status may be present because the quality of the roentgenograms is not consistent.

Many of the dogs included in this summary were euthanized because they had developed bone tumors and a lesser number were similarly disposed of when they had fractures of appendicular bones and/or anemia. Only a few of the living (as of February 1961) dogs included in this study have ever experienced one or more fractures. The most recent complete radiographic study was referred to for the living dogs. If this radiographic series was negative for evidence of fractures no further study was made but when positive, all previous series were also read to obtain the chronological history of fracture occurrence. Only those dogs which have experienced one or more fractures are included in the tables presented here.*

Average radiation dose rates (in rads per day) and cumulative doses (in rads) to the whole skeleton have been calculated at the times of fracture recognition. The method of these calculations has been previously described in detail.[18,19] Because of non-uniform deposition of the radionuclides, the local dose within a bone and the average doses among individual bones are greater or less than this skeletal average. For example, the average

---

* The significance of a single fracture within any level is questionable. This is especially so when the possibility of a non-radiation induced traumatic fracture is considered. However, no fractures have been observed in control dogs so far.

dose to the ribs is about 1·4 times the average skeletal dose for Ra[226], and about 1.6 for Pu[239].[20]

TABLE 1

Data at First Fracture Recognition with Ra[226]

Days age when injected	Injected μc/kg	Days from injection to first fracture	Rad/day at time of first fracture	Total rads at time of first fracture	Dog research number
460	0·0576	2267	0·051	130	F3R1
592	0·387	1642	0·352	650	M2R2
572	0·331	1212	0·310	420	F8R2
523	0·345	2007	0·308	700	M10R2
486	1·14	1781	1·028	2060	F6R3
470	3·55	830	3·46	3250	M2R4
486	3·44	1227	3·22	4450	F6R4
514	3·88	856	3·78	3650	M7R4
474	3·14	832	3·06	2880	F8R4
496	2·81	1434	2·59	4180	F12R4
473	10·5	686	10·5	8130	M1R5
470	10·8	675	10·8	8220	M2R5
380	10·1	364	10·8	4470	F3R5
408	10·6	688	10·5	8220	M4R5
458	10·1	569	10·2	6640	M5R5
486	10·2	542	10·4	6410	F6R5
453	11·9	514	12·4	7140	M7R5
474	9·68	400	10·2	4660	F8R5
420	9·48	535	9·70	5900	F9R5
527	10·2	261	11·3	3380	M10R5

In the 20 Ra[226] dogs thus far experiencing any fractures (Table 1), the first fracture generally occurs sooner if the dose rate is high. One dog had a fracture within 261 days when dose rate was 11·3 rad/day while another dog experienced its first fracture on or shortly before 2267 days following injection of the radium dose, when the dose rate was only 0·051 rad/day. To emphasize this difference in another way, the first dog had accumulated dose of 3380 rad to the skeleton while the second had only 130 rad after 2267 days. It may be somewhat invalid to employ average figures here; however, they show that the first fracture appeared within 966 days when the dose rate was 6·25 rad/day and the accumulated dosage was 4280 rad to the skeleton.

Fifteen of the 69 dogs injected with Pu[239] have given evidence of experiencing fractures to date (Table 2). One dog had a fracture as early as 394 days following injection of the isotope when the dose rate was 4·06 rad/day. In comparison another dog had a fracture within 1857 days when the dose rate was 0·443 rad/day. The total rads necessary to produce the first fracture varied from 380 to 4900. An average dose-rate of 2.68 rad/day was received by the skeleton when the first fracture occurred on or before 928 days following injection and the average total dose was 2160 rad.

TABLE 2

Data at First Fracture Recognition with Pu²³⁹

Days age when injected	Injected μc/kg	Days from injection to first fracture	Rad/day at time of first fracture	Total rads at time of first fracture	Dog research number
417	0·261	1249	0·378	490	M1P3
422	0·312	1857	0·443	860	F2P3
599	0·309	790	0·454	380	M11P3
442	0·823	1618	1·18	2000	M1P4
485	0·929	620	1·38	890	M3P4
420	0·811	1356	1·18	1650	F6P4
598	0·838	764	1·24	980	M12P4
417	2·67	1213	3·88	4900	M1P5
1150	3·30	842	4·86	4260	F2P5
566	3·17	867	4·67	4210	M4P5
691	2·77	585	4·13	2500	F5P5
407	2·57	583	3·83	2340	F6P5
482	2·99	437	4·52	2050	F7P5
497	2·69	394	4·06	1680	M8P5
552	2·73	759	4·04	3180	F9P5

The ribs were most vulnerable to the activity produced by the two radionuclides under consideration. Although a portion of their vulnerability may lie in their size and use, most important is the fact that they usually continue to grow for a few weeks or months after injection. The rib fractures were tabulated for the two groups of dogs providing the most information. These two groups were the dogs injected with an average of 10·4 μc Ra²²⁶/kg and those injected with an average of 2·86 μc Pu²³⁹/kg. An attempt was made to differentiate between the healed and unhealed fractures on the basis of the appearance in the roentgenogram.

The comparatively high doses of Ra²²⁶ caused fractures to appear before the 300th day in some dogs and each dog had one or more before the 700th day. At the time of euthanasia these 10 dogs had an average of 18·9 rib fractures, 6·8 of which were unhealed and 12·1 healed. One of these died before the 500th day and had at that time 3 fractured ribs while at the other extreme there were 41 fractures in another surviving nearly 1300 days.

When rib fractures of the living dogs were totalled for each 50 day period an average number was obtained and plotted with the accumulated rads for that particular period (Fig. 1). The healed and unhealed ribs were separated to provide some information regarding their ability to recover.

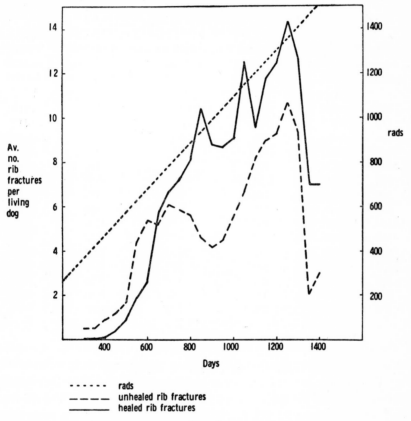

FIG. 1.

Healed and unhealed rib fractures in beagles injected with 10·4 μc Ra^{226}/kg.

As long as 4 or more dogs were included in the calculation there was a consistent tendency for more fractures to occur with each 50-day period. At 650 days the number of healed fractures began to outnumber the unhealed and this tendency was never reversed. There is only a suggestion that the rate of new fracture occurrence may have decreased around 900 days and that the rate increased again thereafter. Eight of these 10 dogs were euthanized because they developed bone tumors. Close observation failed to provide evidence that these dogs suffered pain as a result of these fractures.

The information gained from a study of the rib fractures occurring in the dogs injected with the highest dose of Pu^{239} was similarly plotted (Fig. 2). The first fracture occurred before the 400th day in one dog while 8 of the 9 included in this group all had one or more fractures sometime before day 1250. One dog died before the 500th day and exhibited no evidence that fractures had occurred although another had 27 rib fractures on day 1576. At the time of euthanasia these 9 dogs had an average of 12·5 rib fractures, 5·4 of which were unhealed and 7·1 healed.

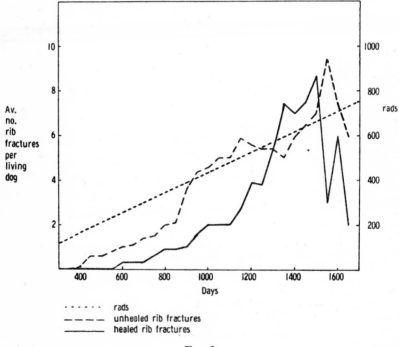

- - - - - rads
- - - - unhealed rib fractures
———— healed rib fractures

FIG. 2.

Healed and unhealed rib fractures in beagles injected with 2·86 μc Pu^{239}/kg.

As long as 2 or more dogs were included in this fracture total versus time study the average number increased quite steadily with each 50 day period. At 1300 days the number of healed fractures began to outnumber the unhealed but this trend is probably not significant because of the small number of living dogs at that time which was shortly before they all were euthanized.

When healed and unhealed rib fractures are added together and plotted with the accumulated dosage (Fig. 3) a comparison of effects is indicated. In the period from 300 to 800 days there is less than one fracture average for each 100 rads from Pu^{239} and thereafter the ratio changes gradually until around 1400 days there are two fractures per 100 rads. In a similar approach for the dogs given Ra^{226}, each has more than one rib fracture per 100 rads before 800 days have elapsed but never reach the point of experiencing two or more rib fractures/100 rads.

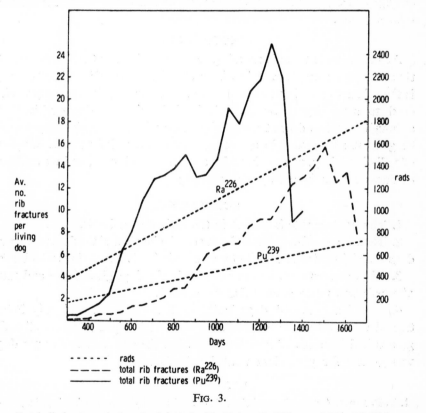

FIG. 3.

Total rib fractures in beagles injected with 10·4 μc Ra^{226}/kg or 2·86 μc Pu^{239}/kg.

The use of additional information is helpful in showing that there are other variations in the effects of Ra^{226} and Pu^{239} as regards bone fractures. The same two groups of dogs used to illustrate the effects on ribs will serve for this purpose. When Ra^{226} was used the ribs tended to fracture proximal to the costo-chondral junction while with Pu^{239} most ribs fractured at or near the point where the costo-chondral junction was at the time of injection. Three of the radium treated dogs had fractures of the appendicular skeleton with an average of 2·3 fractures for the three. One plutonium treated dog had a transverse fissure in some of the cortical bone at one point but there was not a complete separation of the bone.

Seven of the radium treated dogs had an average of 3·7 fractures of irregular bones, primarily processes of the vertebrae while 6 plutonium dogs had an average of 5·7 fractures of the same type of bone. One striking difference is obvious in that four of the plutonium treated dogs had an average of 1·5 pelvic fractures while none of these occurred in the radium treated group.

DISCUSSION

At the moment there is no adequate explanation for the occurrence of these fractures; however, it has been stated that impaired circulation[21] is the primary cause in a succession of events. The bone is eventually weakened to some degree by the radiation-induced resorption cavities[22,23] although fractures do not necessarily occur where resorption appears to be greatest as revealed in a roentgenogram. It is likely that a complex of radiation injury, manner in which any one bone is used, and the amount of stress results in a fracture occurring.

SUMMARY

1. The fracture rate is highest in the highest dose levels.
2. There is a good correlation for fracture incidence and the dose rate when dogs were injected with Ra^{226} but such correlation is less obvious with Pu^{239}.
3. Rib fractures were more numerous in the dogs given Ra^{226} and rate of repair was much greater than with Pu^{239}.
4. Only Ra^{226} treated dogs had long bone fractures and only Pu^{239} treated dogs had pelvic fractures. Approximately equal numbers of both groups had fractures of irregular bones but the average number per dog was greater for plutonium treated animals.

REFERENCES

1. F. B. FLINN, A case of antral sinusitic complicated by radium poisoning, *Laryngoscope* **37**, 341–349 (1927).
2. H. S. MARTLAND, Occupational poisoning in manufacture of luminous watch dials, *J. Am. Med. Assoc.* **92**, 466–552 (1929).
3. H. S. MARTLAND, The occurrence of malignancy in radioactive persons, *Am, J. Cancer* **15**:4, 2435–2516 (1931).
4. J. C. AUB, R. D. EVANS, L. H. HEMPELMANN and H. S. MARTLAND, The late effects of internally–deposited radioactive materials in man, *Medicine* **31**:3, 221–329 (1952).

5. W. B. LOONEY, R. J. HASTERLIK, A. M. BRUES and E. SKIRMONT, A clinical investigation of the chronic effects of radium salts administered therapeutically, *Am. J. Roent. and Rad. Therapy* **73**:6, 1006–1037 (1955).

6. A. J. FINKEL, C. E. MILLER and R. J. HASTERLIK, Late effects of radium deposition in dial painters (abstract) *Rad. Res.* **11**:3, 442–443 (1959).

7. F. R. SABIN, C. A. DOAN and C. E. FORKNER, Production of osteogenic sarcoma and the effects on lymph nodes and bone marrow of intravenous injection of radium chloride and mesothorium in rabbits, *J. Exptl. Med.* **56**, 267–285 (1932).

8. M. ROSENTHAL and E. J. GRACE, Experimental radium poisoning. I. Bone marrow and lymph node changes in rabbits produced by oral administration of radium sulphate, *Am. J. Med. Sci.* **191**, 607–618 (1936).

9. W. P. NORRIS and H. B. EVANS, Studies of the metabolism and toxic action of injected radium, Report No. CH-3852, Metallurgical Lab., Biol. Div., Univ. of Chicago, AECD-1965 (June 1946).

10. R. D. EVANS, R. J. HARRIS and J. W. M. BUNKER, Radium metabolism in rats, and the production of osteogenic sarcoma by experimental radium poisoning, *Am. J. Roent. and Rad. Therapy* **LII**:4, 353–373 (1944).

11. M. P. FINKEL, A. M. BRUES and H. LISCO, Sequalae of plutonium administration to laboratory carnivores (abstract) *Rad. Res.* **5**:1, 496 (1954).

12. C. E. REHFELD, Veterinary group report, Radiobiology Laboratory, Univ. of Utah Semiannual Report, AECU-3109, 44–45 (Sept. 1955).

13. W. R. CHRISTENSEN and E. LEIDICH, Radiological findings, Radiobiology Laboratory, Univ. of Utah Annual Report 24–28 (March 1956).

14. C. E. REHFELD, G. N. TAYLOR, W. FISHER and W. R. CHRISTENSEN, Clinical section radiology report, Radiobiology Laboratory, Univ. of Utah Annual Report AECU-3522, 23–33 (March 1957).

15. C. E. REHFELD, Report of the clinic group, Research in Radiobiology, Univ. of Utah COO-220, 35–39 (March 1960).

16. M. P. FINKEL, R. J. FLYNN and B. O. BISKIS, Pathological consequences of Sr^{90} in growing beagles: Interim observations. (abstract) *Rad. Res.* **11**:3, 443 (Sept. 1959).

17. T. F. DOUGHERTY, Study of the long term biological effects of internal irradiation in adult beagles, This vol. p. 3.

18. BETSY J. STOVER, D. R. ATHERTON and C. W. MAYS, Studies of the retention and distribution of Ra^{226}, Pu^{239}, Ra^{228} (MsTh$_1$), Th^{228} (RdTh) and Sr^{90} in adult beagles, This vol. p. 7.

19. C. W. MAYS, B. J. STOVER, B. W. GLAD and D. R. ATHERTON, Skeletal dosimetry in Utah beagles, Radiobiology Laboratory, Univ. of Utah Annual Report COO-218, 121–145 (March 1959).

20. D. R. ATHERTON, C. W. MAYS and B. J. STOVER, Radionuclide distribution in adult beagle bone, Radiobiology Laboratory, Univ. of Utah Semiannual Report COO-217, 118–125 (Sept. 1958).

21. W.S.S. JEE, J. S. ARNOLD, T. H. COCHRANE, J. A. TWENTE, and R. S. MICAL, Relationship of microdistribution of alpha particles to damage, This vol. p. 27.

22. H. HOLLINGSHAUS, Spontaneous fracture of bones, Mechanical Engineering, 85–89 (April 1959).

23. D. H. TAYSUM, F. G. EVANS, W. M. HAMMER, W. S. S. JEE, C. E. REHFELD and L. W. BLAKE, Radionuclides and bone strength, This vol. p. 145.

DISCUSSION

MOLE: What is the histological basis of the large overgrowth of cortical bone and scoopings out of bone shown by Dr. Christensen?

CHAIRMAN JEE: It is the response of bone to an alteration in the circulation. I will have more to say on this subject in my second paper.

CHRISTENSEN: The fact that there is tremendous variation in local dose, and the fact that these five nuclides produce changes which have actually the same general radiological appearance, strongly suggests that there is a common factor in all of these changes. From gross evidence, at least, this common factor must be vascular in origin.

VAUGHAN: I would like to ask, first of all, for a point of clarification only because I think. I may have misheard something this morning. I thought I heard Dr. Rehfeld say that he could distinguish between the picture of plutonium and radium damage in his dogs.

This contradicted what Dr. Christensen said, that he could not make this distinction.

REHFELD: I did report a difference. Rib fractures in the plutonium dogs occur primarily at the hot line, while in radium dogs they do not. A further distinction is that on the roentgenograms the fractures in the radium dogs healed more readily than those in plutonium dogs, and they heal in a somewhat different fashion. Pelvic fractures have appeared in plutonium dogs but not in radium dogs, while the radium dogs suffered long bone fractures and the plutonium dogs did not.

ROWLAND: We have had the very good fortune to discover what appears to be a break in a human radium bone. Usually there is too much local damage to study a spontaneous fracture, but we have discovered a microscopic crack in a long bone which went from the endosteum to the periosteum on only one side of the shaft. We know that the crack occurred during the six or seven years this person was a dial painter, because, we find that callus had formed, had entered the crack, and was highly radioactive. The crack went through solid compact cortical bone, through no resorption cavities, and in fact it went through rather than around haversian systems. It went through hot spots. It went through highly calcified regions of bone which we think are atypical and typical of radium poisoning. We can do local dosimetry along the crack. It would be of interest to see how many hot spots the crack followed in its spiraling course from periosteum to endosteum.

Also, we have found that there is no correlation between average dose and the breaking of bones, but we are aware that vascularity is vitally impaired in some of these cases. Have you ever tried to do anything in terms of vascularity versus breaking strength?

CHAIRMAN JEE: I would like to comment that the crack described by Dr. Rowland is the kind of injury that could happen to any of us and may not be strictly the result of the radium. With respect to the relationship of vascularity and spontaneous fractures, this is another case where serial sacrifice animals are needed.

HASTERLIK: I will comment on the fractures in the human. We have not seen a person who had a spontaneous pathological fracture, who did not have complete healing of the fracture. One patient who has the most spectacular destructive changes in the bone, and who carries a body burden of about 3.+microcuries, had a fracture of each femoral shaft and had complete healing in a normal time.

Dr. Rehfeld reported this morning that some of the fractures healed and some did not. I had the feeling that one could not put too much stock in that. I think the capacity for complete healing exists if the part is treated with ordinary orthopedic care, such as either splinting or internal or external fixation. So, I am not quite sure that the fact that one can demonstrate radiographically that these bones did not heal, and that a false joint was formed, meant that the lesion was more "severe" than if it did heal.

REHFELD: I reported that many rib fractures had not healed at the time the dog died.

CHAIRMAN JEE: In high-level radiothorium dogs our vascular injection studies have shown that the marrow cavity is quite fibrotic. There are very few blood vessels and it is likely that the local concentration of radioactivity prevents the blood supply from re-establishing itself.

REHFELD: I did not count fractures through the tumor site. With respect to the X-ray shown of a radiothorium dog with tibial fractures, I wish to report that that dog was not allowed to live in that state. It is difficult to give these dogs the kind of orthopedic care that a human would receive.

CHAIRMAN JEE: Dr. Ray, do you have a comment about the vascularity factor?

RAY: I disagree that there is a very varied response with the alteration to circulation to bone, for we see dramatic changes with different types of alteration. In radiation damage we are first impressed with the fact that there is very frequently a hyperemia. This you see when you get a radiation burn on the skin, which is followed, as the radiation damage continues, with thrombosis and hemorrhages and necrosis. We can follow these same changes in the medullary canal of the bone.

I was interested in Dr. Vaughan's sections showing marrow changes, because we have seen similar changes following obstruction of the nutrient artery. We see degenerative changes in the marrow; and then, as the vascularization is re-established, regeneration and reappearance of the marrow cells occur.

With regard to the fractures shown, they resemble in many respects the looser zones that one sees in osteomalacia, symmetrical fractures that fail to heal.

Concerning Dr. Hasterlik's point that these fractures heal, we can call on another type evidence, the patients who have been treated with radium for pathological lesions of the uterus and who develop pathological fractures of the femur. It has been my experience that these fractures very frequently go on to aseptic necrosis and non-union.

CHAIRMAN JEE: How is the vascularity?

RAY: The vascularity is poor.

CHAIRMAN JEE: It is possible that the vascular destruction is transient, and after perhaps a couple of months, it is re-established and then there may be too many or too few blood vessels. If the radiation dose is fairly high, vascular destruction tends to be fairly progressive.

RAY: I think some of these problems can be solved by microangiographic techniques, and we are working on this.

T. F. DOUGHERTY: I would like to comment that there is a lack of pain at the site of these fractures. Where are the nerve endings?

RAY: We have some recent data on a patient with a pathological fracture secondary to metastatic carcinoma where the pain was completely relieved by periarterial stripping of the sympathetic nerve fibers.

T. F. DOUGHERTY: This was pointed out by John Hunter.

RAY: Yes.

T. F. DOUGHERTY: The second experiment we tend to forget constantly is the experiment of John Hunter, in which he split the periosteum, inserted a silver ring, and then sewed the periosteum together again and showed there were two layers of periosteum. The outer layer is a fibrous capsule which is avascular, and the inner layer is vascular and contains the nerve supply to the bone. He showed that if were not intact you would get no bone regeneration at this site, whereas if the silver ring is on the inside bone regenerates over the ring not under it.

In considering these problems we should not ignore what is known of the nature of the organization of the bone.

VAUGHAN: Do any of the tumors arise on the periosteal surface of the bone? With strontium we have never seen tumors arising there, although both dose rate and accumulated dose appear to be the same on both endosteal and periosteal surfaces. This seems to me an interesting point in general pathology, quite apart from radiobiology.

CHAIRMAN JEE: Thus far I have not seen any arising from the periosteum. One of the reasons is that some of these tumors are pretty good sized when the dog is autopsied and the site of origin is difficult to determine. I take approximately 700 sections per animal, and I have not seen anything arising from the periosteum yet.

CHRISTENSEN: The whole problem of the analysis of the damage in bone and the susceptibility to fracture may be greatly aided by the use of external radiation in which the dosage can be fairly clearly established, and the changes in histological pattern of the bone followed a little more definitely than they can with the internal emitters.

The point Dr. Ray raised about the treatment of carcinoma of the cervix is a case in point. This is a case of external irradiation in which 4000 to 5000 roentgens are delivered. There is very little gross change apparent in the femoral necks and the femoral heads of these female patients. Perhaps a slight increase in density. The damage is vascular. They go on to fracture with substantially complete necrosis through the areas in which the 4000 roentgens have been delivered.

CHAIRMAN JEE: I would like to re-emphasize our present belief that the principal effect of internally deposited radionuclides is on the blood vessels of bone. Strong evidence in support of this observation is given in a recent paper (W. S. S. JEE and J. S. ARNOLD, *Proc. Soc. Exp. Med. Biol.* **105**, 351, 1960).

WARREN: I think, as far as the external radiation group is concerned, the description that Dr. Christensen has already given to you is entirely sound.

One of the impressive things in the sharply localized radiation of internal emitters unevenly deposited is that there may be relatively little change in the vascularization of the bone as a whole, chiefly perhaps dilated sinusoidal spaces in the bone marrow. Most trabecular bone is relatively poorly vascularized. When we are talking about vascularization on a scale that can be shown by microangiography we have to restrict our discussion pretty largely to the cortical bone, and depend on microscopic observations as far as the trabecular bone is concerned.

CHAIRMAN JEE: I agree that the most difficult problem will be the vascularity in the spongy bone. We do have some ideas on how to study vascularity in trabecular bone and we hope to find time to do it soon.

EVANS: I want to return to Dr. Christensen's remarks about the difference in the healing of fractures with radium and with mesothorium. This to me is one of the delightful things about the dog observations. Dr. Hasterlik's patients have been mainly radium patients. Our series has about one-third persons whose major burden is mesothorium, and our observations in the human are substantially exactly the same as in the dog. The radium fracture is an ordinary fracture, and it heals well. But in a person whose major insult has been from mesothorium, and in our series these are people in whom about 90 per cent of the radiation dose has been due to mesothorium and its daughters, the fractures do not heal well and generally they don't heal. Moreover, they occur in general without pain.

I have to add one more thing which, I think, has very broad meaning. We have talked about the use of ratios of the effectiveness of plutonium and radium, and mesothorium and radium, and so on, in the dog, wondering whether this ratio would be the same in other species, particularly in man. Here we have an internal check. We do see mounting evidence that the ratio of the effectiveness of radium and mesothorium in these dogs is qualitatively the same as it is in man, and this gives us courage when later we must extrapolate the ratios and say, "What are we going to do about estimating plutonium and Sr^{90} in man?" So, to me, it is a conclusion of very broad generality and a very happy one.

RADIONUCLIDES AND BONE STRENGTH

D. H. Taysum, F. G. Evans,* W. M. Hammer, W. S. S. Jee
C. E. Rehfeld and L. W. Blake

*Radiobiology Division, Department of Anatomy, University of Utah
College of Medicine, Salt Lake City, Utah*

INTRODUCTION

THE observations of fractures in humans[1] whose skeletons contain radium accidentally ingested or therapeutically administered and the incidence of fractures of the bones of beagles injected with radionuclides prompted the examination of the physical properties of bones and bone substance in an effort to assign a causal relationship between fractures and radiation dose.

The fractures have long been termed spontaneous because they apparently arise without the application of large forces. Fractures arising in this fashion may be thought of as being derived from either of two sources: (1) weakened bone substance, or (2) a localized fault in the bone as a structure.

The first source may be evaluated directly by measurement; the second only inferentially since if bone substance is not weakened by an amount sufficient to account for spontaneous fractures then the bone as a structural member must fail because of a localized interruption of its strength.

The first measurements, which are not dealt with here, were made on tibiae tested as a simple beam by Hollingshaus and Mays.[2]

The work reported here is a further extension of the problem in which regularly shaped test specimens were subjected to pure tensile stresses in such a fashion as to allow better measurements of strain than were possible when tibiae were tested as a simple beam.

MATERIALS AND METHODS

The tibiae used were derived from the dogs of the chronic toxicity program of the Radiobiology laboratory. The bones were removed at autopsy. Because of the basic design of the experiment, this did not permit selection of specific elapsed times and radiation doses.[3]

---

* Department of Anatomy, University of Michigan Medical School, Guest Investigator.

145

Test specimens were produced on a jeweler's lathe from defleshed, deep frozen (–20°C) tibiae and were refrozen until two hours before testing. The machining was done in a glove box to contain the bone dust.

The testing jaws for assuring pure tensile forces, the extensometer and a test specimen are shown against a one inch grid in Fig. 1.

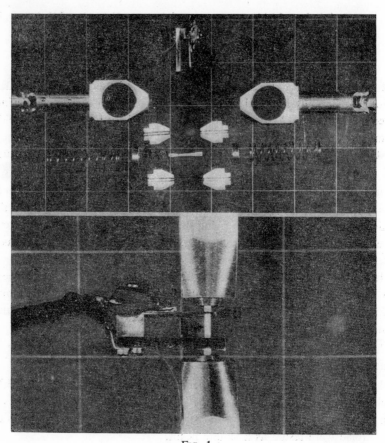

FIG. 1.

a. Flexible leaf; b. Specimen.

The extensometer is a flexible leaf cantilever on which a SR-4 strain gage is bonded. It was read by means of a conventional strain gage bridge and amplifier and was calibrated with a micrometer repeatedly during each experiment to monitor drift.

The testing machine was a standard Baldwin 120,000 lb capacity machine with a Tate Emery load cell with an accuracy ± 0·5 lb in the range used.

The injection schedule to identify the animals from the tabular listing is contained in Dr. T. F. Dougherty's paper.[3]

The tests were carried out at room temperature. The rate of loading was kept at approximately 15 lb/min with stress and strain readings taken in 2 lb increments. A plot was then made for each specimen and the proportional limit determined. All of the values used in this study are values taken at the proportional limit. The proportional limit was first determined using the 25 per cent offset method[4] but no advantage was found and values determined by eye were subsequently used.

Because the tabular listings are listings of stress at the proportional limit, a factor is given here so that interested persons may arrive at breaking stresses by using the following general relationship: Breaking stress is approximately 25 per cent greater than proportional stress.

A further note; to make the control number larger, animals receiving less than 200 rads are considered to be controls. This is believed to be acceptable because of the small effect even at thousands of rads of dose.

The two parameters investigated were age and radiation dose versus stress to proportional limit and energy absorbed to proportional limit. The other values, strain and Young's modulus, are omitted for brevity of presentation.

The data are presented in the form of three independent experiments because the test periods were separated by as much as a year, which represents the time required to collect sufficient tibiae, and the extensometer, as it was read by the bridge amplifier unit, showed a change in calibration. There was no change in calibration of any significance during a test period.

RESULTS

There is no significant correlation in change of stress or energy with increasing age or dose.

Fig. 2 shows a plot of stress versus age for the three experiments. The lines were fitted by the method of least squares. Regression analysis and a test of significance of the regression coefficient indicates that the slopes are not different from the no slope condition of no correlation at the 0·05 level of confidence.

Fig. 3 shows a plot of energy absorbed versus age. The conclusions are the same as for Fig. 2; no correlation at the 0·05 level of confidence.

Fig. 4 shows a plot of stress versus dose. There is no correlation at the 0·05 level of confidence.

Fig. 5 shows a plot of energy absorbed versus dose. There is no correlation at the 0·05 level of confidence.

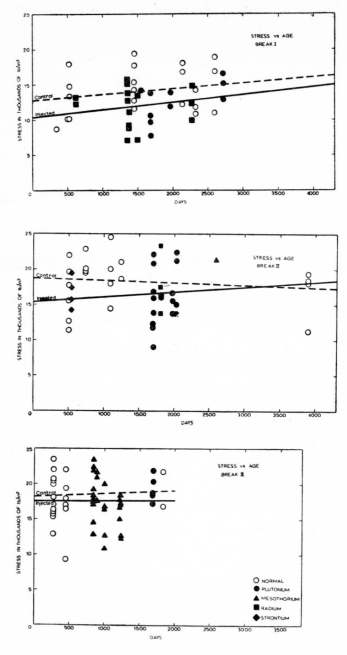

FIG. 2.

Stress vs. Age.

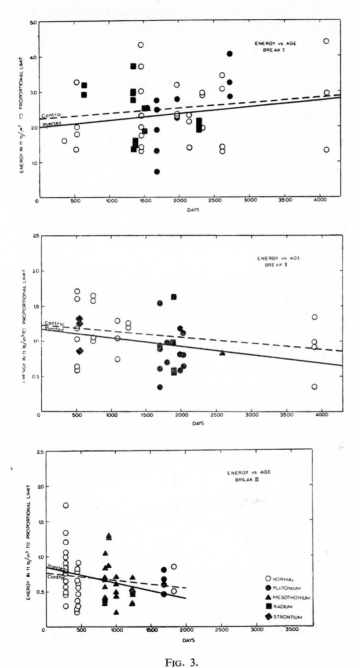

FIG. 3.

Energy vs. Age.

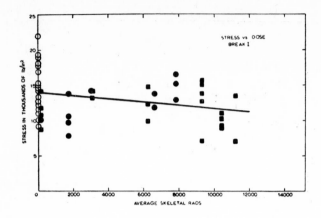

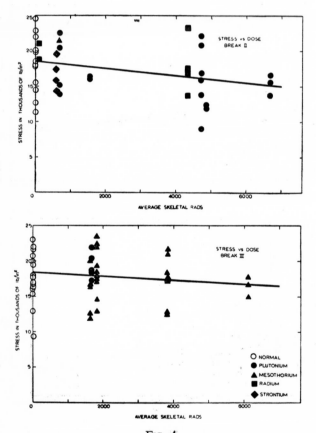

Fig. 4.

Stress vs. Dose.

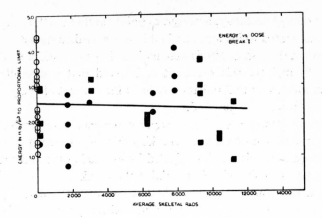

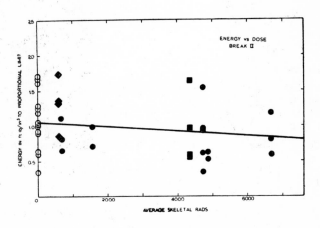

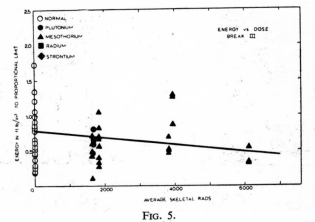

FIG. 5.

Energy vs. Dose.

152   D. H. TAYSUM *et al.*

It is considered necessary, however, to point out that the three experiments
demonstrate trends which agree and all indicate weakening with increasing
dose. Further, these same trends were indicated by the work of Hollingshaus
and Mays[2] and for this reason it is believed that a carefully worded
statement which says that radiation reduces the amount of energy required
to produce fractures is justified.

During the preparation of this paper comments were received by the
author that indicated that the most striking thing was the scatter in the data.
As a consequence, this was investigated by examining the amount of bone
actually present in sites closely adjoining the break in two different specimens from the same tibia which showed widely different energy values.

Fig. 6 shows soft X-ray pictures of four toxicity specimens and compares

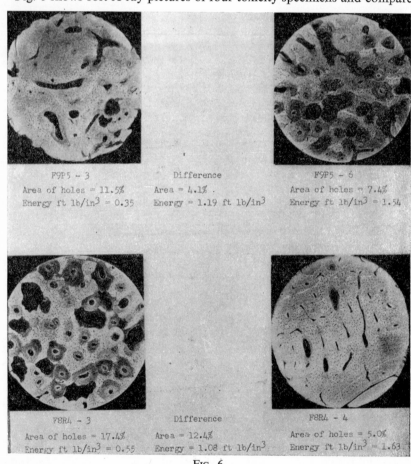

FIG. 6.

Toxicity specimens cross-sections closely adjoining breaks.

the bone area and energy absorbed. Fig. 7 shows four control specimens and compares bone area and energy absorbed.

This information serves to indicate that the scatter is related to a variable that has not been controlled, amount of bone per unit volume actually present, and is not simply measurement uncertainty. It also aids in drawing conclusions about the experiments.

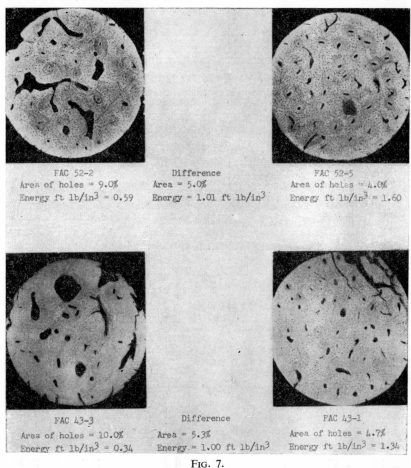

FAC 52-2	Difference	FAC 52-5
Area of holes = 9.0%	Area = 5.0%	Area of holes = 4.0%
Energy ft lb/in^3 = 0.59	Energy = 1.01 ft lb/in^3	Energy ft lb/in^3 = 1.60
FAC 43-3	Difference	FAC 43-1
Area of holes = 10.0%	Area = 5.3%	Area of holes = 4.7%
Energy ft lb/in^3 = 0.34	Energy = 1.00 ft lb/in^3	Energy ft lb/in^3 = 1.34

FIG. 7.

Control specimens cross–sections closely adjoining breaks.

CONCLUSIONS

Age and radiation dose as expressed by the ranges investigated do not weaken bone substance enough to account for the observed fractures and the cause of spontaneous fractures is tentatively assigned to localized faults.

ACKNOWLEDGEMENTS

It is a pleasure to acknowledge the support and direction of Prof. Thomas F. Dougherty, the director of the project, the guidance and thorough care with which Dr. C. W. Mays treated the problems as they arose and the gracious cooperation extended by William Boyd, Lee R. Jackson, Renate Tegge and Douglas Brammer in various phases of this study.

REFERENCES

1. J. C. AUB, R. D. EVANS, L. H. HEMPELMANN and H. S. MARTLAND, The late effects of internally-deposited radioactive materials in man, *Medicine* **31**, 3, 222–329 (1952).
2. H. HOLLINGSHAUS and C. W. MAYS, Changes in mechanical strength of bone due to internally deposited radioelements, Radiobiology Laboratory Annual Progress Report COO-215, 158–179 (1958).
3. T. F. DOUGHERTY, Study of the long term biological effects of internal irradiation in adult beagles. This vol. p. 7.
4. E. P. POPOV, *Mechanics of Materials*, Prentice-Hall, New York (1955).

TABLE 1

Calculated Values Obtained from the Measurements of Experiment One

Bone	Age (days)	Av. dose to skeleton (rads)	Stress ($1b/in^2. \times \times 10^3$)	Strain ($in/in. \times \times 10^{-2}$)	Young's modulus ($1b/in^2. \times 10^5$)	Energy absorbed (ft $1b/in^3.$)
M1R5–1	1381	10,400	8.8	4·20	2.10	1.54
M1R5–3	1381	10,400	11·1	3.48	3.19	1·61
M1R5–5	1381	10,400	9·2	3.92	2·35	1·50
M10R5–1	1352	9300	12·7	5·64	2·25	2·98
M10R5–2	1352	9300	15·1	5·92	2·55	3·72
M10R5–3	1352	9300	7·1	4·60	1·54	1·36
M10R5–4	1352	9300	12·7	5·60	2·50	2·96
M10R5–5	1352	9300	15·7	4·20	3·74	2·75
M10R5–6	1352	9300	13·8	5·24	2·63	3·01
T2R5–1	2287	6270	12·3	3·88	3·17	1·99
T2R5–2	2287	6270	14·8	3·12	4·74	1·92
T2R5–3	2287	6270	9·9	5.24	1·89	2·17
T9R5–1	2334	170	14·2	5·00	2·84	2·96
T9R5–1	2334	170	10·8	6·40	1·69	2·92
T9R5–4	2334	170	11·8	4·00	2·95	1·97
T8R5–1	348	170	8·7	4·44	1·96	1·61
T12R5–3	622	3100	13·2	5.24	2·52	2·88
T12R5–4	622	3100	14·2	5·40	2·63	3·19
F6R5–1	1501	11,200	13·5	4·48	3·01	2·52
F6R5–4	1501	11,200	7·1	2·96	2·40	0·876
F7P4–1	1683	1730	13·8	4.80	2·88	2.76

TABLE 1 (Cont'd)

Bone	Age (days)	Av. dose to skeleton (rads)	Stress (1b/in².× ×10³)	Strain (in/in.× ×10⁻²)	Young's modulus (1b/in².×10⁵)	Energy absorbed (ft 1b/in³.)
F7P4–2	1683	1730	7·8	2·20	3·55	0·715
F7P4–3	1683	1730	13·8	4·32	3·19	2·48
F7P4–4	1683	1730	9·7	4·76	2·04	1·92
F7P4–5	1683	1730	10·6	2·96	3·58	1·31
T3P5–1	1552	3040	14·2	4·28	3·32	2·53
T12P5–1	515	140	10·1	3·24	3·12	1·36
F2P5–2	2726	7830	15·2	6·40	2·38	4·05
F2P5–3	2726	7830	12·9	5·28	2·44	2·84
F2P5–4	2726	7830	16·5	4·72	3·50	3·25
F7P5–4	1973	6630	13·8	4·84	2·85	2·78
F7P5–6	1973	6630	11·0	4·92	2·24	2·25
FAC 10–1	2605		16·9	4·40	3·84	3·09
FAC 10–2	2605		18·9	4·40	4·30	3·46
FAC 10–3	2605		11·0	2·40	4·58	1·10
FAC 10–4	2605		11·0	3·12	3·53	1·43
MAC 3–2	1451		17·7	5·04	3·51	3·72
MAC 3–3	1451		15·3	4·72	2·50	3·01
MAC 3–4	1451		19·4	5·36	3·62	4·33
MAC 3–6	1451		11·6	4·80	2·42	2·32
MAC 37–1	4089		22·0	4·80	4·58	4·40
MAC 37–2	4089		9·18	3·44	2·67	1·32
MAC 37–3	4089		14·4	4·92	2·93	2·93
MAC 37–4	4089		18·6	5·68	3·27	4·40
MAC 3–1	1451		11·4	2·80	4·07	1·33
MAC 3–2	1451		14·3	2·96	4·83	1·76
MAC 3–3	1451		15·0	3·20	4·69	2·00
MAC 3–4	1451		12·7	2·72	4·67	1·44
FAC 17–3	2145		12·2	2·80	4·36	1·42
FAC 17–5	2145		16·8	3·08	5·45	2·16
FAC 17–8	2145		18·1	3·12	5·80	2·35
MAC 35–1	529		17·9	6·72	2·66	5·01
MAC 35–3	529		14·7	5·36	2·74	3·28
MAC 35–4	529		13·3	3·64	3·65	2·02
MAC 35–5	529		10·2	4·28	2·38	1·82
MAC 36–2	1971		15·2	3·68	4·13	2·33
MAC 36–4	1971		15·2	5·04	3·02	3·19
MAC 36–6	1971		14·3	3·96	3·61	2·36

TABLE 2

Calculated Values Obtained from the Measurements of Experiment Two

Bone	Age (days)	Av. dose to skeleton (rads)	Stress (1b/in.$^2\times$ $\times 10^3$)	Strain (in/in.$\times$ $\times 10^{-2}$)	Young's modulus (1b/in.$^2\times 10^5$)	Energy absorbed (ft 1b/in^3.)
M10R1·7–1	1247	107	21·07	1·43	14·73	1·25
M10R1·7–3	1247	107	18·67	1·53	12·12	1·19
F9P5–1	1697	4720	13·88	1·53	9·071	0·884
F9P5–2	1697	4720	15·95	1·41	11·31	0·936
F9P5–3	1697	4720	9·04	0·93	9·720	0·350
F9P5–4	1697	4720	22·14	3·14	7·050	2·89
F9P5–5	1697	4720	16·88	0·88	19·18	0·618
F9P5–6	1697	4720	20·80	1·78	11·68	1·54
F6P3–1	2032	680	15·09	1·03	14·65	0·647
F6P3–2	2032	680	13·77	1·41	9·765	0·807
F6P3–3	2032	680	21·27	1·28	16·61	1·13
F6P3–5	2032	680	22·44	1·20	18·70	1·12
M8P4–1	1808	1560	16·38	1·03	15·90	0·702
M8P4–2	1808	1560	16·03	1·47	10·90	0·981
T15P5–1	738	5·61	19·88	1·27	15·65	1·05
T15P5–2	738	5·61	19·68	1·24	15·87	1·01
T15P5–3	738	5·61	20·10	1·63	12·33	1·57
T15P5–4	738	5·61	22·89	1·74	13·15	1·65
M6S5–1	539	603	15·78	1·37	11·51	0·900
M6S5–2	539	603	17·34	1·74	9·965	1·25
M6S5–3	539	603	19·48	1·63	11·95	1·32
M6S5–4	539	603	14·28	1·44	9·916	0·856
F7P5–2	1973	6670	16·66	1·71	9·742	1·18
F7P5–3	1973	6670	13·72	1·04	13·19	0·594
F7P5–4	1973	6670	15·56	1·24	12·54	0·803
M8P5–1	1689	4870	11·78	1·07	11·00	0·525
M8P5–2	1689	4870	12·33	1·21	10·19	0·621
F8R4–2	1798	4350	17·45	1·33	13·18	0·966
F8R4–3	1798	4350	13·77	0·96	14·34	0·550
F8R4–4	1798	4350	23·33	1·68	13·88	1·63
F8R4–5	1798	4350	16·66	0·84	19·83	0·582
F1M2–4	2588	676	21·42	0·93	23·03	0·830
FAC 43–1	3881		19·38	1·67	11·60	1·34
FAC 43–2	3881		18·07	1·20	15·05	0·903
FAC 43–3	3881		11·27	0·73	15·43	0·342
FAC 43–4	3881		18·46	1·28	14·42	0·984
FAC 51–2	1089		14·43	1·24	11·63	0·745
FAC 51–3	1089		20·00	1·25	16·00	1·04
FAC 51–4	1089		24·56	1·27	19·33	1·29
FAC 51–6	1089		17·95	1·24	14·47	0·927

TABLE 2   (Cont'd)

Bone	Age (days)	Av. dose to skeleton (rads)	Stress $(1b/in.^3 \times 10^3)$	Strain $(in/in. \times 10^{-2})$	Young's modulus $(1b/in.^2 \times \times 10^5)$	Energy absorbed (ft 1b/in.^{3})
FAC 52–1	509		15·55	1·60	9·718	1·03
FAC 52–2	509		11·32	1·25	9·056	0·589
FAC 52–3	509		12·65	1·21	10·45	0·637
FAC 52–4	509		19·60	2·10	9·33	1·71
FAC 52–5	509		21·98	1·75	12·56	1·602
FAC 52–6	509		17·77	1·60	11·10	1·18

TABLE 3

Calculated Values Obtained from the Measurements of Experiment Three

Bone	Age (days)	Av.dose to skeleton (rads)	Stress $(1b/in.^2 \times \times 10^3)$	Strain $(in/in. \times 10^{-2})$	Young's modulus $(1b/in.^2 \times 10^5)$	Energy absorbed (ft 1b/in.^{3})
T10T3–1	455	40	17·7	0·841	21·0	0·620
T10T3–2	455	40	19·4	0·684	28·4	0·553
T10T3–3	455	40	22·0	0·995	22·1	0·912
T10T3–4	455	40	17·0	0·362	47·0	0·470
T10T3–5	455	40	17·0	0·944	18·0	0·293
F1S1–1	1832	20	16·8	0·720	23·3	0·504
F1S1–4	1832	20	21·7	0·940	23·1	0·851
T9T3–1	448	10	16·4	0·547	30·0	0·374
T9T3–2	448	10	22·1	0·854	25·9	0·786
T9T3–3	448	10	17·9	1·11	16·1	0·828
T9T3–4	448	10	9·31	0·515	18·1	0·200
T9T3–5	448	10	17·6	0·342	51·1	0·251
T9T3–6	448	10	19·3	0·822	23·5	0·661
Normal–10 (R)	275		23·5	1·37	17·1	1·34
Normal–9 (R)	275		15·7	0·602	26·1	3·94
Normal–7 (R)	275		22·0	1·32	16·7	1·21
Normal–6 (R)	275		16·3	1·18	13·8	0·801
Normal–5 (R)	275		17·1	1·39	12·3	0·990
Normal–4 (R)	275		16·1	1·58	10·2	1·06
Normal–3 (R)	275		20·7	2·01	10·8	1·73
Normal–1 (L)	275		16·3	0·432	37·7	0·293
Normal–2 (L)	275		19·9	0·790	25·2	0·655
Normal–3 (L)	275		18·1	0·653	27·2	0·492
Normal–4 (L)	275		22·6	0·816	27·7	0·786
Normal–5 (L)	275		20·4	0·995	20·5	0·846

TABLE 3 (Cont'd)

Bone		Age (days)	Av. dose to skeleton (rads)	Stress (1b/in.^{2}× ×10^3)	Strain (in/in.^{2}× ×10^{-2})	Young's modulus (1b/in.^{2}×10^5)	Energy absorbed (ft 1b/in.^{3})
Normal–6	(L)	275		22·0	0·995	22·1	0·912
Normal–7	(L)	275		12·9	1·07	12·1	0·575
Normal–8	(L)	275		15·3	0·720	21·3	0·459
M4M4–3		896	3940	21·7	1·44	15·1	1·30
M4M4–4		896	3940	20·9	1·46	14·3	1·27
M4M4–6		896	3940	17·7	1·18	15·0	0·871
F2M4–1		1238	3820	17·1	0·704	24·6	0·507
F2M4–2		1238	3820	12·7	1·37	9·05	0·708
F2M4–3		1238	3820	18·4	0·685	26·9	0·525
F2M4–5		1238	3820	12·4	—	—	—
F2M4–6		1238	3820	17·3	0·653	26·2	0·465
M3M4–1		997	1640	16·8	0·858	21·1	0·601
M3M4–2		997	1640	16·4	0·720	22·8	0·492
M3M4–3		997	1640	12·7	0·394	32·2	0·208
M3M4–4		997	1640	20·0	0·858	23·3	0·715
M3M4–5		997	1640	11·9	0·858	13·9	0·425
M3P4–1		1683	1680	18·7	0·598	31·3	0·466
M3P4–2		1683	1680	17·2	1·13	15·2	0·810
M3P4–4		1683	1680	18·4	0·771	23·9	0·591
M3P4–5		1683	1680	21·9	0·736	29·7	0·672
M3P4–6		1683	1680	20·3	0·752	27·0	0·636
T2M4·5–1		1218	6110	15·0	0·547	27·4	0·342
T2M4·5–2		1218	6110	17·8	0·736	24·2	0·546
T2M4·5–4		1218	6110	16·7	0·480	34·8	0·334
T1M4·5–1		843	1830	17·4	0·925	18·8	0·671
T1M4·5–2		843	1830	17·1	0·563	30·4	0·401
T1M4·5–3		843	1830	12·9	0·618	20·9	0·332
T1M4·5–4		843	1830	17·8	0·771	23·1	0·572
T1M4·5–5		843	1830	23·5	0·720	32·6	0·705
T1M4·5–6		843	1830	18·4	0·547	33·6	0·419
T1M4·5–1		843	1830	14·6	0·618	23·6	0·376
T1M4·5–2		843	1830	19·3	0·714	27·0	0·574
T1M4·5–3		843	1830	17·4	0·771	22·6	0·559
T1M4·5–4		843	1830	18·4	0·736	25·0	0·564
T1M4·5–5		843	1830	22·4	1·13	19·8	1·05
T1M4·5–6		843	1830	21·9	0·909	24·1	0·829

DISCUSSION

CHAIRMAN JEE: We will open this discussion session with Dr. Mays. He will discuss the paper "Radionuclides and bone strength in beagles".

MAYS: Several years ago a number of us, Dr. JEE, Dr. VAN DILLA, Dr. ARNOLD and I, became interested in how radiation causes bones to fracture.

I was able to interest Harry Hollingshaus, a mechanical engineering student, in measuring the strength of intact tibiae as a thesis project. (H. Hollingshaus, *Mech. Eng.* **85**, April 1959, and H. Hollingshaus and C. W. Mays, Annual Progress Report, Radiobiology Laboratory COO-215, 158, March 1958). I would now like to compare his findings with the more recent results of Taysum *et al.* on test specimens machined from cortical bone.

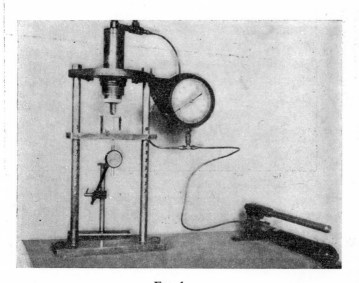

FIG. 1.

The testing machine used by Hollingshaus to break intact tibia. A defleshed beagle tibia was supported near each of its ends. The bone was then loaded at the center by a hand-pumped hydraulic ram until it broke. The breaking stress was computed from the dimensions of the bone and the maximum load before failure.

Harry built the testing machine shown in Fig. 1. In the terminology of the histologist, Harry could have been classified as an osteoclast (bone-breaker). You might ask why he picked the tibia. The answer is that not all of the bone-seekers in our laboratory are in the kennels and the tibia was the only major long bone not claimed by somebody else.

A plot of breaking stresses in control dogs versus their ages at sacrifice is shown in Fig. 2. The data of Fig. 2 suggested a slight increase in breaking strength with age. However, I would like to point out that if you disregard the rightmost two points on the figure, little if any change in breaking stress with age is indicated.

Keeping this in mind, refer back to the control values on Taysum's Fig. 2. The stress to the proportional limit in his test specimens machined from compact bone tended to (a) increase with age in his first experiment, (b) decrease with age in his second experiment, and (c) remain independent of age in his third experiment. Thus, these results support the idea that there is no large consistent change in bone strength with age in normal beagle bone within the age limits tested.

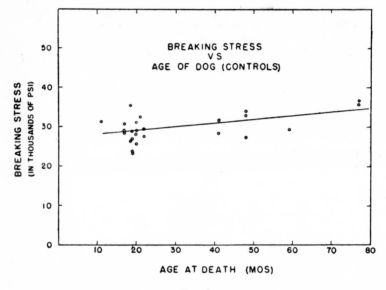

FIG. 2.

Breaking stresses in the intact tibiae of control beagles versus their ages at sacrifice.

Now for the effects of irradiation on bone strength. Each of the three experiments of Taysum *et al.*, showed a tendency for the stress to decrease with increasing skeletal dose (see Taysum's Fig. 4). This confirmed the earlier work of Hollingshaus shown in Fig. 3. As the skeletal dose increased, the breaking strength decreased, but the important thing to note is that the average reduction in bone strength was not more than about a factor of two. It indeed seems most unlikely that a uniform weakening by a factor of only two would cause the large number of fractures which have been observed in some of these dogs. Taysum's conclusion that radiation fractures are the result of local weakening rather than a uniform loss in bone strength seems quite plausible.

Both Dr. Rehfeld and Dr. Christensen pointed out in their papers that most of the radiation fractures in our beagles have occurred in ribs and vertebral spinous processes. Small zones of weakness in these slender bones should be much more serious than weak zones of the same size in larger bones such as the tibia. Attempts by Hollingshaus to measure the strength of ribs were not successful. Ribs from both control and radioactive dogs bent like green twigs.

David Taysum showed some very interesting slides in which a major decrease in energy absorption was associated with a very minor decrease in the fraction of remaining bone (see Taysum's Figs. 6 and 7). For example two specimens from the control dog FAC 52 differed by a factor of three in energy absorption whereas their fractions of remaining bone differed by only 5%.

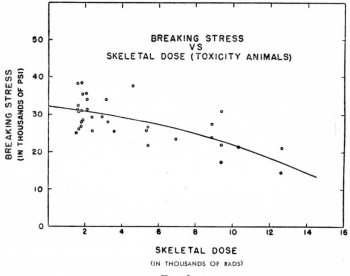

FIG. 3.

Breaking stresses in the intact tibiae of internally irradiated beagles versus their average skeletal doses in rads.

Clearly the resorption of bone can drastically weaken the remaining bone substance. At least part of this weakening definitely results from the concentration of stress along the boundaries of resorption cavities when the bone is loaded. I will also venture the speculation that (a) certain substances are released during the process of resorption, (b) these substances permeate into the bone adjacent to the resorption cavities and (c) weaken this remaining bone substance. Consider the way that even weak acid can seep into mortar and rot its strength to great depth.

It is important to emphasize that resorption and variations in local bone strength occur both in control and irradiated bone. But in control bone this process is presumably more orderly and is less likely to create local areas of weakness extensive enough to result in fracturing.

EVANS: I would like to point out that these tests, which have been run by mechanical engineers, are either breaking or tensile strength tests. I think compression tests have not been done. However, a number of us have worried about this.

The factor which seems to be missing is a test in torsion; that is, the person's bone generally breaks in torsion, and all these standard mechanical engineering tests do not yet involve a test of torsion.

MAYS: We are currently saving tibiae in order to do torsion tests.

SPIERS: Why didn't you use a fatigue test? This would seem to me to be the right way to look for a developing failure, where you might have things like cracks in metal.

11

MAYS: Sometimes a fatigue test is fatiguing to the experimenter, too.

TAYSUM: I do not think any good information would be obtained from a fatigue test if the proportional limit were not known. Now that we have this information we could probably do a fatigue test, and we might be able to do the ribs this way.

CHAIRMAN JEE: In our lower dose level dogs we have seen very few spontaneous fractures.

LAMERTON: Maybe this is a way of leading the discussion on to perhaps a broader subject. I am wondering if quite a lot of the scatter in those curves was not, in fact, because the abscissa was the mean skeletal dose. In a way you showed very conclusively yourself that the local concentrations were extremely important in producing lots of changes, and it would seem to me that this is one of the places where you certainly should not use mean skeletal dose. I am not sure where you should use it, but I am fairly sure you should not use it here.

MAYS: I must insist on answering this question. In the control dogs the mean skeletal dose is very, very small, and we got just about as much variation in the control specimens as we did in those which were radioactive.

MARINELLI: What happens if you change the humidity during the testing?

TAYSUM: If the bone is allowed to dry out its strength goes up markedly, so we made our specimens from deep-frozen tibia. These were immediately refrozen and kept frozen until just two hours before testing. We presume that the state of hydration in all of these specimens is comparable, and about what it is when it comes out of the dog.

LAMERTON: I would like to raise the question again about your use of mean skeletal dose. I quite understand that it is one of the very few parameters that you can get and use. However, it would seem to me that to use it when you are attempting to measure a very general function of bone, is very dangerous since the changes you are measuring almost certainly have been the result of intense local irradiation.

CHAIRMAN JEE: I agree, wholeheartedly, that this is so, but at this time we have very little local dose information, and do not feel that we should suppress the result we have until the local dose measurements are made. We also need proper support and more capable personnel in order to make these measurements.

We are going to take these little specimens and take micro-X-rays close to the break. We will also do the local dose work, and then try to put the information together.

I think we must close the discussion on bone strength to permit time for other topics.

EYE CHANGES INDUCED BY INTERNAL IRRADIATION

G. N. Taylor, C, E. Rehfeld, G. Schneebeli and H. A. Johnson

Division of Radiobiology, Department of Anatomy
University of Utah College of Medicine
Salt Lake City, Utah

INTRODUCTION

ONE of the earliest clinical changes that is seen in beagles following the intravenous injection of Ra^{226}, Ra^{228} or Th^{228} occurs in the eye. Lesser and unpredictable changes are induced by Pu^{239}. Previous investigations [1,2,3,4] have determined that these alterations are limited to the pigmented regions and are related to the treatment level and the duration of burden time except in the case of Pu^{239}.

The clinical features coincide with analytical studies dealing with the regional distribution of these radionuclides in the ocular structures. It has been established that the concentration of Ra^{226}, Th^{228} and Pu^{239} residual in eye tissues is significantly above the plasma level at post-injection periods of over 1000 days, and that most of the burden is present in the pigmented structures. [5,6]

This paper will present some of the clinical and microscopic features of the ocular changes seen in beagles following treatment with Ra^{226}, Ra^{228}, Th^{228} and Pu^{239}.

METHODS

The beagles used in this study are those of the Division of Radiobiology, University of Utah, and the radionuclide dose "levels" referred to are as defined in the general introduction of this symposium. [7]

All retinal photographs were taken with a Bausch & Lomb retinal camera. Prior to photography the irises were dilated with one of several mydriatics, and the desired level of sedation was achieved by the intravenous administration of a tranquilizing agent (promazine). Iris photographs were taken with a 35 mm Exakta camera, bellowscope attachment, 135 mm lens, and electronic flash.

Sections used for light microscopy were Zenker-formol fixed tissues, embedded according to standard paraffin techniques, and stained with hematoxylin and eosin.

11*   163

Tissues used in electron microscopy were prepared as follows: The animals were placed under nembutal anesthesia for enucleation and subsequent euthanasia. The eyeball was divided at a plane through the ora serrata, and the vitreous humor was removed. The retina and choroid were then separated from the sclera and immersed in cold 1 per cent osmium tetroxide for 30 min (within $2\frac{1}{2}$ min after enucleation), washed in several changes of cold distilled water, and dehydrated in graded alcohols up to 80 per cent. The specimens were kept under refrigeration at this dilution for 12 hr and embedded in epoxy resin (Epon 812, Shell Company). The sections were placed on bare grids and carbonized directly.

RESULTS

Iris Changes

Grossly visible changes on the anterior surface of the iris were induced by Ra^{226}, Ra^{228}, Th^{228} and Pu^{239}. These alterations were characterized by the formation of melanotic plaques at the low levels and depigmentation at the higher levels. Thus, there was a dose related effect involving the pigmented tissues of the iris.

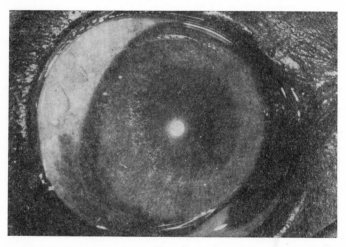

FIG. 1.

Iris photograph showing normal beagle iris. It is noted that there are no hyperpigmented plaques and that the stromal elements are largely obscured. × 10.

In the case of Ra^{226}, plaque formation was the only ocular symptom noted at the 1, 1·7 and 2 levels. These consisted of circumscribed dark brown hyper-pigmented regions varying up to four or five millimeters in diameter (Fig. 2). They were seldom raised above the surface of the iris and did not produce any apparent structural change. Depigmentation was not observed with these doses.

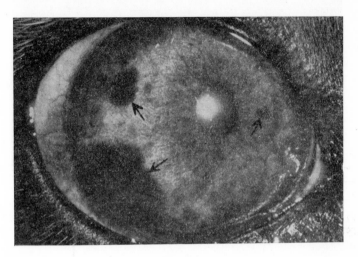

FIG. 2.

Iris photograph of beagle injected with 0·154 μc/kg of Ra[226] (1·7 level) taken 1932 days post injection showing the typical hyper-pigmented plaques (arrow) that are formed at this dose level. × 10.

At the higher levels of Ra[226] treatment the alterations were related to the progressive loss of pigment which exposed the stroma and left the iris with a threadbare appearance (Figs. 3 and 4). This also produced a color transition from the normal dark or golden brown to a faded blue-gray. Hyper-pigmented plaques were produced at these levels, especially at the 3 level, but they were usually not as intensely pigmented as were those of the lower doses and they did not occur in some of the 4 and 5 level dogs. The 3 level dose was transitional in that melanotic plaque formation was a prominent feature during the early post-injection period, with depigmentation becoming the more significant symptom in the later post-injection phases.

Iris changes preceded the tapetal alterations at the lower levels but not at the higher levels. A few of the latent periods, relative to the formation of hyper-pigmented plaques induced by Ra[226], are given in Table 1.

Ra[228] and Th[228] induced iris changes qualitatively similar to those just described. The hyper-pigmented regions were equally as prominent, but the

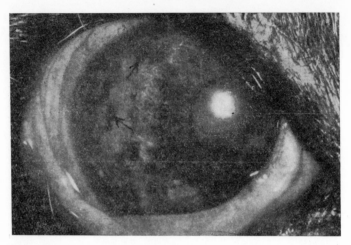

FIG. 3.

Iris photograph of beagle injected with 0·883 μc/kg of Ra²²⁶ (3 level) taken 1897 days post injection which shows both a moderate degree of depigmentation and hyper-pigmented plaque formation (arrow). The depigmentation in this black and white photograph is represented as an increase in the extent to which the fibrillar or stromal elements (S) can be seen. × 10.

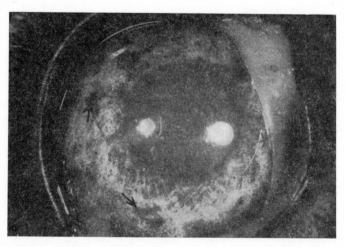

FIG. 4.

Iris photograph of beagle injected with 10·8 μc/kg of Ra²²⁶ (5 level) taken 1329 days post injection which shows an extreme degree of depigmentation that is evidenced by the marked extent to which the stromal elements are seen, especially in the pupillary region. A moderate number of plaques (arrow) are also evident. It is noted that the hyper-pigmented plaques at this level and post-injection interval are less sharply circumscribed than they are at the lower doses. × 10.

TABLE 1

Time Interval between Injection with Ra^{226} and the First Appearance of Melanotic Plaques on the Anterior Surface of the Iris

Injection dose level	Injected μc/kg	Approximate latent period (months)
5	10	7–[a]
4	3	7–[a]
3	1	3–4
2	0·3	undetermined[b]
1·7	0·15	undetermined[b]
1	0·05	undetermined[b]

[a] Melanotic plaques do not appear in some instances at these levels.
[b] In excess of 11 months.

degree of depigmentation did not become as pronounced as in the case of Ra^{226}.

Iris symptoms induced by Pu^{239} were infrequent and were not clearly correlated with the injected dose. Occasional hyper-pigmented plaques were formed, but depigmentation was not observed, even at the highest levels.

Gross Changes in the Tapetum Lucidum

The canine eye, as do those of many of the other carnivores, contains a tapetum (tapetum lucidum, tapetum cellulosum). This is a specialized region of the choroid, positioned in the dorsal fundus just above the optic papilla (Figs. 5, 6 and 7). It is unique in having the highest zinc content of

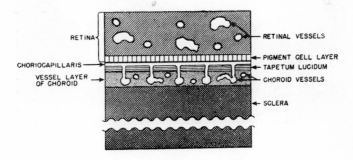

FIG. 5.

Diagramatic cross-section of the canine fundus illustrating the general anatomical arrangement in the region of the tapetum. ×450.

any known tissue. Amounts up to 8·5 per cent of the dry weight are found in dogs, with the zinc in the form of zinc cysteine.[8] This tissue is the site of one of the earliest symptoms seen in beagles following treatment with

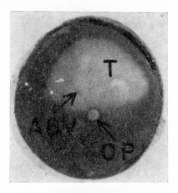

FIG. 6.

Photograph of a normal beagle fundus illustrating the shape and relationship of the tapetum (T) to the optic papilla (OP). The retinal arteries and veins (A & V) emerging in the vicinity of the papilla are faintly visible. This is the right eye with the anterior aspect of the eyeball removed at the level of the posterior aspect of the ciliary body. It is positioned such that the top of the photograph is in the dorsal position of the eye. × 2·5.

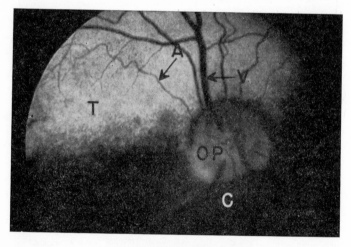

FIG. 7.

Retinal photograph showing a normal beagle fundus in the region of the tapetum (T) and the optic papilla (OP). The retinal arteries (A) and veins (V) are clearly seen. Note the smooth, finely stippled appearance of the tapetum. The choroid (C) is seen in the lower half of the photo. Choroidal vessels are not evident. × 11.

Ra²²⁶ and the pathogenesis as induced by the five dose level will be presented, first, since this treatment produces the full gamut of changes. Comparison of lower levels and the other three radionuclides will be made to this baseline.

On ophthalmoscopic examination, tapetal alterations were evident as early as 20 days post injection. Slight dullness and coarsening of the normally smooth, finely stippled tapetum were the first symptoms noted. With increasing post-injection times (30–200 days) the tapetum became increasingly more grainy and the smooth bright yellow appearance, seen normally (Fig. 7), was transformed to one composed of yellow, blue and blue-green granular-like particles (Fig. 8). Later in the syndrome (85–300

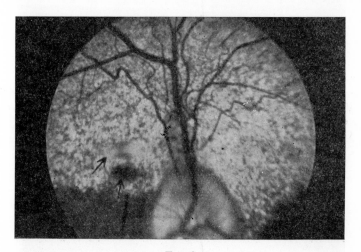

FIG. 8.

Retinal photograph of a beagle injected with 10·4 μc/kg of Ra²²⁶ (5 level) taken 84 days post injection, showing a moderate degenerative change in the tapetum. Transition from the finely stippled appearance seen normally to that of a coarse grainy condition is evident. When viewed *in vivo* much of the yellow brilliance had been lost and yellow, blue and blue-green granules and melanotic foci are beginning to appear. Artifacts indicated by arrows. ×11.

days) the iridescent material became progressively more sparse, exposing the underlying choroid to an extent that was determined by the degree of tapetal degeneration (Fig. 9). Ultimately (approximately 120 to 365 days), the tapetum was entirely lost and the dorsal and ventral aspects of the fundus appeared very much alike (Fig. 10).

Changes qualitatively similar to the above were induced by the Ra²²⁶ 4 level dose. Only the earlier phases were seen at the 2 and 3 levels and the tapetum was never entirely lost. During post-injection intervals

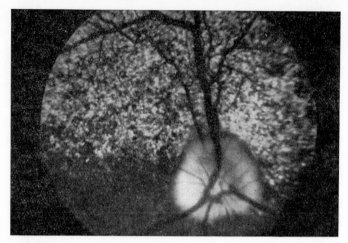

Fig. 9.

Retinal photograph of a beagle injected with 10·4 μc/kg of Ra²²⁶ (5 level) taken 161 days post injection, showing a marked degenerative change in the tapetum. Much of the iridescent material of the tapetum has been removed thus, partially exposing the underlying choroid. ×11.

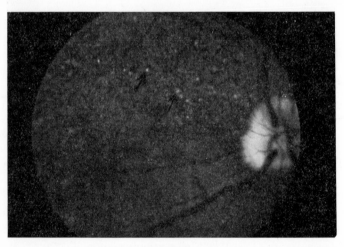

Fig. 10.

Retinal photograph of a beagle injected with 10·4 μc/kg of Ra²²⁶ (5 level) taken 161 days post injection. The tapetum is almost entirely gone and the underlying choroid is clearly seen. Only very scanty amounts of the iridescent substance of the tapetum remain (arrows). The choroidal vessels are not evident. This is the same eye as the normal which is shown in Fig. 7. ×11.

of five to eight years, tapetal changes have not been observed in dogs treated at the 1 and 1·7 levels. As the dose was decreased the latent periods for the comparable stages were increased (Table 2).

TABLE 2

Time Interval between Injection with Ra^{226} and the First Change that is Seen in the Tapetum

Injection dose level	Injected μc/kg	Latent period (months)
5	10	1*
4	3	4–5
3	1	6–7
2	0·3	undetermined
1·7	0·15	no changes noted
1	0·05	no changes noted

* Changes seen as early as 20 days post injection.

Other radionuclides which affected the tapetum include Ra^{228}, Th^{228} and Pu^{239}. Ra^{228} and Th^{228} induced changes qualitatively similar to those described for Ra^{226}. However, at comparable dose levels the degree of alteration was less in the case of Ra^{228} and much less for Th^{228}. Also, the respective latent periods were longer.

Pu^{239} produced changes in the tapetum but of an unpredictable type and degree. The alterations included loss of lustre, slight to moderate granulation, and in some cases dark pigmentary changes. In many instances, even at the 5 level, the fundic examinations remained negative. Yet changes occurred occasionally at the 2 level. This unpredictable incidence and pathogenesis precludes any dose-time-change relationship.

Gross Changes in the Choroid

Ra^{226} at the 2 through the 5 dose levels induced depigmentation of the choroid to an extent that was clearly apparent on opthalmoscopic examination. The normal beagle choroid is heavily pigmented, and the vascular system of the vessel layer is usually not seen (Fig. 7). However, as the loss of pigment progresses, the choroid vessels became exposed to an extent that was related to the amount of depigmentation (Fig. 11). The clearness with which these vessels were seen was the principal criterion used in approximating the degree of depigmentation. Variations in the amount of choroidal pigment normally present and the inherent difficulties in

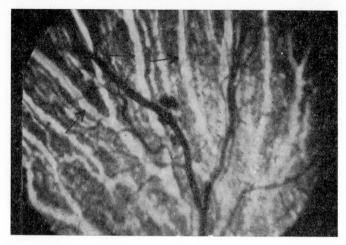

FIG. 11.

Retinal photograph of a beagle injected with 9·48 μc/kg of Ra²²⁶ (5 level) taken
1242 days post injection. The tapetum is entirely gone and marked depigmentation
of the choroid has occurred. The larger choroidal vessels (arrows) are clearly
evident. × 16

evaluating small changes produced latent periods with significantly wider
ranges. The latent periods at which the choroid vessels appeared in dogs
injected with Ra²²⁶ are summarized in Table 3.

TABLE 3

Time Interval between Injection with Ra²²⁶ *and the First Appearance of
the Choroid Vessels*

Injection dose level	Injected μc/kg	Latent period (months)
5	10	3+
4	3	23–40
3	1	46–60
2	0·3	60–83*
1·7	0·15	choroid vessels not seen
1	0·05	choroid vessels not seen

* The choroid vessels were seen in only 25% of the dogs injected at this level.

Depigmentation to the extent that the choroid vessels can be seen is also
induced by Ra²²⁸ at the 5 level. Latent periods at this dose averaged
approximately two years. The lower levels did not produce any alterations
observable on ophthalmoscopic examination.

Pigmentary changes in the choroid have not been observed in dogs injected with Pu^{239} or Th^{228}.

Microscopic Changes in the Tapetum Lucidum

The beagle tapetum is a stratified layer varying up to about 10 cells deep in the central region and tapering to one or two cells thickness at the margins (Fig. 12). It is positioned immediately peripheral to the retina (Fig. 5). The component cells, as seen with electron microscope, were characterized by densely packed osmophilic rods which were oriented in planes parallel to the surface of the tapetum (Fig. 14).

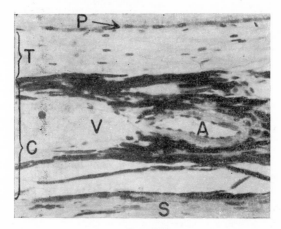

FIG. 12.

Photomicrograph of a section from a normal beagle taken through the pigment cell layer of the retina (P), the tapetum (T), the choroid (C), and sclera (S) showing the stratified cellular tapetum and the heavily pigmented, vascular choroid. The manner in which the choroidal vessels (A & V) are abscured by choroidal pigment on opthalmoscopic examination is clearly seen. × 510.

In animals injected with Ra^{226} at the 5 level, the tapetal cells were completely lost and the pigment cell layer of the retina came to lie in apposition with the choroid (Fig. 13). This has been observed on tissue sections at 177 days post injection and, based on clinical observations, presumably occurred earlier in some instances.

Three level Ra^{226} burdens did not induce significant microscopic lesions as viewed with the light microscope. However, cytological changes were evident in studies with the electron microscope. These included a general disorganization and loss of the osmophilic rods and the formation of vesicle-like structures at various points along these rods (Fig. 15). This

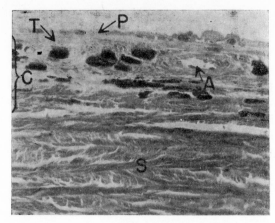

Fɪɢ. 13.

Photomicrograph of a cross-section through pigment cell layer of the retina (P), the region formerly occupied by the tapetum (T), the choroid (C), and the sclera (S) of a beagle injected with 10·4 μc/kg (5 level) of Ra²²⁶, 216 days post injection. The section was taken from a region similar to that of the section shown in Fig. 12. Complete loss of the tapetum and marked depigmentation of the choroid are clearly seen. Note that the choroidal vessel (A) is no longer obscured from the retinal surface by pigment. The line of demarcation between the choroid and sclera is much less distinct. × 500.

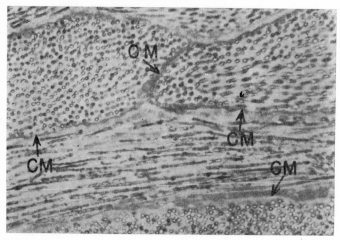

Fɪɢ. 14.

Electron photomicrograph of a cross-section of a normal beagle tapetum which illustrates the numerous densely packed osmophilic rods within the cytoplasm of the respective tapetal cells; the elongated uniform shape of the rods and their similar orientation within the respective cells. It is noted that these rods are all arranged in the same plane, parallel to the surface of the tapetum. The cell membranes (CM) are indicated. × 4000.

probably represented a degenerative change in the cell but not a lethal factor, since the tapetum was never entirely lost at this level. It is surmised that the derangement of the osmophilic cytoplasmic inclusions accounted for the color changes that occurred following treatment with some of the radionuclides presented in this study.

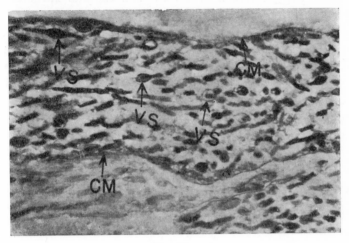

FIG. 15.

Electron photomicrograph of a cross-section through the tapetum of a beagle injected with 0·883 μc/kg of Ra²²⁶(3 level), 1897 days post injection. This micrograph illustrates the general disorganization of the normally uniform arrangement of the osmophilic rods; the marked variation in osmophilia; and the formation of vesicle-like structures (VS) on many of the rods. The cell membranes (CM) are indicated. ×4000.

Histological and cytological features similar to those induced by Ra²²⁶ occurred in animals treated with Ra²²⁸. Complete loss of the tapetum occurred only at the 5 level, with lesser effects being apparent at the 3 and 4 levels. As is the case with Ra²²⁶, the changes resulting from a 3 level burden were primarily cytological alterations and were similar to those shown in Fig. 15. Microscopic lesions were not seen at the lower doses, but observations with the electron microscope were not made.

DISCUSSION

The results of this study present an example of a soft tissue organ in which Ra²²⁶, Ra²²⁸, Th²²⁸ and Pu²³⁹ concentrate in an amount significantly above that of the plasma and induce a characteristic syndrome. The ocular tissue involved was very susceptible to the effects of these respective radionuclides, and in the beagle the eye was a sensitive indicator of relatively low burdens.

The respective alterations occurred without any serious visual impairment to the dog. Night vision was no doubt reduced at the high levels when the tapetum was lost and photophobia occurred in some of those animals with marked depigmentation of the iris and choroid. However, visual acuity appeared to remain unchanged, and cataracts and other ocular diseases did not occur in the treated groups at a rate greater than that of the controls. The incidence of retinal detachment was not increased in spite of the severe degeneration of the tapetum occurring at the high levels. This was probably due to the gradual sequence of the lesions. Intraocular neoplasms have not been seen in any of the groups thus far.

The total amount of radionuclide residual in the eye is small: 10 to 100 $\mu\mu$c in the case of dogs injected at the 5 level with Ra^{226}.[4,5] However, it is localized within only a limited part of the eye and probably within this faction is still further regionalized to a cytological component of a given cell type such as a melanocyte or melanophore. This specificity would greatly increase its effect on a cell type and could account for the ability of the very low total eye burdens to produce the pronounced pigmentary changes.

Densely packed osmophilic cytoplasmic inclusions have been described in the cat tapetum and tentatively have been considered to be a melanin product.[9] They bear many similarities, microscopically, to those seen in the beagle eye. The concurrent depigmentation of the tapetum with that of the other pigmented ocular structures, as described in this study resultant to radionuclide treatment, lends some support to the thesis that these inclusions are related to melanin or, at least, that they have some properties similar to melanin.

Another radionuclide which is known to localize in the eyes of beagles to a much lesser extent and without producing any apparent effects is Sr^{90}. Concentrations approximately 1·5 times greater than that of the plasma have been observed at about 1000 days post injection with the highest burden present in the pigmented parts.[4,5] In a double tracer study, 0·10% and 0·002% of the total injected dose of Ra^{226} and Sr^{85}, respectively, were found in one of the eyes eight days following injection.[10] Again most of the eye burden was in the pigmented parts.

Strontium is also known to concentrate in the eyes of some of the other species. Greater concentrations of Sr^{90} are present in rabbit eyes following intravenous injection than in striated muscle, with most of the burden residual in the pigmented structures.[11] Higher concentrations of stable strontium are found in the iris and choroid than in the non-pigmented tissues of the bovine and rabbit eye.[12]

Other trace metals, including zinc, copper and iron, have been shown to localize in the pigmented eye parts but not in the corresponding tissues of the albino counterparts.[13] These observations, plus the propensity of the radionuclides, presented in this study for the pigmented eye tissues, tentatively suggest that melanin or some factor associated with it has an affinity for some of the trace metals. In beagles this makes the melanotic structures of the eye one of the target sites in the toxicity syndrome following injection with Ra^{226}, Ra^{228}, Th^{228} or Pu^{239}.

SUMMARY

Grossly apparent iris and choroidal changes were induced in the dog (beagle) by the intravenous injection of Ra^{226}, Ra^{228}, Th^{228} or to a lesser and variable extent by Pu^{239}. Alterations were not seen following treatment with Sr^{90}. Changes were limited to the pigmented parts which coincides with the studies of Stover and Atherton, who have shown these regions to retain relatively significant amounts of Ra^{226}, Th^{228} or Pu^{239}. The principal symptoms included hyperpigmentation of the iris at low doses and depigmentation of the iris, choroid, and tapetum lucidum at higher doses. A dose-time-effect relationship exists except for Pu^{239}. Intraocular neoplasms or an abnormal incidence of cataracts were not observed. Loss of iris and choroidal pigment and degeneration or complete loss of the tapetum lucidum layer at higher doses were seen microscopically.

REFERENCES

1. CARL E. REHFELD, Veterinary group leader, Annual progress report of the radiobiology laboratory, Univ. of Utah, p. 20–21 (1956).
2. G. N. TAYLOR, C. E. REHFELD, G. SCHNEEBELI and W. FISHER, Observations regarding the pathological alteration in the eyes of beagles carrying burdens of Ra^{226}, Semiannual progress report of the Radiobiology Laboratory, Univ. of Utah, COO-217, p. 66–84 (1958).
3. G. N. TAYLOR, C. E. REHFELD, G. SCHNEEBELI and W. FISHER, pathogenesis of eye changes in beagles resulting from internal burdens of Ra^{226}, Semiannual progress report of the Radiobiology Laboratory, Univ. of Utah, COO-219, p. 26–41 (1959).
4. C. E. REHFELD, B. J. STOVER, G. N. TAYLOR, D. R. ATHERTON and G. SCHNEEBELI, Eye changes in beagles, *J.A.V.M.A.* **136**, 562–564 (1960).
5. B. J. STOVER, D. R. ATHERTON and C. W. MAYS, Studies of the retention and distribution of Ra^{226}, Pu^{239}, Ra^{228}(MsTh), Th^{228}(RdTh) and Sr^{90} in adult beagles, This vol., p. 7.
6. B. J. STOVER and D. R. ATHERTON, Note on Ra^{226} in beagle eyes, Semi-annual progress report of the Radiobiology Laboratory, Univ. of Utah, COO–217, p. 102–103 (1958).

7. T. F. DOUGHERTY, Study of the long-term biological effects of internal irradiation in adult beagles, This volume, p. 3.

8. G. WEITZEL, E. BUDDECK and A. M. FRETZDORFF, Structure of zinc compounds in the eye of the dog and fox, *Z. Physiol. Chem.* **299**, 193–219 (1955).

9. MAURICE H. BERNSTEIN and DANIEL C. PEASE, Electron microscopy of the tapetum lucidum of the cat, *J. Biophysic. & Biochem. Cytol.* **5**, 35–40 (1959).

10. B. W. GLAD, C. W. MAYS and W. FISHER, Strontium studies in beagles, *Rad. Res.* **12**, 672–681 (1960).

11. R. H. MOLE, A. PIRIE and J. M. VAUGHAN, Differential distribution of radio-active strontium and yttrium in the tissues of the rabbit's eye, *Nature* **183**, 802–807 (1959).

12. ELEANOR SOWDEN and ANTOINETTE PIRIE, Barium and strontium concentrations in eye tissue, *Biochem. J.* **70**, 716–717 (1958).

13. J. M. BOWNESS, R. A. MORTON, M. H. SHAKIR and A. L. STUBBS, Distribution of copper and zinc in mammalian eyes. Occurrences of metals in melanin fractions from eye tissues, *Biochem. J.* **51**, 521–529 (1952).

THE EFFECTS OF CHRONIC IRRADIATION BY INTERNALLY DEPOSITED RADIONUCLIDES ON CORTICOSTEROID BIOSYNTHESIS*

D. L. BERLINER, M. L. BERLINER, and T. F. DOUGHERTY

*Division of Radiobiology, Department of Anatomy,
University of Utah College of Medicine,
Salt Lake City, Utah*

INTRODUCTION

THE influences of internally-deposited radionuclides on the synthesis, release and metabolism of adrenal cortical steroid hormones has not been previously studied. The fact that X-irradiation in a wide range of doses induces a typical stress response has been demonstrated by showing that a portion of the radiation effect on the lymphocytes,[1] eosinophils and adrenal cholesterol is mediated by ACTH secretion. Also, X-irradiation initially increases blood corticosteroid levels[2] similar to other stressors. X-irradiation produces a biphasic adrenal response. Single exposures resulted in a rise in corticosteroid output for 2–3 days which was maintained until the 7th day and then the level of corticosteroid sharply decreased.[3]

In addition to this typical stress effect of releasing corticosteroids from the adrenal gland, it has been reported that irradiation of the gland is followed by alterations in the capacity to synthesize adrenal cortical steroids. Ungar et al.[4] found that when perfused calf adrenals were subjected to radiation from a Co[60] source, hydroxylations at C-11, C-17 and C-21 were markedly inhibited. Similar findings were also reported by Rosenfeld et al.[5]

The biosynthesis, biotransformation and excretion of adrenal steroids have been reviewed extensively in many reports.[6,7,8] The hydroxylations of the progesterone molecule to form corticosteroids has been shown to occur in the following order: 17α, 21 and then 11β.[9] The presence of an hydroxyl group at C-17 characterizes the glucocorticoids (cortisol). Mineralocorticoids (deoxycorticosterone) do not possess this hydroxyl group (Fig. 1).

In this report we will present data on the influences of various internal emitters (Sr^{90}, Th^{228}, Ra^{228} [$MsTh_1$], Ra^{226} and Pu^{239}) on the biosynthetic

* Supported by AEC (No. AT(11–1)–119 and ACS (38–5203).

12*

179

capabilities of the adrenal glands of dogs which were sacrificed from 24 hr to 6 y after injection of the radionuclides. Evidence supporting the thesis that adrenal reticuloendothelial cell function is an important factor in the

ADRENAL BIOSYNTHESIS OF CORTICOSTEROIDS FROM PROGESTERONE

response of the adrenal to internal emitters will be presented and that addition of TPNH (reduced triphosphopyridine nucleotide) can restore the hydroxylating activity of the adrenal gland of irradiated animals.

MATERIALS AND METHODS

Adrenals were removed immediately after sacrifice and placed in cold phosphate buffer. Within three minutes the adrenals were minced and incubated in the following manner: 0·5 g portions of minced adrenal tissue were incubated with progesterone-4-C^{14} (20,000 cpm; specific activity $1·2 \times 10^7$ cpm/mg) in a phosphate buffer pH 7·4 at 37° for three hours. Some incubations contained TPNH (2·5 μM) and glucose-6-phosphate (2·5 μM) and some did not. Incubation mixtures were extracted with warm acetone. Subsequently, the acetone was removed *in vacuo*. The water residue was re-extracted with chloroform which was removed and evaporated to dryness. The residue was redissolved in a chloroform-methanol mixture (1:1) containing 100 μg of the following non-radioactive carriers: cortisol, corticosterone, cortisone, 11β-hydroxyprogesterone, 17α-hydroxyprogesterone, and deoxycorticosterone. The steroids were identified by the chromatographic methods of Zaffaroni.[10] Quantities of steroids were determined by area measurements of chromatograms obtained in a Geiger-Müller strip counter, corrections for self-absorption of $C^{14}\beta$ rays in the paper chromatograms were determined by the measurements of known quantities of radioactive steroids added to samples of the same grade of

TABLE 1

Life Clinical History of Dogs from which Adrenal Steroidogenic Abilities were Studied

Dog*	Treatment	Nuclide dose (μc/kg)	Skeleton dose (rads)	Days with nuclide	Age at death (days)	Lesions
MAC 8	No	—	—	—	3745	none
FAC 1	Sr⁹⁰ 24 hr prior sacrifice (153 μc)	—	—	—**	1383	none
F6R5	radium (Sr⁹⁰ 24 hr prior sacrifice — 141 μc)	10.2	11200	1015**	1501	tumor right humerus
T8P5	plutonium (Sr⁹⁰ 24 hr prior sacrifice — 177 μc)	2.67	3540	863**	1390	rib fracture & bone tumor
F2M4	mesothorium & radiothorium	3.41 0.012	3820	778	1357	tumor 13th vertebra
M2T2	thorium	0.0875	540	1234	1717	tumor 6th thoracic vertebra
F12R3	radium	0.883	1690	1897	2394	tumor left tibia

* The first letter tells the sex of toxicity animals (M = male, F = female) and T is a test animal. M, F or T is followed by a number which denotes a chronological order. Next comes a letter for the radioactive isotope. The final number is the dose level number.

** Injected with Sr⁹⁰ 24 hours prior to sacrifice.

paper.[11] Identification of the steroids was by formation of various derivatives such as oxides or acetates and thus constant specific activity was determined and the radio purity of the compounds was proved.[12]

Seven dogs were thoroughly studied and in each case at least 4 incubations of the adrenal tissue obtained from these dogs were performed. The life span and experimental history of each dog used in this study is given in Table 1.

RESULTS

The percentages of conversion of progesterone-4-C^{14} to total corticosteroids and to cortisol and corticosterone are shown in Tables 2, 3 and 4.

TABLE 2

Adrenal Biosynthesis of Cortisol and Corticosterone from Progesterone-4-C^{14}

Dog	Total conversion	Cortisol %	Corticosterone %
MAC 8	96·8	14·4	14·1
F2M4	61·0	5·0	25·1
M2T2	33·9	8·1	30·1

Table 2 shows a comparison of a control dog (MAC 8) in relation to dogs F2M4 and M2T2. It is noticeable that the total per cent conversion of the adrenals of dogs containing the internal emitter has dropped considerably and that the conversion of progesterone to cortisol is most affected. Corticosterone production not only does not seem to be affected, but it is increased in relation to the control. This indicates that the hydroxylation which was mainly inhibited in these adrenals was C-17 hydroxylation. However, all hydroxylations (C-17, C-21 and C-11) were affected. Figure 1 illustrated the pathway by which progesterone can be transformed to cortisol and corticosterone. If hydroxylation of progesterone at position C-17 takes place first to form 17-hydroxyprogesterone, then cortisol and cortisone will be formed. However, if progesterone is hydroxylated first at position C-21, desoxycorticosterone and corticosterone will be produced, since there is no hydroxylation at C-17 of a compound having a hydroxyl group at position C-21[9] due to steric hindrance.

Table 3 presents data from a study performed on 2 dogs which bore burdens of Ra^{226} or Pu^{239} for some time (F6R5 and T8P5). The results obtained from these dogs were compared with those from a normal dog which received Sr^{90} 24 hours prior to sacrifice (FAC 1) and a normal non-

TABLE 3

Adrenal Biosynthesis of Cortisol and Corticosterone from Progesterone-4-C^{14}

Dog	Total % conversion	Cortisol (%)	Corticosterone (%)
MAC 8	96·8	14·4	14·1
FAC 1[a]	91·8	15·6	45·4
F6R5[a]	77·2	7·7	34·6
T8P5[a]	57·2	19·8	25·3

[a] Sr^{90} 24 hours prior to sacrifice.

treated control (MAC 8). Both F6R5 and T8P5 dogs also were given Sr^{90} 24 hours prior to sacrifice. It is interesting to note that FAC 1 and MAC 8 gave approximately the same total per cent conversions and also that cortisol formation percentage-wise was similar; but the formation of corticosterone was increased in FAC 1, indicating that Sr^{90} given acutely stimulates the formation of corticosterone (C-21 and C-11 hydroxylations). It does not seem to stimulate 17-hydroxylation, at least to any marked degree. In dogs F6R5 and T8P5 the total conversion of progesterone to corticosteroids was decreased as compared to the controls. F6R5 formed quite a small amount of cortisol as compared to the others (Table 3), indicating again that C-17 hydroxylation was inhibited.

In summary, these data show that even with chronic radiation, if there is stimulation 24 hours prior with Sr^{90}, there is a response of the adrenal gland and this response is mainly taking place via the formation of corticosterone. Dog FAC 1 which is a dog radiated acutely with Sr^{90} showed a significant increase in corticosterone biosynthesis and no abolishment of 17-hydroxylation at all as the cortisol level was in the normal range This study indicates again that chronic radiation will inhibit the formation of 17-hydroxylated compounds in the adrenal gland.

TABLE 4

Adrenal Biosynthesis of Cortisol and Corticosterone from Progesterone-4-C^{14}

Dog	Cofactors	Total % conversion	Cortisol (%)	Corticosterone (%)
MAC 8	no	96·8	14·4	14·1
	TPNH+Gl-6-P	97·2	21·8	24·0
F12R3	no	30·2	7·1	21·7
	TPNH+Gl-6-P	100·0	22·5	42·8

The data from a study in which adrenal minces from dogs MAC 8 and F12R3 were divided into two portions is shown in Table 4.

One portion was incubated in the presence of TPNH and glucose-6-phosphate. The other half was incubated without the cofactors. It was observed that the adrenals of dog F12R3 without cofactors had a lower total per cent conversion and cortisol formation was mainly affected, again showing a decrease in 17-hydroxylation. However, when the other half of the adrenal was incubated in the presence of glucose-6-phosphate and TPNH the conversion of progesterone to the corticosteroids was increased to 100% and the production of cortisol was increased to the same level as the control. Corticosterone also was increased significantly. The presence of the coenzymes in this study corrected the inhibitory effect on 17-hydroxylation caused by this internal emitter.

DISCUSSION

The effect of internal emitters on adrenal steroidogenesis appears to be a decrease in 11-, 17- and 21-hydroxylations. The most marked effect is the reduction of 17-hydroxylation. The immediate damage could be due to destruction of the requisite enzyme or of TPNH, the cofactor which has been shown to be necessary for these hydroxylations to occur.[16] The incubations with and without cofactors (Table 4) show that the damage to 17-hydroxylation can be repaired by the addition of TPNH. The demonstration that TPNH can re-establish normal activity indicates that radiation is not acting directly on the enzyme. It therefore appears possible that this coenzyme is destroyed or altered by the energy the cell receives from radiation. Also, it is possible that radiation alters availability of TPNH to the cell or the enzyme system. It has been demonstrated that 17α-hydroxylation in the adrenal gland is mainly quantitatively located in the R. E. cell.[13] This work is confirmed by experiments to be reported elsewhere on cell fractions from the adrenals of beagles injected with radionuclides. The cellular site of 17-hydroxylation is in the reticuloendothelial cell of irradiated dogs and this hydroxylation is markedly reduced in these animals. It can be regenerated by addition of TPNH.

Other investigators have also found that X-irradiation did not affect a large number of enzyme activities but that the fundamental defect following irradiation was due to inadequate function of cofactors.[14,15] These investigators showed that addition of appropriate cofactors to the irradiated animals' enzyme systems restored normal functioning. The fact that a wide variety of enzyme systems other than those solely concerned with steroid metabolism are affected in the same fashion would tend to emphasize the fact that a fundamental action of ionizing radiation on cellular function is the alteration of cofactor function. It is interesting that Krebs[16] pointed out some years ago that it was far more likely that irradiation of animals did not affect the amount of enzymes but rather it affected the pacemaker reactions which, in turn, reduced the enzyme system activity.

Although the total amount of radiation in the adrenal gland is low, radionuclides such as Pu^{239} and Th^{228} are found deposited in R. E. cells of the adrenal gland.[17] Deposition appears to be mainly in the zona fasciculata; whether this direct irradiation accounts for the inhibition of 17-hydroxylation which has been shown to take place in the R. E. system[18] cannot be answered at this time since other radionuclides such as Ra^{226} also diminished hydroxylations but apparently do not localize in the R. E. cells. This question is being explored further.

REFERENCES

1. T. F. DOUGHERTY and A. WHITE. Influence of hormones on lymphoid tissue structure and function. The role of the pituitary adrenotrophic hormone in the regulation of the lymphocytes and other cellular elements of the blood, *Endocrinology* 35, 1–15 (1944).

2. A. B. FRENCH, C. J. MIGEON, L. T. SAMUELS, and J. Z. BOWERS. Effects of whole body X-irradiation on 17-hydroxycorticosteroid levels, leucocytes and volume of packed red cells in the Rhesus monkey, *Am. J. of Physiol.* 182, 469 (1955).

3. A. TONKIKH. The role of the adrenals in the pathogenesis of radiation sickness. United Nations: Peaceful uses of atomic energy, *Proc. II. International Conf.* 22, 219–224 (1958).

4. F. UNGAR, G. ROSENFELD, R. I. DORFMAN and G. PINCUS. Irradiation and adrenal Steroidogenesis. Influence of irradiation of isolated ACTH-stimulated calf adrenals on their cortical output, *Endocrinology* 56, 30–36 (1955).

5. G. ROSENFELD, F. UNGAR, R. I. DORFMAN and G. PINCUS. Irradiation and adrenal steroidogenesis. Steroid transformations by irradiated isolated perfused calf adrenals, *Endocrinology* 56, 24–29 (1955).

6. L. T. SAMUELS. Metabolism of steroid hormones. *Chemical pathways of metabolism,* ed. D. M. GREENBERG, Academic Press, New York, 431–480 (1960).

7. R. I. DORFMAN. Biosynthesis of adrenocortical steroids. *Cancer* 10, 741–745 (1957).

8. O. HECHTER. Conversion of cholesterol to steroid hormones. *Cholesterol,* ed. P. O. COOK. Academic Press, Inc., New York, 309–348 (1958).

9. O. HECHTER, A. ZAFFARONI, R. P. JACOBSEN, H. LEVY, R. W. JEANLOZ, V. SCHENKER and G. PINCUS. The nature and the biosynthesis of the adrenal secretory product. *Rec. Progr. Hormone Res.* 6, 215–246 (1951).

10. A. ZAFFARONI. A micromethod for the analysis of adrenocortical steroids, *Rec. Progr. Hormone Res.* 8, 51 (1953).

11. D. L. BERLINER, O. V. DOMINGUEZ and G. WESTENSKOW. Determination of C^{14} steroids on paper chromatograms. *Anal. Chem.* 29, 1797–1800 (1957).

12. D. L. BERLINER and H. A. SALHANICK. Microchemical identification of radioactive and non-radioactive steroids. *Anal. Chem.* 28, 1608–1610 (1956).

13. D. L. BERLINER, C. J. NABORS, JR. and T. F. DOUGHERTY. Biosynthetic capabilities of isolated adrenal reticuloendothelial cells, *Endocrinol. Soc. Proc.*, 44 (1961).
14. H. MAASS and G. SCHUBERT. Early biochemical reactions after X-irradiation. U. N. Peaceful uses of atomic energy. *Proc. II. International Conf.* 22, 449–454 (1958).
15. T. N. RYSINA. The content of free nucleotides, nucleosides, purine and pyrimidinie bases in some tissues of healthy and irradiated rabbits, *Biochemistry* 24, 518 (1959). (Translation from Russian).
16. H. A. KREBS. The effects of extraneous agents on cell metabolism. *Ionizing radiation and cell metabolism.* Ciba Foundation Symposium. ed. G. E. W. WOLSTENHOLME and C. M. O'CONNOR. Little Brown & Co., Boston 92–105 (1956).
17. W. S. S. JEE (personal communication).
18. D. L. BERLINER and T. F. DOUGHERTY. Hepatic and extrahepatic regulation of corticosteroids, *Pharm. Rev.* 13, 329–359 (1961).

DISCUSSION

T. F. DOUGHERTY: I should like to add that it has also been shown with external irradiation that hydroxylations of 11, 17 and 21 are also inhibited. The interesting thing is that similar findings are being reported here by Dr. Berliner following internal irradiation and this may be related to some of the hematological findings which have been described in this meeting.

Also, it should be emphasized that inhibition of hydroxylation reduces the capacity of the adrenal to form cortisol which is very necessary for the maintenance of life of the animal and the capacity to withstand stressful circumstances.

In addition to these comments, I should like to add one more point which I consider of some interest and that is, that this is a remarkable example of a radiation induced alteration which can be completely reversed.

CHAIRMAN WARREN: Those added comments are very helpful, Dr. Dougherty.

NORRIS: I would like to ask the obvious question, and that is whether you ever treated any of your dogs with cortisol?

TAYLOR: We very seldom treat a dog with cortisol. About the only animals that have been so treated were those with ocular injections, and they were treated optically. With very few exceptions we don't treat the dogs in our experiments with cortisol.

PART II

SOME BIOLOGICAL EFFECTS OF IRRADIATION

ROLE OF HORMONES IN RADIATION CARCINOGENESIS*

JACOB FURTH and KENJIRO YOKORO

Department of Experimental Pathology, Roswell Park Memorial Institute, and the Graduate School of the University of Buffalo, Buffalo, N. Y.†

CONCEPTS are speculations on the fundamental nature of events rooted in observations. As one's horizon is broadened, concepts are modified or abandoned. If we would relate the evolution of our present concept of radiation carcinogenesis, we would be writing a chapter of a biography covering three decades (1930–1960) initiated by the chance finding of ovarian tumors in whole body irradiated mice,[9] followed by demonstration of the vital role of hormones in their genesis (Gardner, *et al.*[15]). These and subsequent observations with thyroid, pituitary and adrenal tumors[6,13,22] and related findings on chemical[19] and viral carcinogens[16,17,25] led to a unified concept of carcinogenesis.[14,7] This communication will be limited to a defense of this concept with a review of recent, in part unpublished, data supporting it.

The hypotheses of mutation or virus being the sole cause of the neoplastic transformation proved to be mere attractive dogmatic general terms covering a vast unknown related to the genesis of radiation-induced cancers. Probing deeper into the mechanism of carcinogenesis led to newer observations and to newer hypotheses. We shall attempt to discuss a few of the findings and concepts evolved in the course of recent studies on carcinogenesis. The following topics will be discussed:

> I. Basic Components of Radiation Carcinogenesis.
> II. Analysis of MtH–carcinogen–MT Relationship.
> III. Latent Cancer Cell.
> IV. Basis of Promotive Action of Hormones.
> V. Fundamental Nature of Neoplasms.
> VI. Nature of Radiation Change.
> VII. Comments on Endocrine Related Tumors other than MT.
> VIII. Comments on Viruses and Tumors.
> IX. Dose Response Curve. Inhibition by Large Doses.

The abbreviations used are as follows:

> MT = mammary tumor; Mt = mammotrope; MtH = mammotropic hormone; MtT = mammotropic tumor; TT = thyroid tumor; TH = thyroid hormone: 3-MCA = 3-methylcholanthrene.

* Supported by the Atomic Energy Commission and the National Cancer Institute.

† Present address: Columbia University–Francis Delafield Hospital, 99 Ft. Washington Avenue, New York 32, N.Y.

I. COMPONENTS OF CARCINOGENESIS

Carcinogenesis has three basic components: carcinogens, hormones (by which we mean homeostatic regulators of numbers and functions of cells) and genetics.

(1) *Carcinogens* are agents which bring about an apparently irreversible modification of the cells' hereditary NA (nucleic acid) with loss of proper response to homeostatic regulators. (2) *Hormones* are promoters and inhibitors in cell homeostasis. They regulate growth and function of cells but, in physiologic concentrations, do not produce cancers. The water soluble pituitary and thyroid hormones were never proven to be carcinogenic, not even in large doses. Steroid hormones are structurally related to carcinogenic hydrocarbons and may be non-specific carcinogens in large doses. We suggest that if cancer arises in a hormone stimulated organ, forces other than the hormone alone are at play. (3) *Genetic factors* lend potentialities to cells determining their physiologic and pathologic response to environmental influences.

Fig. 1 is an introductory survey of the known hormone related tumors induced by radiation. Those underlined are related to endocrine organs.

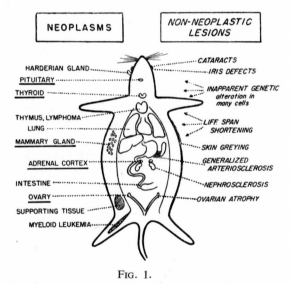

FIG. 1.

Events triggered in mice by single exposure to ionizing radiation.

II. MtH-CARCINOGEN-MT RELATIONSHIP

Let us begin to illustrate this concept by sketching recent experiments on the genesis of breast tumors in mice and rats. In these experiments the three classes of carcinogens (radiation, chemical and virus) were applied with and without hormones. The carcinogens were used in quantities which alone produced no or few tumors. The hormone used was mammotropin (MtH), the most powerful and nearest known stimulant of the mammary gland.[2,10,19] MtH alone is not carcinogenic. Table 1 summarizes these experiments. It shows that the carcinogens did not produce tumors in the concentrations used, within 7 to 12 months, when the animals were sacrificed and carefully autopsied. In general, MtH enhances tumor appearance. In the present experiments, MtH was the determining factor whether tumors developed at all after administration of the carcinogen.

TABLE 1

Mammary Tumor Induction with
Subcarcinogenic Doses of Carcinogens

Carcinogen	Radiation	Chemical[a]	Virus
Dose	50r	10 mg	0·1 ml milk
Species	Rat	Rat	Mouse
Carcinogen alone	0	0	0
MtH alone	0	0	0
Carcinogen + MtH	58%	85%	40%
Reference	(26)	(19)	(25)

[a] 3-methylcholanthrene.

III. LATENT CANCER CELLS

One of the major lessons derived from these experiments is that carcinogens, notably when used in small concentration, often create latent cancer cells, most of which seem to be hormone responsive. They can be activated by administration of the normal stimulant of the cell (or by reduction of its inhibitor).

Fig. 2 sketches the situation observed with 3-MCA. Rats exposed to a single dose of 10 mg of 3-methylcholanthrene and deprived of MtH live with latent cancer cells, the number of which is dependent on the dose of the carcinogen applied. The existence of these latent cells can be disclosed long after exposure to the carcinogen by administration of MtH. In the present experiment (right lower quadrant), MtH was given 9 months after the carcinogen. MtH promotes the growth of these latent tumor cells to form macroscopic tumors. Alone, it did not produce tumors.

Similar studies in radiation carcinogenesis are in progress. Hormone responsiveness of primary tumors is usually retained in the first few transplant generations. In a recent experiment a radiation plus MtH induced fibroadenoma grew only in MtH stimulated rats. When MtH was withheld for $7\frac{1}{2}$ months, mammary tumors appeared in all rats stimulated with MtH and in none without it. Evidently this tumor grows only at elevated levels of MtH.

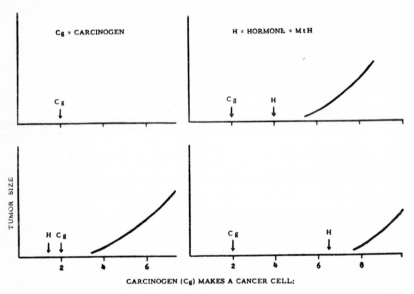

FIG. 2.

Mammary tumor latency in rats treated with carcinogen in relation to time of administration of mammotropic hormone.

The figure in Kim and Furth's paper[18] shows a rat whose carcinogen (3-MCA) induced tumor regressed following hypophysectomy. When this rat was treated with MtH not only did the original tumor recur but many new MT's appeared. This rat was heavily cancerized. Radiation induced tumors thus far studied behave essentially the same way as the chemically induced tumors.

When the carcinogenic dose is large, diverse types of tumor cells are created and the autonomous clones outgrow the dependent ones, forming macroscopic tumors in normal hosts.

IV. THE MODE OF ACTION OF HORMONAL STIMULATION

In these experiments this is conceived merely as causing cell proliferation. The old idea that regenerative hyperplasia favors carcinogenesis was considered by us in radiation leukemogenesis as early as in 1942.[21] "X-rays injure the bone marrow and lymphoid organs; and when they are administered in a single large dose, destruction of these tissues is followed by a regenerative hyperplasia with numerous mitoses and often with atypical cell formations. This tissue derangement may be expected to hasten the effect of another carcinogen administered at this state and be productive of both myeloid and lymphoid leukemia." The experiments performed[8] bore out this contention. They may also explain the increased efficiency of leukemogenesis by fractionation of a dose, well demonstrated by Kaplan. Increase in mitotic activity may also explain acceptance of virus.

Presently, popular concepts link tumor formation with *maturation arrest* and with disturbance of *differentiation*. In the genesis of MT and TT studied by us extensively, differentiation is not involved. The specific hormones appear to do no more than bring about proliferation of a fully differentiated cell. "Whoever has seen a motion picture of mitosis with the extraordinary pinocytic movements, can well visualize how viruses, other particles and solutes can gain entry into cells during mitosis, aside from the associated physical changes which may facilitate entry of extraneous matters into cells during this phase."[7]

Briefly, radiation can both initiate and promote tumor growth; but it can also do the opposite, namely prevent tumor growth, as will be discussed. There is this difference between the promoting action of radiation and hormones: the hormonal stimulation can be more intense and lasting, that of radiation is usually more fleeting. Radiations, on the other hand, alter cell genetics; i.e., they are carcinogens, hormones are not.

V. FUNDAMENTAL NATURE OF NEOPLASMS

Cancer, as we see it, is a state of homeostatic derangement of a cell type. Yet, radiation carcinogenesis is still commonly conceived as a consequence of a direct chromosomal (DNA) damage of a cell. The evidence is overwhelming that ionizing radiations of all types can produce mutations in all cells, and that in transmission of hereditary characteristics deoxyribonucleic acid (DNA) is involved and that these changes may be induced directly or indirectly in DNA. In the course of radiation carcinogenesis, striking exceptions were discovered which broadened the concept of cancer to include homeostatic host disturbances.

In case of pituitary tumor induction by radiothyroidectomy it was found that the tumors arose not in irradiated cells but in their regulating organ, the pituitary gland, and that the initiating and maintaining cause of the tumor was damage to the thyroid with resulting drop in the physiologic inhibitor of thyrotropes.[4] This and other neoplasms induced by similar mechanisms[12] are composed of basically unaltered cells and are reversible.

VI. NATURE OF RADIATION CHANGE

Thus, radiation can affect both the regulating system and the regulated cells. At least three types of lasting radiation modifications are conceivable in the cell: (1) a chromosomal change; (2) modification of an organelle which may or may not be related to the homeostatic control of the cell; or (3) entrace or unmasking of a virus in the cell which may interfere with its homeostasis.

The overwhelming number of changes appear to be non-neoplastic. Witness the vast number of chromosomal abnormalities caused by irradiaton of the normal liver and disclosed by inducing multiplication of liver cells by means of resecting part of this organ. Resection of the liver goes with increase in production of "hepatopoietin". Yet, these altered liver cells are not known to yield a tumor.

A cell can be permanently altered but until it loses the basic function of responding properly to its homeostatic inhibitor, it is not a cancer cell. When animals are treated intensely with a carcinogen, a vast number of cells are permanently altered. Some acquire full autonomy, others do not; the autonomous clones outgrow the dependent clones and form tumors, while the vast number of altered cells remain latent and unsuspected.

Surprisingly, most radiation-induced autonomous tumors proved to be hormone responsive when they were challenged with their physiologic regulator.

Conceivably the base line of inducing permanent modifications in cells by radiations is lower than that of inducing cancer cells and it is possible that the radiation change, as mutation in general, is directly related to the dose and has no threshold. Autonomous cancers require a greater damage and therefore may have a threshold or a different damage. In attempts to disclose this, the use of tropic hormones is of great value.

VII. ENDOCRINE RELATED TUMORS OTHER THAN MT

These will not be fully discussed as they have been the subject of several recent reviews.[2,15,12] The pathogenesis of most of these is still not well understood. The importance of hormones is indicated in numerous situations shown in Table 2 which lists examples of specific hormonal inhibition of neoplasia development after irradiation. Five of the tumors listed are endocrine related.

TABLE 2

Inhibition of Tumor Development after Irradiation

Organ	Inhibitor
Ovary	Ovarian hormone (Gardner[15])
Thyrotropic pituitary tumor	Thyroid hormone
Mammotropic pituitary tumor	Gonadectomy
Myeloid leukemia	Splenectomy (Upton[22])
Lymphoid leukemia	Thymectomy
Thyroid tumor	Thyroid hormone
Mammary tumor	Gonadectomy

Leukemia inhibition is poorly understood. Thymic lymphoma is linked to a virus. Following thymectomy, the virus persists but lymphoma fails to develop. The thymic lymphomas are large lymphocytic and such cells are present in ample numbers in other organs. The pathogenesis of myeloid leukemia and its relation to the spleen is even less well understood.

While the usual major force in genesis of tumors of endocrine-related organs is their specific pituitary tropic hormone, significant minor forces are also operative. For example, there is a relation between adrenals and gonads, adrenals and thyroid, thyroid and the breast, thyroid and gonads. Gonadectomy before irradiation markedly decreases or even prevents pituitary tumor induction by radiation. Gonadectomy enhances adrenal tumor induction.

The best understood influence is that of the inhibitory effect of adrenal corticoid on the thymus, discovered by our Chairman, Dr. Dougherty.[5] Most other situations are poorly understood and will not be discussed. A characteristic pattern is that of ovarian and thyroid tumor induction with small doses. The facts on ovarian tumorogenesis are as follows: (a) Radiations are known to induce ovarian tumors only in mice. Rats are equally sensitive to ovarian tumorogenesis by hormonal imbalance. (b) Direct irradiation of the ovaries alone will induce tumors. (c) Shielding of one ovary, or estrogen, given after irradiation, will prevent ovarian tumor development. (d) The threshold dose is low, about 30r, larger doses will produce ovarian tumors in most mice. (e) Almost all ovarian cells can become tumorous. (f) Most, if not all, ovarian tumors induced by radiations seem to be autonomous; most tumors are functional and benign with rare exceptions.

In both ovary and thyroid, tumors are induced when the organ is in the beam of irradiation. In both, depression of function leads to specific increase of the regulatory pituitary tropic hormone driving the altered cell. Clifton discovered that some alterations go with acquisition of a heightened sensitivity to a tropic hormone.[3] In most endocrine organs such tumors are of the so-called benign type. The hormones implicated are usually assumed; their identifiication and quantitation are still outstanding. For example, three pituitary hormones are related to ovarian function; their relative involvement, if any, in ovarian tumorigenesis is entirely speculative.

Years ago, when viruses were conceived as parasite agents, we emphasized the fact that all cells of the ovary can become tumorous and that tumors of each cell type breed true upon successive passages. In terms of viral causation this meant that there are as many viruses as there are cells. Now that we know of viruses which can become integrated with the cells genome,* we may conceive causation of diverse types of ovarian tumors by a single virus and radiations as a dynamic force to bring this about. Nevertheless, until such viruses are proven, we prefer the mutation concept to explain the modification of the diverse ovarian cells and conceive hormones as their dynamic driving force.

VIII. COMMENTS ON VIRUSES AND TUMORS

Speculation about the nature of viruses and their mode of action is the privilege of the next speaker, Henry Kaplan, whose experience is based on studies of lymphoma viruses in mice. Allow us a few relevant comments based on our experience.

It is reasonable to postulate the existence of a lymphocytopoietin and to suppose that heightened levels of this hormone will enhance lymphoma induction by either virus or chemicals or radiations. The attractive theory of Gregoir-Metcalf of a lymphocytosis stimulating factor residing in the thymic reticulum still lacks solid confirmation.

While adrenal corticoids destroy lymphocytes, they have not been proven to be the physiologic inhibitor of lymphopoiesis. Therefore, to illustrate virus-hormone relationship, we turn to the best model, namely that of MtH-virus-MT and shall illustrate it in Table 3.

---

* Integration on subgenetic level leading to neoplasia is also conceivable.

TABLE 3

*Role of Mammotropic Hormone (MtH) in Induction
of Mammary Tumors in Mice by Virus*

Treatment	No. mice in group	No. mice with tumor
MtH + Virus	37	15(40%)
Estrogen + Virus	30	0
Virus only	30	0
MtH only	39	0
Estrogen only	30	0
None	30	0

Note that virus was given to adult mice of a strain in which MT is almost non-existent. A single dose of less than 0·01 ml of milk is highly infectious to adult mice when the mammary gland is stimulated with MtH but not without it. If a virus is as ubiquitous as this and can be as harmless a passenger as this or the lymphoma or the polioma viruses, then the determination of the dynamic forces which enter into carcinogenesis are perhaps more vital than the mere identification of a virus. In case of MT the pituitary cell MT or, more correctly, mammo-somatotrope, is this dynamic force.

The situation with thymic lymphoma seems similar to that with mammary tumors, the stimulating factor residing in the thymus in case of lymphomas. Gross[16] and Kaplan[17] presented observations implicating virus in radiation-induced thymic lymphomas. Experiments in our laboratory have shown that myeloid leukemia induction in RF mice by X-rays is approximately tripled by resident "lymphoma" virus (cf. Furth, Yokoro and Takemoto, *Ciba Foundation Symposium on Tumor Viruses of Murine Origin*. J. & A. Churchill Ltd., London, 1962, pp. 139–149.

The evidence is strong that viruses may play a role in the induction of neoplasms by radiation. Whether this role is major or minor remains to be seen. However, to attribute *all* neoplasms to viruses is equivalent to abandoning the idea of chromosomal mutations as conceived by Boveri and to negate the existence of conditional neoplasms as those induced by thyroidectomy and controlled by TH. Perhaps the problem merely centers around the understanding of what virus is. To those who, as Luria,[20] believe that viruses and genes are the same, it doesn't exist at all.

IX. INHIBITION OF CARCINOGENS BY LARGE DOSES OF RADIATIONS

We shall close with a euphoric statement to counteract the gloom about radiations and cancers that radiations can also be anti-carcinogenic. Radiotherapists will, of course, agree with this. Earlier we[13, 20] noted a puzzling decrease of some tumors, as mammary sarcomas in mice, by irradiation. Decrease of neoplasia by large doses, recorded by several investigators, is well understood. Fig. 3 shows simple dose response curves of pituitary tumor induction, the left is based on work in mice,[11, 24] the right on that of Van Dyke, et al., in rats.[23]

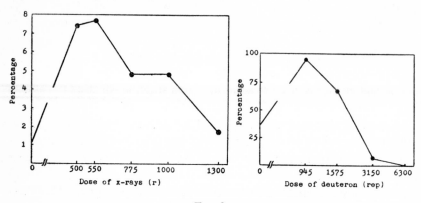

FIG. 3.

Dose-response in induction of pituitary tumors in mice and rats; left, experiments with mice;[11,24] right, experiments with rats.[23]

An organ, whose regenerative capacity is abolished, cannot give rise to a tumor. Or, if an organ secretes a stimulating hormone, destroying that organ will diminish tumor incidence in its target tissue. This dose response curve of Van Dyke from nearly 100 to a drop of nearly zero % response, is most illuminating.

Bond et al.,[1] studying MT induction in the rat, were impressed by the linearity of the dose-response. On the basis of the circles in their Experiment III, we would be inclined to accept the near-plateau at about 500–600r as real and suppose that irradiation at higher doses, topically applied, would have resulted in further decrease of tumor induction rates.

This situation was reviewed by us at the Third Australasian Cancer Congress[14] under the heading, "The Right Side of the Dose Response Curve". Earlier, at the Burlington Radiation Research Congress,[13] we pointed out the importance of this event as follows: "Neoplasia calls for cells capable of proliferation. If radiation causes atrophy of an organ with inhibition of its regenerative capacity, it is conceivable that the probability of neoplasia will be reduced by very large doses. This theory could be tested by local application of large doses to induce neoplasms that arise either from scopal or abscopal effects. Although the prophylactic value of topical large doses remains in doubt, the theoretical importance of the problem warrants experimental exploitation. For example, to what extent would very large topical doses inhibit induction of thymic lymphoma (which is abscopal), ovarian tumors (which are scopal but conditioned on pituitary factors), or sarcomas (which are scopal but are presumably not modified by factors at distant sites)?" Experiments to verify this concept are in progress. In one experiment, performed by Dr. Takemoto, irradiation of the thymic area 4 to 6 weeks after infection with virus reduced the leukemia incidence from about 70 to 6% (cf. Furth, Yokoro and Takemoto, Ciba Symposium on Murine Tumor Viruses).

SUMMARY

Radiation carcinogenesis is a complex process and radiation-induced tumors vary in character. Hormones are powerful promoters of all carcinogens, including radiations. They act by increasing cell numbers, by bringing many cells in stages with heightened sensitivity to ionizing radiations or acceptance of virus. When tumors are induced in large numbers in endocrine-related organs, notably with low doses, hormones are likely to be at play.

Radiations can produce progressively growing tumors either by direct alteration of a cell or by disturbing its homeostatic regulating organ. The tumors resulting from the former are likely to be autonomous, though often hormone responsive, while those resulting from the latter are usually hormone dependent when initiated. Later on, some cells may acquire autonomy and outgrow the dependent cells.

Hormones greatly enhance not only initiation but also growth of many tumors. Hormones can activate latent cancer cells and do the reverse, "silence" progressively growing dependent tumors. As concerns breast cancer, induction by either radiation, virus or chemical, the pituitary mammotropins have a determining position. It is postulated that other pituitary tropic hormones occupy a similar position in tumorogenesis of organs which they control, as the thyroid, adrenal and gonads.

Carcinogenesis calls for cells capable of proliferation. Large doses of radiations which inhibit proliferative capacity of cells will diminish the likelihood of tumor development in those cells. One example of this is prevention of lymphoma in virus-infected mice 4 to 6 weeks after massive irradiation of the thymic area.

REFERENCES

1. V. P. BOND, E. P. CRONKITE, S. W. LIPPINCOTT and C. J. SHELLABARGER, Studies on radiation-induced mammary gland neoplasia in the rat. III. Relation of the neoplastic response to dose of total-body radiation, *Radiation Research*, **12**, 276–285 (1960).
2. K. H. CLIFTON, Problems in experimental tumorigenesis of the pituitary gland, gonads, adrenal cortices, and mammary glands: A review, *Cancer Research* **19**, 2–22 (1959).
3. K. H. CLIFTON and J. FURTH, Estrogen sensitivity of normal, and of dependent and autonomous mammotropic pituitary tumor cells, *Fed. Proc.* **20**, 184 (1961).
4. J. N. DENT, E. L. GADSDEN, and J. FURTH, On the relation between thyroid depression and pituitary tumor induction in mice, *Cancer Research* **15**, 70–75 (1955).
5. T. F. DOUGHERTY, Effect of hormones on lymphatic tissue, *Physiol. Rev.* **32**, 379–401 (1952).
6. J. FURTH, Radiation neoplasia and endocrine systems. In *Radiation Biology and Cancer* Univ. Texas Press, pp. 7–25 (1959).
7. J. FURTH, Vistas in etiology and pathogenesis of tumors, *Fed. Proc.* **20** 865–873 (1961).
8. J. FURTH and M. C. BOON, Enhancement of leukemogenic action of methylcholanthrene by pre-irradiation with X-rays, *Science* **98**, 138–139 (1943).
9. J. FURTH and J. S. BUTTERWORTH, Neoplastic diseases occurring among mice subjected to general irradiation with X-rays, *Am. J. Cancer*, **28**, 66–95 (1936.)
10. J. FURTH and K. H. CLIFTON, Experimental observations on mammotropes and the mammary gland. In *Endocrine Aspects of Breast Cancer* (A. R. CURRIE, and C. F. W. ILLINGWORTH, eds.). Edinburgh, E. & S. Livingstone Ltd., pp. 276–282 (1958).
11. J. FURTH, N. HARAN-GHERA, H. J. CURTIS and R. F. BUFFETT, Studies on the pathogenesis of neoplasms by ionizing radiation, I. Pituitary tumors, *Cancer Research* **19**, 550–556 (1959).
12. J. FURTH, U. KIM and K. H. CLIFTON, On evolution of the neoplastic state; progression from dependence to autonomy, *Nat. Cancer Inst. Monograph* No. 2, 149–177 (1960).
13. J. FURTH, A. C. UPTON and A. W. KIMBALL, Late pathologic effects of atomic detonation and their pathogenesis, *Radiation Research, Supp.* **1**, pp. 243–264(1959).
14. J. FURTH and K. YOKORO, Components of radiation carcinogenesis. *Proc. 3rd Austr. Conf. Radiation Biology*, August 1960, Butterworth Scientific Publications, In print.
15. W. U. GARDNER, C. A. PFEIFFER and J. J. TRENTIN, Hormonal factors in experimental carcinogenesis. In *The Physiopathology of Cancer* (F. Homburger, ed.). Hoeber-Harper, New York (1959).
16. L. GROSS, B. ROSWIT, E. R. MADA, Y. DREYFUSS and L. A. MOORE, Studies on radiation-induced leukemia in mice, *Cancer Research* **19**, 316–320 (1959).

ROLE OF HORMONES IN RADIATION CARCINOGENESIS

17. H. S. KAPLAN, Experimental alteration of host response to an occult tumor virus: Induction of thymic lymphosarcomas in X-irradiated mice, *Nat. Cancer Inst. Monograph* No. **4**, 141–150 (1960).

18. U. KIM and J. FURTH, Relation of mammary tumors to mammotropes. II. Hormone responsiveness of 3-methylcholanthrene induced mammary carcinomas. *Proc. Soc. Exper. Biol. & Med.* **103**, 643–645 (1960).

19. U. KIM and J. FURTH, Relation of mammotropes to mammary tumors. IV. Development of highly hormone dependent mammary tumors, *Proc. Soc. Exper. Biol. & Med.* **105**, 490–492 (1960).

20. S. E. LURIA, Viruses, cancer cells, and the genetic concept of virus infection *Cancer Research* **20**, 677–688 (1960).

21. D. P. MC ENDY, M. C. BOON and J. FURTH, Induction of leukemia in mice by methylcholanthrene and X-rays, *J. Nat. Cancer Inst.* **3**, 227–247 (1942).

22. A. C. UPTON, A. W. KIMBALL, J. FURTH, K. W. CHRISTENBERRY and W. H. BENEDICT, Some delayed effects of atom-bomb radiations in mice, *Cancer Research* **20**, No. 8 (Part 2), 1–62 (1960).

23. D. C. VAN DYKE, M. E. SIMPSON, A. A. KNOFF and C. A. TOBIAS, Long-term effects of deuteron irradiation of the rat pituitary. *Endocrinology*, **64**, 240–261 (1959).

24. K. YOKORO, J. FURTH and N. HARAN-GHERA, Induction of mammotropic pituitary tumors by X-rays in rats and mice. The role of mammotropes in development of mammary tumors, *Cancer Research* **21**, 178–186 (1961).

25. K. YOKORO, J. FURTH and H. TAKEMOTO, Role of mammotropin in induction of breast tumors by virus, *Proc. Am. Assoc. Cancer Research* **3**, 281 (1961) and the *Ciba Foundation Symposium on Tumor Viruses of Murine Origin*, J. & A. Churchill Ltd., London, 1962, pp. 139–149.

26. K. YOKORO and J. FURTH, Enhancement of induction of breast tumors with X-rays by mammotropin in rats, *Radiation Research*, **14**, 519 (1961).

DISCUSSION

CHAIRMAN DOUGHERTY: Dr. Kaplan's paper* is open for discussion.

FINKEL: I am fascinated. It is a beautiful story. Of course we have to look for virus in our osteosarcomas. We will soon try to isolate virus from some of our radiation-induced osteosarcomas.

WARREN: It is an extremely interesting and worthwhile story, and impresses the need of weighing a large number of factors.

There is one point, however, that I would like to raise with regard to the possible adrenal cortical relationships touched upon in the AK strain. If this is so, why is it only the thymic cell that responds, rather than other lymphoid cells?

KAPLAN: I think that is an extremely good and provocative question. Actually, there is indication that one can override the thymic predilection under certain circumstances, and that other lymphoid tissues are also somewhat susceptible but at a very low level compared to the thymus.

A few years ago, in some unpublished experiments, we made implants of lymph nodes comparable to those of the thymus which I showed you, and we got about a 10 per cent incidence of lymphomas apparently primary in those lymph node grafts, under conditions which would have given us about a 70 per cent incidence if those had been thymic implants.

So, this is not an absolute difference, and I think it would be highly desirable to go back and adrenalectomize some animals and put in lymph node tissue rather than thymus, and see whether we could evoke this same response.

CHAIRMAN DOUGHERTY: We have shown in our laboratory in collaboration with Drs. David and Martha Berliner, that certain lymphocytes, particularly immature cells, and lymphoma cells in mice are able to metabolize cortisol in quite a different manner than normal lymphocytes' of the same strain and age of mouse. This has also been found to be true of leukemic lymphocytes of the human as compared to normal cells. The malignant cells are able to catabolize cortisol much more completely to C-19 compounds than the normal cells. Also, we have shown that cortisol is the only form of the adrenal cortical hormone which destroys lymphocytes and, in the normal physiological state, is able to regulate their rate of mitosis and maturation. The malignant cell converts cortisol to cortisone rapidly, which has no such physiological capacities. We have found that the large lymphocyte, very similar

---

* Dr. Kaplan did not submit a manuscript. The following list of papers covers the material presented. Dr. Furth was absent.

1. H. S. KAPLAN, Systemic interactions in radiation leukemogenesis, *Acta Union Internationale contre le cancer* 17, 143–147 (1961).
2. H. S. KAPLAN, The nature of the neoplastic transformation in lymphoid tumor induction, included in Ciba Foundation Symposium on *Carcinogenesis, Mechanisms of Action* (London: J. & A. Churchill, Ltd., 1959) pp. 233–248.
3. H. S. KAPLAN, On the etiology and pathogenesis of the leukemias: A review, *Cancer Research* 14, 535–548 (1954).
4. H. S. KAPLAN, Possible mechanisms of virus carcinogenesis, submitted to Federation Proceedings (1961). In press.
5. M. LIEBERMAN and H. S. KAPLAN, Leukemogenic activity of filtrates from radiation-induced lymphoid tumors of mice, *Science* 130, 387–388 (1959).

to that described by Dr. Kaplan—but of course, this is purely morphologically distinguished—is much more resistant to the action of cortisol. We have formulated a point of view that regardless of the etiology of leukemia, the malignant cell is able to catabolize the form of the steroid molecule which under normal conditions, regulates its growth, maturation and death. Therefore, an essential feature of the leukemic cell is that it destroys that which normally controls its lifespan.

It has been demonstrated also, in our laboratory, that X-irradiation given in doses comparable to those given by Kaplan and according to his method of administration, produces a situation in which the cells of the thymus acquire gradually such capacity also to catabolize cortisol in the same fashion as the fully developed malignant cell.

We have also demonstrated during the period that this is acquired, that there is deficiency in the capacity of the adrenal cortex to form cortisol from progesterone which is the immediate precursor. This forms a peripheral adrenal insufficiency which, at the same time, is accompanied by a greater capacity of the cell to catabolize this hormone. We believe that this is an etiological factor regardless of the mechanism by which leukemia is produced, which permits these cells to continue their lifespan and reproduce a different biochemically oriented crop of lymphocytes.

ENGLISH: I wonder what the evidence is for the dumping of virus into the system by radiation, and where it came from.

KAPLAN: The evidence is pretty near zero. We know that thymi of the susceptible strains contain virus, since cell-free filtrates reveal activity. We know they suffer great cellular injury after radiation, and the cells do undergo dissolution. There is a great deal of debris. Thus, it would seem reasonable that if the virus is intially intracellular, and if one of its loci is the thymus, then when cells die after irradiation there would be a release of virus at least locally. But I certainly have no direct evidence for this.

EVANS: Could you say a word about the presumed mode of action of the carcinogenic hydrocarbons?

KAPLAN: This work has not been carried to this state of completion yet, unfortunately. I think all we can say is that in certain strains, which are independently susceptible to both irradiation and methylcholanthrene, one can demonstrate synergism of the two agents. Whether the synergism is a consequence of their acting through a common pathway or through different pathways, I can't tell you.

This whole area was under investigation by our late friend, Arthur Kirschbaum, working with the hydrocarbons, and I think his death has set this work back quite a bit. To my knowledge the group that has carried on in his laboratory have not yet come out with definitive information about whether they get a virus-like agent out of the methylcholanthrene-induced tumors. I think this should be done.

HASTERLIK: I especially wanted Dr. Kaplan to hear this before he left. This is the first time it has been talked about publicly.* This information is only about four weeks old.

I came across an "epidemic" of acute lymphatic leukemia in children, in a suburb of Chicago. There have been eight cases of acute lymphatic leukemia (stem cell type) clustered around one parochial school in a suburb of Chicago with six deaths.

* *Ed. Note*: Since reported to wire service by Argonne Cancer Hospital, May 18, 1961.

We called in the Communicable Disease Center of the U.S. Public Health Service to do an extensive epidemiological survey. This type of clustering of cases of acute leukemia in children has happened in the last year in two other communities in the United States; one in New Jersey and one in Wyoming.

I bring this to your attention because there are two children still alive. We are storing sera from siblings and close contacts in the deep freeze, but there will be material from two children in the future. So, for the information of those of you who are interested in material, I think this might be an opportunity to have material from what looks like a virus-induced disease in the human.

EVANS: Isn't it also well established that dairy and beef cattle in the Texas area have a very high incidence of a similar disease?

CHAIRMAN DOUGHERTY: And East Prussia and Czechoslovakia.

KAPLAN: The incidence is increasing in dairy cattle.

CHAIRMAN DOUGHERTY: It should be mentioned that previous to 1950 in the United States a major cause of disaster in the poultry industry was chicken leukemia, which cost about 100 milion dollars a year. Here we have a very definitely demonstrated virus type agent.

CHRISTENSEN: A similar small cell lymphosarcoma is being extensively studied in sections of Africa by British workers. The sarcomas occur in native children, and appear in the mandible and areas associated with the mandible, with almost universal death.

CHAIRMAN RUSHTON: Thank you, Dr. Dougherty. I am sure arrangements will be made for the applause to be transmitted to Dr. Furth, less any reasonable deduction for his "mouthpiece" (Dr. T. F. Dougherty read Dr. Furth's prepared text). May I take this opportunity to say it is a very great privilege that you have asked a foreigner to take the chair. You must anticipate that there might be some language difficulty, but I hope you will make allowances for that.

T. F. DOUGHERTY: The theory that Dr. Furth is proposing has an enormous amount of evidence to back it up and I believe it. This is not only true for induction of mammary tumors, but for other tumors including ovarian and possibly testicular. There is a possibility that lymphatic leukemia may be included in this type of hormonally controlled mechanism for the production of cancer.

Basically there is a feedback mechanism by which the target organ acts back on the pituitary, shutting off trophic hormones. It is possible that if we knew more about controlling mechanisms for peripheral tissues, we might find that types of tumors which are at present unsuspected to be hormonally induced may fall into a similar idealogic pattern. I should like to point out that Dr. Furth has shown many years ago a similar type mechanism for the production of ovarian tumors.

It is interesting too that one can produce a tumor similar to those produced by radiation if the gonad of the animal, particularly the mouse which has been used, is transplanted into the spleen. In this way the blood supply from the spleen, going back through the liver, carries the hormone from the gonad to the liver, where the hormone is inactivated. The lack of circulating hormone, then, does not inhibit the pituitary from producing the trophic hormone in large quantity and the trophic hormone then stimulates the growth of the cells of the gonad in the spleen. In this way autonomous tumors have been formed, producing a situation similar to that which can be produced by radiation.

I should also like to state that I believe that adrenocortical hormones not only destroy lymphocytes, but I also think that they may be the inhibitor of lymphocyte growth.

FURTH: What I meant was that it is not certain that adrenal corticoid hormones are the physiologic inhibitors of lymphocytes in lymphocyte homeostasis.

MARINELLI: In the table where it was shown that mammotropic hormone plus the virus were administered, nothing was said about the estrogen titer or any compensatory drug being given the animal. It seems to me that not all possible permutations were worked out on that table.

FURTH: The biologic effects indicate no increase and possible decrease of estrogen levels following administration of MtH. Estrogens are the natural stimulants of MtH.

DUDLEY: I would like to inquire whether with the Utah dogs there is any tendency for tumors to arise in the region where a fracture previously occurred. Does the cell stimulation presumably associated with the process of fracture repair result in secondary effects of the sort Dr. Furth describes?

CHRISTENSEN: The highest incidence of fractures has been in the ribs and in the spinous processes of the dorsal vertebrae. Out of our maximum number of tumors we have had only one that has been of primary origin in the ribs.

FURTH: Regenerative hyperplasia favors induction of tumors by chemical or physical agents. Regeneration of liver is known to be associated with circulating "hepato-poietins." No "osteopoietin" is known. Fractures may be either associated with some pre-neoplastic changes caused by the radionuclides or may be secondary to tumors. But the regenerative hyperplasia, whatever its cause, favors tumor formation.

JEE: There have been two cases of fractures occuring at sites of bone tumors in the Utah dogs, but to my knowledge no tumor arising from fracture sites.

PROBLEMS OF LOW-LEVEL IRRADIATION

R. H. MOLE

Medical Research Council Radiobiological Research Unit, Harwell, England

THERE is something quite arbitrary about the term "low-level". It is clearly a relative term and one which implies a quantitative comparison. For present purposes low-level will not be defined in terms of any particular dose or dose rate but will be taken to mean a level of irradiation which produces a low level of effect. It is as well to remember that a single dose of whole or part body irradiation of the order of 10–50 rads produces a variety of gross effects in the experimental animal (Table 1), and daily irradiation of mice with gamma radiation at the rate of 0·1 rad per hour may produce well marked reductions in testis weight[9] and in female fertility.[10] Most of these sensitive changes are examples of cell depletion. Exposures of the same order may produce gross disturbances of organ development in the embryo but do not result in a high level of tumour incidence with one exception which will be referred to later on. A high level of tumour incidence requires in general doses of several hundreds or thousands of rads. Thus cell depletion is produced relatively easily, tumours with relative difficulty and, if there are uncommon but specific intracellular events which determine the beginning of a tumour, the laws relating their occurrence to radiation "dose" may well not be the same as the familiar laws of classical cellular radiobiology. Clearly the kind of effect under consideration must be specified in each context, and the degree of effect which is considered to be low-level. In experimental work on leukaemia an incidence of 0·05 is a low-level effect whereas in the human context an incidence of 10^{-4} may amount to a doubling of the natural incidence, that is a 100 per cent increase.

PROPORTIONAL OR ABSOLUTE EFFECTS?

Here at once is a major problem. Are the effects of low-level irradiation to be expressed in proportional or in absolute terms? In genetic discussion the phrase "doubling dose" is common currency and the life-shortening effect of somatic irradiation is often spoken of in terms of per cent shortening of lifespan as compared with controls. Yet the concept of "doubling dose" is really a device to circumvent ignorance: the amount of mutation due to natural environmental radiation is not known. Similarly by expressing

207

TABLE 1

Some Somatic Effects in Mammals of Small Doses of X- or γ-radiation

Organ	Species	Age at exposure	Dose (rads) approx.	Structure or function examined	Magnitude of effect	Ref.
Ovary	Mouse	10 days	10	Primitive oeocytes	50% depletion	(1)
		7–14 days	85 (0·5 r/hr)	Fertility when adult	reduced to ~10%	(2)
		adult	50	Reproductive capacity	more than halved	
Testis	Mouse	adult	20	Spermatogonia (late A–early B)	50% depletion	(3)
Thymus	Rat	weanling	20	Cortical lymphocytes	50% depletion	(4)
Bone marrow	Rat	adult	40	Mature normoblasts	50% depletion	(5)
		adult	50	24-hr uptake of Fe^{59} in blood	halved	(6)
Eye	Mouse	adult	15–30	Lens opacities	detectable	(7)
Stomach	Rat	adult	40	Emptying time	doubled	(8)

life-shortening as a fraction of the control lifespan we are concealing our ignorance as to the true nature of this somatic effect.

Once life-shortening is expressed in proportional terms we are led on to the idea of applying experimental results obtained in one species to other species simply by scaling the results in terms of a common unit, the length of the lifespan. We also begin to mix up the concepts of life-shortening and ageing, so that we accept, without much thought, the idea that halfway through their lifespan animals of different species are equally aged. In my] view non-specific life-shortening is not a consequence of radiation exposure so that most of the rest of this paper will be concerned with carcinogenesis, although the fact is acknowledged that bone damage and fractures may be of great practical importance as consequences of low-level α-irradiation of the skeleton.

Where tumours are concerned the question is sometimes asked whether radiation *really* increases tumour incidence or *merely* makes tumours appear earlier in life than otherwise. The fact that radiation exposure can result in tumour incidences of nearly 100 per cent in species with a natural incidence of less than 5 per cent, makes the question seem a purely semantic one since it depends on an assumption which is in principle unobservable. Nevertheless there is a meaningful distinction in the question if we think in concrete terms about mechanism. Does exposure to radiation add a certain independent probability to a natural probability of tumour appearance or does the exposure scale up the natural probability by multiplication?

Carcinogenesis in Man

It is interesting to note that although there seems to be no experimental evidence in favour, there are two suggestive pieces of human evidence pointing to the idea that tumour induction by radiation is a multiplication of a natural process rather than an independent and additive phenomenon. As Dr. Richard Doll pointed out to me, Harada and Ishida[11] found that the overall incidence of malignant neoplasms in 1957–58 in individuals exposed to the atomic bomb explosion at Hiroshima in 1945 was increased in the same proportion at all ages (though in different proportions for the different kinds of tumour) even though the natural incidence progressively increased with age. Similarly when the cases of leukaemia in ankylosing spondylitics given X-ray treatment[12] were reclassified according to age at exposure it would seem as if the probability of induction of leukaemia by radiation was not independent of age but rather that, as for the Japanese data on radiation-induced cancer, the "doubling dose" of radiation was similar at all ages.[13] At these low levels of effect radiation may appear to be acting as a co-carcinogen, an agent which makes manifest a latent potential, rather than being itself an initiator.

It is of great interest that Armitage and Doll[14] postulated a mechanism for natural, spontaneous carcinogenesis which would allow radiation to work in just this way. In order to account for the observed relation between age and age-specific cancer rates they suggested that cancer was the direct consequence of two successive events in time. The first cellular event was followed by an exponential increase in the number of altered cells due to the natural process of cell division. When one of these altered cells suffered the second change a cancer began to grow. Fisher[15] utilized the same idea of two successive events in time with the difference that the number of cells altered by the first event was supposed to increase thereafter according to the square of the time, not exponentially.

If radiation can cause the second type of event, then on either of these two hypotheses it can be understood that a given radiation exposure will produce the same proportional increase at all ages but a bigger absolute increase in older and older individuals in accord with the natural increase with age in the number of cells carrying the first kind of change. Also either model makes it easy to understand that the annual rate of radiation-induced malignant disease following an exposure limited in time should reach a peak and then decrease. If there is anything in the basic hypothesis, it is clearly significant not only for theories of carcinogenesis but also for the determination of maximum permissible dose levels of radiation.

But there is another respect in which the difference between proportions and absolute numbers can be significant for maximum permissible levels. Table 2 gives the proportions of deaths in England and Wales due to a num-

TABLE 2

Relative Incidence (in Round Numbers) of Some Certified Causes of Death
(From Registrar General's Statistical Review of England and Wales 1959)

All causes	2000		
All cancer	370	All accidents and violence	90
Lung	80	Motor traffic	20
Leukaemia	10	Accidental poisoning	5
Thyroid	1	(solids, liquids and gases)	
Bone[a]	1	Coal-mining	1
Aplastic Anaemia	1	Suicide and self-inflicted	20

[a] The certified rate has been halved to allow for the errors in certification.[16]

ber of different causes relevant to a consideration of the toxicity of environmental radiation hazards. It can be seen that bone tumours are a much less frequent cause of death than leukaemia. Ought the (very small) risks of occupational exposure at maximum permissible levels to be assessed absolutely or in relation to the natural incidence of the different diseases which different radioactive materials are liable to cause?

EXTRACTING INFORMATION FROM DATA

The Necessity of Replication

The general principles of extracting information from data are just the same whatever the level of effect being looked for, but because it is so much more laborious to look for low-level effects there is a strong temptation to lower the standards of experimental planning and of interpretation below the scientifically permissible. Consider the survival curves of the control mice and of the mice given 1·1 r or 0·1 r daily of gamma irradiation until they died in the often cited experiment of Lorenz et al.[17] Are the differences between the curves real or do they merely reflect the natural experimental variability to be expected when doing a survival experiment of this kind? In the absence of any replication or repetition of the observations the choice can only be a matter of taste, not of evidence.

The same logical flaw underlies many attempts to extract information from the data of human epidemiology. A recent survey[18] compared the incidence of leukaemia in different areas of Scotland, one main centre of interest being the city of Aberdeen and its surrounding districts where many of the houses are built of granite. Environmental radiation levels are definitely higher than in other areas where houses are made of brick or other kinds of stone. However, the incidence of leukaemia in Aberdeen and its environs was so much higher than in Dundee and Edinburgh that the authors concluded that the difference in radiation levels could not have been the reason for it. If so there must have been some other, unidentified reason or reasons. But let us suppose that this unidentified reason had been quantitatively less potent than in fact it was, so that a smaller difference in leukaemia incidence had been observed, compatible with the then current ideas about the likely relation between exposure dose and leukaemia incidence. Surely the findings would have been taken as confirmation of this relation. This seems a logically absurd situation but it arises only because the necessity has been overlooked of examining several separate pairs of comparisons between areas differing in environmental radiation levels before firm conclusions can be drawn (as the authors of this survey were well aware). The correlation between cigarette smoking and lung cancer is to be believed in because it has been found repeatedly.

Comparability of Experiments Done at Different Times

One of the ordinary workaday rules of scientific experimentation is that of comparability, and it is especially hard to ensure comparability with experiments which last the lifetime of a mammal. After all each such experiment takes up a sizeable fraction of the useful working life of a scientist and there is a very definite limit to the amount of work which any one person can do properly at any one time. So what all of us engaged in such work have to do is to get information out of comparisons between experiments done many years apart. This can have pitfalls. Apart from the work on dogs carrying skeletal burdens of bone-seeking isotopes, which is a main burden of this symposium, the only large-scale quantitative toxicological information on the delayed effects of these isotopes is to be found in the work of Dr. Miriam Finkel and her colleagues with mice. She has compared the bone tumour production by different α- and β-emitters in terms of tumour formation rates against amount of injected isotope[19] and Lamerton[20] has used the same basic data in order to compare overall tumour incidence against calculated tissue dose in rads. Lamerton, especially, has emphasized the difference between the curves for α-emitters and the curves for β-emitters and a great deal of discussion has centred on the physical reasons which may be supposed to make it unlikely that the dose-response relations for these two different kinds of particles should be similar.

However, the conclusion that the curves of tumour incidence are really different is only justified if the data for the different Finkel experiments are really comparable in a basic biological sense. The experiment with strontium^{90} and calcium^{45} was begun in 1954 and the complete data on control lifespan show that the intrinsic health of the mice was as good as can be expected. In fact some 75 per cent of all the bone tumours were recorded before one fifth of the controls were dead. The radium (and plutonium) experiment was begun some five years earlier and the first reports show that the health of the mice was not satisfactory. In the early stages of the experiment "... disease of epidemic proportions rapidly decreased the population".[21] "The tumours among the radium treated animals (100 μc/kg) were only incidental (and not) of primary importance in contributing to mortality."[22] In fact no tumours at all had been recorded by the time one fifth of the controls was dead.[21,23] The recorded incidence of tumours in animals given radium must therefore be less than would have been noted if the animals had been as long lived as in the 1954 experiment with strontium-90 and calcium-45. The radium experiment was clearly an unlucky one and anyone, as I am very conscious, can have the bad luck for an experiment to go wrong. But the difference in longevity and animal health between the radium experiment and the experiment with strontium[90] and calcium[45] means that they are just not properly comparable, quite apart from any differences in the results, such as the distribution of tumours between different parts of the skeleton or the time of occurrence of the first tumour or "latent period" (only two radium tumours occurred before 280 days). It seems to me on the one hand that the radium (and plutonium) experiment badly needs repetition and on the other hand that there is no reliable evidence from which to conclude that the dose-response curves for α- and β-emitters really are different.

What is remarkable to me is the general similarity of the curves of tumour incidence against tissue dose and against amount of injected isotope in spite of the very real differences in distribution of isotope in bone, in distribution of dose, both in space and in time, and in LET. To me this can mean only that these physical differences are not a source of qualitative differences in response, just as the fact that the same isotopes produce bone tumours in the dog where the bones have haversian systems and in the mouse where the bones do not, should mean, by Occam's razor, that haversian systems as such have no especial relevance to carcinogenesis. But my main point here is to emphasize the importance of biological comparability before conclusions are drawn.

The economical way of ensuring biological comparability in long term experiments seems to me the method adopted at Salt Lake City, and in other laboratories. A group of animals, litter mates if the experiment will allow this, is allocated one at a time to different treatments. Groups are given their treatment at successive moments in time. Properly carried out the experiment will automatically provide information about natural variability while at the same time reducing the systematic contamination of the data by secular variation to a greater and greater degree the longer the period of time over which groups start their treatment.

RADIOBIOLOGICAL ASPECTS OF LOW-LEVEL IRRADIATION

LET and Classical Radiobiology

When α- and β-emitting isotopes and X- and γ-radiation are compared, one main consideration is the difference in density of ionization or in LET. The quantitative importance of LET in itself is properly determinable only in objects which are small compared to track length, such as protein molecules, viruses, microorganisms and perhaps single cells, that is in objects in the field of what may be called classical radiobiology. When we consider low-level effects in whole organisms of the size of the laboratory mammal or man, we may try to focus our thoughts and concentrate on a similarly small volume of tissue in order to be able to use the same relations between LET and effect as are found in classical radiobiology. However there is a weighty biological factor which makes me doubt altogether the wisdom of this approach.

Studies in what I have called classical radiobiology are studies in the maintenance of functional activity of chemical molecules, such as enzymes, or biological units such as cells. In order to estimate how much functional activity has been lost by exposure to radiation, a test system is used which, ideally, gives every still functioning unit an equal chance of manifesting itself. Cell suspensions for example are plated out in such a way that each cell preserving the property of divisibility can divide in isolation and so become scorable. The studies are indeed studies of reproductive ability but not, as is so commonly stated, of reproductive integrity. There is no test at all of the "integrity" of the physiological properties of the "surviving" cells, even of their reproductive properties.

Suppose that carcinogenesis is indeed a process determined by a change in an individual cell. It can be assumed quite confidently that this is not the sort of change which is to be found in every cell which maintains some reproductive ability after any dose of radiation however small. If so, then only some of the surviving cells can be potential cancer cells and we have to recognise that no test is applied to tell us what proportion of the survivors are of this kind. In such a case RBE factors derived from LET experiments can be used to assess tumour production in the whole animal only if after exposure to radiations of all LET's and at all levels of dose cells suffering the malignant transformation form the same proportion of all cells maintaining the ability to divide. This seems a highly unlikely assumption.

Indirect Mechanisms for Low-level Effects

Must the mechanism of a low-level effect be a direct one? Certainly it is natural to assume that when carcinogenesis is due to interference with some physiological feed-back mechanism, as may be the case when thyroid tumours are induced by irradiating the pituitary, for instance, then there will be no tumours unless there is a sufficiently large interference with the feed-back. Of course it should always be possible by choosing just the right amount of interference to get a tumour incidence at any desired level, however low, but it is difficult to imagine that anything one might call low-level irradiation would be able to cause the considerable amount of physiological damage necessary for the appearance of even one tumour via a feed-back mechanism. However it is as well to recall that irradiation of the mouse ovary by as little as 50r may be sufficient to induce a large incidence of tumours[24] and that the indirect nature of the mechanism is proved by the ability of an intact unirradiated ovary to prevent the appearance of tumour in an irradiated ovary even at somewhat higher doses.[25]

This example may possibly provide a clue to a general principle. In mice the radiation dose for the induction of ovarian tumours in any numbers is a dose which grossly affects the physiological function of the ovary, the production of fertilisable eggs. The human ovary is much less radiosensitive as judged by the same two criteria. The sterilizing dose is an order of magnitude larger and radiation-induced ovarian tumours in women have not yet been identified so that they certainly cannot be induced anything like as easily as in the mouse. Presumably pronounced quantitative differences between species in the carcinogenic action of radiation are to be expected when the mechanism is an indirect one and, if so, it will not be possible to extrapolate directly and quantitatively to man from the experimental animal. On the other hand the general principle may perhaps be extended. If tumour production by indirect mechanisms occurs only when gross enough physiological damage is done, then if we can learn the level of radiation exposure which produces a small amount of physiological damage in man, we shall know the safe level of radiation exposure as judged by the particular tumour under consideration. Animal experiment will still be necessary to help define the physiological mechanisms involved.

CANCER AS A RARE EVENT

To the classical radiobiologist low-intensity irradiation is irradiation at a dose rate below the level at which consideration needs to be given to any quadratic or higher terms in the relation

$$E = ax + bx^2 + \ldots$$

This viewpoint has two implicit assumptions: that rare events are of no particular consequence and that the interaction between doses separated by an interval of time is purely summative. If it is sensible to think of the radiobiology of low-level irradiation in terms of average cells and average events then the major problem is merely the problem of how to average events which are distant in space and time. Almost by definition, however, a low level of effect means that the events of interest are rare whatever the assumed mechanism and whatever the importance of fitness and LET. Indeed whether a tumour originates in one cell or a field of cells the originating focus is a very small fraction of the original organ, so that tumour production is always a rare event, even when tumour incidence in a group of animals reaches 100 per cent. The rare event is recognized only because of the expansile nature of tumour growth and of course only at some time after it happened.

As far as α-particle emitters are concerned this idea of a rare event seems to me the only sensible supposition compatible with the idea of malignant transformation of a single cell. If an α-particle goes through the cytoplasm the cell may possibly recover completely. If an α-particle goes through the sensitive part of a cell nucleus the cell must be expected to die. A tumour can result from a change in a single cell only if an α-particle tranversing the nucleus does so in such a way as to preserve its ability to divide while at the same time altering it in a permanent, hereditable and rather particular way. It is postulated that this is a rare event amongst all possible α-particle trajectories through the cell.

Let me now take seriously the idea that a radiation-induced tumour starts in a single small focus, perhaps, though not necessarily, a single cell, and let me suppose one further thing, that a tumour begins only after two different rare events have both occurred, possibly separated by an interval of time. Clearly this is a kind of two-hit model but without any specification in detail except that each event is determined by the occurrence of a particle trajectory, not by a tissue dose in rads. The hypothesis, like all two-event models, requires that at any fixed time after administration of different amounts of the same radioactive material the cumulative incidence of tumours should be proportional to the square of the amount given. None of this is original: Brues[26,27] showed that the data on radiation-induced leukaemia in man fitted such a square law and so did Burch.[28] But it is interesting that the same square law seems to fit all the available data on bone tumour production by internal emitters.

(1) *Dogs given radium or plutonium.*[29] Table 3 gives the tumour incidences at 2100 days after a single injection. The 2 to 4 dose levels differ three-fold from their neighbours so that on the two-event hypothesis the

tumour incidence between dose levels 2 and 4 for radium should differ 81-fold.

TABLE 3

Bone Tumour Incidence in Beagles at 2100 Days[29]

Dose level	Dogs with bone tumours / Dogs at risk	
	Radium	Plutonium
4	11/11	12/12
3	4/8	9/12
2	0/7	2/7
1	0/7	0/6

With experimental groups of 10–12 animals this means that if the incidence at a higher level of dose is 100 per cent then at a level two steps lower it should be zero, as was in fact observed. Similarly the differences in incidence at dose levels 1, 2 and 3 for plutonium are compatible with the hypothesis that they should be in the ratio of 1:36:324. (There is a six-fold difference between dose levels 1 and 2).

(2) *Mice given a variety of α- and β-emitters.*[19] The results of these experiments have been of major interest to all those concerned with comparisons between the carcinogenecity of different bone-seeking isotopes.[20,30] Whatever the solution to this problem of comparative carcinogenicity, the individual dose-response curves for each radioactive material need an explanation. When the tumour incidence is assessed at a fixed time it is striking how steep the dose-response curves are for all the materials investigated. A difference of less than 10-fold in the amount of administered material was associated with an increase in tumour incidence from the control level to nearly 100 per cent for Sr^{90} and Ca^{45}[19,20] just as expected on a two-event model. (The reduction in tumour incidence once the optimum dose is exceeded is a separate problem). For α-emitters the rise was less steep but not much less so, except for radium, and previous discussion has shown that tumour incidence after radium must have been underestimated by comparison with other experiments because of the unfortunate mortality from extraneous causes before the time at which tumours begin to appear. If data were available on the number of tumours, not merely on the numbers of tumour-bearing animals, the curves might well be steeper still. Burch[28] has already commented that tumour incidence rate appeared to be proportional to the square of the dose in the original Argonne experiment in which mice were given monthly injections of strontium^{89}.[31]

218   R. H. MOLE

(3) *Other experimental information.* Bone tumour incidence in rats given ten daily doses of Ca^{45}[33] was proportional to the square of administered dose. Other experiments cited[30] are less easy to interpret: in rabbits retention of the dose of Sr^{90} depended on the size of the dose. Fractionation of injected P^{32} suggested that there was an optimum interval for maximal tumour production.[34]

(4) *Human beings carrying a radium burden.* At the much lower levels of cancer incidence in men carrying a skeletal burden of radium, the annual incidence in excess of the natural may be considered to be proportional to the square of the terminal radium burden,[28] but the basic evidence is clearly sketchy.

Rate of Tumour Development with Time

All two-event hypotheses require that tumour incidence at a fixed time should be proportional to the square of the "dose" but different models lead to different conclusions about the rate of tumour development with time. Instead of discussing the theoretical merits of such models as those of Armitage and Doll,[14] Fisher[15] and Burch,[28] it seemed worthwhile seeing empirically what was in fact the relation between dN/dt and time in the production of bone tumours by injected radioactive material. The best data to attack seemed to be those of Finkel *et al.* on Sr^{90} since there were a number of dose levels of Sr^{90} and large numbers of mice, the time of death of each tumour-bearing mouse was available,[23] and the mortality curves of a number of groups with a definite excess of tumours were also recorded.[35,36] The control mortality curve showed that the experiment had been uninfluenced by extraneous mortality. Thus the tumour rate, dN/dt, could be derived with reasonable confidence over 50-day periods as the number of mice dying with bone tumours in that time divided by the number of mice alive at the beginning of the period under consideration.

Time from the day of injection to the day of death, t, is not the relevant time for consideration since a certain development time, θ, must elapse between the start of the tumour and the moment when it is large enough to be recorded i.e. to be responsible for the death of the animal. The probability of tumour development during the time interval $t-\theta$ to $t + 50-\theta$ depends on the number of radioactive events in $t+25-\theta$ *ex hypothesi* but the daily number of events is not constant since Sr^{90} is excreted from the mouse in such a way that the amount of Sr^{90} remaining in the skeleton is a power function of time.[37] Using this function the total number of radioactive events from $t = 1$ up to any specified time can be determined and in Fig. 1 the tumour rate dN/dt is plotted against the square of this number per μc injected, the average development time of a bone tumour, θ, being taken to be 150 days. It can be seen that the tumour rate appears to be linearly proportional to the square of the total number of radioactive evens per μc injected, and that the slopes of the lines for the different injected doses are in proportion to the squares of the amounts injected.

This method of approach is valid only if the retention of Sr^{90} is independent of the amount injected, which was true over the range examined,[37] and if tumour production is not affected by variations in the "average

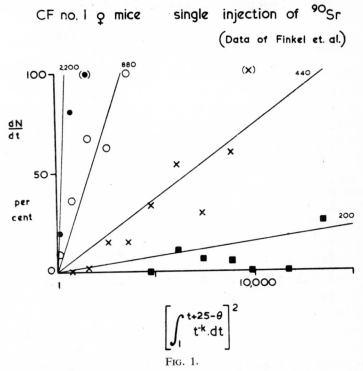

FIG. 1.

The probability of tumour development in successive 50-day periods after a single injection of Sr^{90} and the total time-burden of Sr^{90}.

N is number of tumour-bearing animals. The abscissa is the square of the total number of μc-days per μc injected allowing for the changing retention of a single dose of Sr^{90}.[37] $k = -0.31$. $\theta = 150$ days = the average development time of a bone tumour. The straight lines were drawn by eye and their slopes are proportional to the squares of the injected doses which are shown in $\mu c/kg$.

$$\frac{dN}{dt} = ad^2 \left[\int_1^{t+25-\theta} t^{-k} dt \right]^2 \quad \text{where} \quad a = 3.8 \cdot 10^{-8}$$

and d, the body burden at $t = 1$, is about $0.8 \times$ injected dose.

dose-rate". When the same amount of Sr^{90} was given in one, five or 20 fractions the data show in my opinion that there was little change in the incidence of osteogenic sarcoma in spite of a very great difference in the average dose-rate in the first twenty days.[38] It is also of great interest that the tumour rate at 450–525 days of age in mice exposed since conception to Sr^{90} and continuously fed a diet containing 10 μc Sr^{90} per gram calcium[39] was, within a factor of two, what would be expected from the total number of radioactive events in t-θ using the data of Fig. 1.

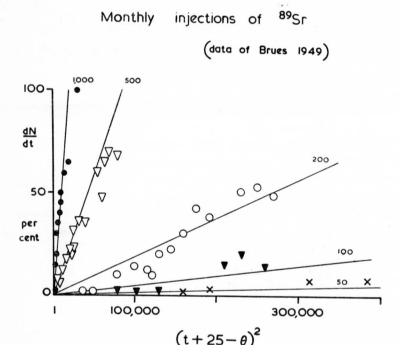

Fig. 2.

The probability of tumour development after monthly injections of Sr^{89} and the total time-burden of Sr^{89}.

$\dfrac{dN}{dt} = 50P_t$ from Figure 2 of Brues[31] so that the scale is the same as Fig. 1. The abscissa is $(t-\theta)^2$ where t is time from the first of a series of monthly injections and $\theta = 150$ days = average development time of a bone tumour. The straight lines were drawn by eye and their slopes are proportional to the squares of the injected doses which are shown in μc/kg.

$\dfrac{dN}{dt} = ad^2(t-\theta)^2$ where $a = 4.6 \cdot 10^{-9}$ and d is the first of the injected doses. If the Sr^{89} was retained like Sr^{90},[37,40] the mean body burden was about $0.5d$ (ignoring changes in body weight during the course of the experiment).

When mice were given monthly injections of strontium[89] in such a way as to keep their body burden constant[31, 32] dN/dt should depend simply on $(t\text{-}\theta)^2$. Figure 2 shows that dN/dt was approximately proportional to $(t\text{-}\theta)^2$ and the slope proportional to the square of the body burden or "dose". For equal tumour rates and equal numbers of μc-days per μc Sr[90] appeared to be twice as effective as Sr[89].* The data on Ca[45] are available for only two dose levels[23, 35] but treated in the same way suggested that Sr[90] was about eight times as effective.

A much more stringent test that these relations generally apply would be in an experiment in which animals were given a single injection of strontium[89]. The daily number of radioactive events in the bone then changes relatively rapidly with time partly because of the excretion of the strontium[89] but principally because the 54-day half life of strontium[89] is small compared to the generation time of the bone tumours. The experiment was done many years ago with mice[31] and the data certainly do not fit very well! However, even a small contamination of the Sr[89] with Sr[90] would be important under the present hypothesis and might account for the second wave of tumours which began to appear some 300 days after the injection.

If these empirical analyses are taken at their face value—and clearly many refinements are possible—then there does appear to be a general kinetic uniformity in the production of bone tumours by bone-seeking isotopes. The range $t-\theta$ available in the relatively short-lived mouse is not large enough to allow real confidence and the data on dogs still to be collected in the next ten years at the University of Utah may be much more decisive.

Kinetics and Mechanism

However establishing a pattern in kinetics does not establish a mechanism. A particular kinetic pattern may positively rule out certain hypotheses but cannot prove a particular one: any pattern is always compatible with a variety of mechanisms. Nothing specific has been postulated here about the intrinsic nature of the two events which have been supposed to be necessary for the development of a cancer to a size which is clinically important, except that they are particular kinds of event. However, if their conjunction is rare, as seems to me to be likely, given the nature of cancer, it must be accepted that in the whole skeleton of a dog with a 3- or 4-level of body burden of radium or plutonium only

---

* It is probably fortuitous that the rate of β-particle emission by 1 μc Sr[90] at equilibrium is also twice that of 1 μc Sr[89].

one, or perhaps a few, of these conjunctions occur in a period of, say, four years. To look down the microscope at tissue preparations in order to find out what this conjunction really is, is indeed like looking for a needle in a haystack without the use of a magnet. Whatever can be recognized microscopically as a true effect of radiation, i.e. seen not once but repeatedly, even if it is found only rarely, will be, almost by definition, something which is *not* the origin of the tumour. This is in many ways a grim conclusion to be forced to and one which it may not be at all easy to accept. Unfortunately, too, even if it is accepted that bone tumour production is proportional to the square of the preceding number of radioactive events for each of a variety of α- and β-emitters, their relative carcinogenic activity can be assessed only if additional information is available about the exact site within the bone where the relevant radioactive events occur.

EXTRAPOLATION

It is sometimes thought that with a sufficient bulk of adequate observations it should be possible to decide whether there is or is not a threshold dose, that is a dose below which no effect of the kind under discussion occurs at all. As explained elsewhere[41] this question of a threshold is a purely theoretical question and cannot be finally decided by any appeal to observation or experiment. However, quite apart from this question, we want to be able to extrapolate from experimental animals to man because we want to know how to control environmental hazards due to radiation.

Can we extrapolate from experimental animals to man without understanding the mechanism of production of, say, radiation-induced cancer? The scientist instinctively feels that this is quite impracticable and, clearly, discussion is impossible in complete ignorance of mechanism. The question is better put thus: how much of the mechanism needs to be known before control is possible? Historically it is fair to say that in no single instance has successful control of an environmental hazard depended on previous knowledge of the cellular mechanisms involved. The nature of the life-cycle of the malarial parasite in the human body and the relative importance of the different kinds of immunity in human tuberculosis are of academic interest but not of first importance in controlling or preventing malaria or infection with tuberculosis. Lead poisoning and dust diseases of the lungs became wholly preventable as soon as it was realised that there was a specific causal agent which could be avoided but their cellular mechanisms are still obscure. We all recognize that we cannot altogether avoid radiation exposure, either of the natural environmental kind, or, if we work with radioactive materials, from the body burden which we must expect to accumulate however scrupulously we work. So we feel we must know what harm small amounts will do, that is, we want to know about the kinetics of radiation damage. More precisely therefore the question is: do we have to know the cellular mechanisms involved before we can make use of the kinetics which can be established in experimental animals?

If this were so, much experimental work with animals would just be of no help to medicine for there is in fact very little human disease of any kind where knowledge of cellular mechanisms is precise and detailed. Are we not altogether too ambitious in expecting to found our rules for prophylaxis of radiation injury on knowledge of cellular mechanisms? Suppose the dose–response–time relations for human bone tumour induction by radiation were known, what more would we need to know from the practical point of view of prophylaxis and control?

This is where the pragmatic and the academic approaches diverge. Any sort of laboratory scale experiment on carcinogenesis deals with limited numbers of animals and even if a mechanism for carcinogenesis can be demonstrated which seems to be true at the 5–100 per cent level of tumour incidence, it must be an act of faith to decide that this particular mechanism *and no other* is responsible for all or the majority of cancers at the level of incidence which is of interest to the public health, say $1 \cdot 10^{-4}$–10^{-5}. Is this act of faith any lesser or greater than that which says that kinetics in animals are transferable to man in the absence of detailed information about cellular mechanisms?

It may be misleading of course to handle even kinetics in an unsophisticated way. If the idea can be seriously entertained that the origin of some kinds of radiation-induced cancer depends on the successive occurrence of two uncommon events with separate probabilities, each depending on the amount of exposure (in appropriate units), we may still have to reckon with the possibility of a change in the dose–response relation as the degree of effect becomes sufficiently low. This may come about if one, or other, or both, of the events may also occur "spontaneously", and especially if the first event can multiply itself by cell division whether on a surface[15] or in a volume.[14]

Several years ago Brues[26] said many of the things that need saying about the somatic effects of low-level irradiation and said them very pertinently. He began with a quotation: "A fool is one who knows nothing but answers—while the wise man knows what the questions are". My purpose in ending with it is emphasize my sense of the inadequacy of the various answers I have discussed.

REFERENCES

1. E. F. OAKBERG, Gamma-ray sensitivity of oocytes of young mice, *Anat. Rec.* **137**, 385–6 (1960).

2. W. L. RUSSELL, L. B. RUSSELL, M. H. STEELE and E. L. PHIPPS, Extreme sensitivity of an immature stage of the mouse ovary to sterilization by irradiation, *Science* **129**, 1288 (1959).

3. E. F. OAKBERG, Gamma-ray sensitivity of spermatogonia of the mouse, *J. Exptl. Zool.* **134**, 343–356 (1957).

4. O. A. TROWELL, The radiosensitivities of the cortical and the medullary lymphocytes in the thymus, *Internat. J. Radiation Biology* **4**, 163 (1961).

5. E. V. HULSE, Quantitative studies on the depletion of the erythropoietic cells in the bone marrow of the irradiated rat, *Brit. J. Haemat.* **3**, 348–358 (1957).

6. E. H. BELCHER, I. G. F. GILBERT and L. T. LAMERTON, Experimental studies with radioactive iron, *Brit. J. Radiol.* **27**, 387–392 (1954).

7. A. C. UPTON, K. W. CHRISTENBERRY, G. S. MELVILLE, J. FURTH and G. S. HURST, The relative biological effectiveness of neutrons, X-rays, and gamma-rays for the production of lens opacities: observations on mice, rats, guinea-pigs, and rabbits, *Radiology* **67**, 686–696 (1956).

8. E. V. HULSE, Observations on the delay in gastric emptying after X-irradiation in the rat and the effect of adrenalectomy upon it, *Brit. J. exper. Path.* **38**, 498–503 (1957).

9. A. B. ESCHENBRENNER, E. MILLER and E. LORENZ, Quantitative histologic analysis of the effect of chronic whole-body irradiation with gamma-rays on the spermatogenic elements and the interstitial tissue of the testes of mice, *J. Nat. Cancer Inst.* **9**, 133–147 (1948).

10. R. H. MOLE, Impairement of fertility by whole-body irradiation of female mice, *Internat. J. Radiation Biology* **1**, 107–114 (1959).

11. T. HARADA and M. ISHIDA, Neoplasms among A-bomb survivors in Hiroshima: First report of the research committee on tumor statistics, Hiroshima City Medical Association, Hiroshima, Japan, *J. Nat. Cancer Inst.* **25**, 1253–1264 (1960).

12. W. M. COURT BROWN and R. DOLL, Leukaemia and aplastic anaemia in patients irradiated for ankylosing spondylitis, Medical Research Council, Special Report Series No. 295, H.M.S.O. London (1957).

13. R. H. MOLE, Radiation and leukaemia, *Lancet* **ii**, 192 (1957).

14. P. ARMITAGE and R. DOLL, A two-stage theory of carcinogenesis in relation to the age distribution of human cancer, *Brit. J. Cancer* **11**, 161–169 (1957).

15. J. C. FISHER, Multiple-mutation theory of carcinogenesis, *Nature* **181**, 651–2 (1958).

16. A. MACKENZIE, W. M. COURT BROWN, R. DOLL and H. A. SISSONS, Mortality from primary tumours of bone in England and Wales *Brit. Med. J.* **i**: 1782 (1961).

17. E. LORENZ, W. E. HESTON, A. B. ESCHENBRENNER and M. K. DERINGER, Biological studies in the tolerance range, *Radiology* **49**, 274–285 (1947).

18. W. M. COURT BROWN, R. DOLL, F. W. SPIERS, B. J. DUFFY and M. J. McHUGH, Geographical variation in leukaemia mortality in relation to background radiation and other factors, *Brit. Med. J.* **i**: 1753–1759 (1960).

19. M. P. FINKEL, Relative biological effectiveness of internal emitters, *Radiology* **67**, 665–72 (1956).

20. L. F. LAMERTON, An examination of the clinical and experimental data relating to the possible hazard to the individual of small doses of radiation, *Brit. J. Radiol* **31**, 229–239 (1958).

21. M. P. FINKEL and G. M. HIRSH, Progress report. Radium 226 and Plutonium 239 toxicities in mice, Argonne National Laboratory ANL-4713, 119–122 (1951).

22. M. P. FINKEL and G. M. HIRSCH, Progress report: The incidence of malignant bone tumors in the long-term toxicity experiments with uranium, plutonium and radium, Argonne National Laboratory ANL-4794, 71–81 (1952).

23. M. P. FINKEL and B. O. BISKIS, The induction of malignant bone tumors in mice by radioisotopes, Acta Unio Internat. *Contra Cancr.* **15**, 99–106 (1959).

24. A. C. UPTON, F. FURTH and K. W. CHRISTENBERRY, Late effects of thermal neutron irradiation in mice, *Cancer Research* **14**, 682–90 (1954).

25. L. LICK, A. KIRSCHBAUM and H. MIXER, Mechanism of induction of ovarian tumors by X-rays, *Cancer Research* **9**, 532–36 (1949).

26. A. M. BRUES, Somatic Effects, in *Low-level Irradiation*, ed. A. M. BRUES, Publ. No. 59, American Association for the Advancement of Science, Washington, D.C. 73–86 (1959).

27. A. M. BRUES, Critique of the linear theory of carcinogenesis, *Science* **128**, 693–699 (1958).

28. P. R. J. BURCH, Radiation carcinogenesis: a new hypothesis, *Nature* **185**, 135–142 (1960).

29. T. F. DOUGHERTY, Research in Radiobiology, Semi-annual Report of work in progress on the chronic toxicity program Sept. 30, 1960, COO-222, Dept. of Anatomy University of Utah College of Medicine.

30. L. F. LAMERTON, Dosimetry aspects of the production of bone tumours by radiation, *Proc. 2nd International Conf. on the Peaceful Uses of Atomic Energy* (United Nations) **22**, 119–125 (1958).

31. A. M. BRUES, Biological hazards and toxicity of radioactive isotopes, *J. Clin. Invest.* **28**, 1286–1296 (1949).

32. M. P. FINKEL, H. LISCO and A. M. BRUES, Toxicity of Sr^{89} in mice. Malignant bone tumours, Argonne National Laboratory ANL-5378, 106–117 (1955).

33. J. F. KUZMA and G. ZANDER, Cancerogenic effects of Ca^{45} and Sr^{89} in Sprague-Dawley rats, *Arch. Path.* **63**: 198–206 (1957).

34. L. F. LAMERTON, Radioisotopes in the skeleton: Considerations of radiation dosage in relation to bone damage, in *Radioisotopes in the Biosphere*, ed. R. S. CALDECOTT and L. A. SNYDER, University of Minnesota, 382–400 (1960).

35. M. P. FINKEL, B. O. BISKIS and G. M. SCRIBNER, Toxicity of Strontium-90 and of Calcium-45 in mice—II. Status of experiment 625 days after injection, Argonne National Laboratory Quarterly Report ANL-5597, 16–20 (1956).

36. M. P. FINKEL, B. O. BISKIS and G. M. SCRIBNER, The influence of Strontium-90 upon life span and neoplasms of mice, *Second International Conference on the Peaceful Uses of Atomic Energy*, Geneva **22**, 65–70 (1958).

37. M. P. FINKEL, B. J. TELLEKSON, J. LESTINA and B. O. BISKIS, The influence of dosage pattern upon the toxicity of Sr^{90} in mice—I. Preliminary experiment and 212-day survey of the long-term study, Argonne National Laboratory ANL-5732, 21–31 (1957).

38. M. P. Finkel, B. O. Biskis and P. J. Bergstrand, Radioisotope toxicity: significance of chronic administration, in *Radioisotopes in the Biosphere* ed. R. S. Caldecott and L. A. Snyder, University of Minnesota, Minneapolis, 461–473 (1960).
39. M. P. Finkel, P. J. Bergstrand and B. O. Biskis, The consequences of the continuous ingestion of Sr^{90} by mice, *Radiology* **74**, 458–467 (1960).
40. M. P. Finkel, A. M. Brues and H. Lisco, The toxicity of Sr^{89} in mice, Argonne National Laboratory ANL-5247, 25–29 (1954).
41. R. H. Mole, Radiation as toxic agent, in *Lectures on the Scientific Basis of Medicine*, Athlone Press, London **8**, 65–86 (1958-9).

DISCUSSION

CASARETT: I would like to make some general comments on both of these excellent papers by Drs. Kaplan and Mole.

They have both pointed up very effectively in different ways the multistage complexity of radiation tumorogenesis. It seems clear that there are at least two essential factors in radiation tumorogenesis — the primary or initiating cellular change, and the secondary or potentiating condition either in the mutant cell or in the tissue environment. It seems that in the case of some types of tumors the secondary or growth-promoting factor may be localized in the tissue of origin of the tumor in the form of localized tissue disorder, and with other types of tumor it may be a more generalized disorder. For example, it can be inferred from the experimental work of Dr. Kaplan and Dr. Furth that the stimulation of secretion of pituitary trophic hormones is important in the radiation induction of some of the tumors of the endocrine glands.

Both Dr. Kaplan and Dr. Furth have shown experimentally, in the radiation induction of certain types of tumors, the relative importance of indirect mechanisms and the relative lack of importance of irradiation of the cells of origin of the neoplasms.

Whatever roles are played by the disturbances of growth-regulating mechanisms or local tissue disorders, it is clear that the ultimate acquisition of malignant characteristics in the neoplastic cell involves a permanent and reproducible change in the cell.

There is perhaps less difference between a somatic mutation and a viral infection of a cell than seems apparent offhand, if we care to regard them both in a broad sense as infection by genic material, either changed inherent genic material in the one case or invading viral genic material in the other case.

In either case there is conferred a survival or proliferative advantage on some cells over other cells not so affected, at least under certain conditions which may develop locally in the tissue of origin of the neoplasm or in more generalized growth-regulating systems.

When we consider the phenomenon of transduction of genetic units of bacteria by means of bacteriophage, the phenomenon of a bacterial transformation, and the transforming activity of DNA, the possible similarities between somatic mutation and viral infection are strong and very provocative. Such interactions closely resemble the re-combination phenomenon in chromosomes in sexual reproduction. In this broad sense of infection, fertilization may be regarded as infection of a cell by genic material.

The property of re-combination is common to chromosomes, viruses and transforming agents. It may be relatively unimportant in tumorogenesis whether the cell mutation is due to identifiable mutagens, viruses, excessive hormonal stimulation or other uncontrolled factors. Mutations of significance in tumorogenesis are probably always with us and increasing in time with ageing processes, irradiation or exposure to other agents.

Perhaps the factors of greatest importance are those which permit the emergence of mutant cells with proliferative advantage and malignant tendencies. It seems imperative, in research on mechanisms of tumorogenesis, to take some of the effort that is put into the study of the behavior of the tumor cell and apply it in an attempt to assess the relative importance of these two factors in tumorogenesis. This requires elucidation of both local and general controls that are responsible for the maintenance of normal tissue function and integrity.

CHAIRMAN DOUGHERTY: I think the points made here are well taken, and in a sense, can be summarized by saying that without radiation at a certain level you may not get a tumor, but if you do give radiation you may get a tumor. The third possibility is that radiation plus something else gives a tumor, and then maybe you don't need anything at all to get a tumor.

It is even questionable in many cases whether a virus is necessary. I am not completely convinced that a virus as a direct inducing mechanism is a factor in all tumorogenesis. At certain levels of radiation there is no question but that we have an inducing mechanism as far as the production of some kinds of cancers is concerned.

When we get to much lower levels, probably those that are more practical from the standpoint of real possibilities of affecting the human race, we get into an area in which we know very little about the role actually played by radiation in inducing the cancer.

MARINELLI: I would like to comment on Dr. Mole's remarks about epidemiological studies and the fact that one cannot demonstrate the existence of a threshold.

A physicist would say that it is impossible to demonstrate by any quantitative experience that A is equal to B; if one knows the laws governing the errors of a particular type of measurement, one can only demonstrate that A is equal to B, "plus or minus" a certain quantity, or state the frequency with which a certain experimental result will appear in an infinite series of identical experiments. The demonstration of threshold effects in radiobiology is no exception to this limitation of quantitative science.

This type of information is not useless, however; from the work of Court-Brown et al. (Brit. Med. J., pp. 15–39, Nov. 1960) it can be estimated that the chances of doubling cancer incidence in the viable progeny of 40,000 pelvic irradiated pregnant mothers are only 1 in 300.

In a scientific sense this statement is more convincing than A. Stewart et al. (Brit. Med. J., pp. 1495, June 1958) computations which were based on the very assumption which her study was designed to prove. Unfortunately, her hypothetical result has been reiterated and assumed valid practically everywhere.

EVANS: There is one factual point I want to ask Dr. Mole. On one of your slides, which was the tumor incidence data from Brues, Lisco and Finkel, paper of 1949, you mentioned a variation of cumulative tumor incidence with the square of dose rate.

If I recall our calculations correctly, the linear relationship between the fractional rate of appearance of tumors, $(1/N_0)\,(dN/dt)$, and elapsed time, t, led to the following expression for the cumulative tumor incidence

$$\frac{N_0 - N}{N^0} = \frac{AR}{2}\,(t - t_0)^2$$

where N^0 is the initial number of animals, N is the number of animals which remain unaffected at time t, R is the dose rate, t_0 is the effective latent period, and A is a constant. Then when $t \gg t_0$, the cumulative tumor incidence would be proportional to $Rt^2/2$ or $(Rt)(t/2)$. In this case one has the opportunity to make an entirely different interpretation, which we used to call jokingly "Brues' law". This was that the total dose is (Rt) and the average time during which this insult has been in the tissue is $(t/2)$. Then the cumulative tumor incidence is proportional to the product of the dose and the elapsed time. This has led several of us to make calculations of radiation insult in terms of "rad days" rather than just rads.

Did I understand correctly that you obtained a mathematical analysis of these same data which gives a cumulative incidence proportional to R^2t^2, that is to the square of the total number of radioactive events per gram, Rt?

MOLE: In the original description by Brues a different latent period was put in for each different dose level in order to use your equation. I just took the same data and assumed there was no latent period but there was a generation time for the tumor, which in a sense is looking at the same thing backwards; and then, just plotting the data, they did fit R^2t^2.

EVANS: So you can have either result from the same data?

MOLE: Yes.

EVANS: Perhaps that is all that needs to be said.

MOLE: There is one comment that ought to be made on what Dr. Marinelli said because this illustrates the problems of human epidemiology, and that is that Court-Brown and Doll's work isn't an exact check on Stewart. Court-Brown and Doll went to the records in maternity hospitals where people were known to be pregnant and also were known to have been exposed to radiation. Thus, there is one group of people who are altogether omitted in Court-Brown and Doll's survey, and that is women who were not known to be pregnant but who received diagnostic radiation. This would be women early in pregnancy receiving such things as intravenous pyelography.

If it were true that the embryo at that stage of development is unusually sensitive, then Court-Brown and Doll have overlooked cases of leukemia induced by diagnostic radiation. However, I think the numbers are such that one need not worry about it.

The special feature of Stewart's kind of investigation is that it depends on memory. The memories of mothers who have lost children are different from the memories of mothers with living children; and there is no built-in control, and there can't be. So, I think one has got to look at this sort of investigation rather carefully each time.

FINKEL: I will never cease to be amazed at the uses to which our data are put. I am very pleased that Dr. Mole availed himself of those that fit his thesis, but I feel I must come to the defense of those he rejected because they did not fit. It is possible, you know, that the thesis is in error, or incomplete, and that the data are really quite all right.

The first experiment that Dr. Mole rejected measured the carcinogenicity of radium in mice. He claimed that the data were not comparable to the Sr^{90} experiment because an infection severely distorted the survival data. And he quoted an ANL report to prove the point. I seriously doubt that he read that report beyond the sentence that he quoted because in it I examined the problem of comparability of experiments done at different times with animals exposed to different levels of infectious disease. My conclusion was that the proportion of animals with bone tumors, even when the number is corrected to the animals alive at the end of some "latent period", can give a completely erroneous impression of the carcinogenic response. So I devised something different, and called it tumor probability.

Tumor probability is obtained at any given time by dividing the tumors still to appear in the population by the number of animals still alive. This procedure constantly corrects for extraneous deaths. As we applied it we discovered that the value was quite constant with increasing time after the first tumor-death occurred. So we were able to obtain an average value for purposes of dose-response evaluations and for comparing the carcinogenicity of different isotopes.

The ANL report appeared in 1952. Since then almost all of our osteosarcoma data have been given in terms of tumor probability, not tumor incidence, as Dr. Mole has implied. He thinks the data from our experiments done at different times are not comparable. Obviously I think they are, or I wouldn't have compared them on numerous occasions!

I am the first to admit that the radium experiment needs to be repeated. In fact, it is being repeated right now. But the reason for the repetition is not that the incidence of tumors was lower than it should have been because the animals died too soon. The reason is that the number of useful animals was drastically reduced by the infection. So the results are less dependable because of small numbers, not because of disease *per se*.

Actually, Dr. Mole even thinks data within the same experiment are not very good if they disagree with his theory. I am referring now to tumor incidence after a single injection and after fractional injections of Sr^{90}. Forty-five mice had an average of one tumor/mouse when 0·25 μc Sr^{90}/g mouse was given all at once. One hundred sixty-five mice had an average of 0·4 tumors/mouse when the same total amount of Sr^{90} was divided into 5 or 20 injections. He dismissed this experiment by saying that these results show little change in incidence associated with fractionation!

Another experiment that Dr. Mole rejected because it didn't fit his theory very well involved Sr^{89} given in a single injection. However, he implied that the data were not very reliable because the work was done so many years ago. On the other hand, the data from the experiment in which Sr^{89} was re-injected monthly did fit, and they were used in some detail to support the theory. The amusing thing is that these were two parts of the same experiment done at exactly the same time on completely comparable animals.

But we need not dwell on the various ways in which data can be misrepresented, misunderstood, or in other ways abused. In spite of differences we may have in the interpretation of some results, there is a lot of good sense in Dr. Mole's paper. I particularly like his points about the futility of searching for a threshold, about the misuse of the concept of non-specific life-shortening, and about the rarity of the neoplastic event.

MAYS: By choosing the specific time of 2100 days after injection and disregarding the 5-levels, Dr. Mole has (in his Table 3) suggested that in dogs injected with Ra^{226} or Pu^{239}, the cumulative bone tumor incidence is proportional to the square of the dose. It is extremely important to realize that other interpretations are possible when the complete data are used. For example, consider the following results previously presented in this book by Dr. T. F. Dougherty in his paper, "Incidence of bone cancer in internally irradiated dogs." The dogs are the same ones referred to by Dr. Mole.

At the injection levels in which osteosarcomas have thus far occurred, nearly all (70–100%) of the deaths were due to bone cancer *regardless of the total rad dose*.

Deaths in Ra^{226}(R) *and* Pu^{239}(P) *Beagles in Utah as of* 31 *March* 1961

Injection level	Deaths (osteosarcoma) / Deaths (total)	Mean days from injection to death from osteosarcoma	Mean rads to skeleton at death from osteosarcoma
R5	9/10 = 90%	1110	12,360
R4	11/12 = 92%	1590	5280
R3	8/9 = 89%	2140	2420
R2	0/1 – – – – –	– – – – – – – – –	– – – – – – – –
R1·7	0/2 – – – – –	– – – – – – – – –	– – – – – – – –
R1	0/1 – – – – –	– – – – – – – – –	– – – – – – – –
R0	0/2 – – – – –	– – – – – – – – –	– – – – – – – –
P5	7/9 = 78%	1480	6470
P4	12/12 = 100%	1320	1790
P3	12/12 = 100%	1650	720
P2	5/7 = 71%	2360	330
P1·7	0/1 – – – – –	– – – – – – – – –	– – – – – – – –
P1	0/1 – – – – –	– – – – – – – – –	– – – – – – – –
P0	0/1 – – – – –	– – – – – – – – –	– – – – – – – –

However, at the lower injection levels it generally took longer for bone cancer to appear. It is thus apparent that this biological response to irradiation depends not only on dose but also on time. Adequate theories of radiation carcinogenesis should consider both of these variables.

In the lowest injection levels most of the dogs are still alive. Will these also die of radiation effects? These delayed effects of radiation can only be observed if the animals do not die of other causes beforehand. This is why it is so important that studies of this kind be done with long-lived animals given the best of veterinary care.

MOLE: From the assumptions (1) that tumour incidence depends on the square of the number of radioactive events between the moment of injection of the radioactive material and the start of the tumour, and (2) that the development time, the interval between the start of the tumour and the moment when it is large enough to kill, is independent of dose, it would be predicted that, as injected dose was increased above the minimal amount required to produce a near 100 per cent incidence of tumours, (a) the time interval between injection and death would shorten and (b) the amount of wasted radiation (absorbed during the development time) would increase. Both predictions seem to agree qualitatively with Dr. Dougherty's table (see page 49).

Some of Dr. Finkel's comments also seem misconceived:

(1) Tumour probability, as she defines it, does *not* always and automatically correct for extraneous deaths during the course of an experiment as a simple

example can show. Suppose 100 mice are alive at time t and that during the next time interval 25 die of tumours and 50 die of extraneous causes. Suppose further that from then on all mice die of tumours. The tumour probability at t is 50 per cent. If there had been no extraneous deaths, tumour probability at t would have been 100 per cent.

(2) A reduction from 1 to 0·4 in numbers of tumours per mouse according to whether Sr^{90} was given in 1, 5, or 20 fractions is indeed a small change in incidence in the light of the hypothesis I have been discussing since it corresponds to a reduction of only about one third in the effectiveness of the Sr^{90} [0·4... $(2/3)^2$].

(3) If there was a small contamination of Sr^{89} with Sr^{90}, this would clearly matter far less when the body burden of Sr^{89} was maintained by monthly injections than when a single injection of Sr^{89} was given.

SOME PROPERTIES OF REPARABLE AND IRREPARABLE RADIATION INJURY*

H. A. BLAIR

Department of Radiation Biology, University of Rochester, School of Medicine and Dentistry, Rochester 20, New York

ANIMAL experimentation has made it clear that shortening of lifespan is a consequence of exposure to ionizing radiation. The dosage may be either single or protracted and the exposure may be terminated sufficiently long before death that such recovery as could occur would have ample time to do so. Consequently, it may be concluded that shortening of life is due to inability of the animal to recover completely from radiation injury.

On the other hand it is equally clear that recovery from radiation injury does take place to a considerable degree. This is evidenced by the fact that animals submitted to substantial exposures may appear to regain complete health. It is also evidenced by the fact that if the dosage is sufficiently protracted to permit concurrent recovery, animals will survive total doses several or many times larger than one which would be lethal if administered briefly. It is also evidenced by the demonstration that following a brief sublethal dose the magnitude of a second dose, necessary to produce lethality, increases as the interval between the two doses is increased. The general properties of recovery and irreparability have been reviewed by Sacher.[18]

Irreparable radiation injury has been likened to ageing because it leads to premature death and because of common pathological changes. For this reason, it is reasonable to quantitate irreparable injury in terms of shortening of lifespan, or, in terms of age-specific increases in mortality rate. It may also be quantitated in terms of increased incidence or advancement in time of various diseases, the neoplastic especially. However, because such measurements are possible only long after the original injury, earlier evidences of the precursors of such long-term effects have been sought in terms of early changes in susceptibility to additional exposure.

In order to discuss the results of various measurements it will be convenient to use an empirical description of the kinetics of radiation injury

* This paper is based on work performed under contract with the United States Atomic Energy Commission at the University of Rochester Atomic Energy Project, Rochester, New York.

233

previously employed.[1] While lacking in generality with respect to certain details, it appears to represent the essential features of the injury process. The assumptions are these:

(a) The total injury produced is proportional to the dose.
(b) Recovery occurs at a rate proportional to the magnitude of the injury in excess of a fraction which is irreparable and accumulates in proportion to the total dose.
(c) Irreparable and unrepaired injury add in all proportions and become lethal when their sum becomes equal to the injury resulting from the acute lethal dose at the time in question.

Representing reparable and irreparable injury by I_r and I_i, respectively,

$$\frac{dI_r}{dt} = (A-\alpha)\gamma - \beta I_r \tag{1}$$

$$\frac{dI_i}{dt} = \alpha\gamma \tag{2}$$

in which γ is radiation dose rate and A, α, and β are constants.

Following exposure for time, t, at constant rate, the injuries become

$$I_r = \frac{(A-\alpha)\gamma}{\beta}(1-e^{-\beta t}) \tag{3}$$

$$I_i = \alpha\gamma t \tag{4}$$

If the exposure is sufficiently brief that $e^{-\beta t}$ approximates $1-\beta t$,

$$I_r = (A-\alpha)\gamma t \tag{5}$$

and the total injury

$$I = I_r + I_i = A\gamma t \tag{6}$$

or I is measured by the total dose.

If the exposure is sufficiently long, repair and production of injury will become essentially equal, or $e^{-\beta t}$ becomes negligible and

$$I_r = \frac{(A-\alpha)\gamma}{\beta} \tag{7}$$

and the total injury I becomes

$$I = I_r + I_i = \frac{(A-\alpha)\gamma}{\beta} + \alpha\gamma t \tag{8}$$

Under these circumstances the total injury increases linearly with time of exposure as represented in Fig. 1. If exposure is stopped when the line reaches the just lethal level, as usually defined, the animal concerned will die within 30 days.

According to Equation 6, direct verification of this linear relation could be obtained in separate groups of animals by measuring the added brief dose necessary to produce lethality at various times after the beginning of exposure. As far as is known such verification is available only in data by Mole.[2]

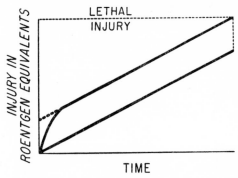

FIG. 1.

According to Equations 3 and 4, when added, the total injury resulting from continued constant exposure should curve upward, as represented by the upper curve, until the amount of reparable injury sustained each day is equalled by the amount which repairs each day. This equilibrium of reparable injury is represented by the intercept on the vertical axis. After equilibrium is reached the total injury increases linearly, according to Equation 8, parallel to the lower line which represents irreparable injury, only, according to Equation 4. If radiation is stopped, only that injury represented by the intercept will repair.

Mole's data are listed in Table 1 and are plotted in Fig. 2. Female CBA mice were irradiated daily, 5 days per week, at the dose rates 10, 25 and 50 r per day with X-rays of kvp about 250. The additional brief single dose necessary to produce LD_{50} was determined in groups of mice, under each regimen, at various times after beginning of exposure. The data points in the figure represent normal LD_{50}, 792 r, less the values of LD_{50} at these times. Consequently, they measure the injury accumulated from the continued exposure in roentgen-equivalents of brief dose.

It will be seen that the data, as expected from Equation 6, appear to yield a linear relation for each dosage schedule. For the most complete case, 50 r per day, it will be seen that the intercept is 180 r. This presumably is the equilibrium value, from Equation 7, of reparable injury $(A-\alpha)$ γ/β which will continue at this equilibrium value during exposure and will be repaired if the exposure is stopped short of lethality. The values on the line, less the intercept, presumably represent irreparable injury, as measured in roentgens. This increases at the rest of 13 r per day. The constant α is, therefore, 13/50. Consequently, about one-fourth of the injury is irreparable and would presumably persist if the exposure were stopped.

The intercept of the 25 r per day line is about 90 r, about one half of that for 50 r, as expected from Equation 5. However, the slope of this line is only 2·2 r per day corresponding to a value of, α, of about one-

TABLE 1

Mole's Data[2] on LD$_{50}$ for Brief Doses Following Daily Irradiation

Daily dose r	Total dose r	Time days	LD^{50} r	Residual dose r
50	250	5	541	251
	500	12	467	325
	750	19	373	419
	1000	26	239	553
	1698	49	0	792
25	250	12	671	121
	500	26	622	170
	1000	54	574	218
	1500	82	593	199
10	200	26	769	23
	500	68	762	30

Normal LD$_{50}$ is taken as 792 r, the average of 2 measuerd values 768 r and 815 r. Total dose is total exposure at 5 days per week. Time days is period of daily exposure including off days. LD$_{50}$ is brief lethal dose just following daily exposure. Residual dose is normal LD$_{50}$, 792 r less LD$_{50}$ just described.

tenth. The slope of the 10 r per day line is poorly determinable but, as drawn, it is considerably less than 1 r per day, so that α is less than one-tenth. These results indicate that the parameter, α, is not a constant for a particular radiation, as implied in the postulates above, but is dependent on dose rate and increases, within certain limits at least as dose rate increases.

Incidentally, in consideration of Equation 7, the intercept at 25 r per day should be somewhat greater than one half that at 50 r per day, owing to the change in α, providing the other factors of the equation remain constant.

In Fig. 2 is marked, also, the point at which radiation at 100 r per day produces LD_{50} in 30 days. Earlier points were not determined, but if a line is drawn back to an intercept twice that for the 50 r per day line, its slope is 24 r per day. This value of α, 24/100, is similar to 13/50 at 50 r per day. This result suggests that α is constant in the region between 50 and 100 r per day and possibly above some dose rate less than or equal to 50 r per day.

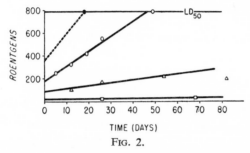

FIG. 2.

The curves from below upward represent, respectively, Mole's data from Table 1 on accumulation of injury, in roentgen equivalents, in mice exposed at 10 r, 25 r, 50 r and 100 r per day, 5 days per week. The data points are determined by subtracting LD_{50}, as measured at the times indicated, from the normal LD_{50}, 792 r. The intercepts on the vertical axis represent the equilibrium levels of reparable injury which would repair on cessation of exposure. The slopes of the lines represent the daily accumulations of irreparable injury which are less than 1 r per day, 2·2 r per day, 13 r per day and 24 r per day for exposures at 10 r, 25 r, 50 r and 100 r per day, respectively. The uppermost horizontal line is at 792 r, the normal LD_{50}.

It seems probable that the high rate of accumulation of irreparable injury shown by Mole's data with 250 kvp X-rays is not general for all energies of X or γ rays. For example, Spalding et al.[3] found the median lethal dose for mice in a continuous Co-60 γ ray field of 50 r per day to be about 5500 r in contrast to Mole's value 1700 r. Assuming similar recovery rates, α, for Mole's data, is at least 3 times as great.

A similar difference between moderate and high energy X-radiation is shown by Moos et al.[4] in the rat. Whereas LD_{50} for 400 KV and 22 MV X-rays was 600 r and 750 r, respectively, for brief doses, it was 2600 r and 4800 r for protracted exposure at 51 r per day, 5 days per week. Thus protraction of high energy wave radiation decreases its effectiveness relatively more than that of low energy radiation because, presumably, the high energy injury is more reparable.

That there are species differences also is shown by the data of Trum et al.[5] in swine who found the median lethal dose of continuous γ radiation at 50 r per day to be 8500 r. These data indicate a low rate of accumulation of irreparable injury. On the other hand Rust et al.[6] found burros to succumb to 1500 r of γ radiation at 50 r per day indicating a high degree of irreparability.

It will be realized that the considerations above are not exact because both rate of recovery and irreparability are concerned in resistance to continuous exposure. In particular, the burro may recover slowly. However, fast recovery could not account for the small values of α indicated by the other data.

The data in Fig. 2, by themselves, do not prove that the so-called irreparable component of the injury retains this property indefinitely. Conceivably this injury could be quasi-irreparable, either possessing a very slow rate of recovery or the property of recovery wholly or in part after exposure has stopped.

These possibilities could be investigated best by testing, from the cessation of sublethal exposure for a considerable time afterward, to determine how much of the accumulated injury repairs and how much remains.

Mole[2] has made some observations on these points although not beyond 18 days post exposure. These data are given in Table 2.

By ignoring irreparable injury and assuming recovery would go to completion, Mole purported to show that the rate of recovery became markedly slower as the total prior daily exposure increased. Actually if it is assumed from the intercepts in Fig. 2 that only 180 r is recoverable after exposure at 50 r per day and only 90 r is recoverable after 25 r per day, it becomes apparent from Table 5 that 26% or less of the reparable injury remains after 5 days. Consequently, the half-times for recovery are about 2·5 days.

According to Fig. 2 recovery should not proceed beyond 145 r in the 50 r per day case. Actually it goes to 97 r at 11 days. With 1000 r and 1500 r at 25 r per day it should not proceed beyond 128 r or 109 r, respectively, whereas it goes to 91 r and 105 r after 18 days. In view of the several factors involved these values are probably within the experimental error. Consequently, it may be concluded that Mole's data are consistent with normal rapid recovery of that portion of the injury measured by the intercept in Fig. 2.

Another index of recovery rate is provided by Fig. 2. Since 13 r accumulates per day at 50 r per day exposure, 50–13 or 37 r per day must recover. Because about 180 r on the average is reparable the average rate of recovery is 37/180 or about 20% per day. Similarly at 25 r per day about 23 r per day must recover from the average level of 90 r. Consequently, the recovery rate is about 25% per day. These recovery rates correspond, also, to half-times of recovery of 3 days or less.

TABLE 2

Mole's Data[2] on Recovery after Extended Daily Exposure

Daily dose r	Total dose r	Interval days	LD_{50} r	Residual dose r	Irreparable part r	Reparable part r
50	500	0	467	325	145	180
		5	600	192		47
		11	695	97		−48
25	500	0	622	170	80	90
		5	718	74		−6
25	1000	0	574	218	128	90
		5	656	136		8
		18	701	91		−37
25	1500	0	593	199	109	90
		5	660	132		23
		18	687	105		−4

Normal LD_{50} is taken as 792 r the average of 2 measured values, 768 r and 815 r. Total dose is accumulated exposure at 5 days per week. Interval days is time between end of daily exposure and determination of LD_{50}. Residual dose is normal LD_{50} less the value during recovery. The reparable part of residual dose is taken from the vertical intercept in Figure 2. The irreparable part is residual dose less the reparable part.

It will be realized that these estimates are somewhat inexact because they would be strictly valid only in ideal experiments in which the exposure was continuous over 7 days per week instead of intermittent over 5. Nevertheless, they preclude, on experimental grounds, any such slowness of recovery as postulated by Mole.[2] It is evident also that there is no indication that recovery rate is significantly dependent on rate of exposure, or, as hypothesized by Storer,[14] decreased on duration of exposure or number of exposures. If it were, the accumulations of injury in Figure 2 would not be linear but would curve upward increasingly with time.

There are no data, for the mouse, at present, systematically examining the post-exposure sensitivity, both during recovery and for a long time beyond it, to determine the constancy of the irreparable injury. In particular, this phase may be complicated by early over-recovery. Following a single initial exposure it has been shown by Cronkite et al.[7] and others that the mouse may exhibit what may be called "over-recovery", in that, following exposure, the initial period of hypersensitivity may be succeeded by a transient period of hyposensitivity, maximal at about 2 weeks. While this increased resistance is probably due to recruitment of various physiological resources rather than a peculiarity of the recovery process itself, it may be expected to mask, initially, irreparable injury or lead to an underestimation of its value. Consequently, it may be necessary, following single doses, at least, to allow several weeks to elapse before a direct determination of irreparable injury can be made.

Returning to the question, raised previously, as to whether the injury designated irreparable in Fig. 2 is really maintained indefinitely, it will be noted that animals irradiated continuously until just short of death will contain more recuperable injury (greater vertical intercept) and therefore less irreparable injury at high daily rate than at low. In consequence, animals allowed to recover from a nearly lethal dose delivered at high rate will survive longer than those which had been subjected similarly to a low dose rate. This effect was, in fact, commented upon by Mole (Fig.[16,2]) who found numerous deaths in the 9 month period following nearly lethal exposure at 25 r per day, a lesser number of deaths following similar exposure at 50 r per day and few deaths following exposure at 100 r or 200 r per day. Clearly these results are qualitatively, at least, in conformity with the designations of reparable and irreparable injury in Fig. 2 and with the view that irreparable injury is maintained and that it contributes to mortality.

The attempts to measure irreparable injury directly, in terms of decreased resistance to additional exposure, following an initial exposure, have given conflicting results. Two methods have been employed, the one using a single test dose and the other a succession of daily doses.

Krebs et al.,[8] using C_3H female mice and 250 kvp X-rays, measured LD_{50}, 4 to 20 weeks after exposure to 600, 900, 1200 and 1500 r, in 300 r increments, 3 weeks apart. The animals were 9 ± 1 weeks of age at the beginning of irradiation. The LD_{50} was reduced in each case by about 10% of the initial total dose. Consequently, these results may be interpreted as showing that, of the injury produced by the initial radiation dosage under these particular circumstances, 10% in roentgen equivalents is irreparable and additive to new acute injury.

On the other hand Alexander and Connell[9] using CBA male mice and 250 kvp X-rays found no change of LD_{50}, 3 weeks after 600 r, or 1100 r, given in increments of 300 r, 3 weeks apart (excepting a last dose of 200 r in the 1100 r case).

The only apparent differences between these experiments and those of Krebs et al.[8] are the sex and strain of the mice and that testing was done at 3 weeks instead of 4 to 20 weeks. The conditioning doses and dosages were very similar. It may be that "over-recovery" is masking irreparable injury at three weeks. However, superficially it can be concluded from these latter experiments that prior irradiation of the type given has no influence on LD_{50} after a 3-week interval, even though the conditioning doses were shown in separate experiments to produce median life shortening of about 26% and 43%, respectively, for the 600 r and 1100 r exposures. It may be significant, however, that Mole[2] found less than 50% recovery 18 days after 1000 or 1500 r at 25 r per day in female mice of the same strain. Consequently, his animals presumably would have shown a significant decrease in LD_{50} at 21 days when Alexander et al.[9] found none. This points to a sex difference or to some dependence on dose fractionation.

Hursh et al.[10] found that rats subjected to a single dose of 650 r and tested with single doses 60 days later, showed an LD_{50} of 548 r in contrast 703 r for controls. This result shows irreparable damage equivalent to nearly 25% of the initial dose.

That the same effect occurs in the dog was shown by Miller and Coulter.[11] They exposed a group of 20 dogs to 300 r of X-radiation at intervals of 1, 2 or 3 months. Since the LD_{50} was 450 r, under the conditions used, there was no lethality from the initial dose but the lethality was 15%, 50% and 70% after the second, third and fourth doses, respectively. These results are compatible with the assumption that injury equivalent to about 75 r remained after each 300 r dose.

Michaelson and Howland,[12] using Co-60 γ radiation, re-exposed, after 3 to 8 months, dogs which had survived doses of X-rays or Co-60 γ rays in the lethal range. The LD_{50} was found to be 265 r in comparison to 335 r for controls. That irreparable injury measurable by a single test dose is observable at one month and is maintained over at least many months appears to be well established in the dog.

The alternative method of testing for residual injury by prolonged exposure until death, first proposed by Sacher,[15] was employed by Spalding et al.[3]

RF female mice at 3 to 4 months of age were given the total initial doses of Co-60 γ rays listed in Table 3 in 5 semi-weekly, approximately equal, fractions. At 90 days post–exposure the animals were re-exposed until death to a continuous γ–ray field of intensity about 50 r per day.

Assuming that these data conform to a linear relation, similar to that in Fig. 1, it will be seen that the control group (lethal dose 5561 r) will accumulate injury according to the relation.

$$5561\,x + C = LD_{50} \qquad (9)$$

where C is the constant $(A-\alpha)\,\gamma/\beta$ of Equation 8 and x is the irreparable fraction of the protracted dose.

Similarly, if y is the irreparable fraction of the prior exposure, y times this exposure will be added to the intercept. In the case of 1200 r pre-exposure, for example,

$$3382\,x + 1200\,y + C = LD_{50} \qquad (10)$$

In consequence of Equations 9 and 10,

$$5561\,x = 3382\,x + 1200\,y \text{ or } y/x = 1\cdot83 \qquad (11)$$

and so on, for the other pre-doses. These relations yield the values of y/x in Table 3. The average is 1·83 and there is no discernible systematic trend with dose.

According to this result the residual injury per roentgen from the pre-exposure is 1·83 times that which accumulates from the continuous test exposure. These data permit the conclusion that with the particular dosages employed the irreparable injury is greater, from separated brief doses of γ radiation, than from continuous exposure. However, since α appears to be a function of dose rate, presumably, some dose rate might have been chosen, such that $y/x = 1$ since, in this case at least, there is no indication that α varied with the dose or dosage of the pre-exposure.

With pre-exposure to fission neutrons, of average energy 1·4 MeV, the ratio y/x is 8·6. This is compatible with a relative effectiveness of fast neutrons to γ radiation of 8·6/1·83, or 4·7, for production of irreparable injury by brief divided dosage, or, a relative effectiveness of 8·6, for divided brief doses of neutrons, in relation to continuous γ radiation.

These data conform, approximately, to the linear equations analogous to Equation 11.

$$D = 5561 - 1\!\cdot\!83\, d \text{ for } \gamma \text{ radiation} \tag{12}$$

and

$$D = 5799 - 8\!\cdot\!6\, d \text{ for neutron radiation} \tag{13}$$

in which D is the lethal dose in rads for continuous γ exposure and d is the dose in rads for pre-exposure.

Doull et al.[13] using CF mice of both sexes, gave pre-exposures of single doses of γ radiation ranging from 100 to 900 rep, followed first, by a recovery period of 4 weeks and then by brief daily doses of 50 rep, 5 days per week, of γ radiation until death. Co-60 was the source of radiation. LD_{50} for single doses was 900; consequently, there was some mortality from pre-exposure.

These authors plotted lethal dose for the protracted test exposure against pre-exposure obtaining an approximately linear relation in conformance with Equation 12. Its value was approximately

$$D = 4400 - 2\!\cdot\!6\, d \tag{14}$$

D and d being the test and pre-exposure doses, respectively, in rep.

It will be seen that irreparable injury from pre-exposure is 2.6 that of test exposure in contrast to $1\!\cdot\!83$ as in Equation 10 from the data of Spalding et al.[3] Presumably this difference may be related to the differences in experimental plan, the pre-exposures being single rather than multiple and the test exposures, being divided rather than continuous, as for the data of Equations 14 and 12, respectively.

It is noteworthy that, in each of these studies, the irreparable fraction of injury from the initial exposure is constant throughout the rather wide range of doses used, although in the one case the doses were single and in the other case divided into fractions of different sizes. In the latter case it is not clear why the irreparable fraction is independent of the size of the conditioning doses given twice weekly while it is dependent on size of the test doses given daily.

It should be noted also, that if, as postulated by Mole and Storer,[2,14] r, recovery rate were diminished as pre-exposure dose increased, Equations like 12 and 14 would not obtain.

It is a factor of considerable practical interest that a test exposure rate can be chosen that produces less irreparable injury per roentgen than that consequent to at least certain pre-exposure dosages. The use of such test

TABLE 3

Data of Spalding et al.[3] *Using Continuous Irradiation to Death as an Index of Previous Exposure*

Initial dose γ rad	Test dose γ rad	y/x	Initial dose neutron rad	Test dose γ rad	y/x
240	5043	2·16	92	4719	11·8
480	4825	1·54	182	4231	8·6
720	4109	2·02	271	4059	6·1
960	4029	1·60	355	3074	7·7
1200	3382	1·82	451	1752	9·0
0	5561		0	5799	

Initial dose is prior exposure accumulated in fractions. Test dose is continuous exposure at 50 rad per day required to produce lethality. y/x is ratio of irreparable fraction of injury from pre-exposure to that of test exposure.

rates has the effect of magnifying the results of preexposure which may be of special value when these are small, the effects from small single doses, for example.

There is so much evidence indicative of the existence of irreparable injury, measurable by diminution of resistance to subsequent exposure, that it appears reasonable to ascribe failure to observe it in mice, at times just following recovery, to the phenomenon of transient "over-recovery", occurring sometimes, if not always, in that species. A decision on this point depends on extending the observations on recovery for longer times to see if the irreparable component re-appears.

The properties of irreparable injury are clearly not such that they can be described for all dosages of a given radiation in a given species by a single constant of proportionality with dose as was hypothesized earlier.[1]

From the data reviewed and other considerations it appears tentatively that the constant, α, or the fraction of injury, α, which is irreparable, has the following properties.

(a) In protracted daily dosage of wave radiation it is a function of dose rate at least in certain ranges, but is constant with a particular dose rate through the whole period of its application.

(b) With substantial single doses, or, with widely separated fractionated doses over a considerable range of size of fraction, it is proportional to total dose over a wide range of doses.

There is an inconsistency apparent between conclusions (a) and (b), requiring investigation, in that fractionated doses, widely separated, act like single doses whereas fractionated doses given daily and continuous doses do not.

(c) With single doses close to or within the lethal range α appears to exceed 20%, a value probably considerably larger than with single doses well below lethality, but, probably no larger than values attained with high daily dose rates.

(d) In the dog, at least, α appears not to change significantly over a period of many months after exposure.

(e) It is indicated that the degree of irreparability may differ in different species and that it is less in a given species for high energy wave radiation than for low.

(f) The finding that α is a function of daily dose rate and, according to present indications, decreases in certain ranges as the dose rate decreases, leaves open the possibility that irreparability of injury from very low dose rates may be significantly less than predicted from studies using exposures in the range of 1 or more r per day.

(g) The dependence of irreparability on dosage is of so much importance both for theoretical reasons and for practical reasons, in relation to permissible exposure, that it should be widely investigated in a number of species.

(h) It seems likely that life-shortening and other late effects of radiation are consequent to and closely related to irreparable injury but quantitative relations have yet to be established.

(i) Although not considered here, except that from neutrons, there are reasons to believe that irreparable injury from particle radiation may be considerably greater than from wave radiation.[17] Therefore, conclusions regarding wave radiation may not apply to particles.

REFERENCES

1. H. A. BLAIR, *University of Rochester AEC Reports*, UR 206 and UR 207 (1952); *Proc. Int. Conf. Peaceful Uses of Atomic Energy* **11**, 118–120, United Nations, New York (1956).
2. R. H. MOLE, *Brit. J. Radiol.* **30**, 40–46 (1957).
3. J. F. SPALDING, V. G. STRANG and F. C. V. WORMAN, *Radiation Research* **13**, 415–23 (1960).
4. W. S. MOOS, J. B. FULLER, W. J. HENDERSON, F. DALLENBACH and R. A. HARVEY, *Radiation Research* **3**, 44–51 (1955).
5. BERNARD F. TRUM, JAMES N. SHIVELY, U. S. G. KUHN and WALTER T. CARLL, *Radiation Research* **11**, 326–342 (1959).
6. JOHN H. RUST, BERNARD F. TRUM, JOHN J. LANE, U. S. GRANT KUHN, JOHN R. PAYSINGER and THOMAS J. HALEY, *Radiation Research* **2**, 475–482 (1955).
7. E. P. CRONKITE, C. R. SIPE, D. E. ELGHOLTZ, W. H. CHAPMAN, and F. W. CHAMBERS, Jr., *Proc. Soc. Exptl. Biol. Med.* **73**, 184–186 (1950).

8. JOHN S. KREBS, RALPH W. BRAUER and HARVEY KALBACH, *Radiation Research* **10**, 80–88 (1959).
9. PETER ALEXANDER and DOROTHEA I. CONNEL, *Radiation Research* **12**, 38–48 (1960).
10. JOHN B. HURSH, FLORENCE VAN SLYKE and GEORGE CASARETT, University of Rochester AEC Report UR 318 (1954).
11. R. W. MILLER and MOLLY P. COULTER, University of Rochester AEC Report, UR 260 (1953).
12. SOL M. MICHAELSON and JOE W. HOWLAND, *Radiation Research* **9**, 153 (1958)
13. J. DOULL, V. PLZAK, M. ROOT and J. COWAN, *University of Chicago USAF Radiation Laboratory Quarterly Report* No. 37, AEC Report NP-9443, 69–84 (1960).
14. JOHN B. STORER, *Radiation Research* **10**, 180–196 (1959).
15. G. A. SACHER, Argonne National Laboratory Report ANL-4163, 83–85 (1948).
16. R. H. MOLE, *J. Nat. Canc. Inst.* **15**, 907–914 (1955).
17. J. N. STANNARD, H. A. BLAIR and R. C. BAXTER, University of Rochester AEC Report, UR 395 (1955).
18. G. A. SACHER, Chapt. 12 in *Radiation Biology and Medicine* (Atoms for Peace Series Geneva), ed. W. D. CLAUS, Addison-Wesley, Mass, 1958.

DISCUSSION

MOLE: I found what Dr. Blair said to be a fascinating experience. I have often manipulated other people's data.

FINKEL: I was so glad to see it happen!

MOLE: This is the first time I have been in on the receiving end, and it was indeed most interesting.

I think some of the data are sufficiently precise perhaps not to fit to the straight lines shown, but I would much rather ask a question about biological discontinuities.

If one takes animals that have been given an exposure to daily irradiation and then gives them a single large dose, they appear to die with severe bone marrow damage, in the same way as animals given a single large dose without any preconditioning exposure. Supposing you take animals that have been irradiated for the same length of time and don't give them any single dose (i.e. don't determine a LD_{-50}) but leave them alone. Then, if you choose the right duration of exposure, you can get 80 to 100 per cent of mouse leukemia. That would seem to me to mean 100 per cent's worth of irreparable damage in a biological sense. I don't see how you can get away from that; yet there is a very different degree of irreparable damage as measured by the single dose LD_{-50} kind of test. It seems to me that there are a number of biological discontinuities in response to radiation which interfere with trying to interpret things in a global kind of way.

I haven't got the slide with me, but if one gives daily radiation at 50 r a day for about eleven weeks all the mice die in a very short time. If one stops treatment after 10 weeks, some of them die just before you stop the exposure, some just afterwards, all with acute marrow damage. If you stop the radiation a week earlier, still a proportion will die of the same kind of illness, and then nothing whatever happens for some months, but after that time the survivors start dying of leukemia; so you get a time-mortality curve with a long horizontal plateau in the middle of it.

If, of course, you reduce the exposure a little further there are no acute deaths, you get nothing at all for six months but then leukemia develops at the same kind of rate. So, within 12 or 15 months all the animals are dead.

You get a number of similar curves after shorter and shorter exposures, and then all of a sudden when you reduce the duration a little further you get the mortality curve going right out to 30 months. You get some leukemia at 6–15 months, and then something else later on. So again you are getting a sudden stepwise change in response, looking at it in terms of biology looking at the animal. It is this kind of thing that worries me a bit. Perhaps I could show one slide.

This slide (*International J. Radiation Biology*) doesn't have any biology on it, only numbers. It is plotted in a slightly unusual way, so I had better explain it. The points refer to animals given certain limited periods of daily irradiation and then left alone to see when they would die. I plotted the duration of exposure against the mean survival time and deliberately put them in different units so as not to get confused. Clearly, if you expose animals for the duration of their life, their mean survival time will equal the duration of exposure, and that is the diagonal. You cannot get any results below and to the right because all the animals are dead. The point of the slide is to show that there is a sort of plateau with each of several different levels of weekly dose. If you expose these animals, shall we say, for 20 weeks or 30 weeks or 40 or 50 weeks, you do not get an appreciable increase in effect as

248   DISCUSSION

judged by mean survival time, and yet the total accumulated dose here is something like three times that. This is true of all of these data. It looked as if the last two-thirds of the dose didn't produce any measurable damage as just measured by mean survival time.

This is crazy in a sense if one thinks of radiation damage accumulating in an irreparable kind of way whether one thinks of it in terms of algebra or in terms of chromosome changes or what-have-you. On the other hand it is very easily explained in biological terms, because these different sets of animals with the same mean survival time die of the same kind of illness. I think you only want a certain amount of radiation to initiate a biological process; and then the biological process goes on at its own rate regardless of how you started it or whether you continue to ra-diate the animal. And as soon as you got in a certain minimal amount of radiation, the biological thing (here it is mouse leukemia) takes charge, and it is the mouse leukemia that determines the mean survival time. As soon as you get a real reduction in mouse leukemia then these survival times start getting longer and the time-mortality curves getting steeper.

BLAIR: I think Dr. Mole's data can be used to predict the effect he has just described. If animals are irradiated daily, at different dose rates, to points just short of death, all will accumulate the same total injury but those exposed at the higher dose rates will bear a greater proportion of reparable injury than those exposed at lower rates. In consequence those exposed at the higher rates will recover more and, within certain limits, will live to a greater age than those exposed at lower rates. These limits are imposed by the decline of LD_{-50} with age which becomes important when the dose rate is sufficiently low so that the time of exposure becomes long.

These factors, taken together, tend also to narrow the spread of times of death of animals exposed at moderate to high dose rates and, presumably, also, the times of onset of other manifestations arising from irreparable injury.

As specific examples one would expect animals exposed at 100 or more r per day until just short of death to live longer than those exposed at 50 r per day and possibly 25 r per day but not as long as those exposed at lower rates such as 10 r per day. The insight provided by Dr. Mole's data clarifies the apparent anomaly that the after effects of irradiation to levels just short of death may differ with different dosage schedules.

MOLE: The facts are that the 100 r animals did live longer than the 50 r, but the 50 r lived slightly shorter than the 25 r animals.

CHAIRMAN DOUGHERTY: It seems to me that Dr. Warren presented some data that bear on this question in an indirect way. For instance, he showed that if you induced a local amount of radiation which would be enormous, you could produce a type of tumor that you did not see spontaneously, and yet in terms of summation of irreparable events at much lower doses this animal might die of something quite different. So, it seems to me that one of the problems that is going to eventually be facing us is that we have to know more about mechanism—what the causes of death are at any one point—because some cells survive enormous doses delivered locally or absorbed locally—the cells that survive beautifully and could become tumorous because they can survive, whereas the other cells could not.

I wonder if this isn't one of the problems—that we have a gradation of cell survival with any given localized dose, and therefore a whole host of various physiological events can occur because of this.

B. VAUGHAN: If I understood Dr. Blair correctly, you would like to know why in some instances the continuous exposure gave a smaller irreparable injury than a divided dose type of exposure.

I think we have experiments in our laboratory which may shed some light on this. We are using rather high initial doses, 2/3 of an LD_{-50}, and then repeating on a divided dose basis and determining the LD_{-50}. For rats, mice and hamsters we have good statistical control now, such that we can draw the probity of mortality and detect a definite change in the probity slope as we decrease the interval for the divided dose. That is to say, if you repeat the dose at a 3-day interval rather than a 14-day interval or a 30-day interval, you markedly depress the probity slope.

It suggests to us that the differences in the so-called irreparable injury are influenced primarily by hangovers from the preceding dose for these relatively short periods. It is difficult to say whether this will raise or lower the LD_{-50}, since the LD_{-50} may be considerably down on slopes having a non-regular shape. Perhaps someone else here would care to comment on this.

I have the feeling about these data that perhaps on a continuous exposure basis, we have in a sense averaged out this kind of error. This may be a more realistic approach than the divided dose technique.

CHAIRMAN DOUGHERTY: I would like to close with one comment, and that is that every day you live is one of irreparable damage. This should influence our statistics.

RADIOLOGIC AGING, GENERALIZED AND LOCALIZED

(with special reference to internal irradiation)

G. W. Casarett

Department of Radiation Biology, University of Rochester School of Medicine and Dentistry, Rochester, New York

ALTHOUGH it is not yet possible to define and compare the essential processes of aging and of late radiation effects, their late manifestations can be compared.

The manifestations of aging in adult mammals comprise a progressive deterioration of tissues, with concomitant decline of functional reserves and adaptive powers, which leads eventually to disease and inevitably to death.

Aging is not uniform with increasing time, but varies in rate among individuals and among organs of an individual. The rate of aging, the development of disease, and the lifespan are the net results of many variable modifying, conditioning and correlating forces, both environmental and inherent, including genetic constitution. The integration of these forces determines the physical status of the aging individual.

There are four general types of data which are often used as criteria of alteration of aging process by irradiation. These are: data pertaining to mortality, pathology and disease incidence, subclinical histopathology, and physiology (including biochemistry). It is fruitful to examine these criteria critically in relation to one another, in a general manner.

An agent is ideally regarded as causing premature aging if it causes the force of age-dependent mortality to increase earlier in the treated than in the control population, brings forward in time the age of onset of diseases which affect the controls, without greatly altering the sequence or the incidence of diseases and causes of death, and if it causes characteristic morphologic and physiologic manifestations of the aging process to appear and develop at an earlier age.

* This paper is based on work performed under contract with the United States Atomic Energy Commission at the University of Rochester Atomic Energy Project, Rochester, New York.

If the agent produces aging changes prematurely, but from that point on the changes progress at the usual rate, the effect is simple, *precocious* aging. If the agent causes an increase in rate of the process, as judged by the manifestations, the effect is not simply precocious but one of *acceleration* of aging.

1. *Mortality Data*

With increasing age in the adult there is generally a progressive increase in the probability of disease and accident and in the probability of death.

Inherited body constitution establishes essentially the baseline in an individual with respect to the aging process and its rate and the maximal lifespan even under optimal conditions.

However, a comparison of mean or median longevities alone is meaningless in terms of the process or rate of aging, since many age-independent factors are capable of shortening or prolonging the median or mean lifespan of a population. Comparisons of the temporal distribution of deaths together with causes of death are more meaningful. Even in this case, however, the relative age-dependence of causes of death, and the existence of genetically transmitted susceptibility to any particular cause of death which is more or less independent of age, must be recognized.

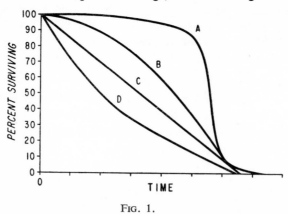

FIG. 1.

For a group of mammals maintained under excellent environmental conditions the shape of the arithmetic survival or mortality curve tends toward the rectangular (Fig. 1A), indicating a relatively low incidence of age-independent causes of death. At the other extreme, a group of mammals kept under poor environmental conditions and subject to a very high incidence of age-independent causes of death, with few living to senescence, exhibits an arithmetic survival curve which resembles a logarithmic decay curve (Fig. 1D). When multiple life-shortening factors independent of age modify an arithmetic rectangular survival curve they tend to reduce it in the direction of a straight line (Fig. 1B and C) or, if the effect is marked, toward the logarithmic decay curve.[1] Combinations of the damage of premature aging and increases or decreases of age-independent causes of death at various times can result in survival curves of many shapes, especially if some of the changes produced and their consequences have long latent periods while others are capable of rapid and substantial recovery. Furthermore, when an agent is capable of producing a prophylactic or therapeutic effect in relation to any serious age-independent or age-dependent disease in a population this could result in change of survival curves and even in life lengthening. On the other hand, an activating effect on preexisting chronic or latent infectious disease can alter survival curves in other ways. The most that can properly be said of a survival or mortality curve is that it is compatible or incompatible with a supposed process.[1]

It is well established experimentally in mammals that exposure of the whole body or parts of the body to ionizing radiation in substantial but sublethal doses can shorten lifespan. Numerous mathematical analyses and interpretations of such data have been performed in relation to the aging problem.[2-8] In the case of partial body exposure, the life-shortening effect is variable in degree, depending on the kind and amount of tissue irradiated as well as the dose.[3]

The mortality curves for populations of adult animals suffering life shortening after total body irradiation in a brief period of time, as in single exposures, are often similar in shape or slope to control curves but displaced to earlier time periods in a manner compatible with the concept of precocious aging. However, sometimes the curves are flattened and are compatible either with accelerated aging or increase in age-independent mortality.

After the brief total body irradiation, despite the waxing and waning at different times of morphologic and functional aberrations in different physiologic systems, there is observed generally, over a period of weeks or months, a gradual reduction of the sum of damage present, with disappearance of most of these aberrations. This improvement is also manifest by the return of the LD_{50} from a depressed level toward pre-exposure levels.[9] However, the observation of life-shortening, the reduced LD_{50} in comparison with nonirradiated animals of the same chronologic age, and the residual damage and delayed effects long after irradiation, all indicate that some of the injury or its consequent damage is irreparable.

Limited experimental observations indicate that irreparable injury is detectable after an interval of presumed maximal repair as a reduction in acute lethal dose, and that the LD_{50} dose for irradiation decrease with increasing age.[9] According to Blair's theory of radiologic life shortening[3] the injury of aging and the irreparable injury of radiation are additive in producing or contributing to acute radiation lethality, and the irreparable component of the injury is equivalent to premature aging in an actuarial sense, in that it ultimately deprives the animal of part of its expected lifespan.

Limited experience with measurement of irreparable injury by decrement in radiation LD_{50} dose at various times after brief, total body irradiation, in comparison with the LD_{50} of nonirradiated animals of the same age, suggests that the irreparable injury may remain more or less constant after irradiation until the point in time where age-dependent disease increases considerably in incidence prior to this occurrence in the non-irradiated population[9] (Fig. 2).

Populations of animals receiving protracted total body irradiation from external sources sometimes have shown increased slope of mortality curves and sometimes the curves have been similar in shape to those for controls, but simply advanced in time. The increased slope is compatible

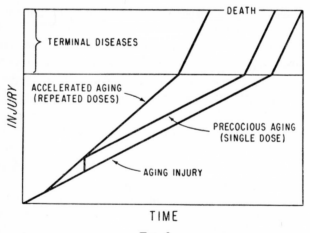

FIG. 2.

either with the concept of accelerated aging or with the concept of increased incidence of age-independent causes of death. The continuous or repeated accumulation of irreparable injury may reasonably be expected to increase the slope of a plot representing irreparable injury with passing time (Fig. 2), and the constant production and existence of unrepaired radiation injury of the reparable type, may act more or less as well as irreparable injury in contributing throughout the period of irradiation to increased susceptibility to age-independent as well as age-dependent causes of death. This would depend on the dose rate and the balance between injury and recovery rates. However, the simple temporal displacements of survival curves, without change in slope, are compatible with the concept of precocious, but not accelerated, aging. This has led some investigators[7] to the interpretation that at comparatively low daily dose rates, shortening of life is likely to be determined mainly by the irradiation during the early part of the lifespan.

It can be seen that mortality data alone are greatly limited as criteria of effect of total body irradiation on the aging process. They are even more limited for partial body irradiation. We must turn to the pathophysiologic data for aid in interpreting mortality data and for more refined criteria.

2. Pathology and Disease Incidence

A well-kept aging population of genetically heterogeneous animals tends to die as a result of a relatively wide variety of age-dependent causes of death. Many highly inbred or genetically more homogeneous aging populations of animals tend to show a lesser variety of causes of death and unusually high incidence of certain specific causes of death. In general, the age-dependent diseases or the so-called diseases of aging are essentially either degenerative or neoplastic in character, and it is well known that many of the neoplastic diseases develop in relation to previously developing degenerative tissue states either at the site of origin of the neoplasms or in some physiologically related tissue.

As in the case of aging manifestations, the propensity for development of diseases is not uniform with respect to individuals of a population or organs of an individual. Some diseases are progressively age-dependent. Other age-dependent diseases show considerable age-specific propensity, the incidence rising to a peak with advancing age and then declining after those individuals with a genetic tendency for the disease have died.

In order to establish a baseline for interpretation of the aging process by means of data on disease incidence or cause of death it is necessary to know the age-dependent diseases in a well-kept aging population, and to recognize the possibility that diseases or causes of death which are relatively age-independent, whether they be infectious diseases or degenerative or neoplastic diseases for which there is very strong genetic propensity, may be extraordinarily increased in incidence or advanced in time of onset by relatively little tissue injury, relatively independent of change in aging process. Such an effect may change markedly, in relative fashion, the age-specific incidence of age-dependent diseases expected in an undisturbed control population. Furthermore, for a better understanding of the disease picture in relation to the aging process, it is necessary to distinguish between temporal advancement of disease and true induction of disease.

If an agent results in the earlier appearance of a disease in a population, with increase in age-specific incidence at earlier ages and without a significant increase in absolute or life-time incidence, as compared with controls in a well-kept aging population, then the disease may be regarded as having been temporally advanced by the agent. When the agent results in a considerable increase in absolute incidence of diseases as compared with the incidence expected within the maximal life span of the species or strain, then the excess incidence of the diseases may be regarded as having been induced by the agent.

It is well known that the median or average lifespans of experimental animal populations often fall far short of their potential averages because infectious diseases kill or damage large numbers of individuals well before the senescent period of life. Some age-dependent diseases of long latency may rarely or never develop spontaneously within the observed lifespan in many individual experiments. Consequently it is possible in some instances that some of the diseases regarded as induced by the experimental treatment under these circumstances may have been instead diseases of relatively long latency with their time of onset greatly advanced temporally in individuals with some propensity for them.

The effect of total body irradiation on lifespan with respect to mechanisms involving alteration of the aging process is often judged according to ideal standards and assumptions which may not be true. Total body irradiation is often regarded as having shortened life solely through the causation of generalized precocious aging if it causes no induction of disease and if it causes a proportionately equal temporal advancement of all diseases common to the species or strain. In practice this ideal concept implies the assumptions that all of the diseases in question are age-dependent to the same degree, that the irradiation is always applied uniformly throughout tissues and that the irradiation, if it alters the degree or rate of aging at all, must alter the relative rates of aging process in various parts of the body to a degree proportionate to their relative rates of aging in nontreated animals. The truth of this latter assumption depends greatly on the fundamental nature of the aging process, which, of course, is not yet known.

In the case of total body irradiation experiments on rats and mice, some experiments, especially among those with single dose exposures shortening life with a simple temporal displacement of the survival curve, show approximately the same diseases in approximately the same incidence in irradiated and control groups,[2] i.e., a simple temporal advancement of disease. Other such experiments show about the same diseases, although not necessarily in the same incidence. Still other experiments show, in addition to advancement of certain diseases, a considerable induction of certain other diseases. This tends to occur more in inbred strains with a high genetic susceptibility to certain diseases, e.g. leukemia or ovarian tumor in certain inbred strains of mice.

The observed strain variation in life shortening in irradiated mice can be partially attributed to genetic differences in the sensitivity to the leukemogenic effects of irradiation.[10] When leukemia mortality is excluded, life shortening due to all other causes is found to vary comparatively little between strains.

In the case of total body irradiation of most hybrid or heterogeneous animal-populations advancement of disease is relatively of greater importance in life shortening than induction of disease, while in the case of highly localized irradiation, particularly with the use of the more intense or larger doses possible to administer without acute lethality, induction of disease at the site of irradiation or indirectly in a physiologically related site, is relatively of increased importance.

Intensive highly localized irradiation, as with internal radioisotopes which concentrate in certain tissues, enhances greatly the tendency to diseases related to the part irradiated, with relatively less enhancement of the tendency to disease development in unrelated parts of the body. Whether we regard these diseases as induced or advanced, the incidence depends greatly on the latent periods for the diseases in relation to the temporal proximity of development of other terminal diseases in other parts of the body to which the animals are susceptible. This, in turn, depends on the age of the animals at the time of irradiation.

In general, however, irradiation of experimental animals increases the incidence and/or the severity of clinically recognized diseases at given chronologic ages.[2,3,6,11–14] One could perhaps assume that total body irradiation induces each of the diseases of advanced age separately. However, it is more reasonable to regard such uniformity of response as a temporal advancement of the diseases and as evidence that total body irradiation causes a nonspecific diffuse, subclinical deterioration of the body tissues that advances the onset of many diseases to a roughly equal degree.[2] There are data which suggest that similar effects may occur in man.[15]

3. Subclinical Histopathology

Most of the so-called diseases of aging do not develop suddenly to clinical proportions to be recognized as pathologic entities, but are the eventual results of slow insidious subclinical deteriorations in tissues or organs.

Aging animal populations are seen by gross examination and by microscopic examination to deteriorate slowly but generally in progressive fashion before clinically or pathologically recognizable age-dependent diseases occur. These changes have been observed to occur prematurely following irradiation.[16,17]

A fundamental aging change in the adult animal may be defined as a change which occurs consistently and progressively with the passage of time in all temporally aging individuals of the population in the general phase of life in which the change may be expected, and which is generally qualitatively independent of variations in clinical history among individuals. Such a change may be detectable initially at different chronologic ages among individuals of the same chronologic age or may vary quantitatively with disease history or variations in genetic constitution or environment.

The fundamental histopathologic changes of aging seem to be in general degenerative and atrophic changes, the end result of which may be described generally as fibroatrophy. This fibroatrophy involves decrease in number of parenchymal cells associated with increase in density and amount of connective tissue, constituting an increase in the histohematic barrier (connective tissue barrier between blood and parenchymal cells), and decrease in fine vasculature in a process of arteriolocapillary fibrosis.

The hypertrophic cellular changes and hyperplastic or metaplastic tissue changes seen with increasing age are generally not among the fundamental aging manifestations and most of them do not occur in all senescent individuals. These changes seem to be either normal physiologic compensatory responses of less affected cells to degenerative changes in related cells or tissues or, like many degenerative changes observed, are secondary to specific disease processes.

It is not clear at the histopathologic level which of the three components of the tissue fibroatrophy of "normal aging", i.e., the changes of parenchymal cells, of connective tissue, and of fine vasculature, are primary and secondary with respect to one another; or what are the relative contributions of one component to another, since they have mutual or reciprocal influences; or to what extent these relationships or contributions differ among tissues of different kinds.

Aging and death of fixed postmitotic parenchymal cells, or such a degree of destruction and loss of self-reproducing parenchymal cells that regeneration is markedly delayed, may be followed by a process of replacement fibrosis and reduction in fine vasculature secondary to reduced parenchymal cellularity. Also, nonspecific damage of the endothelium of fine vasculature may result in interruption or impedence of circulation, increase in interstitial colloid and in fibrillar density of connective tissue, increase in histohematic barrier, consequent loss of parenchymal cells through hypoxia and reduced nutrition, replacement fibrosis, and reduction in fine vasculature. The success of regeneration of parenchymal cells depends greatly on the adequacy of the microcirculation and on the permeability of the histohematic barrier.

None of these histopathologic components of the tissue fibroatrophy of aging are due necessarily to inherent changes in the tissue components involved. Even the increasing fibrillar density of interstitial connective tissue may be caused by forces originating elsewhere in the body. All of these changes are nonspecific changes which may be brought about by a variety of agents or factors, including adrenal corticoids and perhaps any agent eliciting a response of the adrenal cortex, as in stress phenomena. The nonspecificity of basic histopathologic aging changes is compatible with the concept proposed by Jones[18] that aging is a result of the accumulation of nonspecific injuries.

Sublethal, life-shortening total body irradiation and localized irradiation, by means of external or internal sources of radiation, produce permanent changes in the tissues of experimental mammals which, according to the histopathologic criteria discussed, seem to me to be essentially identical with the histopathologic manifestations of premature aging.[11,12,19-21]

This radiation fibroatrophy comprises increase in amount and density of connective tissue, and increase in amount of interstitial mesenchymal elements, constituting an increase in histohematic barrier, reduction of fine vasculature in a process of arteriolocapillary fibrosis, and reduction in number of parenchymal cells (Fig. 3).

Following brief total body irradiation, or during the course of protracted daily total body irradiation, at dosage levels causing temporal advancement of age-dependent diseases and lifespan shortening, the nonspecific damage of endothelium of fine vasculature, by direct or indirect mechanisms, seems to be the change of greatest importance, among

the early radiation changes, in the eventual development of the tissue
fibroatrophy of "radiologic aging". Although some of the damage of the
fine vasculature may be due to relatively direct effects of the radiation
on endothelial cells, some of it is probably indirect. Much of the indirect
damage on fine vasculature in some tissues seems to be due to the initial

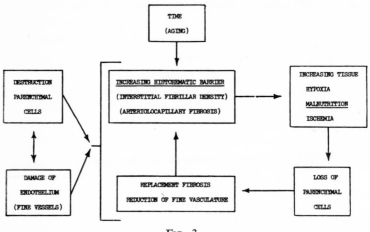

FIG. 3.

destructive effect on parenchymal cells, which varies according to their
nature and radiosensitivity from one tissue to another. Secondary to
damage of capillary and arteriolar endothelium, there is some degree of
pericapillary edema and increase in amount of interstitial colloid, followed
soon by an increase in fibrillar density of the interstitial connective tissue.
There also develops some increase in subendothelial connective tissue
in arterioles. These changes in connective tissue constitute an increase
in the histohematic barrier and a temporal advance in the development
of arteriolocapillary fibrosis, which are progressive processes in "normal"
aging. This manifestation increases progressively with passing time in
the irradiated tissue as it does in nonirradiated tissues, but remains temporally advanced in degree in the former as compared with the latter.
As these changes gradually reduce the capacity of the vasculoconnective
tissues to support the full complement of parenchymal cells, owing to
the development of relative hypoxia and malnutrition, the parenchymal
cells gradually become decreased in number either as a result of precocious aging and death in the case of nonrenewable cells or as a result
of decrease in cell reproduction in the case of renewable cells. This loss
of parenchymal cells occurs earlier in the irradiated tissues than in the
nonirradiated tissues, according to the earlier changes in histohematic

barrier and vasculature. With the gradual decrease in number of parenchymal cells there occurs a "replacement fibrosis" with further increase in interstitial mesenchymal elements and histohematic barrier, and further reduction of fine vasculature secondary to the loss of parenchyma.

The influence of the early parenchymal response to irradiation on the early changes in vasculoconnective tissue and on the late effects or aging manifestations is best described for different types of tissue in terms of the nature and relative radiosensitivity of the parenchymal cells they contain. *Vegetative intermitotic parenchymal cells*, which divide regularly but differentiate little or not at all, e.g. basal cells of epidermis, are generally highly sensitive to destructive action of radiation. *Differentiating intermitotic cells*, which divide regularly and differentiate to some extent between divisions, e.g., myelocytes, are somewhat less sensitive but still relatively sensitive cells in general. Certain mesenchymal elements, including endothelial cells of fine vasculature, are intermediate in sensitivity between these highly sensitive cells and the relatively resistant *reverting postmitotic parenchymal cells* and the extremely resistant *fixed postmitotic parenchymal cells*. The *reverting postmitotic parenchymal cells* are highly differentiated cells which do not divide regularly but are capable of dividing upon appropriate stimulus, e.g., the hepatic cell when a partial hepatectomy is performed. The *fixed postmitotic parenchymal cells* are highly differentiated cells which have lost completely their ability to divide under any circumstances, e.g., the neuron. Some of these, like the neurons, are long-lived, age and die without replacement; others, like polymorphonuclear leukocytes, are relatively shortlived, age and die, but are replaced by the activity of vegetative and differentiating intermitotic precursor cells.

In tissues containing the radiation sensitive vegetative and differentiating intermitotic parenchymal cells, such as epidermis, gastrointestinal mucosae, and hematopoietic tissues, the radiation destruction of these cells depends relatively little on the early radiation damage of vasculoconnective tissue, but the degree of damage of fine vasculature, pericapillary edema, and the change in connective tissue seems to be generally greater in such tissues than in tissues with radiation resistant parenchymal cells. Following doses such as those received total body in the sublethal range, the radiation sensitive parenchyma is regenerated to normal or subnormal levels of cellularity while vasculoconnective tissue changes are "fixed" irreversibly and are progressing with passing time at an advanced level as compared with nonirradiated tissue. Eventually there is a second phase of gradual loss of parenchymal cells secondary to these progressive changes in supporting tissues and premature as compared with nonirradiated tissues.

The intermediate period of maintained parenchymal cellularity between the period of regeneration and the beginning of the period of the age involution is shorter the larger the dose, owing to the fact that the vasculoconnective tissue changes are greater the larger or more intense the dose. This intermediate period corresponds with the period of low mortality rate between the period of acute or subacute mortality and the late period of age-dependent mortality.

With the larger doses possible to administer to such tissues under conditions of localized irradiation, there is greater damage of vasculoconnective tissue, greater destruction of parenchyma, directly and sometimes also secondary to marked vascular damage, reduced and delayed regenerative activity of remaining parenchymal cells, due to damage of fine vasculature and connective tissue, and a shorter intermediate period between the regenerative phase and the later involutional phase. In fact, with sufficiently high dose, there is no intermediate period due to failure of regeneration and the development of early fibroatrophy of the tissue.

In the case of tissues containing the radiation resistant reverting postmitotic parenchymal cells, such as liver and kidney and many other epithelial glands, and tissues containing the irreplaceable radiation resistant fixed postmitotic parenchymal cells, such as muscle and brain and spinal cord, early radiation destruction of considerable numbers of parenchymal cells in direct or indirect fashion requires large doses. Consequently, early destruction of these parenchymal cells is not seen with total body irradiation in the sublethal dose range but only with more intensive localized or generalized irradiation. However, with sublethal irradiation of the whole body the vasculoconnective tissue changes may be advanced temporally, and the parenchyma, although not appreciably damaged histopathologically in earlier phases, may show precocious loss of parenchyma in the phase of age-involution secondary to these changes. With increasing doses in localized exposures the temporal advancement of these processes is progressively greater.

Localized "radiologic aging" changes have been produced in many of the organs of the body by external sources of radiation,[3] in radiotherapy patients and experimental animals, and by internally deposited radioactive isotopes.[11,12] The tissue changes involved in the development of radiation-induced or advanced nephrosclerosis caused by localized or generalized irradiation from external sources[3,6] or by internal administration of polonium^{210}[11,12] are histopathologically of the aging type, since the fundamental histopathologic process in aging of the kidney is essentially a nephrosclerotic process.

Internal radioactive substances distributed more or less diffusely throughout the body, such as P^{32}, tend to mimic the picture produced by total body irradiation from external sources.

Intermediate types of exposure from internal emitters which, although diffusely deposited throughout the body, concentrate differentially among the soft and hard tissues, may result in different degrees of premature aging change in different parts of the body. For example, polonium^{210} is widely distributed in the body, but tends to concentrate highly in spleen and kidney and certain other organs. Consequently, although the fibroatrophy may be a widespread effect, it tends to be more advanced generally in organs of highest polonium concentration or exposure, and the causes of death related to nephrosclerosis, hypertension and renal failure are high in incidence.[11]

4. *Physiologic Changes*

Associated with the gradual development of the degenerative aging changes generally described as fibroatrophy or involutional changes is a gradual decline in functional abilities, or more exactly a decline in reserve functional capacities in related tissues and organs. This gradual decrease of reserve capacity is detectable provided suitable sensitive tests of the functions are used and provided the functions are stressed. If not stressed but tested under basal conditions, the functional decline may not become apparent until all or nearly all reserve capacity has been lost, when the decline becomes manifest as symptoms. As the functional reserve of tissue is decreased gradually to a point where ordinary stresses tax function, or function is deficient even under basal conditions, the tendency to disease from internal conditions and the susceptibility to diseases from environmental factors are gradually increased, as is the probability of death.

A decrease in functional reserve of one vital part by precocious localized aging far in advance of other vital parts tends to increase relatively the probability of disease in the affected part or dependent parts with respect to the natural probability of other common diseases of the species.

Once the degenerative changes and decreasing functional reserve capacities of aging have reached the point at which serious diseases begin to develop, especially the various chronic progressive disorders of later life, the correlated effects of aging and disease on physiologic processes tend to contribute to the pathogenesis of related disorders, perpetuate themselves by circular reactions, exacerbate other preexisting difficulties, and cause further changes characteristic of aging, further decreasing functional reserves. The pathogenesis of nephrosclerosis and the renal-hypertensive syndrome with consequent generalized arteriosclerosis following irradiation is a good example.[11]

Unfortunately there has been relatively little study of long-term effects of irradiation on body functions, especially functional reserve capacities, with respect to aging manifestations. However, some of the functional studies which have been done suggest that functions which decline with age tend to decline prematurely as a result of life-shortening irradiation in accordance with the deterioration of tissue as observed histopathologically.

There is a paucity of biochemical information on effects of irradiation directly related to manifestations of aging or the aging process. However, some pertinent data have been obtained which indicate premature aging manifestations following irradiation. One of the most notable examples is the work of Sobel[22] showing premature decrease of hexosamine-collagen ratio following irradiation of skin, indicating a relative decrease of ground substance and a relative increase in collagen. Whether this change is primary or secondary to histopathologic effects of irradiation in vasculature or parenchyma, or represents only the increase in collagenous tissue in replacement fibrosis, is not yet clear.

CONCLUSION

The foregoing general considerations of actuarial, pathologic, histopathologic, and physiologic changes following irradiation, in comparison with the manifestations of "normal" aging, indicate a strong resemblance between the late effects of life-shortening total body irradiation and the manifestations of premature aging, especially with respect to the histopathologic manifestations preceding disease. The histopathologic changes preceding disease development at the site of localized irradiation from external sources or from internal radioisotopic sources also bear a strong resemblance to the histopathologic manifestations of aging and therefore suggest the concept of premature localized aging resulting from localized irradiation. Although the processes and manifestations of "normal" aging and "radiologic aging" at the histopathologic level are similar, their nonspecificity makes it impossible to predict whether or not the more fundamental underlying processes, whatever they may be, will be similar or quite different.

REFERENCES

1. A. COMFORT, Natural aging and the effects of radiation, *Rad. Res. Suppl.* **1**, 2 16–234 (1959).
2. H. A. BLAIR, Data pertaining to shortening of lifespan by ionizing radiation, USAEC Document UR-442 (1956).

3. Report of the Subcommittee on Long-Term Effects of Ionizing Radiations from External Sources, Committee on Pathologic Effects of Atomic Radiation, NAS-NRC Publication 849, Washington, D.C. (1961).

4. A. M. BRUES and G. A. SACHER, Analysis of mammalian radiation injury and lethality, in *Symposium on Radiobiology*, ed. J.J. NICKSON, Wiley, N.Y. 441–465 (1952).

5. R. H. MOLE, Shortening of life by chronic irradiation: the experimental facts, *Nature* **180**, 456–460 (1957).

6. J. FURTH, A. C. UPTON and A. W. KIMBALL, Late pathologic effects of atomic detonation and their pathogenesis, *Rad. Res. Suppl.* **1**, 243–264 (1959).

7. G. J. NEARY, R. J. MUNSON and R. H. MOLE, *Chronic Radiation Hazards*, Pergamon Press, London (1957).

8. G. A. SACHER, A comparative analysis of radiation lethality in mammals exposed at constant average intensity for the duration of life, *J. Natl. Cancer Inst.* **15**, 1125–1144 (1955).

9. J. B. HURSH, G. W. CASARETT, A. L. CARSTEN, T. R. NOONAN, S. M. MICHAELSON, J. W. HOWLAND and H. A. BLAIR, Observations on recovery and irreversible radiation injury in mammals, *2nd UNIC on Peaceful Uses of Atomic Energy*, Vol. 22, 178–183 (1958).

10. D. GRAHN, The genetic factor in acute and chronic radiation toxicity. *2nd UNIC on Peaceful Uses of Atomic Energy*, Vol. 22, 394–399 (1958).

11. G. W. CASARETT, Histopathology of alpha radiation from internally administered polonium. USAEC Document UR-201 (1952).

12. G. W. CASARETT, Acceleration of aging by ionizing radiation. *J. Gerontology* **11**, 436 (1956).

13. A. C. UPTON, Ionizing radiation and the aging process. A review. *J. Gerontology* **12**, 306–313 (1957).

14. P. ALEXANDER, Accelerated aging—a long term effect of exposure to ionizing radiations. *Gerontologia* **1**, 174–193 (1957).

15. SHIELDS WARREN, Longevity and causes of death from irradiation in physicians. *J.A.M.A.* **162**, 464–467 (1956).

16. S. RUSS and G. M. SCOTT, Biological effects of gamma irradiation. *Brit. J. Radiol.* **12**, 440–441 (1939).

17. P. S. HENSHAW, Experimental roentgen injury. IV. Effects of repeated small doses of x-rays on blood picture, tissue morphology, and life span in mice. *J. Natl. Cancer Inst.* **4**: 513–522 (1944).

18. H. B. JONES, A special consideration of the aging process, disease and life expectancy, in *Advances in Biol. and Med. Physics*, Academic Press, N.Y. **4**, 281–337 (1956).

19. G. W. CASARETT, Acceleration of aging by ionizing radiation. USAEC Document UR-492 (1957).

20. G. W. CASARETT, Acceleration of aging by ionizing radiations, in *The Biology of Aging*, ed. B. STREHLER, A.I.B.S., Washington, D.C. 147–152 (1960).

21. G. W. CASARETT, Interactions between cells and tissues following radiation, in *Radiobiology At The Intra-Cellular Level*, ed. T. G. HENNESSY *et al.*, Pergamon Press, London, 115–135 (1959). Also USAEC Document UR-521 (1958).

22. H. SOBEL, Studies on the measurement of aging, in *The Biology of Aging*, ed. B. STREHLER, A.I.B.S., Washington, D.C. 274–278 (1960).

DISCUSSION

BLAIR: I shall not attempt to discuss the papers just presented in detail but I should like to comment briefly on the necessity for correlations and generalizations in radiation biology, such as those discussed in their various ways by Doctors Jones, Mole and Casarett, because of our ultimate concern in the problems of relative toxicities.

I think it is true, that, except for acute lethality, we do not have acceptable criteria for quantitative expression of the relative toxicities of pairs of radioactive substances such as radium and strontium. On the other hand it seems clear that the relative toxicity of one dose of radium to another may be quantitated because both doses presumably enter the same sites and produce the same effects in different degrees.

If tumors, for example, were the only toxic effect of radioactive materials it would be practical and understandable to express relative toxicity in terms of tumor incidence, even if the tumors, or the mechanisms of their origin, were different. However, it is clear that tumors, on the whole, are rather improbable events occurring in an established pathological setting and their incidence is not known to be simply related to the degree of injury from which they arise.

Therefore, when two substances are distributed differently and have potentialities for injuring in different ways, it is not at all clear whether extrapolations from such data as tumor incidence can be used to predict accurately the effects of lesser doses in the ranges of importance in human exposure.

For reasons such as these it would be desirable to be able to express a relationship between injury and dose for all significant doses of each toxic material, this injury being measured in terms of its effect on vitality of the organism. On the basis of such relationships for two toxic materials their relative toxicities for a given dose, or, their relative doses for a given toxicity, could be expressed quantitatively.

Unfortunately, measures of vitality are difficult to acquire. Shortening of lifespan is perhaps one of the more acceptable, but, even in the shortlived species of mammals, its determination is difficult and is uncertain at lower dose levels. However, the tendency of lifespan shortening to be linear with dose permits some confidence in extrapolations.

Whether or not this problem of equating the overall effects of different injuries can ever be resolved acceptably it seems likely that the efforts of analysis and generalization involved in attempting its solution cannot fail to be profitable in increasing understanding of the impact of various degrees of organ pathology on the vitality of the whole organism.

MOLE: Even though this is just about the end of a most interesting and, if I may say so, entertaining symposium, I feel I must not abdicate altogether my critical responsibilities. I feel perhaps the one man out of step when it comes to talking about radiation and aging.

I am quite certain I didn't entirely understand what Dr. Hardin Jones was talking about: I am sure that is a defect in me. Suppose we take the over-all age specific in the human race against time or age (and they are not necessarily the same thing), we have to accept that the straight line is really the sum of a very large number of different causes of death.

I might put it this way: In my country there is a measurable mortality for 13-year-old children, especially boys, from riding bicycles on the road. Does the idea that radiation accelerates aging mean that instead of dying at 13 these children are going to die at 12, and also that people who have cancer of the pancreas are going to die a little earlier, and that the toddler infant who kills himself by eating his mother's iron sulfate tablets or aspirin tablets is going to die a little earlier, and that his grandfather's coronary thrombosis is going to come on just that little bit earlier, and that all these things as well as all other causes of death are going to move together in such a way that global line just shifts a certain amount? I find the suggestion frankly incredible.

On the other hand if the idea is put in another form, that a certain number of particular causes of death are going to be shifted in time so that the global line appears to shift as a whole, then I think one is getting away from the idea of a nonspecific effect on aging.

This is my difficulty about this general sort of idea, and I feel that the human evidence, as far as it goes, suggests that it is specific causes of death that are really important and not nonspecific ones. British radiologists showed no shortening of life compared with other medical men, or with other people within the same kind of income bracket.

I am quite certain also that, if one wants to talk about aging, one ought to get away from numbers and time and start looking in the way that Dr. Casarett does. But at the same time I am not sure that there is anything we might call aging.

I would like to illustrate that by talking about intelligence. I am sure each of us thinks we are (shall we say) above the 50 per cent bracket in intelligence, although we might not think that to be true of each of our neighbors: Twenty or thirty years ago, when people tried to measure intelligence, they thought there was something that could be measured, and that tests could be devised from which you could extract a number that would tell you how much intelligence you had. But after a while it became clear that each test of intelligence measured a particular kind of skill and, however many tests you did, you ended up with one fewer equations than you had unknowns to solve for. So, you never could discover any measure of intelligence. We can still talk about it, though, and it makes horse sense in common, ordinary language.

I feel this is also true probably of aging—that we can test all kinds of individual functions, look at changes in structures, but we will always have one more unknown than we have got equations to solve. And so, although I think aging is a perfectly sensible thing to talk about in common, ordinary language, I am not at all sure it makes any sense to try and investigate it as a thing in itself. That is just a point of view.

Before sitting down, I do think I ought to say what beautiful pictures of the eyes Dr. Taylor and his colleagues have made. I feel these changes in the eyes are an index perhaps that we have got to think fairly hard about unexpected forms of radiation damage. We commonly think of the alkaline earth isotopes as going where calcium goes; but there is certainly an undue concentration of them in the tapetum lucidum of the eye out of proportion to the amount of calcium you expect to find there, and this is presumably related to the highly specific biochemical properties of that part of the eye.

All I know about tapetum lucidum is what Mrs. Antoinette Pirie has told me (*Endeavor* **17**, 181, 1958). She has shown that in one species of mammal the reflecting layer is made of pure crystalline vitamin B. In carnivores such as the dog and for some 10 per cent of the tapetum lucidum by dry weight is zinc, and in fact the reflecting layer is crystals of zinc cysteine.

I would suspect that all kinds of specialized organs, like the parathyroid, for example, might have highly specific chemical properties which would lead to unexpected concentrations of elements whose metabolic properties are still somewhat obscure.

So, I am looking forward with great interest to learning some more in time about what these particular nuclides that are being studied in Salt Lake City do in the eyes of dogs.

JONES: May I have a slight rebuttal?

CHAIRMAN CHRISTENSEN: By all means.

JONES: In reply to Dr. Mole, I want to make it quite clear that I do believe great radiation probably generates very specific effects. I don't think in the long run it is going to run down the course of natural aging all the way along. The remarkable thing is that there is so much similarity, and the other remarkable thing is that there is so much contrast. I never want my interpretations to mean that I have a blanket endorsement of radiation effect paralleling aging.

I also think that almost everything will sometime be found in terms of a given cause and effect relationship. However, as we investigated cause and effect relationships we found they are terribly complex, and there are secondorder interactions between almost any partial cause and causative system in other directions.

So, even in the case of the boy on the bicycle, if he had been irradiated rather severely I think he would probably be more accident prone than the non-accident prone, whereas I prefer to believe with you that for small effects you wouldn't see any differences on bicycles, whereas in Tennessee you would see differences in cancer development.

On British radiologists and American radiologists, two extensive studies have been done comparing the specific mortality ratio for radiologists compared to other physicians. In this there is one fallacy and that is that radiologists in practice have on the average not been in practice very long, and what one is really comparing is physicians to radiologists, whereas the difference in radiation exposure is considerably less than 50 r of whole body equivalent.

MOLE: That is not true of the British people.

JONES: I know it is true of the American radiologists, because I have all the information on the date of registration of radiologists and how the radiologists' basic population has grown in time. Almost all the radiologists have been registered radiologists only a very short period of time here in the United States. I presume that the same might be true in England, and this is why I think the American radiologists do not show this effect.

However, for American radiologists you calculate age with compared death rates, and if you compare it by death rates you find radiologists over 55 are considerably different from physicians at large. It will take a long time to clear up these differences.

THE RESPONSE OF THE BLOOD-FORMING TISSUES OF THE RAT TO CONTINUOUS IRRADIATION AT VARIOUS DOSE RATES

L. F. LAMERTON

Physics Department, Institute of Cancer Research, Royal Cancer Hospital Fulham Rd., London, S.W. 3. England

INTRODUCTION

IN INTERPRETING the response of the blood and of the blood-forming tissues to internally deposited radioactive isotopes one has to consider the effects both of protraction of radiation exposure and of non-uniformity of radiation dose. There are many gaps in our knowledge with regard to both of these factors. This paper will be concerned principally with the effects of protraction, and although the experiments have been done with an external source of radiation they have a considerable relevance to the problems of internal radiation.

Any attempt to forecast the response of a given tissue to protracted radiation exposure is difficult because one is concerned with the problem of simultaneous damage and repair and so little is known quantitatively about the repair capacities of the various tissues of the body. It is not surprising that a considerable difference in the capacity of the different renewal tissues of the body to withstand continuous irradiation has been reported by various workers.[1]

Our own work on this subject has been done using rats continuously irradiated by an external gamma source. The design of the unit has already been described.[2] It consists essentially of a source of about 6c of Cs^{137}, around which the rats are arranged in aluminium cages. By alteration of distance and filters a selection of dose rates from 415 rad/day down to 4 rad/day can be obtained. A second Cs^{137} unit is now also in use, in which a group of up to 65 rats can all be exposed to a dose rate of about 50 rad/day. The animals are exposed continuously day and night except for a period of about one half-hour during the day taken up by cleaning, feeding, etc.

MODE OF DEATH UNDER CONTINUOUS IRRADIATION AND RESPONSE OF SMALL INTESTINE

Even at the highest dose-rate we have used (415 rad/day) the rats do not die as a result of intestinal damage, but from failure of the blood-

269

270 L. F. LAMERTON

forming system. A series of investigations carried out[2,3] has, in fact, indicated that the epithelium of the small intestine is remarkably resistant to continuous irradiation and can maintain function under a much higher dose-rate than the blood-forming tissue. Within the first two days of irradiation at 415 rad/day, the crypts and the villi of the epithelium of the small intestine show cellular depopulation, but thereafter the cell population appears to be maintained for a period of time with the rate of cell division, determined by mitotic index and by percentage labelling with tritiated thymidine, not very different from normal. Following removal of the animal from the unit after 5 days irradiation at 415 rad/day, the mitotic index increases and a normal cell population in crypt and villus is quickly achieved. Using tritiated thymidine, the generation time of cells in the crypts can be determined autoradiographically by the method of labelled mitoses, and Quastler (unpublished) has shown that the generation time is the same in animals after 5 days' irradiation as in the normal animal, that is, about $10\frac{1}{2}$ hr.

BLOOD STUDIES

The response of the peripheral blood count has been studied at dose rates of 176, 84, 50, 16, and 4 rad/day. The blood counts for the three higher dose rates have been published before,[4] but all the counts are collected together in Figs. 1 to 5 for the sake of completeness.

At the dose rate of 176 rad/day (Fig. 1) there is a rapid fall in numbers of all cell types in the peripheral blood, with no sign of establishment of a steady state. At 84 rad/day (Fig. 2) there is again an initial fall in platelets, mononuclears and polymorphs but at about 20 days there is a transient recovery in all blood elements, though afterwards the counts fall again until death with severe thrombocytopenia and haemorrhage. At lower dose rates there is again a change in pattern of response. At 50 rad/day (Fig. 3) and 16 rad/day (Fig. 4) there is still an initial fall in platelets, mononuclears and polymorphs, but the recovery that follows may be maintained for a considerable period of time. So far as the mononuclear count at 50 rad/day is concerned we have found recently that the pattern of change is to some extent dependent on the initial level of the count. With a much higher initial mononuclear count than for those animals in Fig. 3, there is again an initial fall to about 20 days, but then a levelling off rather than a recovery as shown in Fig. 3. However, the final level of mononuclear count was about the same in both sets of experiments.

With most of the animals irradiated at dose rates of about 50 rad/day

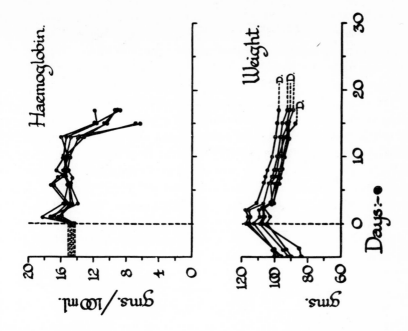

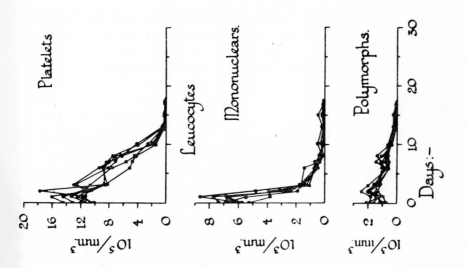

FIG. 1.

Blood response of hybrid rats to continuous irradiation at 176 rad/day.

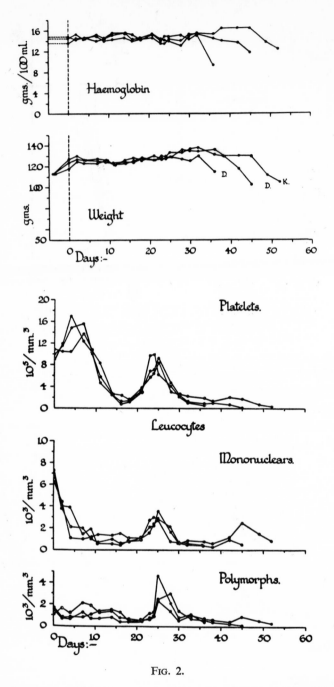

FIG. 2.

Blood response of hybrid rats to continuous irradiation at 84 rad/day.

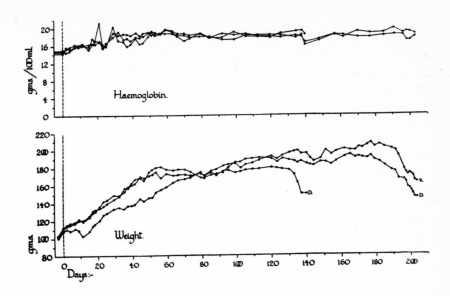

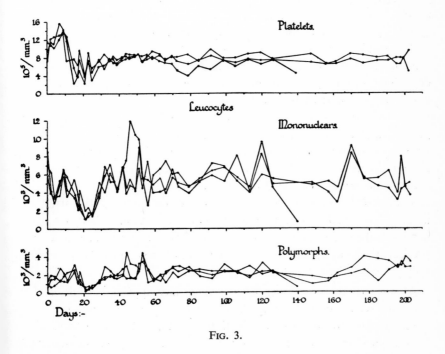

FIG. 3.

Blood response of hybrid rats to continuous irradiation at 50 rad/day.

18

there is no sign of haemorrhage at death and frequently the platelet count is not greatly below normal. Also, autoradiographic studies with tritiated thymidine on the epithelium of the small intestine have demonstrated that proliferation in the crypts is little different from normal. In fact, we do not yet know the major cause of death at this dose rate. Death is generally preceded by weight loss and it could be that there is a late functional failure in the gut which we have not yet detected.

The blood-counts for four rats exposed to 16 rad/day until death are shown in Fig. 4. There is recovery after an initial fall and a fairly normal count is maintained for a long period of time. In each of these four animals the cause of death was different. The first died at 325 days, with a blood and bone marrow picture indicative of a myeloid leukaemia. However, for some nine weeks before death the haemoglobin had been falling steadily, which was not the result of a platelet deficiency since there was, in fact, an intermittent thrombocytosis during the period of fall. From evidence presented below it would appear very unlikely that this anaemia was the direct result of radiation on the erythropoietic system and it would seem that the anaemia was the first manifestation of the leukaemic process. The second death at 16 rad/day was from a subcutaneous tumour at 416 days, the third animal was sacrificed at 445 days because of middle ear disease and the fourth animal died at 497 days with a collapse of the platelet-forming and polymorph systems.

At 4 rad/day (Fig. 5) we have had five rats exposed for about 500 days. The only difference in blood count from the controls is that the mononuclear count of the irradiated animals fell to a value about 20% below the control values and has remained so since. The difference in growth rates of the control and irradiated rats, starting at 160 days, is probably nothing to do with the irradiation but is the result of moving the control animals into somewhat larger cages. The other difference between the groups is that 3 out of 5 of the control animals have died (probably from endemic lung infection) while none of the irradiated animals have died so far. It must be noted that though both irradiated and control animals were individually caged they could not be kept under precisely the same conditions, since we have not as yet a similarly designed unit for control animals.

At none of the dose rates used is there any appreciable fall in haemoglobin value until terminally. The extent to which this represents a maintenance of red cell production and the extent to which blood volume changes are of importance is at present being investigated. Data on red cell production from Fe^{59} studies will be discussed below.

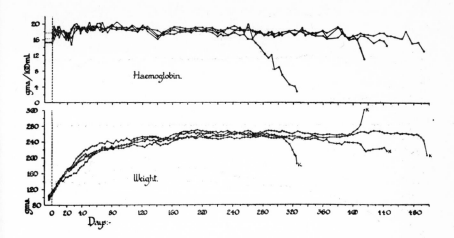

Blood changes in hybrid rats during chronic irradiation.   16 rads. per day.

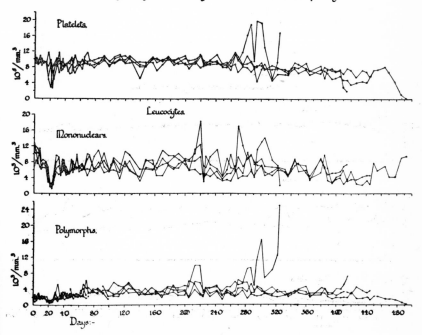

FIG. 4.

Blood response of hybrid rats to continuous irradiation at 16 rad/day.

18*

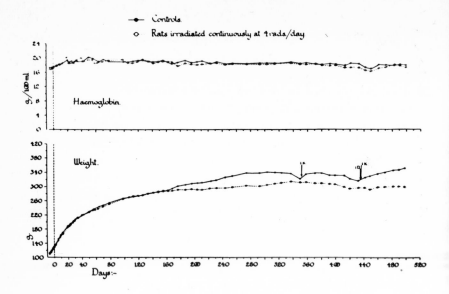

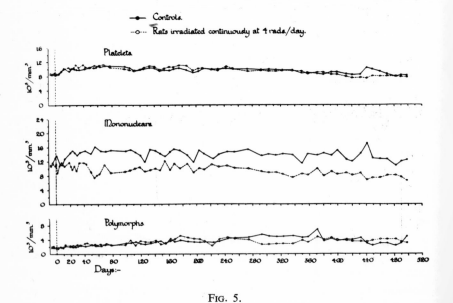

FIG. 5.

Blood response of hybrid rats to continuous irradiation at 4 rad/day.

EFFECT OF SPLENECTOMY

These findings on the response of blood to continuous irradiation raise a number of very obvious questions for investigation. The first is why there should be the recovery in platelet and white cell count at about 20 days. As reported in the previous publication[5] splenectomy prior to radiation exposure will markedly affect the pattern of response. In splenectomised animals, at both 84 and 50 rad/day, splenectomy eliminates the rise in mononuclear count at 20 days and a low level of mononuclear count is maintained until death. However, at both dose rates, the platelet fall is much less severe in splenectomised than in intact animals, which could be a result of a longer life of the platelets in the absence of the spleen, or possibly the removal of some inhibitory effect the spleen normally has on bone marrow activity. It is of interest that splenectomy increased survival time at both the dose rates studied.

It is possible that at about 20 days after the start of irradiation there is a release of mature blood elements from the spleen into the circulation and that this is followed by regeneration if the dose rate is not too high. However, we have at the moment no real explanation for such a phenomenon, but hope that our present studies with tritiated thymidine in the various tissues will give a lead.

THE "STEADY STATE" AT 50 RAD/DAY

Of the dose rates we have investigated the highest at which there is evidence of a "steady state" so far as the peripheral blood count is concerned, is 50 rad/day. It is of importance to find out to what extent this represents a steady state in the blood-forming tissues themselves since factors such as changes in blood volume and changes in release of blood cells from extra-vascular stores may be of significance in maintaining a steady peripheral count for a considerable period of time.

Our previous studies on mitotic index in femoral bone marrow two hours after colchicine injection indicated that in the first week of irradiation there was some reduction in division rate but that from 4 weeks on the division rate was somewhat higher than normal. However, these results were not very conclusive and there are various criticisms one can bring against the use of colchicine techniques in such experiments. Recently we have been studying the problem using tritiated thymidine. Animals that have been exposed for various periods of irradiation at 50 rad/day have been sacrificed 3 hours after injection of tritiated thymidine. The thymidine uptake of the marrow has been measured by Dr. G. G. Steel and autoradiographs made of marrow smears by Mr. B. Lord. A number of experimental difficulties remain to be overcome, but preliminary results are shown in Fig. 6. The autoradiographs indicate that, after the first week of irradiation, there is an increase in percentage labelling of the nucleated cells, but that it falls again to levels possibly lower than normal

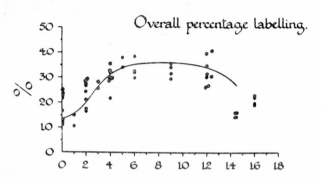

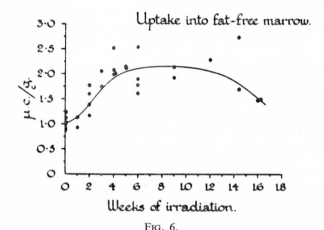

FIG. 6.

Tritiated thymidine uptake in femoral bone marrow of rats irradiated for various periods at 50 rad/day.

by about 16 weeks. The assay measurements on the bone marrow confirm this general pattern, but it is not yet possible to give any firm figure for the extent of the increase in percentage labelling. The factor of increase might be as high as two.

The detailed autoradiographic studies indicate that this change in percentage labelling during irradiation at 50 rad/day is not the result of a change in the spectrum of cell types in the marrow but of a true change in percentage labelling of the individual cell types. The work which is being carried out at the moment by Mr. Lord indicates, however, that there may be a difference in response between the white cell and the red cell precursors, in that the percentage labelling of the white cell precursors does not remain at a high level, while that of the red cell precursors is maintained, possibly until death. It would seem that, towards the end of the life of a rat exposed at 50 rad/day, there may be a steady state of cell proliferation in the bone marrow for the red cells, but not for the white cells.

Any comprehensive treatment of the kinetics of cellular proliferation in the bone marrow demands a knowledge of changes in total marrow cellularity. This is a difficult parameter to measure, but we have evidence, both from the previous studies[5] and from recent determinations by Dr. Steel of the fat content of the marrow, that the cellularity of the femoral bone marrow falls substantially soon after the start of exposure at 50 rad/day.

If an increased percentage labelling does represent a decreased generation time of the cells, the picture we have at 50 rad/day is of a reduced marrow population dividing more rapidly, at least for some time, and thus maintaining a stable blood count. This is not an unreasonable conception but it does not fit in with the hypothesis of Alpen & Cranmore[6] concerning regeneration of red cells after bleeding, where the evidence pointed to increase in input of stem cells, but little change in generation time of precursors. We hope soon to be able to have direct information on the generation time of the bone marrow cells, normal and irradiated.

RED CELL PRODUCTION

To test the red cell production in rats irradiated at 50 rad/day we have employed the radioactive iron technique previously described.[5] Fe^{59} is given intravenously and 24 hours after the Fe^{59} injection a series of daily injections of 'Imferon', an inactive iron-dextran compound was started, in order to eliminate as far as possible the reutilisation of Fe^{59} and the transfer to erythropoietic tissues of Fe^{59} initially taken up elsewhere. Periodically blood samples were taken from the tail and counted and the blood content expressed as a percentage of the injected dose. The results for control animals and for animals irradiated for different periods of time at 50 rad/day, are shown in Fig. 7 and Fig. 8. Each curve represents the mean for three animals and the level reached by the curves can be taken as the iron incorporating capacity of the erythropoietic tissues at the time of Fe^{59} injection. Owing to the limitation of space in the irradiation unit the experiment had to be done in two parts, one concentrating on the shorter periods of exposure and the other on the longer periods. It can be seen that the Fe^{59} uptake by the rat is never very greatly below normal values and at 140 days, when some of the same group of animals had already died, the Fe^{59} uptake was almost normal.

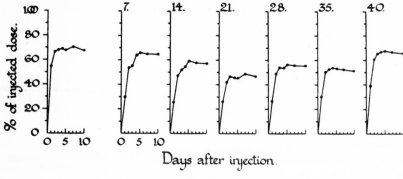

FIG. 7.

Rate of appearance of injected Fe^{59} in blood of rats irradiated at 50 rad/day for various periods from 7 to 40 days.

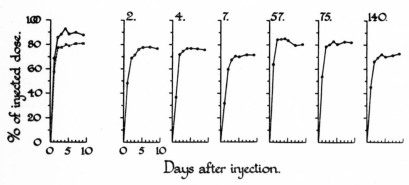

FIG. 8.

Rate of appearance of injected Fe^{59} in blood of rats irradiated at 50 rad/day for various periods from 2 to 140 days.

The conclusions from these results will be affected if there are substantial changes in blood volume during the course of irradiation and this is being currently studied.

Our Fe^{59} data at 84 rad/day is much less comprehensive than that at 50 rad/day, but there is again evidence of a practically normal uptake of Fe^{59} just before death, when the white cell and platelet count are low.

This finding certainly lends support to the view that the erythropoietic system is much more capable than the granulocytic or thrombocytic systems of maintaining function under continuous irradiation. Measurements made at 176 rad/day give no evidence of maintenance of erythropoietic function at this dose rate.

BLEEDING EXPERIMENTS

The maintenance of normal output of new cells under continuous irradiation does not necessarily imply that the tissue will react to stress as effectively as normal tissue. To test the capacity for regeneration of the erythropoietic system we have measured the rate of recovery of haemoglobin after removal of one-third of the blood volume by cardiac puncture. The results are shown in Figs. 9 and 10. There is no evidence of any reduced capacity to make new red cells after 94 days or 130 days exposure at 50 rad/day. So far as the leucocytes are concerned the main difference in response after bleeding is that, whereas control animals show a rapid leucocytosis, it is either much less marked or absent in the irradiated animals. This could be the result of depletion of extra-vascular stores of leucocytes by continuous irradiation.

EFFECT OF A SHIELDING PROCEDURE

One experiment has been carried out on the effect of non-uniform irradiation. Great difficulties are presented by shielding experiments with continuous irradiation and therefore the effect of shielding was investigated using daily doses of X-radiation. Doses of 100 rads were given to a group of rats once per day, at a dose rate of 30 rad/min, with one hind leg shielded by lead and the response compared with that of non-shielded animals. The blood counts for the two groups are shown in Fig. 11. Previous work[7] had shown that divided doses of radiation were more effective than a continuous exposure, and the pattern of response in the unshielded animals was very similar to that reported previously. It can be seen, however, that shielding of one hind limb is effective not only in reducing the severity of the platelet and polymorph fall, but also in reducing the severity of the mononuclear fall. This was rather a surprising observation since only small amounts of lymphoid tissue could have been included in the shielded area. The animals lived longer and there was a much less severe haemoglobin fall. Studies with tritiated thymidine in the various tissues of the shielded rat are at present in progress.

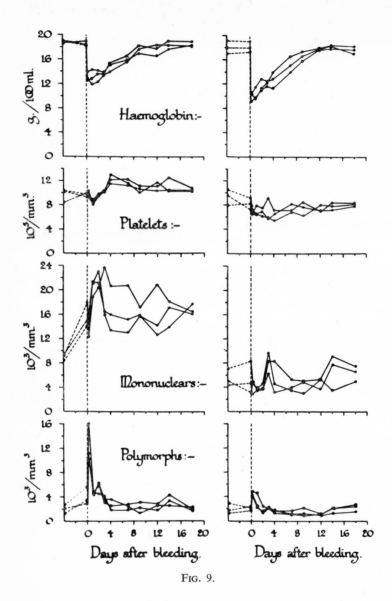

FIG. 9.

Blood recovery after removal of $\frac{1}{3}$ of blood volume. Rats given 50 rad/day for 94 days before bleeding.

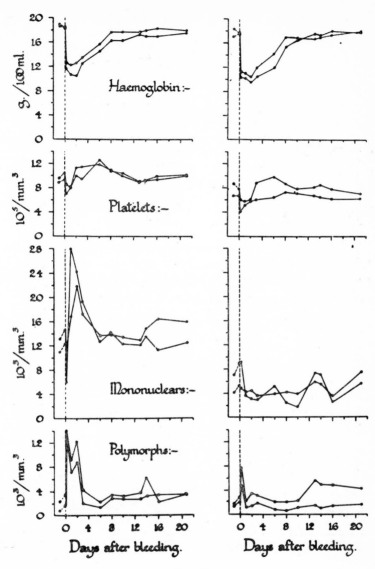

FIG. 10.

Blood recovery after removal of $\frac{1}{3}$ of blood volume. Rats given 50 rad/day for 130 days before bleeding.

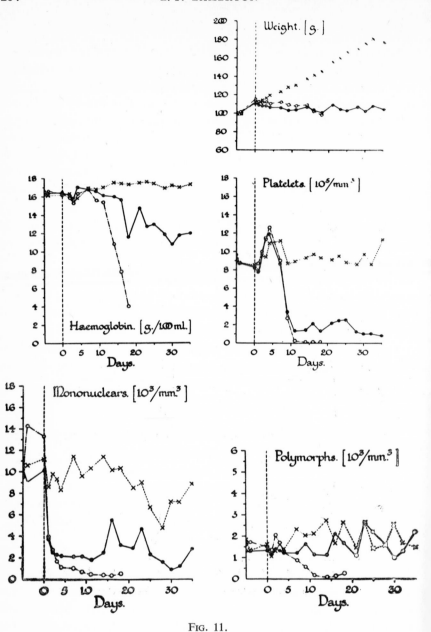

FIG. 11.

Comparative blood response of hybrid rats given fractioned irradiation (100 rad
daily at 30 rad/min).

——○—— Whole body.
———●——— One leg shielded.
··· × ··· One leg irradiated.

GENERAL DISCUSSION

Without a great deal more data on the cellular kinetics, and particularly on changes in generation time in the bone marrow under continuous irradiation it is not very profitable to speculate on the factors determining the dose-rates at which cell population and function can be maintained for periods of time. However, there is evidence that the erythropoietic system can withstand higher dose rates of continuous irradiation than either the granulocytic or thrombocytic systems. It is not possible to say at the moment whether this results from a greater radioresistance of the red cell precursors or from a greater efficiency of red cell homeostatic mechanisms.

The finding that the epithelium of the small intestine can maintain function under a much higher continuous dose rate than the blood-forming tissues offers a very fruitful field for investigation. It may be here that the shorter generation time of the intestinal epithelial cell is the most significant factor, but there are a number of factors, including the speed and efficiency of the homeostatic mechanisms, and the possibility of acquisition of radiation resistance which have to be explored.

The one example given in this paper of the effect of a shielding procedure illustrates how greatly the response may be modified by non-uniform irradiation.

SUMMARY

The response of the blood and blood-forming tissues of the rat to continuous irradiation at dose rates from 176 to 4 rad/day is discussed. A special study has been made of the response at 50 rad/day, at which dose rate a steady state of the peripheral blood count can be maintained for a considerable period of time. The effect of shielding one hind limb on the response to daily doses of radiation is also described.

ACKNOWLEDGEMENTS

This paper is a summary of work done, or being done, by a number of colleagues and I would like to express my gratitude especially to Miss Kay Adams, Dr. G. G. Steel, Mr. B. Lord, Dr. N. M. Blackett and Dr. J. P. M. Bensted. I am very grateful to Miss I. Yeatman for her help in preparing the manuscript.

Finally, I wish to express my appreciation to Professor W. V. Mayneord, Director of the Physics Department, Institute of Cancer Research, for his continual support and encouragement.

REFERENCES

1. G. J. NEARY, R. J. MUNSON and R. H. MOLE, *Chronic Radiation Hazards*, Pergamon Press, London (1957).
2. H. QUASTLER, J. P. M. BENSTED, L. F. LAMERTON and S. M. SIMPSON, II. Adaptation to continuous irradiation: Observations on rat intestine, *Brit. J. Radiol.* **32**, 501–511 (1959).
3. Unpublished observations.
4. L. F. LAMERTON, A. H. PONTIFEX, N. M. BLACKETT and K. ADAMS, Effects of protracted irradiation on the blood-forming organs of the rat, I. Continuous exposure, *Brit. J. Radiol.* **33**, 287–301 (1960).
5. L. F. LAMERTON, E. H. BELCHER and E. B. HARRISS, Blood uptake of Fe^{59} in studies of red cell production, in *The Kinetics of Cellular Proliferation*, ed. F. STOHLMAN Jr., Grune & Stratton, New York & London, p. 301–311 (1959).
6. E. L. ALPEN and D. CRANMORE, Observations on the regulation of erthropoiesis and on cellular dynamics of Fe^{59} autoradiography, in *The Kinetics of Cellular Proliferation*, ed. F. STOHLMAN Jr., Grune and Stratton, New York & London, p. 290–300 (1959).
7. A. H. PONTIFEX and L. F. LAMERTON, Effects of protracted irradiation on the blood-forming organs of the rat, II. Divided doses, *Brit. J. Radiol.* **33**, 736–747 (1960).

DISCUSSION

BASERGA: I just wanted to comment about the increase in the percentage of cells labeled with tritiated thymidine and Professor Lamerton offers as the most logical explanation the fact that the generation time is shorter than normal.

Could that be due to a lengthening of the "S" phase? In fact, we have observed that some Ehrlich ascites tumor cells in the mouse, that have a mean generation time of 20 hr, have a percentage of labeled cells of about 50 per cent because they have an "S" phase of 13 to 14 hr, whereas the cells of the crypts of the intestine have a percentage of labeled cells of about 35 to 40 per cent and a mean generation time of 14 hr, but an "S" phase much shorter than tumor cells.

LAMERTON: This is extremely interesting. We had rather assumed that one would not get a specific lengthening of the "S" period. If this occurred, it could explain our result.

EFFECTS OF FETAL X-IRRADIATION ON AGING CHANGES IN CEREBRAL CORTEX

K. R. Brizzee, Xenia Kharetchko and L. A. Jacobs

Department of Anatomy, College of Medicine, University of Utah, Salt Lake City, Utah

INTRODUCTION

Recent reports on aging changes in nervous tissues have described certain definite alterations in neurons which appear to be related to the aging process. These include a decrease in basophilia, loss of definition of the nuclear membrane, satellitosis and neurophagia.[1,2] In an earlier study, Brody[3] reported an overall loss of neurons in aged human brains together with some change in relative numbers of granule and pyramidal cell types.

Some authors, however, have been inclined to view such changes as artifacts due to errors of subjective interpretation or due to inadequate methods of fixation and subsequent preparation of tissues. For example, Gellerstedt[4] believed that the hypochromatism seen in many cells of senile human brains was due to the occurrence of "preagonal changes" which he ascribed to a greater vulnerability of cells in aged brains. In recent studies by Andrew[2] an effort was made to eliminate the possibility of such preagonal changes by the use of perfusion fixation of tissues to insure rapid, uniform fixation and thus permit more valid histological comparisons of young and old tissues. Similarly, Kharetchko et al.,[5] employing perfusion fixation and quantitative histological methods, described definite histological changes in the aging cerebral cortex in rats including a decrease in mean neuron soma volume and an increase in packing density of glial cells. Thus, it appears that in the more recent studies of aging changes in the nervous system, if not in some earlier ones, real tissue alterations incident to the aging process have been demonstrated.

Investigations of aging effects of radiation exposure have given very little attention to effects on nervous tissues and the few reports dealing with late effects or long-term effects of radiation on nervous system[6] have not attempted to relate such effects to the aging process. In the present study, therefore, we have endeavored to determine whether fetal X-irradiation administered in fractionated doses during a period in which neuroblasts and spongioblasts of forebrain structures are particu arly susceptible to irradiation results in any alteration in the type or sequence of changes observed in our previous study.[5]

MATERIALS AND METHODS

A series of pregnant white rats of the Sprague–Dawley strain were exposed to a fractionated dose of whole body X-irradiation totalling 300 r at the rate 60 r/min on gestation days 10 through 14. A Westinghouse Quadrocondex unit was employed for the radiation and operated at 250 kV, 15 mA, with a filtration factor of $\frac{1}{2}$ mm Cu+1 mm Al. The animals were irradiated from the dorsal aspect in a perforated Lucite box. Dose and rate calibrations were carried out with the use of a Victoreen r-meter in the center of a wax phantom of the approximate dimensions of the adult rats. Sixteen animals from the irradiated litters were sacrificed at 100, 200, 300 and 400 days of age and the brains were prepared for histological evaluations as described in previous papers.[7,8,9,10] Mean neuronal nuclear, perikaryal and soma volumes, neuron and neuroglial packing densities and cortical thickness measurements were carried out as described in the earlier reports.

RESULTS

Neuron nuclear, perikaryal and soma volumes in irradiated animals decreased between the 100- and 400-day stages while in the controls no significant changes were observed in this period (Table 1, Fig. 1). In older controls (730 days), however, the values for all 3 of these parameters decreased to about the same levels as were observed in 400-day irradiated groups (Fig. 1). The nucleocytoplasmic ratio (Table 1) was not significantly different in irradiated and control groups at comparable age levels, nor was the mean value in the oldest control animals different from that of 400-day controls. The mean values for gray/cell coefficient (Table 1) were lower at the 100- and-200 day stages in irradiated than in control groups but were approximately the same in 300- and-400 day groups. An increase in the gray/cell coefficient was observed between the 400- and 730-day stages in the control group, the highest value attained being 18·38.

No significant changes in neuron packing density (Table 1) were observed in either control or irradiated groups at any age levels. Glial packing density (Fig. 2) in control animals increased between the 100- and 400-day stages but showed a more marked increase in the 730-day animals. In irradiated specimens, however, the glial density increased greatly between the ages of 100 and 400 days, the final value being somewhat

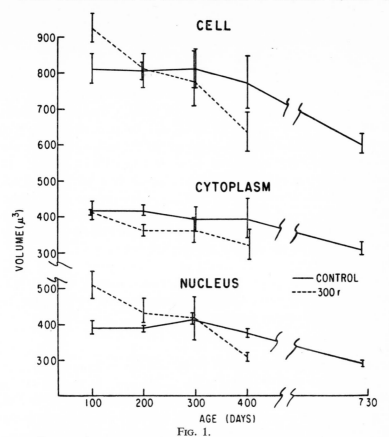

FIG. 1.

Decrease in neuron nuclear, cytoplasmic and soma volumes.

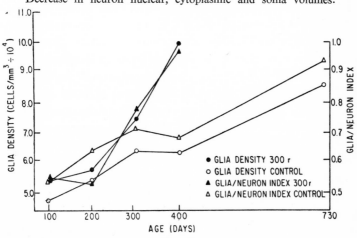

FIG. 2.

Increase in the glia packing density and glia/neuron index.

TABLE 1

Comparison of Morphological Changes in Control and Irradiated Animals

Control

Age (days)	Glia density/mm³	Neuron density/mm³	Glia index	Nuclear volume	Cyt. volume	Cell volume	N/C ratio	Gray/Cell
100	47·564±2·422	87·998±5·298	0·54±0·011	396±18	420±25	816±42	0·94±0·02	14·20±1·23
200	53·837±4·283	83·493±3·265	0·64±3·265	390±12	421±13	811±24	0·92±0·02	14·91±0·99
300	63·818±5·334	83·663±8·314	0·71±0·09	416±20	397±34	813±53	1·06±0·05	13·50±1·02
400	63·616±6·235	94·119±6·884	0·68±0·08	374±13	398±54	773±74	0·96±0·08	13·96±0·34
730	85·402±2·742	91·353±3·232	0·94±0·04	293±7	307±18	600±22	0·96±0·05	18·38±0·93

Irradiated

Age (days)	Glia density/mm³	Neuron density/mm³	Glia index	Nuclear volume	Cyt. volume	Cell volume	N/C ratio	Gray/Cell
100	53·874±5·824	100·368±4·620	0·55±0·075	414±7	514±37	928±41	0·82±0·04	11·02±0·79
200	57·576±5·267	110·484±7·598	0·53±0·06	365±17	437±39	802±44	0·86±0·09	11·46±0·57
300	74·552±2·336	96·042±4·956	0·78±0·03	363±35	419±58	782±89	0·89±0·07	14·30±2·60
400	100·343±11·732	102·614±3·456	0·97±0·01	326±41	312±15	638±56	1·04±0·08	15·75±1·76

higher (about 100,000 cells/mm³) than in the oldest controls (about 85,000 cells/mm³). Since the neuron packing density did not change, the glia/neuron index increased directly as the glia density increased.

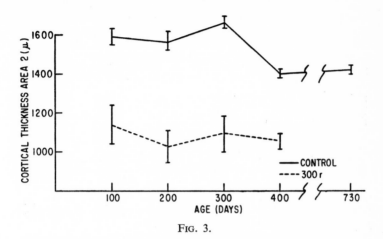

FIG. 3.

Thickness of submolecular layers of cerebral cortex—Area 2.

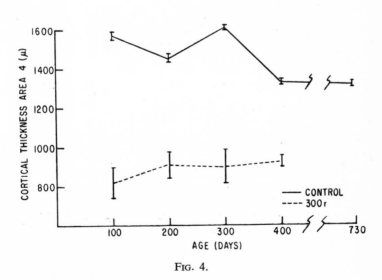

FIG. 4.

Thickness of submolecular layers of cerebral cortex—Area 4.

294   K. R. BRIZZEE *et al.*

In control groups significant decrease in cortical thickness occurred between the 100- and-400 day stages in areas 2 and 4, with smaller decreases occurring in areas 17 (Table 2, Figs. 3–5) and 41 (Fig. 6). No marked changes occurred between the 400- and-730 day groups in any of the areas

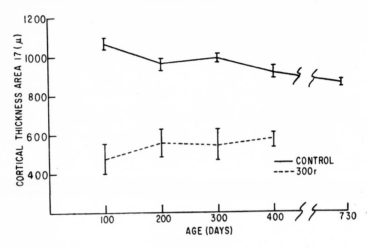

FIG. 5.

Thickness of submolecular layers of cerebral cortex—Area 17.

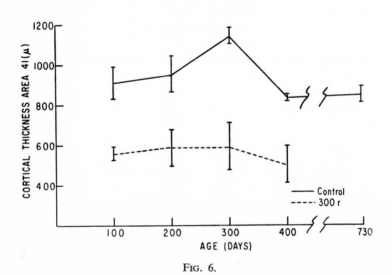

FIG. 6.

Thickness of submolecular layers of cerebral cortex—Area 41.

TABLE 2

Thickness of Submolecular Layers of Cortex (μ)

Age (days)	Area 2		Area 4		Area 41		Area 17	
	Control	Irrad.	Control	Irrad.	Control	Irrad.	Control	Irrad.
100	1596±45	1153±99	1573±17	825±80	910±82	556±28	1074±31	484±82
200	1582±52	1038±78	1460±24	907±70	956±86	593±86	974±30	560±70
300	1679±26	1110±94	1618±11	896±87	1150±45	588±123	1001±22	550±77
400	1424±32	1072±44	1344±12	934±34	839±20	508±93	931±12	583±45
730	1482±25	—	1326±20	—	888±31	—	903±21	—

studied. In the irradiated animals no significant changes in any cortical areas occurred between the 100- and 400-day stages but cortical thickness in the irradiated animals was very significantly lower in all areas than in controls. The relative thickness of all cortical layers, however, appeared to be in the normal range.

TABLE 3

Comparison of the Total Brain Weight and the Brain Wt./Body Ratio in Control and Irradiated Animals

Age (days)	Total brain weight (gms)		Brain wt./body wt.	
	Control	Irrad.	Control	Irrad.
100	1·7840±0·098	0·8707±0·056	0·0063±0·0002	0·0041±0·0002
200	1·8625±0·047	1·0658±0·065	0·0068±0·0002	0·0041±0·0002
300	1·9875±0·032	1·1102±0·058	0·0053±0·0001	0·0034±0·0002
400	1·8049±0·125	0·9866±0·045	0·0048±0·0007	0·0044±0·0001
730	1·9940±0·044	—	0·0046±0·0005	—

Changes in brain weight (Table 3, Fig. 7) were not significant in control or irradiated groups, but mean brain weight in irradiated animals was significantly less than in controls. The ratio of brain weight to body weight (Table 3, Fig. 8) was higher in control animals of 100 to 300 days of age, than in the irradiated rats of the same age group. A decrease occurred,

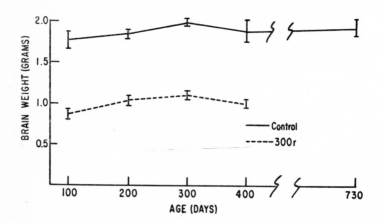

Fig. 7.

Total brain weight.

however, in the control animals of the 300-day group and at 400 days the values decreased to a level not significantly different from the irradiated animals.

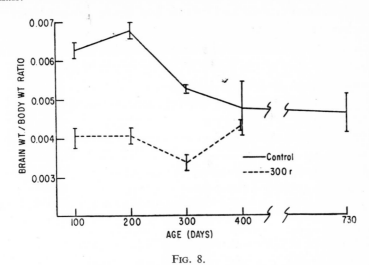

FIG. 8.

Changes in the total brain wt./body wt. ratio.

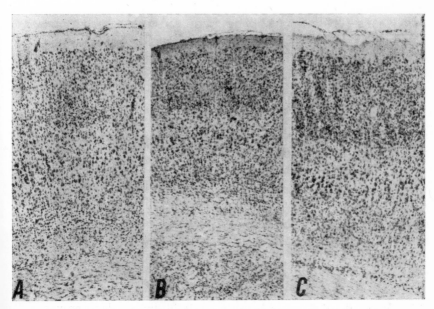

FIG. 9. Effect of fetal X-irradiation on cortical thickness ($\times$ 40). A. 400 days control. B. 400 days irradiated. C. 700 days control.

DISCUSSION

Studies of aging changes in nervous tissues in many species have revealed a definite decrease in brain weight[11,12,13,14] associated with the aging process. In the rat, however, it is known[15] that brain weight normally does not decrease in older animals. In the present study no significant change in brain weight was observed in either control or irradiated animals although the values in the irradiated rats were significantly lower than in controls at any given age level.

Several workers have reported a loss of neurons in aging brains,[3,16,17,18] Wilcox,[19] however, did not observe any loss of neurons in the pyramidal layer of cerebral cortex in aged guinea pigs. Our findings in the cerebral cortex in the rat appear to support those of Wilcox in that no significant change in neuron packing density was observed in older animals in either the control or irradiated series.

A decrease in nuclear volume in aged brains in man was reported by Hodge.[20] In our own studies a definite decrease in mean nuclear and soma volume in neurons was observed in older animals in both radiated and control groups, appearing to substantiate the work of Hodge. Since a decrease in soma volume appears to be a constant finding in aged brains the steady decrease observed in irradiated brains at a much earlier age than in controls probably can be considered a definite aging change resulting from the early radiation exposure.

Accompanying the decrease in mean neuron soma volume, the gray/cell coefficient $\left(\dfrac{\text{volume of cortex}}{\text{volume of neuron somae in cortex}} \right)$ increased significantly between the 100- and 400-day stages in irradiated animals but not in controls. However, in controls an even greater increase occurred between the 400-day and 730-day groups. The increase in irradiated animals thus occurred earlier and approximated the levels attained at a much later stage in control animals. From these results it appears that the gray/cell coefficient may serve as a useful criterion of aging in the cerebral cortex.

The mean thickness of the submolecular layers of cerebral cortex decreased somewhat in control animals between the 100- and 400-day stages in areas 2, 4, and 17 but failed to decrease in area 41. No significant changes occurred between the 400- and 730-day levels, however. In the irradiated groups mean cortical thickness increased slightly between the 100- and 400-day levels in areas 4 and 17 and decreased slightly in areas 2 and 41 but none of the differences between levels in any of these groups were significant. It would appear from our observations to date that the decrease i n neuron soma volume (with a probable decrease in dendrite volume as well) is balanced by an increase in neuroglia volume in both irradiated (400 day) and non-irradiated (730 day) animals thus precluding any marked decrease in cortical thickness or brain weight in the older animals. Since the marked increase in glial density is seen to occur in irradiated animals at a much earlier age than in controls and actually exceeds the level seen in the oldest controls we have studied it appears that the increase in glial density may constitute the most definite criterion of aging of any we have considered.

Hicks[21] has suggested the use of fetal X-irradiation as a research tool for the purpose of altering brain structure for experimental purposes. Our results from the present study as well as in an earlier investigation[10] suggest that fractionated doses of fetal X-irradiation may be more useful for this purpose than single exposures, since greater cumulative doses can be given with fractionated than with single doses without severe alterations of structural features or relationships, yet with a consistent reduction in cell numbers apparently affecting all cortical layers about equally. Our findings in the present investigation suggest that the use of fractionated doses of fetal irradiation constitue a useful procedure for the study of aging processes as well as developmental processes in nervous tissues.

SUMMARY

Morphological aging changes were studied in the cerebral cortex of the progeny of pregnant albino rats exposed in utero to a fractionated dose of whole body X-irradiation totalling 300 r. The neuron nuclear, cytoplasmic and soma volumes in irradiated animals between 100 and 400 days decreased to approximately the same levels observed in the control animals at 730 days of age. The mean value for gray/cell coefficient in 400-day irradiated animals was significantly higher than the gray/cell coefficient in controls at the same age, but the gray/cell coefficient in 730-day control rats was higher than that in 400-day irradiated specimens.

The glia packing density and glia/neuron index in 400-day irradiated animals increased to a level higher than that in the 730-day controls, while no significant changes in the neuron packing density were observed in either irradiated or control animals after 100 days of age.

A significant decrease in mean cortical thickness was observed in areas 2 and 4, with smaller decreases in areas 17 and 41 in control groups between 100 and 400 days of age. Between 400 and 730 days of age, however, no marked changes in cortical thickness occurred in any of these areas in the control series. In irradiated rats at 400 days there were no significant differences in cortical thickness in any cortical areas as compared with younger animals. Mean values for cortical thickness ,however, were significantly lower in irradiated than in control groups at all age levels. No significant change in brain weight was observed in control or irradiated groups although the mean values for brain weight were significantly lower in irradiated than control rats.

The decrease in neuron nuclear, cytoplasmic and soma volumes, together with a significant increase in the glia density, glia/neuron index and gray/cell coefficient in irradiated as compared with control animals at 400 days of age, suggests that these parameters may be useful in establishing criteria of the aging process and of aging effects of fetal X-irradiation in cerebral cortex.

REFERENCES

1. W. ANDREW, Structural alterations with aging in the nervous system, *Proc. Assn. Res. & Ment. Dis.* **35**: 129–170 (1956).
2. W. ANDREW, The reality of age differences in nervous tissue, *Jour. Geront.* **14**, 259–267 (1959).
3. H. BRODY, Organization of the cerebral cortex, III. A study of aging in the human cerebral cortex, *J. Comp. Neur.* **102**, 511–556 (1955).
4. N. GELLERSTEDT, Zur Kenntnis der Hirnveranderungen Bei der normalen Altersinvolution. *Upsala lakaref. forh.* **38**, 193–408 (1933).
5. X. KHARETCHKO, K. R. BRIZZEE and L. A. JACOBS, Quantitative histological study of aging changes in cerebral cortex of rat, *Anat. Rec.* **139**, 245 (1961).
6. D. COWAN and L. M. GELLER, Long term pathological effects of prenatal X-irradiation on the central nervous system of the rat. *Jour. Neuropath. and Exper. Neurol.* **14**, 488–527 (1960).
7. K. R. BRIZZEE and L. A. JACOBS, Post-natal changes in volumetric and density relationships of neurons in cerebral cortex of cat, *Acta Anat.* **38**, 291–303 (1959).
8. K. R. BRIZZEE and L. A. JACOBS, The glia/neuron index in the submolecular layers of the cortex in the cat, *Anat. Rec.* **134**, 97–106 (1959).
9. K. R. BRIZZEE and L. A. JACOBS, Early post-natal changes in neuron packing density and volumetric relationships in the cerebral cortex of the white rat, *Growth* **33**, 337–347 (1959).
10. K. R. BRIZZEE, L. A. JACOBS and X. KHARETCHKO, Effects of total-body X-irradiation in utero on early post-natal changes in neuron volumetric relationships, *Rad. Res.* **14**, 96–103 (1960).
11. R. BOYD, Philosophical trans. 1860. Ref. in *Quains Anatomy, vol. III*—Part I, E. A. SCHAFER and G. D. THANE, Longmans & Green, London, p. 219 (1895).
12. R. PEARL, Biometrical studies on man, *Biometrika* **4**, 13–104 (1905).
13. F. W. APPEL and E. M. APPEL, Intracranial variation in weight of human brain, *Human Biol.* **14**, 48–68 (1942).
14. F. W. APPEL and E. M. APPEL, Intracranial variation in weight of human brain, *Human Biol.* **14**, 235–250 (1942).

15. H. H. DONALDSON and S. HATAI, A comparison of the Norway rat with the albino rat in respect to body length, brain weight, spinal cord weight and the percentage of water in both the brain and the spinal cord. *J. Comp. Neurol.* **21**, 417–458 (1911).
16. M. CRITCHLEY, *Problems of Aging*, Williams & Wilkins, Baltimore, p. 518 (1942).
17. W. RIESE, The cerebral cortex in the very old human brain, *J. Neuropath. and Exp. Neur.* **5**, 160–164 (1946).
18. H. KUHLENBECK, Senile changes in the brain of Wistar Institute rats, *Anat. Rec.* **88**, 441 (1944).
19. H. H. WILCOX, Changes accompanying aging in the brains of guinea pigs, *J. Gerontol.* **6** (suppl. to No. 3), 168 (1951).
20. C. F. HODGE, Changes in ganglion cells from birth to senile death, Observations on man and honeybee, *J. Physiol.* **17**, 129–134 (1894).
21. S. P. HICKS, Radiation as an experimental tool in mammalian developmental neurology, *Physiol. Rev.* **38**, 337–352 (1958).

SPECIFIC EFFECTS OF IRRADIATION ON THE LUNG*

S. Warren

Cancer Research Institute, New England Deaconess Hospital, Boston, Massachusetts

The lung reacts to injury by exudation, humoral or cellular, desquamation of alveolar cells into the lumen, secretion of mucus, fibrosis, less frequently by metaplasia and rarely by neoplasia. The most common neoplastic response in the lung in rats and mice is the so-called pulmonary adenoma,[1,2] usually a benign tumor, which in most instances appears to arise from alveolar lining cells. This tumor may be spontaneous or may be induced by a number of agents, and appears in a variety of strains of mice. Progress to a malignant form with metastases may occur. It is quite different from most pulmonary tumors in man. It is possible to induce tumors similar to the lung (bronchial) cancer of man in mice[3] and rats[4] by heavy doses of radiation.

The human lung appears quite resistant to radiation damage[5] and to radiation neoplasia.[6,7]

Radiation reaction in the lung may lead to the formation of a hyaline membrane that tends to line the alveolar and atrial spaces. It is neither constant nor consistent in appearance and is not pathognomonic, although strongly suggestive. The alveolar and atrial cells increase in size, usually the nucleus hypertrophies as well but does not do so always. Changes of this type may be difficult to differentiate from chronic inflammation. As time goes on, if the dose of radiation has been large, several thousand roentgens or more, these cells tend to increase in size, to become more and more bizarre and some eventually resemble closely tumor giant cells. Cells of this type sometimes persist for long periods in areas of dense fibrosis, as the only evidence of previous respiratory structure. These cells apparently have little proliferative power and, although they are extraordinarily abnormal in appearance, I have not seen a cancer arise from them. The endothelial cells including those of the capillaries tend to become more prominent and some of these show the giant cell forms seen after heavy irradiation. The septal cells of the alveolar walls may also swell. Varying degrees of mononuclear phagocytic infiltration may

* Supported by USAEC and US Public Health Service grant C-3003.

303

develop but is rarely, if ever, marked. Special stains for elastic tissue bring out the fact that soon after the initial edema of the alveolar walls is passed, thickening and splitting of the elastic fibers occurs. The bronchial epithelium reacts to radiation by enlargement and distortion of bronchial cells, ultimately with loss of cilia. Some keratinizing metaplasia may occur and at times this is marked. At times the submucosa is covered only by distorted or flattened epithelial cells, at other times there is a building up of a multilayered lining of epithelial cells showing various degrees of keratinization. The lymphatics and blood vessels initially are dilated but later show to a mild degree the radiation changes commonly expected in the vascular tree.

Few adequate data exist on carcinogenic dose levels of internal emitters in the lung in animals; these have been summarized by Gates and Warren.[3] No dose of external radiation sufficiently great to produce lung cancer in animals or man has been achieved.[8] A basic difficulty with the dosimetry of particulate sources of radiation in the lung is that uniform distribution must perforce be assumed, but observation shows the distribution to be spotty. Tumors seem to arise in foci where relatively large aggregates of radioactive particulates occur, and, hence, the local dose is well above the average to the lung.

Dosimetry can be made somewhat more accurate by the use of a single source, such as a short Co^{60} wire directly implanted. This is the technique used in our laboratory. The beta component of Co^{60} can be ignored, thanks to absorption in the source and immediately adjacent tissues. Sometimes by necrosis or movement by adjacent muscles the source may be translated in space; usually it remains *in situ*. By determining the strength of source, distance of tumor from source, and time interval, the carcinogenic dose can be determined. The exact time of carcinogenesis cannot be determined, and hence there is some wasted radiation, but the small size of many of the tumors, the often short time periods at which they are observed, and the fact that the animals often die of intercurrent problems, such as malnutrition from dysphagia secondary to esophageal radiation, and that the tumors do not occur at the point of maximal dose to viable tissue, but rather arise in a nearby zone of injury and reaction, suggest the doses are not grossly distorted.

In estimated doses from a slowly decaying source such as Co^{60}, time measured in days is not too great a factor, and by use of suitable graphs, quite accurate total doses can be determined. The doses given are so obtained.

The source is placed within the mouse lung by trocar (Fig. 1).

Most of our experiments were made with RAP mice; however, small-scale experiments with C3H, LAF, A/J, BALB and DBA strains gave similar results.

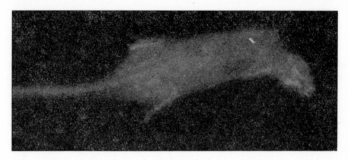

FIG. 1.

Roentgenogram of mouse with Co⁶⁰ source.

While other tumors, such as carcinoma of skin, of the esophagus and leukemia may be induced, lung cancers originating from bronchial epithelium (Fig. 2) can be obtained in a number of the mice.

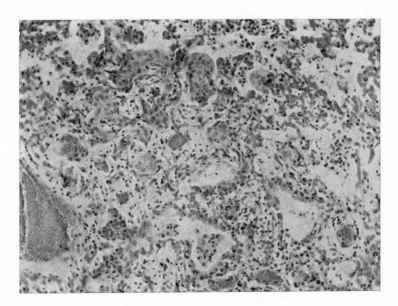

FIG. 2.

Radiation-induced epidermoid carcinoma arising from bronchial epithelium ($\times$ 170).

The shortest induction time for a lung cancer was 66 days. The lowest dose was 90,000 r to the tumor site. The longest exposure time over which mice have failed to show lung cancer is 315 days, the highest dose 450,000 r.

Most of the pulmonary cancers had not metastasized, probably due to their small size.

REFERENCES

1. M. SLYE, H. F. HOLMES and H. G. WELLS, The primary spontaneous tumors of the lungs in mice, *J. Med. Res.* **30**, 417–442 (1914).
2. H. L. STEWART, Pulmonary Tumors in Mice, in *The Physiopathology of Cancer*, edited by HOMBURGER and FISHMAN, Paul B. Hoeber, Inc., New York, P. 93–112 (1953).
3. O. GATES and S. WARREN, Histogenesis of carcinoma of the lung in mice induced by gamma radiation, *Arch. Path.* **71**, 693–713 (1961).
4. H. LISCO, Autoradiographic and histopathologic studies in radiation carcinogenesis of the lung, *Lab. Invest.* **8**, 162–170 (1959).
5. S. WARREN and O. GATES, Radiation pneumonitis. Experimental and pathologic observations, *Arch. Path.* **30**, 440–460 (1940).
6. B. RAJEWSKY, Berichte über die Schneeberger Gruben, *Krebsforsch.* **49**, 315 (1939).
7. R. D. EVANS, Quantitative aspects of radiation carcinogenesis in humans, *Acta Union Internationale Contre le Cancrum* **6**, 1229–1237 (1950).
8. O. GATES and S. WARREN, The production of bronchial carcinoma in mice, *Am. J. Path.* **36**, 653–671 (1960).

DISCUSSION

MOLE: I was very interested particularly in Dr. Warren's clear demonstration that radiation can produce new kinds of tumors at a high level dose. I guess you would agree that at low levels of dose, in general, radiation appears to produce tumors that are indistinguishable from those that occur spontaneously?

WARREN: Yes; this is absolutely right.

MOLE: More specifically, I would be very interested to know if there was any difference in the pattern of tumor production depending on whether the strain of mouse did or did not carry the polyoma virus. I think you said you had the two different strains.

WARREN: Yes. As far as these particular tumors were concerned, there was not any variation.

HASTERLIK: I just want to thank Dr. Warren for confirming in the mouse what Dr. Asher Finkel and I have been seeing in the human, that is the production of the tumor which never occurs in the human except under the influence of radiation This is the occurrence of mastoid air cell carcinomata in radium watch dial painters and other persons administered radium by their physicians. The pathologist knows well the carcinoma that appears first in the middle ear after many years of chronic infection and then penetrates into the mastoid air cells. However, the tumor arising *de novo* in the epithelium of the mastoid is rarely seen or described by pathologists.

Here again if the radiation can irradiate the tissue, then the possibility for the production of the tumor does exist even though it is otherwise rarely seen.

I think Dr. Warren might be able to sort out some of his problems if he uses a different isotope than the high energy, gamma emitting radiation from Co^{60}. I would like to suggest that perhaps something such as Pd^{103}, which has a 20 kV X-ray. This might sort out some of these problems of the tremendous dose that you have to the surrounding stroma. This may sort out whether the stromal damage is important, too, or whether it is only the large dose to the epithelium itself that is of some importance.

I think this would also do away with your seeing these accompanying osteosarcomas and skin tumors.

KINETICS OF POPULATION OF BONE-FORMING CELLS IN THE NORMAL AND IRRADIATED RAT

N. F. Kember

Brookhaven National Laboratory, Upton, Long Island, New York

THE work of Reichard and Estborn;[1] Friedkin, Tilson and De Wayne;[2] Amano, Messier and Leblond[3] and Hughes[4] has shown that tritiated thymidine is a reliable tracer for DNA synthesis in cells. If an animal is killed within a few hours of an injection of tritiated thymidine, autoradiographs of tissue sections taken from the animal will show the positions of cells engaged in DNA synthesis, so that by this method the sites of active cell proliferation within a tissue may be determined.

In Fig. 1 the position of each cell that has taken up tritiated thymidine in one tissue section of bone is indicated, the uptake of labelled thymidine having been detected by stripping film autoradiography. The particular region of bone shown in Fig. 1 is the proximal third of a tibia from a young female rat (6–8 week old hybrid of August and Marshall strains). The animal was killed 6 hr after the injection of the labelled thymidine so the cells that had been labelled originally were in various stages of the mitotic cycle, some being still in the synthetic (S) or pre-mitotic (G2) phases, some undergoing division and others having completed division so that many pairs of labelled cells were seen on the autoradiograph. Previous studies[5] have shown that by 6 hours these labelled cells will not have moved appreciably from the site at which they were labelled nor will appreciable numbers have differentiated into other cell types.

No attempt was made to classify each labelled cell according to cell type but some general remarks can be made about the types of cells seen labelled in the various anatomical regions of the bone. The labelled cells in the epiphyseal cartilage plate could obviously be classified as chondrocytes together with the few labelled cells within the articular cartilage. The greatest concentration of labelled cells was found in the metaphysis in the band, about 500 μ in depth, immediately below the cartilage plate, that is, in the region of primary spongiosa. Most of the labelled cells in this band had little cytoplasm and large reticular nuclei and could be classified as the stem cells of the bone-forming series, together with a proportion of endothelial cells. Labelled cells with scant cytoplasm and large nuclei were also seen in the vascular spaces above the cartilage plate, in the zone of epiphyseal osteogenesis at the interior surface of the articular cartilage, on the periosteal surface of the metaphysis, where active re-sorption was in progress, and at the junction of the metaphysis and the diaphysis, where large clusters of osteoblasts were found on the endosteum. No labelled osteoclasts or osteocytes and few labelled osteoblasts have been seen in bone at this interval, i.e. 6 hr after injection of tritiated thy-midine.

At all other regions within the bone, the bone cell elements were indis-tinguishable from the marrow cells and these regions, where labelled marrow cells were observed, are indicated in Fig. 1 by shading. In these areas, wherever large nuclei which lay near the bone surfaces were seen labelled, these were included as "labelled cells", that is, labelled bone-forming cells, on the diagram. It should be noted that some of the other cells might also have been detected as lying on bone surfaces had serial sections been studied. It is likely, however, that more primitive progenitor marrow cells may be present in the metaphysis than in the diaphysis since the marrow space grows in length within the metaphysis.

Labelled cells were also found in the periosteum, particularly in the epichondral zone, and some labelled cells were seen within the cortical blood vessel canals.

The detailed pattern of cellular labelling shown in Fig. 1 agrees with the general descriptions of Messier and Leblond[6] and of Tonna[7] who have also used tritiated thymidine in bone cell studies.

This diagram (Fig. 1) represents just one instant in the distribution of labelled thymidine in bone. Bone growth is a dynamic process and the pattern of cell labelling is continuously changing. In a previous paper[5] the author has described in some detail the sequence of thymidine labelling in the cells of the rat metaphysis and it is relevent to outline those results here. In Fig. 2 are shown the results of this experiment in which a series of animals were killed at intervals ranging from 1 hr to 28 days after the injection of tritiated thymidine so that the time sequence of events could be followed. The results are plotted to show the numbers of labelled cells of each of four types counted within successive 125 μ depth bands down through the metaphysis, beginning immediately below the cartilage plate. The origin (base of the cartilage plate) has been moved progressively to the right at each time interval to show the movement of the cartilage plate relative to the diaphysis during growth. By plotting the results in this form the sequences of two changes in the pattern of cell labelling can be followed. The first change is the actual movement or migration of cells up through the metaphysis as the bone grows, the rate of migration being about 130 microns per day in a female rat of this age. The second change that occurs is the differentiation of one cell type into another, these results indicating that the bone-forming cells increase in numbers largely by the division of the mesenchymal cells which then differentiate into osteoblasts or osteoclasts. Labelled osteocytes are only found when the labelled precursors (probably osteoblasts) become embedded in bone. This differentiation sequence of the bone-forming cells is not yet fully established nor is there any standard nomenclature for the cell types seen within the metaphysis.

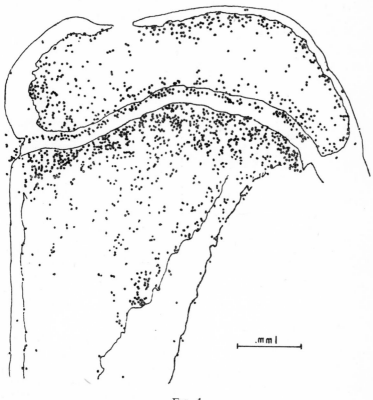

.m m l

FIG. 1.

Diagram showing the position of each labelled bone cell on an autoradiograph of one section from a rat injected with tritiated thymidine 6 hr before sacrifice.

The results plotted in Fig. 2 are derived from data on the metaphysis where the rates of cell migration are probably more rapid than at other sites within the bone. It is possible that other differentiation patterns may be found at other sites.

Under abnormal conditions more cells and cell types may take part in proliferative activity than under normal conditions. The uptake of tritiated thymidine in bone cells at intervals after a bone had been fractured was studied by Tonna and Cronkite[8] in the mouse femur. They describe a rapid and extensive response in the cells of the periosteum, the percentage of labelled cells increasing from 3 to 20 per cent of the population by

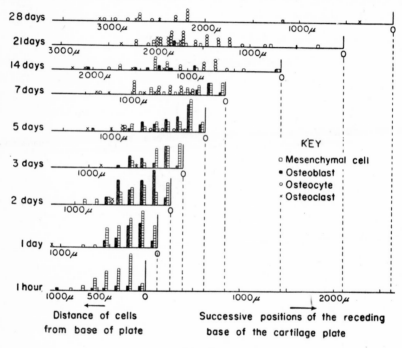

KEY

- ▫ Mesenchymal cell
- ● Osteoblast
- ○ Osteocyte
- × Osteoclast

Distance of cells
from base of plate

Successive positions of the receding
base of the cartilage plate

FIG. 2.

Distributions of labelling among four types of cells in the metaphysis at intervals of 1 hr to 28 days after injection of tritiated thymidine. The diaphysis of the bone is regarded as fixed and so the base of the epiphyseal cartilage plate has been shifted progressively to the right by distances equal to its growth at the various time intervals shown. Reproduced by courtesy of the British Editorial Society of Bone and Joint Surgery.

3 days after fracture. This response is seen in the periosteum in all ages of animals although the effect does decrease somewhat with age. It is likely that the flattened, mature osteoblasts in the periosteum take part in this proliferative activity and this implies that a diagram, such as Fig. 1, showing the sites of active proliferation in a normal bone does not include potential sites of abnormal cellular proliferation.

The endosteal cells do not appear to show much activity following fracture and it is felt that the internal callus is formed by periosteal cells that "leak" in before repair starts and by osteogenic cells lining the trabeculae in the marrow cavity. There are also the possibilities that reticulum cells in the marrow or wandering mesenchymal cells in the blood may take part in fracture repair. Thus, there are many types of cells present in bone that may increase their proliferative activity when stimulated by some injury to bone tissue.

Effects of Radiation on Bone Cell Proliferation

The effects of radiation on the proliferation of bone cells have not been studied in any detail but some preliminary studies using tritiated thymidine have been carried out and will be described briefly. Young female rats that had been irradiated were killed in pairs two hours after an injection of tritiated thymidine. Autoradiographs were prepared from sections of the tibia and standard areas in the primary spongiosa were scanned for labelled cells. The areas chosen were 500 by 500 μ squares immediately below the base of the epiphyseal cartilage plate. Three such areas were scanned on each section and the numbers of labelled cells in each were counted. The mean of these three counts gave a number which was used as an index of cell labelling in the metaphysis.

The first experiments were carried out on animals that were given single acute doses of 230 Kvp X-rays to one hind limb. The use of this quality of radiation made it necessary to calculate the actual dose absorbed by the cells in the intra-trabecular spaces. Following Spiers' method[9] an average factor of $\times(1\cdot75)$ was derived to correct from incident dose to the radiation dose absorbed by cells in the primary spongiosa.

In Fig. 3 are shown the variations in the chosen index of cell labelling with time after irradiation. The top series of curves are plotted from the results of the acute irradiation experiments and demonstrate that the bone cells have a similar radiation response to that observed in other biological materials. The initial fall in numbers of labelled cells is followed by an abortive recovery and then after the lower of the two doses there is a full recovery to normal by 16 days while the higher dose produces a more severe effect so that few cells were seen labelled even at 28 days after irradiation. These results are in good agreement with the studies of Woodard and Spiers[9] who used the alkaline phosphatase levels in bone as an index of radiation damage to the bone cells.

In the next series of curves the results of labelled cell counts on bones from continuously irradiated animals are presented. The rats were exposed to whole body irradiation from a Cs^{137} gamma source for 23 hours each day. It is seen that at high continuous irradiation levels the numbers of labelled cells fall off rapidly but that at 84 rads per day the bone is able to adapt to the continuous irradiation conditions so that the cells continue to divide but at a reduced rate. Even at 176 rads per day there is some

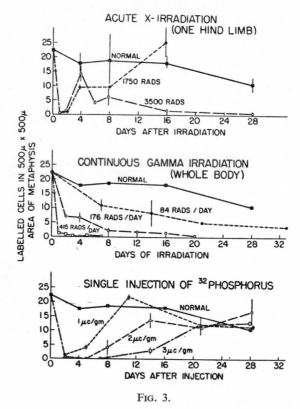

FIG. 3.

The effects of radiations on the numbers of metaphyseal cells taking up tritiated thymidine. Data based on counts of labelled cells in a 500 micron square area of the primary spongiosa at 2 hr after an injection of tritiated thymidine.

evidence of a leveling off after 4–8 days. This adaptation to continuous irradiation is analogous to that found in the gut epithelium and in the bone marrow (see paper by Lamerton in this volume). Labelled cells were found in a section from one animal that had been exposed for 9 weeks at 84 rads per day.

Although in this continuous irradiation experiment the whole body was exposed, the irradiation of the metaphysis was similar to that produced by bone-seeking isotopes emitting long-range beta rays and it should be possible to predict from these results the levels at which such bone-seeking isotopes will produce a sufficiently high initial dose rate in the metaphysis to stop cells taking up tritiated thymidine. In the lowest series of curves in Fig. 3 are plotted the results from tritiated thymidine uptake experiments at three injected dose levels of P^{32}. From autoradiographic studies[10] of radiation dosimetry it is known that all three injected dose levels delivered more than 300 rad to the cells of the primary spongiosa in the first day following injection, so that the immediate drop in numbers of labelled cells that occurred in all three P^{32} experiments was in agreement with the results of the continuous irradiation experiment. These results were also confirmed in one study using Am^{241} where the initial irradiation of the primary spongiosa is very non-uniform. Rats were injected with 1·5 micro-curies per kg weight, an injected dose that delivers an initial mean radiation dose of 82 rads per day (range: 20–400 rads per day) to the primary spongiosa and no significant fall in numbers of labelled cells was detected in these animals over the first few days following injection. If certain bone cells are able to adapt to continuous irradiation at some levels and not at others it follows that quite different patterns of irradiation damage may follows radiation dose rates that differ by not more than a factor of 2 or 4.

The series of graphs plotted in Fig. 3 show only the overall effect of various irradiation schemes on the numbers of cells synthesising DNA in the primary spongiosa. All types of labelled cells in the area, apart from obvious marrow cells, were included in the counts. Some evidence of the effects of radiations on the proportions of each cell type in the metaphysis was obtained. The most striking example is hidden in the data plotted in Fig. 3 from the results of the P^{32} experiments. It is seen that the numbers of labelled cells return to the normal value fairly rapidly, there being a complete recovery by 21 days even after the highest dose injected. Differential cell counts showed that 80 to 100% of the labelled cells in the metaphysis at these later times were spindle-shaped cells which normally comprise only 25 to 30% of the labelled cell population. It was not clear how this abnormal population of spindle cells arose and there are a number of possible explanations: (a) they could be more resistant as a cell type and divide rapidly to fill the spaces left by less resistant cells; (b) other types of surviving cells could differentiate abnormally into spindle cells; (c) migration could have taken place from regions outside the irradiated area. This proliferation of spindle cells was not observed in any of the other irradiation experiments.

These results have shown that there are a large variety of cells that may be a risk for the production of late radiation damage in bone. These include not only the cells in the areas of high or prolonged radiation dose but also cells that may migrate in from regions of low or zero dose to take part in repair processes. It is conceivable that such non-irradiated cells could eventually become cancerous. It is felt that these problems will only be solved by study of the responses of the cellular components of bone to irradiation, during both initial injury and also attempts at repair, remembering that these cellular effects are dependent on the distribution of radiation dose both in time and in space and that they will also be affected by vascular and hormonal disturbances.

ACKNOWLEDGEMENTS

Part of this work was carried out in the Physics Department of the Royal Cancer Hospital, London and part at the Brookhaven National Laboratory under the auspices of the U.S. Atomic Energy Commission. I wish to record my thanks to Prof. L. F. Lamerton and to Dr. H. Quastler for their encouragement and advice.

REFERENCES

1. P. REICHARD and B. ESTBORN, The Utilization of desoxyribosides in the synthesis of polynucleotides, J. Biol. Chem. **188**, 839–846 (1951).
2. M. FRIEDKIN, D. TILSON and R. DE WAYNE, Studies in DNA biosynthesis in embryonic tissue with thymidine C^{14}, J. Biol. Chem. **220**, 627–637 (1956).
3. M. AMANO, B. MESSIER and C. P. LEBLOND, Specificity of labelled thymidine as a DNA precursor in radioautography, J. Histochem. **7**, 153–155 (1959).
4. W. L. HUGHES, The metabolic stability of DNA, Kinetics of Cellular Proliferation, ed. F. STOHLMAN, Grune and Stratton, New York and London, p. 83 (1959).
5. N. F. KEMBER, Cell division in endochondral ossification, J. Bone and Joint Surg. **42B**, 824–839 (1960).
6. B. MESSIER and C. P. LEBLOND, Cell proliferation and migration as revealed by radioautography after injection of thymidine-H^3 into male rats and mice. Am. J. Anat. **106**, 247–285 (1960).
7. E. A. TONNA, The cellular complement of the skeletal system studied autoradiographically with tritiated thymidine during growth and aging, J. Biophys. Biochem. Cytol. (in press).
8. E. A. TONNA and E. P. CRONKITE, Cellular response to fracture studied with tritiated thymidine, J. Bone and Joint Surg. **43A**, 352–362 (1961).
9. H. Q. WOODARD and F. W. SPIERS, The effect of X-rays of different qualities on the alkaline phosphatase of living mouse bone, Brit. J. Radiol. **26**, 38–46 (1953).
10. J. P. M. BENSTED, N. M. BLACKETT and L. F. LAMERTON, Histological and Dosimetric considerations of bone tumour production with radioactive phosphorus Brit. J. Radiol. **34**, 160–175 (1961).

PART III

SOME ASPECTS OF Sr^{90} TOXICITY

PATHOLOGIC SEQUELAE IN BEAGLES FOLLOWING CONTINUOUS FEEDING OF SR^{90} AT A TOXIC LEVEL*

A. C. ANDERSEN AND M. GOLDMAN

School of Veterinary Medicine, University of California, Davis

IN 1956, a continuous Sr^{90} feeding program was established with a preliminary experiment to determine the toxicity of body burdens calculated to reach values of about 27 μc Sr^{90}/kg body weight at 19 months of age (one month after completing the feeding schedule). This report discusses clinical, subclinical, and postclinical syndromes manifested by the dogs throughout the experiment.

Late in 1956, a female beagle of normal size and conformation was isolated in a metabolism cage after being bred. Throughout gestation and lactation she was fed *ad libidum* a specially prepared radioactive diet; by weight, 60% dry ration containing 3% calcium and 2% phosphorus, 20% water (including the Sr^{90}), and 20% hamburger. Sr^{90} was maintained at a constant Sr^{90} to Ca ratio. In January 1957, the beagle whelped 4 pups (2 males; 2 females), which were maintained on the same diet until 18 months old. While on the radioactive ration, one female (5S2) was bred and whelped a litter of six pups, likewise maintained on the Sr^{90} diet. Ten dogs were kept on the Sr^{90} diet, and except for one survivor (5S2) were studied after sacrifice or death. The information obtained is sufficient to illustrate some of the effects which are found in dogs fed on a toxic level of Sr^{90} from *in utero* to early maturity. The deposition of radiostrontium following feeding and the subsequent retention curves were estimated from radiochemical analyses of bones and whole-body gamma ray (Bremsstrahlung) counting of survivors. Throughout the experiment, the skeletal dose rate was not constant since the fraction of beta energy absorbed increased with growth and size of the skeleton.[1] A smaller fraction of Sr^{90} was deposited during gestation and lactation than when fed directly. After the last feeding, the skeleton loses Sr^{90} by excretion and decay. All of these factors are taken into consideration in the estimate of dose rate and cumulative dose as presented in Fig. 1. During the feeding period, it is estimated that the daily dose rate reached 13 rads dropping to a minimum of 9 rad/day by two years after the radiostrontium feeding.

* Supported by USAEC.

320 A. C. ANDERSEN AND M. GOLDMAN

The dog (5S1) in this study which died from an osteogenic sarcoma 678 days after the last radioactive meal is estimated to have had a cumulative skeletal dose of 13,000 rads, delivered at about 10 rad per day. At the end of feeding, the skeleton was estimated to have had a body burden of 1·9 μc Sr^{90}/gm Ca, or a total body burden of about 400 μc Sr^{90}.

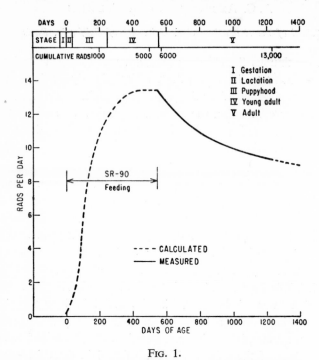

Fig. 1.

Skeletal dosage of beagle 5S1 fed Sr^{90} to 540 days of age.

A dam and stud of lineage comparable to that of the dogs fed Sr^{90} produced two sham-treated controls (male and female). Control data represent these dogs and those from our beagle colony.

Under the conditions of this experiment the effects of a toxic Sr^{90} level in the diet are noticeable quite soon. Histologic examination of the femur from a pup sacrificed at birth gave evidence of disturbed ossification although the skeleton appeared normal upon gross examination. Sections of the femur revealed alternate foci of necrosis and acellularity between active areas of osteogenesis. Despite histological evidence of defective ossification at birth, dogs maintained on the Sr^{90} diet showed normal development of the skeleton throughout growth, except for a sternal bulge. The xiphoid region protruded ventrally 2–3 cm until treated dogs were about one year old; then the defect subsided. Throughout growth, palpable lymph nodes and tonsils were estimated to be about one-half the size normal for the beagle. Peripheral blood examinations at monthly intervals showed the normal trend in values to maturity, but leukocytic values did not exceed 60–70% of the normal mean values for the beagle.[2] Leukocyte counts ranged from 5000 to 7000/mm³, but thrombocyte counts were normal, ranging from 110,000 to 430,000/mm³. At 4 years old, 910 days after Sr⁹⁰ treatment ceased, the surviving dog has not yet attained normal blood values.

Two highly malignant neoplasms were observed during Sr⁹⁰ administration. At 192 days of age (6½ mos.), one dog (5S5) showed signs of anorexia, bloody diarrhoea, and rapid loss of body weight; death occurred 5 days later. Readily apparent at necropsy were marked icterus, widespread hemorrhage, and multiple neoplastic growths. Histological examination revealed the neoplasm to be a primitive type of lymphosarcoma (Figs. 2a, 2b).* As shown in Figure 2a, the lymphoblastic sarcoma had

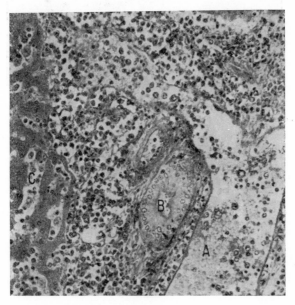

FIG. 2a.

Sr⁹⁰ induced lymphoblastic sarcoma. Invasion of portal triad and hepatic parenchyma. (A) blood vessel containing metastatic cells, (B) bile duct, (C) hepatic laminae. Bouin's nitrocellulose, hematoxylin and eosin (×100).

* Synonyms: malignant lymphoma, reticulosarcoma, reticulum cell sarcoma, large round cell sarcoma.

the characteristic feature of penetrating interstitial tissue; its metastatic ability was evidenced by lymphoblastic cells in peripheral blood during terminal illness and metastatic cells within the lumen of blood vessels after death.

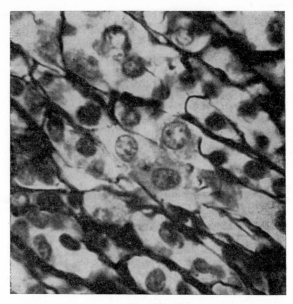

FIG. 2b.

Higher magnification of lymphoblastic sarcoma, shown in Figure 2a, depicting various size cells and reticulum stroma. Bouin's, nitrocellulose, Foot and Menard method for reticulum ($\times$ 1200).

A similar case occurred in one dog (5S3) at 452 days of age. Palpation of the retropharyngeal lymph nodes revealed progressive enlargement as terminal illness progressed. Upon necropsy, at 471 days of age, widespread hemorrhage and metastatic neoplasms resembled the other case. Blood examinations before death demonstrated a total leukocyte count of 9250 per mm^3, of which 83 per cent were lymphoblastic. Features of this neoplasm are unlike leukemia in that the vascular system merely acts as a vehicle for metastases.

Two dogs were maintained for longevity studies. At 1178 days (39 mos.) of age, one dog (5S1) exhibited a posterior paresis that progressed to posterior paralysis. An osseous neoplasm in the 5th lumbar vertebra was seen roentgenographically. The animal had to be sacrificed 7 weeks later. Roentgenograms (Fig. 3) at weekly intervals during the dog's illness gave evidence that the diameter of the neoplasm doubled in volume every 16

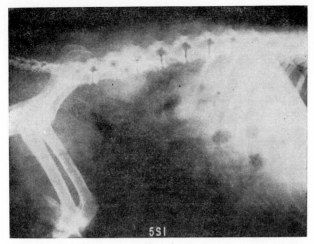

FIG. 3.

Roentgenogram of osseous neoplasm in the 5th lumbar vertebra (551).

days. At death, the tumor had spread to the 4th, 5th, and 6th lumbar vertebrae with extensions into neighboring muscle. The neoplasm was identified histologically as an osteogenic sarcoma (Fig. 3a) with multiple

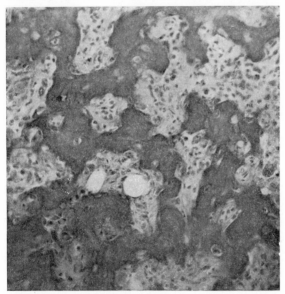

FIG. 3a.

Photomicrograph of osteogenic sarcoma shown in Fig. 3. The primary neoplasm consisted of rather uniformly distributed osseous and osteoid tissue. Bouin's decalcified (formic acid method), nitrocellulose, hematoxylin and eosin (×100).

21*

small metastases to the lung (Fig. 3b). Upon gross and microscopic study, the organ systems (including parathyroids and bulbus oculi) appeared normal. However, other skeletal damage was apparent both radiographically and histologically.

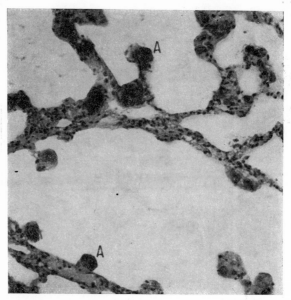

FIG. 3b.

(A) multiple islands of osteogenic sarcoma metastases into lung parenchyma from primary neoplasm in lumbar vertebra. Dog 5S1. Bouin's, nitrocellulose, Hematoxylin and eosin (×200).

A 5-mm slice of the femur revealed two pathognomic lesions from radioisotope damage (Fig. 4). Autoradiograph (Fig. 4, A) demonstrated a circular non-radioactive area about 1·5 cm in diameter in the proximal metaphysis. This semi-solid noncalcified mass contained uniformly distributed pyknotic nuclei as evidence of an aseptic osseous necrosis; the necrotic area was avascular and encapsulated by dense bone. Figure 4, A and B, also demonstrated cortical areas of decreased bone density and radioactivity. Such areas have been studied histologically, and roentgenographically in the last survivor (5S2) in this experiment.

Histological study of cortical bone revealed alternate areas of osseous necrosis and repair. Figure 5a, A, shows an area of cortical bone erosion containing necrotic osseous tissue and mesenchymal elements between spicules of compact bone. Histological study of surrounding areas gave evidence that osseous necrosis precedes fibrous tissue replacement (Fig. 5b,). Thus, this lesion may be described as a circumscribed osteolytic fibrosis that is apparently progressive with advancing age. A similar lesion following radium deposition has been described in humans.[3]

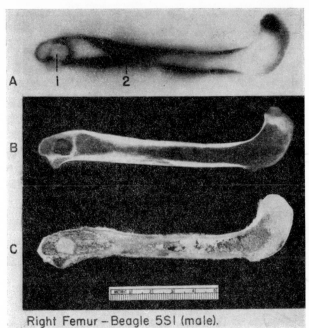

Right Femur – Beagle 5S1 (male).

FIG. 4.

Femur slice, beagle 5S1. (A-1) autoradiograph showing absence of Sr^{90} in aseptic necrotic area and (A-2) decreased Sr^{90} content of circumscribed osteolytic area in diaphysis. (B) roentgenogram. (C) photograph.

We have recently observed the rate of radiation-induced osteolytic fibrosis in the dog. As shown in Figs. 6a and 6b, the lesion is not confined to either endosteal or periosteal surfaces, and almost doubles in severity in about one year. Dogs surviving to maturity on this Sr^{90} level showed an increased radioopacity in the metaphyseal region of certain long bones. This non-specific lesion, easily recognized in roentgenograms of the distal radius, is apparently irreparable.

In summary, this experiment demonstrated the sequence of pathological events in dogs fed a toxic level of Sr^{90} to early maturity (18 months of age). Malignant soft tissue neoplasms (lymphoblastic or reticulum cell sarcomas) preceded bone neoplasia. Similar results have been reported in mice, and the opinion is held that soft tissue neoplasia occur through

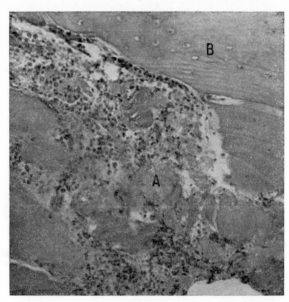

FIG. 5a.

Erosion of compact bone in diaphysis of femur (Fig. 4, A-2). (A) necrotic osseous
mass surrounded by mesenchymal elements—osteoclasts, osteoblasts, and fibroblasts. (B) normal compact bone. Such lesions were repaired by fibrosis. Bouin's,
decalcified (formic acid method), nitrocellulose (×100).

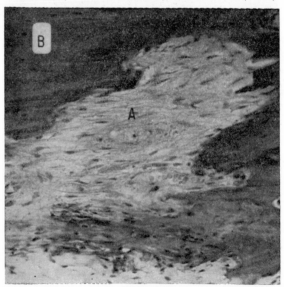

FIG. 5b.

Photomicrograph of osteolytic fibrotic area shown in Figure 4 (A-2). Fibrous tissue
(A) has replaced necrotic bone. (B) normal appearing compact bone. Bouin's, nitrocellulose (×200).

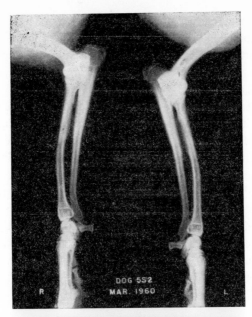

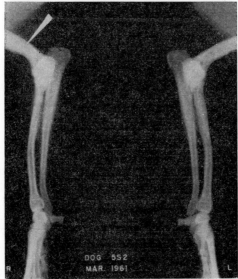

FIG. 6a and 6b.

Anterior limbs of beagle 5S2. Roentgenograms were taken at 3 and 4 years of age (1½ and 2½ years after Sr^{90} treatment). Comparison of the diaphysis of humerus, radius and ulna reveal the slow progression of circumscribed areas of osteolytic fibrosis. A precancerous lesion is present in the distal humerus (arrow, Fig. 6b). Note irregularity and loss of continuity. The intense radioopacity of the metaphyseal region in the distal radii persists.

indirect mechanisms rather than direct irradiation.[4,5] Two years after Sr^{90} administration, one dog succumbed to osteogenic sarcoma in lumbar vertebrae. Spontaneous osteogenic sarcomas are not uncommon in the dog, but their occurrence is largely restricted to long bones of large breeds.[6,7] As discussed by Upton et al., the mechanism of radiation-induced neoplasms appears to be a complex multistage process. The authors are in agreement with the opinions of some investigators that osseous necrosis and stages of fibrosis constitute a pre-cancerous lesion for osteogenic sarcoma.[9,10] The long-term effect of Sr^{90}, besides neoplasms, is a slow process in bone (osteolytic fibrosis) that forms non-osseous low-density tissue. Lacroix[11] has observed that bone remodelling is a continuous process throughout life with individual bone responses to radiostrontium being influenced by age-dependent variables. Consequently, an adequate understanding of the effects of a constant Sr^{90} environment in osseous tissue must include consideration of the complex variables which contribute to the net effect.

REFERENCES

1. C. W. Mays, Escape of beta-energy from the skeleton, Radiobiology Laboratory, Annual Report COO-218, 113–120 (1959).
2. A. C. Andersen and W. Gee, Normal blood values in the beagle, Vet. Med. 53, 135–138 (1958).
3. W. B. Looney, Late skeletal roentgenographic, histopathological, autoradiographic and radiochemical findings following radium deposition, Am. J. Roenthenol. Radium Therapy Nuclear Med. 75, 559–572 (1956).
4. M. P. Finkel, P. J. Bergstrand and B. O. Biskis, The consequences of the continuous ingestion of Sr^{90} by mice, Radiology 74, 458–467 (1960).
5. M. P. Finkel, Late effects of internally deposited radioisotopes in laboratory animals, Radiation Research, Suppl. 1, 265–279, (1959).
6. S. W. Nielsen, J. D. Schroder and D. L. T. Smith, The pathology of osteogenic sarcoma in dogs, J. Am. Vet. Med. Assoc. 124, 28–35 (1954).
7. R. S. Brodey, J. T. McGrath and H. Reynolds, A clinical and radiological study of canine bone neoplasms, Part I, J. Am. Vet. Med. Assoc. 134, 53–71 (1959).
8. A. C. Upton, A. W. Kimball, J. Forth, K. W. Christenberry and W. H. Benedict, Some delayed effects of atom-bomb radiation in mice, Cancer Research 20, Part 2, 1–62 (1960).
9. L. A. Cherkaskii, Bone changes in rats after the injection of radioactive strontium, Voprosy Onkologii 2, 275–284 (1956).
10. L. F. Lamerton, Radiosotopes in the skeleton: Considerations of radiation dosage in relation to bone damage (Section IV), in Radioisotopes in the Biosphere (R. S. Caldecott and L. A. Snyder, eds.), University of Minnesota, Minneapolis, Chapt. 26, 382–400, (1960).
11. P. Lacroix, Bone and Cartilage, in The Cell (J. Brachet and A. E. Mirsky, eds.), Academic Press, N.Y., Vol. V, Part 2, Chapt. 4, 219–266, (1961).

PATHOLOGY OF IMBIBED SR^{90} IN RATS AND MONKEYS*

G. W. Casarett, L. W. Tuttle, and R. C. Baxter

Department of Radiation Biology, University of Rochester School of Medicine and Dentistry, Rochester, New York

The long-term toxicity and tumorigenic effects of radioactive strontium have been studied experimentally in monkeys, dogs, rabbits, rats, and mice following intravenous or intraperitoneal injection,[1-11] and in dogs, rabbits, rats and mice following ingestion.[12-15] Histopathologic studies of effects of radioactive strontium on bone have been done on several experimental species.[16-18] Williams[19] has recently reviewed many of the main lines of biological research on radioactive strontium.

This is a report of the tumorigenic effects and some of the histopathology observed in experiments being conducted by Tuttle and his associates on the long-term toxicity of imbibed carrier-free aqueous solutions of equilibrium mixtures of Sr^{90}–Y^{90} (pH 2·5–3) in Long-Evans rats and Rhesus monkeys.

The handling and treatment of the experimental animals, the *in vivo* monitoring of body burden of Sr^{90} by means of Bremsstrahlen counts, and the determination of total amounts of Sr^{90} in the carcasses at death, are described in a previous publication.[20] Radiation dosage patterns are being worked out by Tuttle *et al.* for future publication.

Skeletal roentgenographs were made periodically and at death for detection of bone tumors. At death the animals were autopsied, gross observations were recorded, and samples of all observed lesions and abnormalities, and samples of femur, were taken for microscopic study.

In the monkey experiments seven young monkeys were given 500 or 1000 μc of Sr^{90} by gavage in equal daily doses over periods of 5 to 10 days. The experimental factors and causes of death are presented in Table 1.

The leukemia found in monkey P was "monocytic", probably a variant of lymphatic leukemia. The differential white cell counts revealed 11 per cent monocytes. Neoplastic growths found in bone marrow, kidney, lymph nodes, stomach, small intestine, liver, spleen and pancreas contained

* This paper is based on work performed under contract with the United States Atomic Energy Commission at the University of Rochester Atomic Energy Project, Rochester, New York.

TABLE 1

Imbibition of Sr⁹⁰ by Rhesus Monkeys

Item	Monkey						
	S	P	B	504	507	508	515
Sex	Female	Male	Male	Female	Male	Female	Female
Dose (μc)	500	500	500	1000	1000	1000	1000
Age at dosing (y)	3–6	4–8	4–9	3–6	3–3·5	2–4	3–7
Survival (months)	35	48	80(alive)	36	4	18	45
Death weight (kg)	4·8	9·0	—	5·3	3·6	4·3	5·8
Sr⁹⁰ burden death(μc)	34·0	45·0	—	75·8	200·0	116·3	33·1
Sr⁹⁰/kg at death(μc)	7·1	5·0	—	14·3	55·6	27·0	5·7
Est. skeletal dose (rad)	4500	4300	—	9500	4500	9100	4700
Cause of death	para-sites	leuke-mia	—	chondro-sarcoma	pancyto-penia	para-sites[a]	osteo-sarcoma

[a] Esophagostomum.

predominantly large cells with the characteristics of monocytes, many lymphocytes, and a small number of immature myeloid cells. The chondrosarcoma in monkey 504 originated in the distal end of the left femur and metastasized to both lungs, inguinal and mediastinal lymph nodes. The osteosarcoma in monkey 515 originated in the humerus and metastasized to lung.

In the rat experiments, groups of rats of different ages were fed various doses of Sr⁹⁰ in their drinking water in equal daily doses over periods of 10 to 30 days, as seen in Table 2.

TABLE 2

Imbibition of Sr⁹⁰ by Long-Evans Rats Experimental Groups

Rat groups[a]	No. of rats male female	Days dosed	Total dose (μc)	Skeletal Sr⁹⁰ 5 months (μc)	Age last dose (days)	Survival days (av.)	Ave. age at death (days)
A–Sr	32 32	10	330	1	425	380	805
A–Con.	26 11	—	—	—	(425)	322	747
B–Sr	40 40	10	650	2	346	372	718
B–Con.	10 10	—	—	—	(346)	328	614
C–Sr	40 40	30	790	11	117	354	471
C–Con.	20 20	—	—	—	(117)	601	718
D–Sr	20 20	10	464	33	40	106	146
D–Con.	20 20	—	—	—	(40)	700	740

[a] Con. = Control, Sr = Strontium.

There was no shortening of lifespan in the A–Sr and B–Sr groups, and the life-lengthening which may be suggested by the figures is questionable, owing to the small numbers of rats in the control groups. Group C–Sr showed moderately marked shortening of lifespan (about 34%), and in group D–Sr this effect was marked (about 80%). The effect on survival time of 464 μc Sr⁹⁰ given in 10 days to the immature 40-day old rats was marked, while there was no effect of 650 μc given in 10 days to adult rats 346 days old.

The incidence of neoplasms is presented in Table 3.

TABLE 3

Imbibition of Sr⁹⁰ *by Long-Evans Rats*
Percent Incidence of Neoplasms[a]

Neoplasm	Experimental groups							
	A		B		C		D	
	Sr	Control	Sr	Control	Sr	Control	Sr	Control
Osteosarcoma	0·00	0·00	0·00	0·00	27·50	0·00	17·50	0·00
Skin Carcinoma (Face)	0·00	0·00	7·50	0·00	11·25	0·00	0·00	0·00
Leukemia	0·00	0·00	3·75	0·00	6·25	0·00	0·00	0·00
Reticulum Cell Sarcoma	6·25	13·50	6·25	5·00	1·25	20·00	2·50	5·00
Other Malignancies	0·00	2·70[b]	7·50[c]	0·00	0·00	0·00	0·00	0·00
Mammary Fibroadenoma[d]	18·75	18·20	12·50	10·00	0·00	5·00	0·00	5·00
Other Benign Tumors	3·10	0·00	1·25	0·00	0·00	2·50	0·00	2·50
All Malignancies	6·25	16·20	26·25	10·00	46·25	20·00	20·00	5·00
All Benign Tumors	12·50	5·40	7·50	5·00	0·00	7·50	0·00	2·50
All Tumors	18·75	21·60	33·75	15·00	46·25	27·50	20·00	7·50

[a] Percent incidence of neoplasms is equal to percentage of rats with neoplasms.

[b] Bile duct carcinoma.

[c] Two hepatic carcinomas, two fibrosarcomas, one mammary carcinoma, and one uterine carcinoma.

[d] Mammary fibroadenomas in females only; incidence calculated for females.

Osteosarcomas were found only in the C–Sr group (27·5%) and D–Sr group (17·5%), the younger rats with the larger skeletal burdens of strontium. The cumulative incidence of rats with osteosarcoma in these groups are plotted in Fig. 1. The lesser incidence in the group with the highest body burden (D–Sr) is probably due to the markedly reduced after-sur-

332　　　　　　　G. W. CASARETT *et al.*

vival (av. 106 days). The survival times for rats with osteosarcoma in the C–Sr group ranged from 199 to 536 days, and for rats in the D–Sr group from 127 to 196 days.

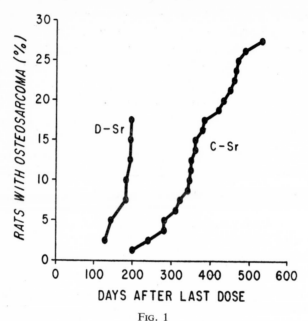

Fig. 1

Cumulative incidence of osteosarcoma.

The osteosarcomas and the metastases were of several types histologically, but were all osteogenic in that some osteoid or bone was formed. There were fibroblastic types, some that resembled angiosarcoma, others producing relatively mature cancerous bone, other anaplastic types resembling reticulum cell sarcoma, some producing cartilage as well as bone, and some mixed types.

Squamous-cell carcinoma of the skin of the face was found only in the B–Sr group (7·5%) and C–Sr group (11·25%). The survival times of rats with this tumor ranged from 378 to 568 days for the B–Sr group and from 297 to 462 days in the C–Sr group. There was probably insufficient dose in the A–Sr group and insufficient after-survival in the D–Sr group for this tumor. Induction of this type of tumor in rats and mice by radioactive strontium has been reported previously,[6,11,14] following both injection and ingestion.

Leukemia (all cases lymphatic except one myeloid type), characterized by hematologic findings and widespread neoplastic growths in various organs, was found only in the B–Sr group (3·75%) and C–Sr group (6·25%). The survival times for leukemic rats ranged from 325 to 463 days in the B–Sr group and from 313 to 545 days in the C–Sr group. Presumably there was insufficient dose in the A–Sr group and insufficient after-survival in the D–Sr group for induction of leukemia.

Reticulum cell lymphosarcoma originating usually in abdominal lymphatic tissue is a fairly common neoplasm in nontreated Long-Evans rats. There was no significant change in the incidence of this neoplasm with strontium treatment, except perhaps for a reduction of incidence in the C–Sr group.

The data suggest a small increase in the incidence of other malignant neoplasms (in the aggregate) in the B–Sr group.

Mammary fibroadenoma, a fairly common tumor in nontreated female rats with advanced age, was not changed significantly in incidence by strontium treatment, except perhaps for the reduction of the incidence to zero in the C–Sr and D–Sr groups, which exhibited reduction of lifespan. There were no significant changes related to treatment in the incidence of other benign neoplasms.

There was significant increase in incidence of chronic interstitial nephritis (mild to marked in degree) only in the B–Sr group (18·7%), as compared with zero incidence in the B–control group. This disease was rare or absent in all other groups, treated or nontreated.

The distal half of the femur was studied routinely microscopically, to observe effects of the strontium on the marrow and on the cartilage plate in the zone of endochondral ossification.

In nontreated rats 34 months old the metaphysial and epiphysial marrow is generally mildly hypoplastic ,and involution of the cartilage plate is marked. In group A–Sr the marrow was generally slightly hypoplastic as compared with A–controls of comparable age, and the involution of the cartilage disc was marked by the 15th month after treatment (29 months of age). In the B–Sr group the marrow was generally mildly hypoplastic as compared with controls, and cartilage plate involution was marked by the 10th month after treatment (21 months of age); and the plate was nearly completely converted to bone by the 16th month after treatment (27th month of age). In the C–Sr group, in femurs not containing osteosarcoma, the marrow was generally moderately or markedly hypoplastic, not only in the epiphysis and metaphysis, but often in the diaphysis as well. In many cases there were regions of fibrous and relatively acellular marrow, with obliterated blood vessels and reduced vascularity, containing scattered atypical connective tissue cells. Associated with this damage was severe damage of the cartilage disc, with detachment of the primary spongiosa and failure of resorption of the secondary metaphysial spongiosa. Cartilage plate involution was markedly advanced in time, being complete or nearly complete, with conversion of most of the plate to bone, by the 12th month after treatment (16 months of age). In the case of the immature rats in the D–Sr group, the femurs not containing osteosarcoma revealed the development of extreme or nearly extreme hypoplasia of the marrow in epiphysis, metaphysis, and diaphysis, with much fibrosis and vascular damage and reduction, and the presence of atypical connective tissue cells. The marrow damage was so severe that in many cases marrow invasion into the columns of cartilage cells of the disc was stopped, while active proliferation of the cartilage cells was resumed, thereby resulting in over-growth of the cartilage into the metaphysis. There was failure of resorption of metaphysial cartilage and spongiosa, and failure of transformation of metaphysial spongiosa to bone. Associated with these changes there was frequent incorporation of cartilage and fibrous marrow into the cortical bone, which was associated in some cases with fracture and de-formation of bone.

Many or most of the rats in the A–Sr, B–Sr, and C–Sr groups, and rela-tively fewer rats in the D–Sr group, showed in epiphysial or metaphysial marrow spaces masses of amorphous or coarse-fibered calcified material, sometimes containing bits of osteoid or bone, suggesting abortive attempts at bone formation. In the A–Sr and B–Sr groups, such masses were often surrounded by relatively normal marrow and showed evidence of resorption. In the C–Sr and D–Sr groups, however, the production of fibrous, hypo-vascular marrow together with continuing attempts at osteogenesis seemed to lead to the production of immature osteoid or bone structures in marrow spaces, and eventually in some cases to the development of bone sarcoma in such structures.

The atypical connective tissue cells which arose in the fibrous marrow prior to the development of immature osteoid structures in the marrow spaces are difficult to ascribe exactly to well established classes, but their structures suggest atypical fibroblasts and reticular cells, and incompletely differentiated osteoblasts and osteoclasts. With the advent of such cells there appeared formations of threads or spicules of osteoid material which developed into more advanced growth of immature cancerous bone, often resembling osteoid osteomata, especially in the metaphysis near the carti-lage disc. These growths usually developed an attachment to the carti-lage plate and progressed through the metaphysis toward the diaphysis. Finally, in tissues of this kind the atypical cells, especially near the edges of the atypical growth, sometimes acquired a pleomorphic or anaplastic character and revealed increased mitotic activity. With these changes the tissue took on the characteristics of a malignant tumor, with more rapid growth and less differentiation, the vascularity of the growing tissue increased, and the growth became invasive, with destruction of the osteoid tissue in the metaphysis and of cortical bone. The osteogenic sarcomas seemed to arise chiefly in metaphysial regions, and extension to the outside of bone seemed to occur most often at the joining of the cortical bone and epiphysis.

REFERENCES

1. G. M. EDINGTON, J. M. JUDD and A. H. WARD, Delayed toxicity of radiostrontium in monkeys, *Nature* 175, 33 (1955).

2. M. P. FINKEL, J. LESTINA, G. M. SCRIBNER, H. LISCO, R. J. FLYNN and A. M. BRUES, Toxicity of radiostrontium in dogs, USAEC Document ANL 5426: 33–37 (1955).

3. M. P. FINKEL, R. J. FLYNN and B. O. BISKIS, Pathologic consequences of Sr^{90} in growing beagles. Interim observations, *Rad. Res.* 2, 3 (1959).

4. W. S. S. JEE, J. S. ARNOLD and T. H. COCHRAN, On the genesis of osteogenic sarcoma in dogs, *Anat. Rec.* 127, 423 (1957).

5. B. J. STOVER, J. H. DOUGHERTY, C. W. MAYS and C. E. REHFELD, Interim report of studies of Sr^{90} in adult beagles, Div. of Radiobiology, Department of Anatomy, Univ. of Utah College of Medicine, COO-221: 1–14 (1960).

6. J. F. KUZMA and G. ZANDER, Cancerogenic effects of Ca^{45} and Sr^{89} in Sprague–Dawley rats, *A.M.A. Arch. Path.* 63, 198–206 (1957).

7. A. M. BRUES, Biological hazards and toxicity of radioactive isotopes, *J. Clin. Invest.* 28: 1286–1296 (1949).

8. H. LISCO, M. P. FINKEL and A. M. BRUES, Carcinogenic properties of radioactive fission products and of plutonium. *Radiology* 49, 361–363 (1947).

9. M. OWEN, H. A. SISSONS and J. M. VAUGHAN, The effect of single injection of high dose of Sr^{90} in rabbits, *Brit. J. Cancer* 11, 229 (1957).

10. M. P. FINKEL, H. LISCO and A. M. BRUES, Toxicity of strontium^{-89} in mice: malignant bone tumors, USAEC Document ANL 5378: 106–117 (1955).

11. M. P. FINKEL, B. O. BISKIS AND G. M. SCRIBNER, The influence of strontium^{-90} upon lifespan and neoplasms of mice, *2nd UNIC on Peaceful Uses of Atomic Energy* 22, 65–70 (1958).

12. A. C. ANDERSEN *et al.*, The effects of continual Sr^{90} ingestion during the growth period of the beagle and its relation to Ra^{226} toxicity. 3rd Annual Progress Report, AEC Project No. 6, U. of California, Davis (1960).

13. E. D. DOWNIE, S. MACPHERSON, E. N. RAMSDEN, H. A. SISSONS and J. VAUGHAN, Effect of daily feeding of Sr^{90} to rabbits, *Brit. J. Cancer* 13, 408–423 (1959).

14. G. W. CASARETT, J. CONLEY, B. J. HENDERSON and L. W. TUTTLE, Late pathologic effects of imbibed Sr^{90} in bones of rats. *Rad. Res.* 9, 100 (1958).

15. M. P. FINKEL, B. S. BERGSTRAND and B. O. BISKIS, Consequences of the continuous ingestion of Sr^{90} by mice, *Radiology* 74, 458–467 (1960).

16. W. S. S. JEE, Autoradiographic and histopathologic studies of beagle puppies administered intravenously with Sr^{90}. USAEC Document AECU 3109: 68–70 (1955).

17. W. S. S. JEE and J. S. ARNOLD, Radioisotopes in the teeth of dogs. I. The distribution of plutonium, radiothorium, and strontium and the sequence of histopathologic changes in teeth containing plutonium. *Arch. Oral. Biol.* **2**, 215–238 (1960).

18. M. HELLER, Bone, in *Histopathology Of Irradiation From External And Internal Sources*, ed. W. BLOOM, McGraw–Hill, N.Y., 70–103 (1948).

19. K. WILLIAMS, Strontium studies. United Kingdom Atomic Energy Authority Research Group Report AERE-R3423, H.M. Stationery Office (1960).

20. L. W. TUTTLE, R. C. BAXTER, M. GOLDMAN and W. F. BALE, The metabolism and toxicology of Sr^{90} in the rat. Rationale, experimental procedures, pilot experiments. USAEC Document UR-424 (1959).

DISCUSSION

RAY: First I have some comments on Dr. Furth's paper. If I am not misquoting him, he said that hormones are not carcinogenic, and he also commented on the fact that the water-soluble hormones of the pituitary had never been shown to be related to cancer.

I would like to recall the work of Moon, Evans, Simpson, Reinhardt, Asling and Chao Ho Li, who showed that pituitary growth hormone given over long periods of time results in a marked incidence of soft tissue and bone tumors.

One of the interesting things in both Dr. Andersen's and Dr. Furth's papers was the reference to injury and repair. Those of us who are involved in clinical medicine frequently see instances when injury results in a stimulus to reparative processes, but other cases where extensive injury caused an inhibition of repair and ensuing necrosis.

I am reminded of some studies on fractures healing in the presence of plutonium. Some of the fractures showed a remarkable acceleration of the healing processes, whereas the fractures we have seen here with isotopes deposited in the callus have in some instances demonstrated delayed healing. Again I think this is a question of the degree of injury versus repair.

One is tempted to become philosophical about this and say that all organisms from single cells to humans and even some societies respond to injury by reparative processes provided the injury isn't too severe.

While looking at Dr. Andersen's beautiful sections the thought arose that it would be a great challenge to compare the changes seen in this slides, and those shown in a previous part of the meeting, with changes due to causes other than radiation: the changes in bone resulting from varicosities (described years ago by Brailsford), the changes resulting from severe arteriosclerosis and the changes in fibrous dysplasia. One can't help but think that there must be some common denominator and that possibly this common denominator is circulation.

One person who is a great protagonist for the theory that many of the changes in bone are the result of altered circulation is Dr. Trueta. He has recently suggested the osteoblast may be derived from the endothelial cell of the blood vessel, and he has some dramatic photomicrographs that are quite convincing.

DOUGHERTY: Bone growth is dependent upon pituitary hormones. I wonder if this isn't a factor in the difficulties in dosimetry, because we are dealing with a constantly changing environment as far as bone cell proliferation is concerned—an hormonal effect. Probably the real baseline animal is the hypophysectomized, irradiated animal in which one produces events occurring in bone which will serve for comparison.

I would wish that all of us should consider the role of growth hormone in growth of bone, the role of thyroid in growth of bone, the role of testosterone in closure of the epiphyses, the role of estrogens in the closure of the epiphyses and the growth of the metaphysis and the importance and absolute necessity for thyroid hormone in order to form chondroitin sulfate, which is the very substrate of calcification.

In other words, I don't think we can leave these things out of our thinking and deal with radiation alone.

WENGER: I have no special comments on the papers, but I wanted to say some words about our work in Geneva. We have started now with the human contamination with strontium at low level; but our work is just beginning, and so we have no results and no bone slides to show to you. I am sorry to come here with so few results.

FINKEL: I shall make only a few comments about the papers given this morning. It is very gratifying to see that other people doing some of the same things that we have done have gotten results very similar to ours. For example, the bone section that Dr. Andersen showed is very much like some of our dog bone sections. And the histologic changes in the rat femur that Dr. Casarett described resemble the histologic changes we have seen in the mouse femur.

In the event that everyone would like to hear what we are doing in the Laboratory at present, I shall take just a few minutes to tell you. It seems from many of the papers that we have heard so far at this Symposium that our chief function has been to provide data for other people to work with. So, if you would like to know what sort of information you will have to play with reasonably soon, I can outline it for you.

We have several different types of experiments in progress. One that may be of particular interest to you involves 2250 CF-1 female mice that have had a single intravenous injection of Ra^{226}. We are looking only for osteosarcomas. This experiment is a year old, and within another year or two we should have a lot of data for you. You may recall that the radium dose-response curve for osteosarcomas in CF-1 mice from a previous experiment is not very satisfactory. That is, it reaches a rather low plateau, and then it decreases as the amount of radium administered increases. Since radium toxicity is often used as a baseline for extrapolating to man, we thought it wise to repeat this phase of the experiment.

The next experiment along this line that we will do, as soon as Finkel's fancy individual mouse cage has been developed, will involve 20,000 CF-1 female mice and a single intravenous injection of Sr^{90}. Here again we will be looking only for osteosarcomas and the dose-response curve.

We have several studies in progress that are much more fascinating than determining dose-response curves. For example, we know that when we give a single intravenous injection of a radiostope, such as Sr^{90}, there is a relatively large amount in the time of injection, but this amount decreases very rapidly. Perhaps 15 per cent of the initial Sr^{90} remains 150 days later. We also know that at about 150 days after injection mice begin to die with malignant bone tumors. We are trying to find out whether the osteosarcomas were induced at the time of injection or at some later time. This information is crucial in estimating the dose that induced the tumor.

The theory of carcinogenesis that Dr. Furth proposed in his paper this morning is consistent with our data on the induction of osteosarcomas in mice. It seems that the potential neoplastic change occurs shortly after injection but that a second event is required before this change can be expressed. The second event occurs in a Gaussian fashion, and the result is that the tumors subsequently appear with a normal frequency distribution. If the amount of material injected is highly carcinogenic, the first tumor can be detected roentgenographically about 100 days after injection, and the first death with tumor will occur at about 150 days.

What we would like to know is how the frequency distribution of tumors changes as the amount of Sr^{90} administered changes. That is, if we give half the amount, will the origin of the curve or its peak occur at the same time, or at a later time. In other words, will the pattern of tumor appearance be similar, or will it be entirely different.

By examining animals radiographically at weekly intervals after injection, we can detect the tumors as they first appear. Recording neoplasia at the time of roentgeno-graphic appearance gives quite a different picture of induction rate than recording them at the time the animals die. With this technique we plan to check the frequency of tumors after different amounts of the same isotope, after different isotopes, among animals of different ages, animals of different strains, and animals of both sexes. Some of these studies are already in progress.

The hormonal influence in tumor induction has been mentioned on several occasions during this Symposium. We are certain that in CF-1 mice there is a marked difference between the sexes in their carcinogenic response to radio-strontium. For once we had enough room to keep CF-1 males in an experiment. They fight and have to be caged individually. In this experiment the incidence of tumors in the females probably will be close to 80 per cent, and the incidence in the males probably will be less than 10 per cent. This difference may well have an hormonal basis.

BONE-SEEKING RADIONUCLIDES IN MINIATURE SWINE*

R. O. McClellan, L. K. Bustad, W. J. Clarke, N. L. Dockum,
J. R. McKenney and H. A. Kornberg

Biology Laboratory, Hanford Laboratories, General Electric Company, Richland, Washington

Sr⁹⁰ TOXICITY

IN ORDER to contribute toward defining relatively safe levels of dietary Sr^{90} intake for man, a long-term daily feeding experiment of this radionuclide in miniature swine was initiated at Hanford in March, 1959. The Pitman-Moore miniature swine used in the study are omnivores which weigh 60–70 kg when mature[1] and whose dietary requirements, gastrointestinal tract and bone mass are quite comparable to those of man. The estimated lifespan is 15–20 years. These favorable physiological factors and the need for extension of Sr^{90} toxicity studies to

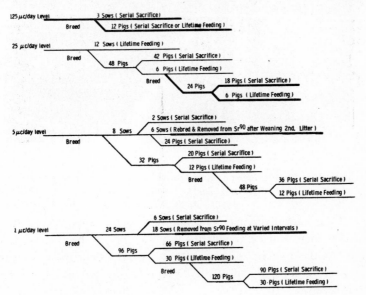

FIG. 1.
Experimental design of Sr^{90} toxicity study in miniature swine.

* Work performed under Contract No. AT(45–1)–1350 between the Atomic Energy Commission and the General Electric Company.

another animal species, in addition to the smaller laboratory animals, dictated use of the miniature swine in this experiment.

The experimental design of the main study on the toxicity of Sr^{90} in miniature swine is shown in Fig. 1. The dosage levels selected were based on our own preliminary observations[2] and data from Argonne National Laboratory[3] and the University of Utah.[4] At the lowest feeding level,

FIG. 2.

Laboratory facility for housing miniature swine showing individual feeding compartments and Sr^{90} pellet being fed.

1 μc Sr^{90}/day (approximately 450 times the occupational MPL), it is estimated that there will be greater than 10 per cent probability of detecting damage. At the 5 μc Sr^{90}/day level there is greater than 50 per cent probability of seeing damage and at the 25 and 125 μc Sr^{90}/day level, 100 per cent probability.

All animals are fed individually, receiving the strontium in a single feed pellet along with the morning ration (Fig. 2). Strontium intake is graduated during the growing period to correlate with increase in feed consumption and calcium intake. A discrepancy does occur, however, during the suckling period because of the discrimination against strontium that takes place in passage of the strontium from the dam's diet to the milk. This discrimination factor for strontium relative to calcium was observed to be approximately 10. The amount of bone produced up to weaning, however, is small in comparison with the adult skeleton (approximately 100 g bone mineral at weaning and 2000 g when adult). The resulting lower concentration of Sr^{90} in the bone of the young would be important from a toxicity standpoint, then, only if the skeleton of the young is more radiosensitive than that of the older animal.

Hematological and blood biochemical determinations which are made routinely include: packed cell volume, hemoglobin, glucose, cholesterol, calcium, inorganic phosphorus, creatinine, urea nitrogen, total protein, and erythrocyte, leukocyte, differential and reticulocyte count. No significant changes in these constituents have yet been noted at the 25 μc/day level following daily Sr^{90} feeding up to a period of two years, nor at the 125 μc/day level through gestation and weaning. Programs are being developed for the storage and analysis of these blood data utilizing an IBM 7090.

Routine radiographic examination of the animals has revealed no significant skeletal changes which may be attributed to the radiation dose from Sr^{90}. All animals have remained clinically normal, and, except for

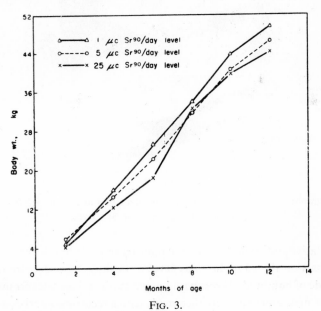

FIG. 3.

Growth rate of miniature swine fed Sr^{90} daily.

a slightly reduced rate of growth, are indistinguishable from control animals. The growth rate of the animals on the three main levels of Sr^{90} feeding is shown in Fig. 3. The weights of control animals closely parallel those on the 1 μc Sr^{90}/day feeding level.

During the past two years more than 200 animals were euthanized at various ages in order to provide specimens for radioanalysis, histological and autoradiographic studies. In Figures 4, 5 and 6 are shown

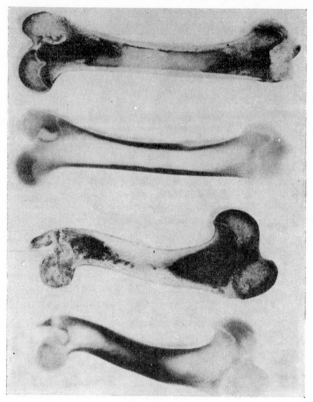

Fig. 4.

Photographs and matching autoradiograms of a femur and a humerus from a one-year-old pig on the 25 μc Sr^{90} level.

representative autoradiograms and photographs of bones from one-year-old animals on the 25 μc Sr^{90}/day level of feeding. Similar autoradiograms were made of bone and sources with known surface dose rates from Sr^{90}. Appropriate measurements were then made with a recording microdensitometer to provide estimates of radiation dose to the bone tissue. Assuming a *uniform* distribution of the Sr^{90} in the skeleton, the radiation dose from $Sr^{90}-Y^{90}$ to the skeleton was 0·02, 0·05 and 0·15 rads/day per microcurie n daily diet for newborn, weanlings and adult swine, respectiv ely.

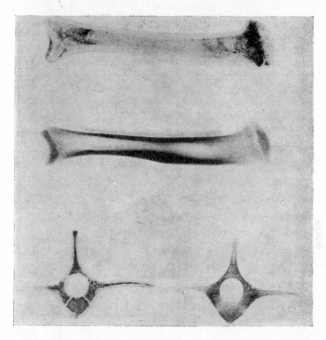

FIG. 5.

Photographs and matching autoradiograms of a tibia and the 4th lumbar vertebra from a one-year-old pig on the 25 μc Sr^{90} level.

The body burdens of the miniature swine (expressed as μc Sr^{90}/kg body weight per μc Sr^{90} in adult ration) as determined from skeletal analysis of the serially euthanized animals are approximately as follows: at birth, 0·04; at weaning, 0·09; and in adults, 0·25. The body burdens of the live animals are being followed by whole-body monitoring utilizing a 9-inch diameter by 4-inch NaI, thallium-activated crystal with a multi-channel analyzer. A photograph of the counting chamber, a large steel tube located in an underground room, is seen in Figure 7. A detailed description of the monitoring facility has been published elsewhere.[5]

Since only two years have elapsed in the main study, no more than predicted minimal changes have been observed to date. Data obtained over the lifetime of three generations of swine will provide an opportunity for observations under steady-state conditions, sufficient numbers of ani-

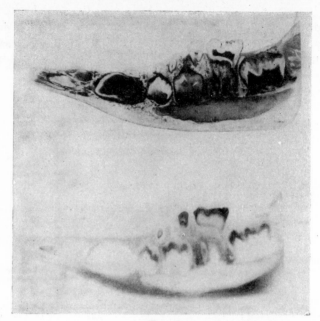

FIG. 6.
Photograph and autoradiogram of mandible frcm a one-year-old pig in the 25 μc Sr⁹⁰ level.

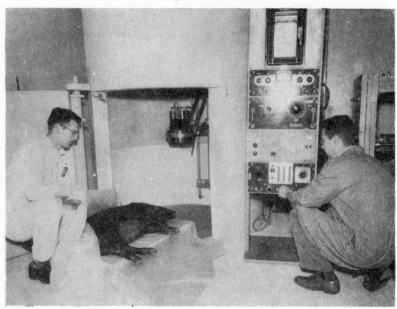

FIG. 7.
Underground whole-body counting chamber for large animals. A movable 9-inch sodium iodide crystal is mounted in a steel tube.

mals from which to draw applicable conclusions and sufficient time to observe long-term effects. Relevant data from other laboratories will also be available and should afford a sound basis for interspecies comparisons.

COMPARATIVE TOXICITY OF BONE-SEEKING ISOTOPES

For comparative purposes, the relative toxicity of a single injection of Sr^{90}, Ra^{226} and Pu^{239} in miniature swine is being studied concurrently. A single intravenous dose of either 64 μc Sr^{90}/kg body weight, 6·4 μc Ra^{226}/kg or 1·3 μc Pu^{239}/kg is administrated at six weeks, six months or one year of age. All animals injected are alive at 18 months following radionuclide administration and show only minimal evidence of damage. A leukopenia was noted immediately following injection, but the leukocyte count returned to normal very rapidly. Bone changes were noted radiographically in some animals, especially those injected at six weeks of age with Pu^{239}. The changes included an increased varia-

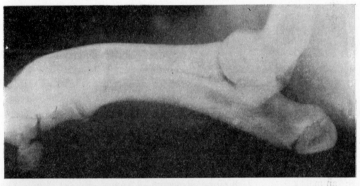
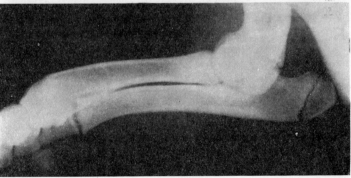

FIG. 8.

Radiographs of a 15-month-old swine injected with Pu^{239} when six weeks old (above) and of a control swine (below) 15 months old.

tion in thickness of cortical bone, outgrowths of cortical bone into the medullary canal with loss of definition of the boundaries and increased trabeculation in the spongiosa. Some of these changes are apparent in Figure 8.

SUMMARY

Progress is reported on a long-term daily Sr^{90} feeding experiment whose objective is to define relatively safe levels of dietary intake of Sr^{90} for man. Miniature swine are fed four levels of Sr^{90}—1, 5, 25 and 125 μc/day. Animals maintained on 25 μc of Sr^{90} per day for over two years appear normal and their 18-month-old offspring exposed to Sr^{90} since conception have manifested only a slightly depressed growth rate. Adult animals fed 125 μc of Sr^{90} per day for eight months, together with their three-month-old offspring, appear clinically normal.

A concurrent study on the comparative toxicity of Sr^{90}, Ra^{226} and Pu^{239} in miniature swine is also in progress.

REFERENCES

1. V. G. HORSTMAN, W. J. CLARKE, P. L. HACKETT, M. E. KERR, R. L. PERSING and L. K. BUSTAD, Anatomical and physiological data in miniature swine, Hanford Biology Research—Annual Report 1959, Document HW-65500, 59–67 (1960).
2. J. R. McKENNEY, W. J. CLARKE, V. G. HORSTMAN, L. A. GEORGE and D. L. ANDERSON, Metabolism of Sr^{90} in swine, Hanford Biology Research—Annual Report 1958, Document HW-59500, 11–15 (1959).
3. MIRIAM P. FINKEL, Mice, men and fallout, *Science* 128, 637–641 (1958).
4. C. N. STOVER, JR., Injection tables, University of Utah Annual Progress Report—Radiobiology Laboratory, COO-215, 1–18 (1958).
5. A. C. CASE AND J. R. McKENNEY, Facilities for measurements of radionuclides in large animals, Hanford Biology Research — Annual Report 1960, Document HW-69500, 28–30 (1961).

DENTAL CHANGES IN RABBITS INDUCED BY SR^{90}

M. A. Rushton

Department of Dental Medicine, Guy's Hospital, London, England

THE studies to be described were carried out on the jaws of rabbits injected by Dr. Janet Vaughan with $Sr^{90}Cl_2$ in a single dose. The injected dose varied between 100 and 1000 $\mu c/kg$ and was given either to weanlings or to older animals. The rabbits were killed at intervals varying from an hour to 9 months after injection. Concurrent with histological studies of one mandible, dosimetrical studies were performed on the opposite mandible by Dr. Maureen Owen.[1] Radiographs of the jaws before demineralization were made by Surg. Rear-Admiral Holgate.[2]

The most severe changes in the teeth and surrounding tissues were produced in weanling rabbits which received a high injected dose and the effects in a series of 34 animals which had 600 $\mu c/kg$ as weanlings will be described. Rabbits now being studied which received the same dose at ages of 1 to 3 years show less severe effects on the teeth, especially those injected at over 3 years. Rabbits injected as weanlings with 100 $\mu c/kg$ showed much slighter effects than with the high doses and in particular did not show arrested growth of the teeth. For this reason the Sr^{90} incorporated in the teeth in those animals was presently removed from the teeth by attrition. In the animals which received 600 $\mu c/kg$ or more as weanlings, on the other hand, growth and eruption of the cheek-teeth were soon arrested, so that the Sr^{90} incorporated in the teeth remained there substantially during the whole period of observation.

Series Injected with 600 $\mu c/kg$ Sr^{90} as Weanlings

Pyknotic cells were seen among differentiating odontoblasts after 24 hours (accumulated dose 150 rads) and pulp cells became separated from the internal enamel epithelium by an exudate. After 14 days (2500 rads) a depletion of pulp cells in this area was evident. At 30 days in length growth of the cheek-teeth had almost stopped (4500 rads) and there was some fibrosis of the pulps. The recently formed parts of the teeth were of diminished diameter and the pulps consisted of immature and mature portions without the normal gradual transition between the two. The incisors continued to grow in length for considerably longer, but became progressively thinner and showed the same kind of segregation of the immature portion of the pulp. Proliferation of pulp cells and differentation of new odontoblasts occurred superficial to this immature portion. The older odontoblasts and adjacent pulp cells in all teeth were rather little affected and continued to produce dentine until teeth were solid. The younger odontoblasts showed great disorder and became often embedded in defective dentine matrix. In general, the mature parts of the pulps became completely replaced by dentine, while the immature part remained as an apparently inactive nodule at the base of each lobe of the tooth up to the end of 6 months observation. The production of enamel and the growth of the enamel organ were arrested, but the enamel organs, though diminished and degenerate in aspect, did not completely disappear. No neoplastic change was seen in any of the dental tissues with the possible exception of cementum.

The periodontal membranes became in 30 days relatively poor in cells; and their deeper part, which is not normally collagenous, became so as the enamel organs diminished and gave place to cementum.

The apposition of cementum was much less affected than that of alveolar bone which diminished soon after the time of injection. By 30 days apposition on the interdental bone had ceased except near the bases of the teeth, but resorption continued so that there was progressive osteoporosis. Most of this bone eventually could be recognized as dead with empty lacunae. Two or three months after injection a vigorous proliferation of pleomorphic osteoblastic tissue occurred on the surfaces of bone forming the deeper halves of the sockets and eventually other areas. This proliferation in some areas seemed to subside, leaving trabeculae of dysplastic bone which greatly narrowed the periodontal membrane but did not unite with the tooth. By six months after injection there were in addition some or many areas where very active pleomorphic growth was associated with resorption of bone and teeth and the production of tumors having the morphology of osteosarcoma. These were in areas which had received an accumulated dose of between 11,000 and 52,000 rads, and in a case where they were still very small it appeared that they had arisen where the accumulated dose had been of the order of 20,000 rads received over a period of six months. This is comparable with the results obtained by Vaughan and co-workers in studies of osteosarcoma in the long bones of these rabbits.[3,4] In the older parts of these tumors, teeth sometimes had become united with tumor-bone.

Series Injected with 600 *μc/kg* Sr^{90} *as Adults*

In a series now being studied where rabbits were injected as adults, effects occurred which were in general similar to those seen in the series injected as weanlings, but took place after a longer time or were less severe and lasting. There was a difference between 3 rabbits injected at under 2 years of age and 3 injected at over 3 years, seen in the growth of the teeth 3 and 6 months after injection. Although the numbers are small, it appeared that in those injected at under 2 years, growth and eruption of teeth were generally arrested or much retarded, as in animals injected as weanlings; but in rabbits injected at over 3 years, continued growth and eruption of teeth were not so much retarded; so that in these, by 6 months after injection, most or all of the dentine which had contained the heaviest burden of Sr^{90} had been lost by attrition. The quality of the tooth pulps and dentine in these older rabbits also showed a high degree of recovery from damage.

Since the teeth, which contain a particularly high burden of Sr^{90} in these adult rabbits, appear to have such a different fate in animals injected at 2 and 3 years, our group of rabbits injected as adults cannot be regarded as homogeneous when considering the changes which occur on the surface of the bone. However, certain general remarks can be made.

Pleomorphic proliferation of osteoblastic tissue from the surface of the walls of the sockets was seen much later in rabbits injected as adults than in those injected as weanlings; only a little at 6 months instead of at 2 or 3 months after injection. Dr. Maureen Owen's dosimetry results show that this was not due to decreased dose rates in the area concerned, for these and the calculated accumulated doses were much increased. Thus, in the weanling group, the maximum accumulated dose between the bases of the cheek-teeth at the time that osteoblastic proliferation was evident was of the order of 9000 rads but in the adult group 47,000 rads or more.

Again, while changes regarded as osteosarcoma were evident in 4 out of 4 rabbits of the weanlings series at 6 months after injection, they could not be recognized in the adult group at 6 months but only in the one rabbit yet available 9 months after injection. This animal injected at 21 months of age had osteosarcoma in both jaws, the massive maxillary tumor showing some cartilage differentiation, the only jaw tumor yet to do so. The maximum accumulated dose between the bases of the mandibular cheek-teeth has been calculated at 123,000 rads, which can be compared with the 20,000 to 50,000 rads associated with osteosarcoma of the mandible in the weanling series.

This series appears to show that although (from the results of Holgate, Mole, and Vaughan[5,6] there are in the rabbit injected as an adult preferential locations of Sr^{90} in the jaws and especially the teeth compared with the distribution in weanlings, and much higher dose rates in the jaws in all areas initially and in many areas throughout, the development of sarcoma in the jaws is slower. Whether this may be due to a different reactivity of the older tissues, to the higher dose rate or other factors is not known. But there seems to be no reason to doubt that, as suggested by earlier work[3,6] the jaws will be the principal site of sarcoma in rabbits injected as adults.

Rabbits Injected with 500 $\mu c/kg$ Sr^{90} *soon after Birth*

The jaws of 4 animals in this group examined show remarkably slight qualitative changes compared with those injected as weanlings. Though it has been shown by Vaughan that they develop carcinoma of the external auditory meatus, rabbits which survived 27 days, 6, $9\frac{1}{2}$ and 16 months showed no osteosarcoma of the mandible and little qualitative disturbance of dental development.

REFERENCES

1. M. A. RUSHTON, M. OWEN, W. HOLGATE and J. VAUGHAN, The relation of radiation dose to radiation damage in the mandible of weanling rabbits, *Arch. Oral Biol.* **3**, 235–246 (1961).
2. W. HOLGATE, The incorporation and retention of Sr^{90} in the teeth, *Brit. dent. J.* **107**, 131, 1–10 (1959).
3. M. OWEN and J. VAUGHAN, Measurement of radiation dose and its relation to damage in the rabbit tibia following a single injection and daily feeding of Sr^{90}, *Brit. J. Cancer* **13**, 424–438 (1959).
4. E. D. DOWNIE, S. MACPHERSON, E. N. RAMSDEN, H. A. SISSONS and J. VAUGHAN, The effect of daily feeding of Sr^{90} to rabbits, *Brit J. Cancer* **13**, 408–423 (1959).
5. W. HOLGATE, R. H. MOLE and J. VAUGHAN, Accumulation of strontium-90 in dental tissues, *Nature* **182**, 1294–1295 (1958).
6. M. OWEN, Sr^{90} dosimetry in rabbits. This vol. p. 409.
7. M. OWEN, H. SISSONS and J. VAUGHAN, The effect of a single injection of a high dose of Sr^{90} in rabbits, *Brit. J. Cancer* **11**, 229–248 (1957).

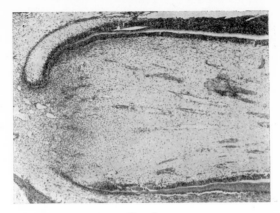

FIG. 1.

Weanling rabbit injected with 600 μc Sr^{90}/kg. Base of lower incisor tooth after 9 days. Irregular dentine and depletion of pulp cells on the lingual side. Haematoxylin and eosin × 40.

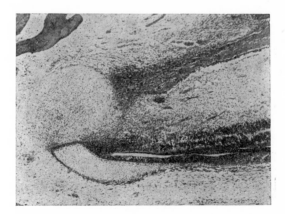

FIG. 2.

Similar incisor 2 months after injection showing segregation of immature pulp, diminution in width, irregular dentine. Haematoxylin and eosin × 40.

FIG. 3.

21-month rabbit injected with 600 μc Sr^{90}/kg and killed after 3 months. Incisor
has ceased to grow, recent dentine has been defective, and pulp is almost obliterated.
Haematoxylin and eosin $\times$ 20.

FIG. 4.

Incisive end of same tooth shows incremental line in dentine corresponding to
injection and its relation to alveolar bone. Haematoxylin and eosin $\times$ 20.

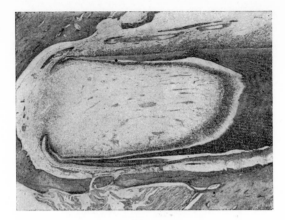

Fig. 5.

38-month rabbit injected with 600 μc Sr^{90}/kg and killed after 3 months. The pulp
of the incisor has almost recovered. Haematoxylin and eosin $\times$ 20.

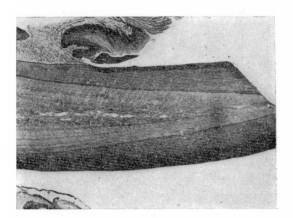

Fig. 6.

Incisive end of same tooth shows incremental line in dentine corresponding to
injection, already partly worn away by attrition and having erupted far past the
level of the alveolar bone. Haematoxylin and eosin $\times$ 20.

23*

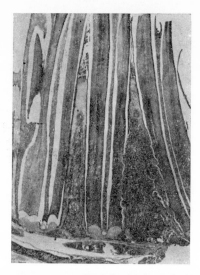

FIG. 7.

Weanling rabbit injected with 600 μc Sr^{90}/kg shows replacement of whole thickness of mandible with osteosarcoma at 6 months. Accumulated dose 11,000–52,000 rads, the higher dose being near the gum. Haematoxylin and eosin × 9.

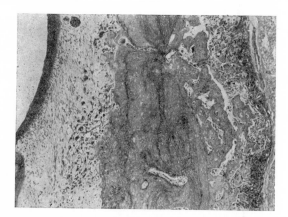

FIG. 8.

12-month rabbit injected with 1000 μc Sr^{90}/kg and killed after 7 months. Section from maxilla shows alveolar bone with empty lacunae covered with successive layers of dysplastic bone. On the left near the tooth this is covered by a pleomorphic osteoblastic proliferation. On the right it is continuous with osteosarcoma. Haematoxylin and eosin × 60.

DISCUSSION

ENGLISH: I would indeed like to make two brief comments on your very interesting paper, but before I do this may I be permitted to do a little missionary work in about half a minute.

I would like to personally applaud Dame Janet Vaughan for interesting Professor Rushton and Dr. Maureen Owen in this work, and also I would like to thank Dr. Dougherty for his support of the work done in his laboratory on the dogs and teeth of these animals; also Dr. Webster Jee and Dr. Christensen.

So very often pathologists and experimental anatomists very carefully take the jaws and teeth and place them in formalin and put them up on the walls of their laboratories, or with equal care they put a paper towel around them and throw them in the waste can. I believe there is some very important material being overlooked and discarded in doing this.

Years ago, in the *Rubaiyat*, Omar Khayyam said that "the hand of time relentlessly writes on and the record, once written, can never be erased." Surely he was thinking of the dentine of the teeth of humans and certain animals, because here we would have a permanent record. He could not have been thinking of the bone which is continually replaced.

So I believe one parameter of confusion might be taken away in certain of the studies by using the dentine of the permanent teeth. Not that I would suggest that we discontinue studying bone.

In certain experimental animals we all know that there are teeth that continue to grow throughout the life of the animal. The incisor of the rat grows 2 or 3 mm a week. We have therefore a built-in Beckmann recorder that nature has provided, that gives us a record of the functioning of the odontoblasts and ameloblasts. I think these records bear considerable study.

To get to the paper—the very important paper by Professor Rushton— I was interested in the fact that in the weanlings given 600 mc of Sr^{90} per kilogram the differentiated odontoblasts continued to lay down dentine until the entire pulp was replaced, and the estimated total dose was somewhere of the order of 13,000 to 15,000 rad.

I speak from the point of view of someone who has worked almost entirely with external radiation and X-rays. This seems like a tremendous dose for these cells to have been subjected to and still to be able to function and lay down relatively normal dentine.

I talked with Dr. Owen, and I realize that this dose was accumulated over a period of six months. Even so if in truth these odontoblasts can function at that level of radiation it is rather astounding to me.

In other words, it seems to me that the change in function of the cells may well be expected. This of course may occur long before any morphologic changes. Changes in the dentine would record functional change in the odontoblasts.

In the second study reported by Professor Rushton he mentioned that in rabbits injected at under 2 years of age with 600 mc of Sr^{90} per kilogram growth and eruption of the teeth were generally retarded, but in rabbits injected at over 3 years, growth and eruption were not retarded, so that six months after injection most or all of the strontium-bearing dentine was lost. I find this hard to understand, and I hope you have a continuing source of rabbits and can follow through on this.

Although the rabbit is a year or so older, the odontoblasts are continually forming, and as new cells it is hard to understand why they would not function quite similarly to the cells of the two-year-old animal. Of course with bacterial colonies we know there is a gradual change in their potential, and this could be possible in the case of new generations of odontoblasts. This is very interesting and if it is verified with further study, I think it may be one place that would provide knowledge regarding basic mechanisms.

EVANS: I might say just a word about the jaw and teeth in humans, and simply remind everyone that radium poisoning in the human was discovered by disorders of teeth and jaw by an oral surgeon, Theodore Bloom in New York. At first it was thought that the difficulties arising in the teeth and gums were the result of local irritation because the girls swallowed radium dial paint. Of course this turned out later not to be so when disorders of the jaw were found in people who had received radium by injection.

Ten years or more ago the radium cases we saw very commonly had necrosis of the mandible. These were people with residual burdens from about 3 up to 20 micrograms of radium. The jaw effects were summarized in the *Medicine* paper in 1952 (Aub, Evans, Hempelmann and Martland, *Medicine* **31,** 222, 1952).

Secondly, Robert Dudley at M.I.T. and C.E. Miller and J.B. Corcoran at Argonne have done some nice work showing that in the human at present a tooth sample or several teeth is a good index of the body burden in a human. If you can't get the human—if he has been buried, for example, but if you do have one or two teeth you can get an estimate of the body burden within a factor of 2 or 3.

BUSTAD: I so wanted to be a successful discussant today but I felt very inadequate to the occasion. After considerable thought I decided—as so many people do when faced with a situation they know little about—to write a paper about it. I will give you only the high points of my paper on *Gamesmanship in Discussions*. First of all, one must decide on the approach to be used. I have noted several approaches have been utilized so far in the conference. Briefly, the choices are these:
1. You may sit near the front, put your pretty legs up on the chairs in front of you, and sit back and look wise, assuming a commendably philosophic attitude as people use and misuse your data.
2. You may post a great deal of data on the blackboard—and then go off and wash your hair and put it up in curlers.
3. You may refuse to comment. (The last—or should I say the next-to-the-last—person in this room that I expected to do this chose this approach Tuesday night).
4. You may come armed with a pocketful of slides which have varying degrees of irrelevance to the subject under discussion.

Obviously some of these approaches are not appropriate for me: Miriam's legs are much prettier than mine and I must say she should be happy that someone uses or misuses her data. No one even reads mine. As regards the second case, I don't have enough hair to wash, and I certainly don't have to put it up in curlers for it's naturally curly. My approach is obviously a 5th type: When you are in doubt about what to do, ham it up! Important as is the approach, one must of course prepare himself (or herself) to be a discussant. Being naive, I believed that all one should have to do was to be up on all the relevant literature—which is defined as all the papers authored by the program participants and conference chairmen. This, I realized last night, is not true. Really all one need review are Webster Jee's publications, Robley Evans' book, and Shakespeare. And, I learned a few minutes ago, Omar Khayyam would also be recommended reading. In being a discussant, it is a real mark of one-upmanship if one gives some indication of having done some research work recently himself, shows some familiarity with the literature and then asks what might appear, on the surface at least, to be a wise question. In keeping with this: I have been interested in reading of the work of Holgate, Vaughan and Mole and in hearing Maureen Owen report that after a single injection of Sr^{90} the teeth are not really good indicators of what the bone burden is, since the burden in each changes with time and not necessarily in the same relationship. In preliminary work with our swine exposed to Sr^{90} throughout their lifetime, the molar teeth expressed as $\mu c/g$ of ash appear to be good indicators of the bone burden.

Secondly, odontogenic tumors are exceedingly rare in domestic animals. There is one tumor of the dog, however, that is described often in the literature of the last decade. It has been named a fibromatous epulis and has been reported to appear most often in young Boxer dogs. It will be interesting to see in the future if the Davis, Argonne or Utah people see this tumor of the periodontal tissue, and if an increased incidence appears following internal radiation exposure.

Lastly, a wise discussant always imparts some sage advice. Mine is this: Take Jee's shoes away from him when he comes to the laboratory so that when he kicks the dogs he will not shorten their life appreciably.

PRELIMINARY STUDY OF THE EFFECT OF INTERNAL IRRADIATION FROM Sr^{90} ON THE BONE MARROW AND PERIPHERAL BLOOD PICTURE OF YOUNG RABBITS

JANET VAUGHAN

Medical Research Council, Bone-Seeking Isotopes Research Unit, Oxford, England

INTRODUCTION

THE effect of external irradiation on haemopoiesis has been extensively studied and attempts have been made to determine the underlying disturbance of haemopoiesis produced by such radiation.[1,2,3,4,5,6,7,8,9] Less work has been done on the mechanisms underlying the disturbances of haemopoiesis caused by internal radiation though the resulting peripheral blood picture had been described both in man and experimental animals.[10,11,12,13,14,15,16,17,18]

The present paper attempts to relate changes seen in the peripheral blood and in the cellularity of the bone marrow to the radiation dose, measured in rads, received by the bone marrow in young rabbits followed for six months after a single intravenous injection of 600 μc/kg Sr^{90}+Y^{90} equilibrium mixture when 6–8 weeks old.[19] Experience has shown that multiple osteosarcoma develop within this period after injection.

EXPERIMENTAL METHODS

(i) *Rabbits*

The rabbits were of the same stock and fed on the same diet as those used in all experiments reported from this laboratory, namely, Dutch rabbits fed on a diet of oats, cabbage and hay.

(ii) *Dosimetry Studies*

Dosimetry studies on the marrow in the tibia and vertebra were carried out on 20 rabbits killed at different time intervals after a single injection of Sr^{90}+Y^{90} equilibrium mixture. The pattern of radiation dose-rate in the marrow is determined by the pattern of distribution of Sr^{90} in the bones.[20,21] No Sr^{90} is retained in the marrow itself though possibly some radiation dose contribution is made immediately following injection by the high level of Sr^{90} in the blood. The detailed technique of measuring radiation dose rates by determining the density of autoradiographs of thick sections and comparing it with that from a known standard is described elsewhere.[20,21]

(iii) Haemotological Studies

(a) *The bone marrow.* The bone marrow in the lumbar vertebrae and tibia was studied in histological sections from all the rabbits in which dosimetry measurements were made. For this purpose bones were decalcified in EDTA and embedded in either celloidin or paraffin. Sections were stained with haemotoxylin and eosin. The marrow in the femur and humerus was also available for study in many rabbits but dosimetry studies were not made in detail on these bones. It is probable that in the long bones the pattern of dose distribution is of the same order as that in the tibia. The degree of cellularity seen microscopically in the marrow at any site in the irradiated animals was expressed as a percentage of the cellularity seen in the unirradiated rabbits killed at the same age. This was estimated by eye for a large number of rabbits. The picture was extremely constant at any time interval and the changes at the points in time at which examinations were made were dramatic. It is recognised that the cellularity of the marrow is no measure of its activity in terms of function.[22] Cellularity is, however, one piece in the jigsaw puzzle that is required to understand the state of haemopoiesis under any particular set of circumstances. Sections of liver and spleen and kidney were prepared and stained with haemotoxylin and eosin.

(b) *Peripheral blood.* For this particular detailed study 6 litter mates were used. Three received 600 μc/kg Sr^{90} by intravenous injection and three were used as controls. After a short control period when examinations were made daily the haemoglobin was estimated and total leucocyte, platelet, differential and reticulocyte counts were made, at first every 3 days and then once a week using methods previously described.[16] Platelets were counted by the method described by Brecher and Cronkite.[23] The differential and reticulocyte counts were made by one individual (J. V.).

RESULTS

The marrow cellularity in relation to radiation dose-rate in rads/hour in the vertebrae below the epiphyseal plate is shown in Fig. 1, and in three sites in the tibia in Figs. 2, 3, 4; namely, in the middle of the marrow of the tibia beneath the plate at the time of injection, in mid-diaphysis and

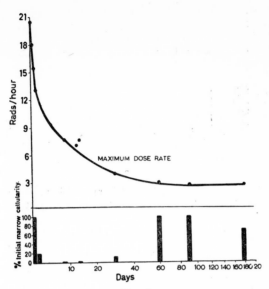

FIG. 1.

Relation of radiation dose-rate to cellularity in the lumbar vertebrae of young rabbits after intravenous injection Sr⁹⁰ (600 μc/kg).

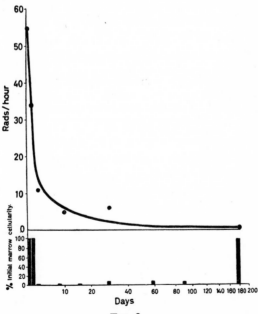

FIG. 2.

Relation of radiation dose-rate of cellularity in the middle of the marrow of the tibia beneath the plate at the time of injection Sr⁹⁰ (600 μc/kg).

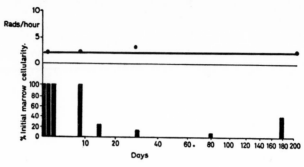

FIG. 3.

Relation of radiation dose-rate to cellularity in marrow in midline mid-diaphysis of tibia after intravenous injection Sr⁹⁰ (600 μc/kg).

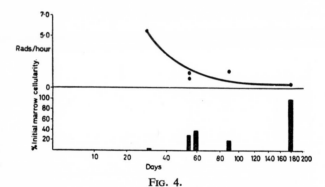

FIG. 4.

Relation of radiation dose-rate to marrow cellularity 3·6 mm below terminal plate tibia after intravenous injection of Sr⁹⁰(600 μc/kg).

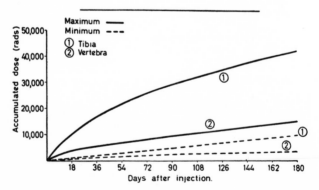

FIG. 5.

The maximum and minimum accumulated radiation dose found in the bone or marrow in the tibia and vertebra. Accumulated doses in rabbits injected with 600 μc/kg of Sr⁹⁰. Aged 5–8 weeks.

at an arbitrary point 3·6 mm below the terminal plate. The maximum and minimum accumulated radiation dose in the tibia and vertebra over six months is shown in Fig. 5. The mean levels for haemoglobin g per cent, reticulocytes per 100 red cells, neutrophils per mm³, and small lymphocytes per cm, in both injected and control rabbits are shown in Figs. 6–9, together with the marrow cellularity in the injected rabbits expressed as a per cent of that seen in the normal controls.

(i) *Total Bone Marrow Cellularity*

Examination of these charts at once shows that the marrow cellularity presents an extremely complex picture even in the two bones studied, leaving out of account the rest of the skeleton (Fig. 10). For instance, beneath the epiphyseal plate, at both the upper end of the tibia and the vertebra, within 3 or 4 days of injection, there is almost complete absence of cells while in mid-diaphysis of the tibia there is 100 per cent cellularity,

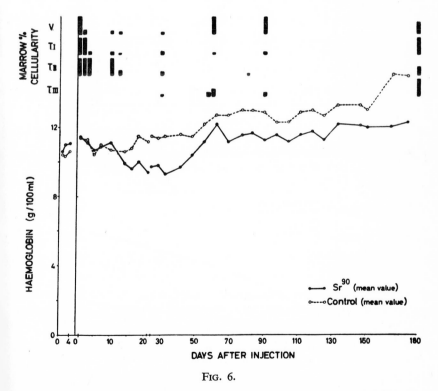

FIG. 6.

Effect of intravenous injection of Sr[90] (600 μc/kg) on circulating haemoglobin (g/per cent mean values) and marrow cellularity in young rabbits.

Cellularity has returned, on the other hand, 100 per cent in the vertebra
between 60 and 80 days after injection while it has fallen to low levels
at this time in the mid-diaphysis of the tibia. It is evident from consideration
of the marrow cellularity in the areas studied that during the first six months
following injection there was no period where there was complete marrow
aplasia in the animals studied though in the period of about 15–50 days
after injection all marrow cellularity was considerably reduced.

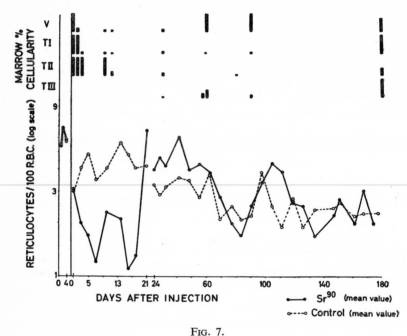

FIG. 7.

Effect of intravenous injection of Sr[90] (600 μc/kg) on circulating reticulocytes (mean
values) and marrow cellularity in young rabbits.

(ii) *Marrow Cells Affected*

In the affected areas aplasia ensued very rapidly after injection in the
areas of high dose-rate. Both granular and early red cells vanished simultaneously, megakaryocytes being left outstanding among a few spindle
cells. In the stage of aplasia large groups of multinucleated giant cells
were noted usually about 9–15 days after injection. As many as 20–50
could sometimes be counted in a low power field. They were usually in
groups often in contact with one another. The origin of these cells is uncertain. They may be giant fibroblasts. A similar unusual number of giant
cells has been noted in the bone marrow of the tibia and femur of rabbits

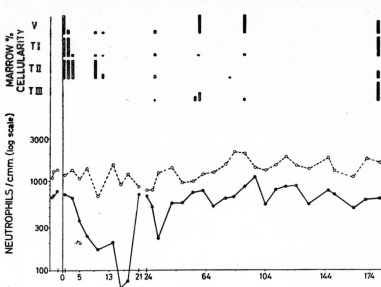

Fig. 8.
Effect of intravenous injection of Sr[90] (600 μc/kg) on circulating neutrophils (mean values) and marrow cellularity in young rabbits.

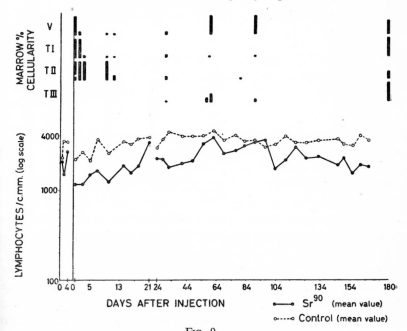

Fig. 9.
Effect of intravenous injection of Sr[90] (600 μc/kg) on circulating small lymphocytes (mean values) and marrow cellularity in young rabbits.

in which certain blood vessels had been ligated.[24] It is possible that the same factor was responsible in the present marrow since damage to blood vessels of the marrow does occur in heavily irradiated areas.[25] Bloom[13] and Puck[26] have also described the appearance of abnormal giant cells as characteristic of the response to irradiation.

(iii) *Relation of Marrow Cellularity to Radiation Dose*

Examination of the charts 1–4 relating marrow cellularity to radiation dose shows that in sites where there is an initial high radiation dose-rate, for instance, beneath the vertebral epiphyseal plate where the dose-rate is about 20 rads/hr and beneath the epiphyseal plate at the proximal end

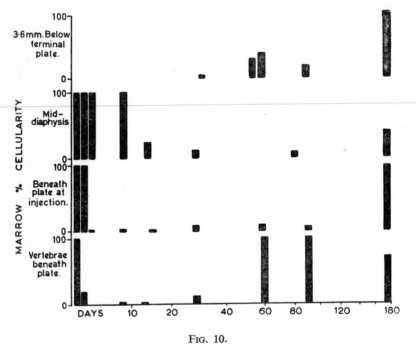

Fig. 10.

Marrow cellularity in vertebrae and 3 sites in tibia after injection of Sr^{90} (600 μc/kg) to young rabbits.

of the tibia where it is 55 rads/hr there is an almost complete and extremely rapid loss of cellularity. Recovery of cellularity, however, takes place and may be maintained, though sometimes at a subnormal level in the face of a persistent dose-rate of about 5 rads per hour, as may be seen in the case of the vertebrae. This recovery takes place more rapidly in the marrow of the vertebra than in the marrow of the tibia beneath the plate at the time of injection, presumably because the initial dose-rate was much higher and therefore the accumulated dose was much higher in the latter site.[27] It is not, however, clear why the low dose-rate in the mid-shaft of the tibia causes severe aplasia in the short time of about 40 days (Fig. 3).

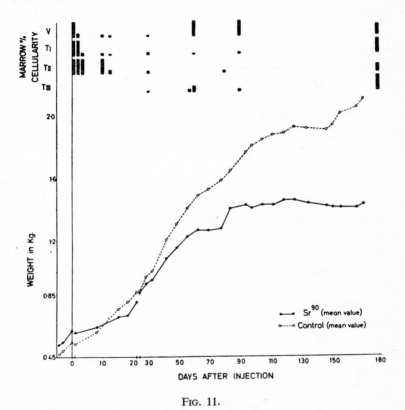

FIG. 11.

Effect of intravenous injection of Sr⁹⁰ (600 μc/kg) on weight of young rabbits.

(iv) *Extra Medullary Haemopoiesis*

Extra medullary haemopoiesis was not found on histological examination in animals killed or dying 9 days after irradiation and later. Unfortunately no examination of histological preparations was made in the initial 9 days during which time increased haemopoietic activity has been reported in the spleen of rats following external irradiation.[3] Eddington and his colleagues[14] found no extra medullary haemopoiesis in monkeys following death from Sr⁹⁰.

(v) *Relation of the Peripheral Blood Picture to the Marrow Cellularity*

Following injection there was a significant fall in platelets, in total leucocytes, in reticulocytes, and in haemoglobin in the injected rabbits. This was followed by a rise and then a second, though less marked, fall in the case of both reticulocytes and leucocytes and their gradual recovery to low normal or subnormal levels, which were maintained until sacrifice 6 months after injection. One injected rabbit died on the 19th day with a haemoglobin the preceding day of 8 g per cent. In the two surviving rabbits the haemoglobin rose slowly from a minimum level of 9 g per cent reaching in one case, a peak of 12·8 g per cent and in the other 11·8 g per cent. The leucocytes started to fall and reached their lowest level rather sooner than the haemoglobin. Both recovered to a low normal level between the fifty-third and sixty-third day though recovery in the white cell count was apparent before that in the haemoglobin. The platelets reached their lowest figure on the 28th day and then started to rise slowly, reaching a low normal level about the 80th day. If these figures are compared with those for marrow cellularity it is at once apparent that the falls in value are associated with the loss of cellularity in the large and important areas of haemopoietic marrow below the epiphyseal plate in the tibia and in the vertebra and that the return to normal values is related to the increased cellularity in the vertebrae and beneath the terminal epiphyseal plate in the tibia. After the period of depression of the reticulocytes in one rabbit there was, on the 23rd day, when the haemoglobin started to rise, a peak value of 11 per cent, the second injected rabbit also showed a raised reticulocyte count at about the same time associated with a rising haemoglobin but it was not noted to have a single peak. This may well be due to the fact that counts were not made daily and therefore the maximum count was missed.

The fall in total leucocytes is largely due to a loss of cells of the myeloid series. Neutrophil leucocytes (Fig. 8) were not seen in the blood of the rabbit that died on the 19th day after injection while in the other two injected rabbits they were reduced to less than 100 per mm^3. In the controls on the same day they ranged from 500 to 1800 mm^3. Eosinophils were rarely seen in the blood of injected rabbits between the 3rd and 80th day while in the controls, though they were occasionally absent as many as 80 per mm^3 were found during this period. Basophils were also lost, the maximum seen being 20 per mm^3. They returned about the 41st day, while in the controls, though occasionally missing for one day, 100–200 or more per mm^3 were almost invariably found. Small lymphocytes (Fig. 9) were also depressed below the level of the controls reaching their lowest figure around 1000 per mm^3 between 3 and 11 days after injection and then rising slowly to figures approximately that of the lowest normal control, but as inspection of Figs. 8 and 9 shows, the fall in lymphocytes, though significant, was not as marked as that in neutrophils. Large monocytes, plasma cells and large lymphocytes were somewhat but irregularly reduced during the same period but they did not entirely disappear as did the basophil and eosinophil leucocytes. No abnormal or immature cells were seen at any time. The neutrophils, however, immediately following injection became extremely toxic showing few and irregular granules. They became normal in appearance as they increased in number.

DISCUSSION

The detailed figures for the peripheral blood picture following a single injection of Sr^{90} to young rabbits resulting from the present study are in agreement with other figures obtained in this laboratory published elsewhere.[19]

The present results suggest certain points for discussion.

(i) *Relation between the Radiation Dose, Marrow Cellularity and Peripheral Blood Picture*

(a) *Acute.* In the first three months following Sr^{90} administration to weanling rabbits the peripheral blood picture, the dose-rate and accumulated dose as measured in the tibia and the lumbar vertebrae and the cellularity of the marrow appear to be related to one another in a logical manner. The initial high dose-rate in certain sites results in aplasia of the marrow in these sites only and loss particularly of myeloid elements in the peripheral blood. When the dose-rate falls, due to removal of Sr^{90} from the bone by the normal physiological processes of exchange, resorption, and growth of new bone containing little or no isotope, the aplastic marrow may recover and the blood picture returns to a low normal or high subnormal level. The fact that the blood picture does not recover completely during the first 3 months is probably associated with the fact that irradiation continues though at a low dose-rate. The capacity of bone marrow to recover and function in the face of continuous radiation at low dose-rate has been emphasised by Lamerton and his colleagues.[8,9] The mechanism underlying this recovery requires further investigation. It is often assumed to be a repopulation by cells moving in from less heavily irradiated areas.[27] It may, however, be due to recovery of stem cells in the irradiated area. The fact that the marrow beneath the epiphysis in the vertebrae when the initial dose-rate is only 20 rads per hour recovers before that in the tibia when the initial dose-rate is about 60 rads per hour suggests this may be so. That recovery from the initial partial aplasia may not always occur is shown by examination of our mortality figures. These figures suggest that the radiation dose to the marrow given by the injection of 600 μc/kg Sr^{90} into rabbits may be sufficient to cause such severe damage that the marrow may not recover quickly enough after the period of severe partial aplasia found between the 10–60 days but that if the animals come through this period and especially the period 10–20 days, survival is likely, at least until osteosarcoma develop.

In the present experiment one rabbit died 19 days after injection when the blood elements were all at their lowest level and the absence of circulating reticulocytes and neurophils indicated functional failure of myeloid haemopoiesis. The post-mortem report on this rabbit showed almost complete aplasia of the marrow in the bones examined. The spleen was small in size showing few cells and no active malpighian bodies. In both liver and kidneys there were many small vessels containing bacteria and areas of necrosis also containing bacteria, but there was little evidence of any inflammatory reaction. The evidence of haemorrhage was also slight. The findings were suggestive of agranulocytosis or pancytopenia in humans. In previous studies involving 31 weanling rabbits[19] receiving 500–1000 μc Sr^{90}/kg (all but 3 of which received 1000 μc/kg) with a planned survival time of 30 days to 9 months, six deaths occurred 14–17 days after injection, the haemoglobin, leucocytes and platelets being greatly reduced. One died 64 days after injection, again with reduced blood values. In the rabbit there is no post-mortem evidence that anaemia due to gross haemorrhage is the cause of death, but there may be considerable extravasation of red cells both into the marrow and adjacent to the connective tissues. Such extravasation resulting in severe anaemia has been suggested by others as a cause of anaemia death following external irradiation.[8,28] It would appear probable that both agranulocytosis resulting in overwhelming infection and anaemia dependent upon haemorrhage and failure of erythropoiesis may cause death from acute strontium poisoning. The character of erythropoietic failure must be variable since in the rabbits it was associated by aplasia of cellular marrow, while hyperplastic marrow is reported in at least one monkey dying with severe anaemia.[14]

(b) *Chronic.* After 3 months the picture of the relationships of radiation dose, marrow cellularity and the peripheral blood may become complicated by factors other than the effect of radiation on the haemopoietic marrow. Examination of the weight charts of the present animals

(Fig. 11) shows that the Sr^{90} rabbits gain weight less rapidly than the controls, a fact which has been confirmed in considerable detail in a larger number of rabbits.[29] This failure to gain weight is evidence of some disturbances of metabolism which may well have an effect on haemopoiesis apart from radiation. It is also known that from about 3 months after injection of 600 μc/kg proliferative changes, resulting in widespread osteosarcoma invading the marrow, begin to develop.[25] The development of such proliferative tissues within the marrow cavity will again have secondary effects upon haemopoiesis. The occurrence of leukoerythroblastic anaemia in human beings with secondary skeletal deposits is well recognized.[22] The part played by disturbed metabolism and the presence of multiple bone tumours rather than radiation in producing the severe fatty gelatinous degeneration that may be found 6–9 months after injection is impossible to assess.[15]

(ii) *The Relation between the Effects of Internal Radiation and External Radiation on Haemopoiesis*

In attempting to make this comparison there are many, perhaps insurmountable difficulties. Firstly, it must be remembered, that apart from anything else, the pattern of radiation dose received by the marrow from external radiation is unlikely ever to be similar to that received from an isotope that is unevenly distributed in bone. The marrow radiation dose received in the two bones studied in the present paper was variable both in time and place though all marrow was probably receiving some, though it may have been a minimal radiation dose. This irregular pattern cannot be exactly paralleled with external radiation. Secondly, with external radiation other potential leukopoietic tissues like liver, spleen, lymph glands and kidney are irradiated while irradiation of these organs even by a long-range beta emitter like Y^{90} is less significant. Finally, even if it were possible to give the same pattern of radiation dose both in time and place to the marrow from internal and external sources, this has not yet been done. It is at present only possible to compare the results on different species made by different investigators using extremely different radiation doses.

(a) *Leukopoeisis.* There is clearly one important difference between the effect of external radiation, at least from Sr^{90}, on haemopoiesis.

Following external irradiation, unless the dose is so heavy as to give complete agranulocytosis, leukopaenia is pre-eminently due to a decrease in circulating lymphocytes while with internal irradiation, again unless the radiation dose is overwhelming,[14] the effect on the granular leukocytes is more striking.[2,12,17] This difference can be explained by the fact that, with internal radiation, the bone marrow, the site of origin of the granular leukocytes is primarily irradiated, while with external radiation the sensitive lymphoid tissues of the body are equally exposed. Without discussing the literature on leukaemia and its relation to irradiation it should also be noted that there is no case of leukaemia reported in human beings receiving internal radiation from bone-seeking isotopes and no satisfactory evidence of myeloid leukaemia in experiments animals. The increase in leukaemia obtained in mouse experiment using Sr^{90} is always of lymphatic origin.[30] Leukaemia of all types occurs in both man and animals following external irradiation though in man it is probable that the myeloid type predominates.[31]

(b) *Erythropoiesis.* The broad effect of internal and external irradiation on the erythroid elements of the peripheral blood and marrow appear in some respects similar, though as already stated the experimental evidence available has been obtained on different species using very different radiation doses. Both types of irradiation, at appropriate radiation dose levels, cause a fall in haemoglobin, reticulocytes and circulating red cells which may be followed by recovery or may result in haemopoietic death usually within 20 days. The experimental data on the possible underlying mechanism of this initial haemopoietic failure is much more detailed for the period immediately following exposure in the case of external irradiation than is available in the present study, though no marrow studies are available.

For internal radiation the mechanism may well vary with radiation dose. In the present studies of internal irradiation the dose-rate in certain sites was high and almost immediate aplasia of the marrow, in areas of extremely active haemopoeisis, such as the vertebrae and the proximal ends of the long bones, resulted. As already discussed this aplasia i.e. complete loss of cells, may well account for the fall in myeloid elements noted. On the other hand it is possible that with smaller doses of radiation such as have been used on some experiments with external radiation other effects on haemopoiesis may come into play.

Lamerton and his colleagues[3] suggests that immediately after an acute exposure to external irradiation a reduced rate of release of mature red cells and excessive haemorrhage may result in the initial fall in haemoglobin and reticulocytes, while later, as shown by radioactive iron studies, there is depression of erythropoietic activity, the duration of this depression depending on the initial dose level. How far this depression of erythropoietic activity is based on actual lack of cells, i.e. aplasia, and how far it is due to inhibition or delay of mitosis in nucleated red cells[2,5] in the experiments with external irradiation we have not the data to judge. Lamerton notes increased activity in the spleen before it occurs in the bone marrow in rats[8] and failure of recovery when splenectomy is performed before irradiation. It may be that in his experiments the marrow was repopulated from the spleen. There is evidence in the case of the rabbits that repopulation may have occurred from less severely irradiated, and therefore still active, marrow.

In conclusion it may be said that the present preliminary study suggests that actual lack of haemopoietic cells in the marrow as well as disturbance in function may well be responsible for changes in the peripheral blood picture following internal irradiation. Further, that aplasia of the marrow is related to radiation dose distribution both in time and space and that an average radiation dose calculated from retention figures in the case of an internally deposited isotope can give little indication of likely marrow damage.

SUMMARY

1. A study of the relationship of the peripheral blood picture to the marrow cellularity in tibia and vertebra and the radiation dose in young rabbits receiving a single intravenous injection of Sr^{90} 600 μc/kg is described.

2. The pattern of radiation dose-rate and therefore of marrow cellularity even in the same bone is complex owing to differences in Sr^{90} distribution.

3. In areas of marrow receiving a high initial dose-rate aplasia occurs within 24–48 hours. As the dose-rate falls there is partial or complete recovery. This may be due to repopulation from undamaged marrow elsewhere or to recovery of stem cells *in situ*.

4. Initial marrow aplasia is associated with a fall in haemoglobin, in total white cells, platelets and in reticulocytes. The white cells most affected are the myeloid cells, i.e. the neutrophil, eosinophil and basophil granulocytes though lymphocytes also show a reduction. Death may occur about the 18th day: if not, there is a recovery of all peripheral blood elements to low normal or high subnormal levels.

5. During the second three months after injection of Sr^{90} 600 μc/kg haemopoiesis may well be affected by factors other than irradiation of the marrow, namely, general metabolic disturbance evidenced by slowing of growth and development of widespread osteosarcoma.

6. These studies emphasize the importance of accurate data about doserate distribution both in time and space in a study of radiation damage.

ACKNOWLEDGEMENTS

I am indebted to Dr. Maureen Owen for the measurements of radiation dose and to Miss Schofield and Miss Scammell for technical help. Dr.Byers reported on the soft tissues of the rabbit that died.

REFERENCES

1. E. H. BELCHER, I. G. F. GILBERT and L. F. LAMERTON, Experimental studies with radioactive iron, Brit. J. Radiol. 27, 387–392 (1954).

2. L. O. JACOBSON, The haematologic effect of ionizing radiation, in Radiation Biology, edited by A. HOLLAENDER, McGraw-Hill Book Co., New York, Vol. 1, High Energy Radiation, 1029–1090 (1954).

3. C. F. BAXTER, E. H. BELCHER, E. A. HARRISS, and L. F. LAMERTON, Anaemia and erythropoiesis in the irradiated rat: an experimental study with particular reference to techniques involving radioactive iron, Brit. J. Haemat. 1, 86–103 (1955).

4. M. COURT-BROWN and J. D. ABBATT, The effect of a single dose of X-rays on the peripheral blood count of man, Brit. J. Haemat. 1, 75–85 (1955).

5. L. J. LAJTHA and H. D. SUIT, Uptake of radioactive iron (^{59}Fe) by nucleated red cells in vitro, Brit. J. Haemat. 1, 55–61 (1955).

6. E. H. BELCHER, E. B. HARRISS and L. F. LAMERTON, Turnover studies with Fe^{59} in the X-irradiated rat, Brit. J. Haemat. 4, 390–403 (1958).

7. R. H. MOLE, The development of leukaemia in irradiated animals, Brit. Med. Bull. 14, 174–177 (1958).

8. L. F. LAMERTON, A. H. PONTIFEX, N. M. BLACKETT and K. ADAMS, Effects of protracted irradiation in the blood-forming organs of the rat. Part I: Continuous exposure, Brit. J. Radiol. 33, 287–301 (1960).

9. A. H. PONTIFEX and L. F. LAMERTON, Effects of protracted irradiation on the blood-forming organs of the rat. Part II: Divided doses, Brit. J. Radiol 33, 736–747 (1960).

10. H. S. MARTLAND, P. CONLON, and J. P. KNEF, Some unrecognized dangers in the use and handling of radioactive substances; with special reference to the storage of insoluble products of radium and mesothorium in the reticulo-endothelial system, J.A.M.A. 85, 1769–1776 (1925).

11. H. S. MARTLAND, The occurrence of malignancy in radioactive persons, Amer. J. Cancer 15, 2435–2516 (1931).

12. E. L. SIMMONS and L. O. JACOBSON, Radiotoxicity of injected Sr^{89} for rats, mice and rabbits. Part IV: The haematological effects of internally and parenterally administered Sr^{89} in animals. USAEC Report, MDDC, 1387 (1946).

13. W. BLOOM and M. A. BLOOM, Histological changes after irradiation, Radiation Biology, Vol. 1. High Energy Radiations, edited by A. HOLLAENDER, New York, 1090–1143 (1954).

14. G. M. EDINGTON, A. H. WARD, J. M. JUDD and R. H. MOLE, The acute lethal effects in monkeys of radiostrontium, J. Path. Bact. 71, 277–293 (1956).

15. W. B. LOONEY, Late effects (25–40 years) of the early medical and industrial use of radioactive materials. Their relation to the more accurate establishment of maximum

permissible amounts of radioactive elements in the body. Part III, *J. Bone Jt. Surg.* **38A**, 392–407 (1956).

16. M. OWEN, H. A. SISSONS, and J. VAUGHAN, The effect of a single injection of Sr^{90} (500–1000 μc/kg) in rabbits, *Brit. J. Cancer* **11**, 229–248 (1957).

17. J, H. DOUGHERTY and K. SEYMOUR, Heamatology Report, Radiobiology Laboratory College of Medicine, University of Utah, Annual Progress Report, COO–218, p. 64 (1959).

18. E. D. DOWNiE, S. MACPHERSON, E. N. RAMSDEN, H. A. SISSONS and J. VAUGHAN, The effect of daily feeding of Sr^{90} to rabbits, *Brit. J. Cancer* **13**, 408–423 (1959).

19. J. VAUGHAN, Preliminary report on damage to bone marrow in relation to radiation dose from Sr^{90} weanlings, *Radiation Damage in Bone*, Conference in Oxford sponsored by International Atomic Energy Agency, Vienna, 36–37 (April, 1960).

20. M. OWEN and J. VAUGHAN, Radiation dose and its relation to damage in the rabbit tibia following a single injection and daily feeding of Sr^{90}, *Brit. J. Cancer* **13**, 424–438 (1959a).

21. M. OWEN and J. VAUGHAN, Dose-rate measurements in the rabbit tibia following uptake of Sr^{90}, *Brit. J. Radiol.* **32**, 714–724 (1959b).

22. J. VAUGHAN, Leuco-erythroblastic anaemia, *J. Path. Bact.* **42**, 541–564 (1936).

23. G. BRECHER and E. P. CRONKITE, Platelet count using 1 per cent ammonium oxalate, *J. Phys.* 365 (1950).

24. M. BROOKES, Sequelae of experimental partial ischaemia in long bones of the rabbit, *J. Anat.* **94**, 552–561 (1960).

25. S. MACPHERSON, M. OWEN and J. VAUGHAN, The relation of radiation damage to radiation dose from Sr^{90}, *J. Bone Jt. Surg.* **42B**, 395 (1960).

26. T. T. PUCK, Quantitative studies on mammalian cells *in vitro*, *Rev. Mod. Phys.* **32**, 433 (1959).

27. D. W. H. BARNES and J. P. LOUTIT, Post-irradiation treatment of mice and rats, in *Ionizing Radiations and Cell Metabolism*, Ciba Foundation Symposium, edited by G. E. W. WOLSTENHOLME and C. M. O'CONNER, published by J. & A. Churchill Ltd., London, 140–153 (1956).

28. M. H. ROSS, J. FURTH and R. R. BIGELOW, Changes in cellular composition of the lymph caused by ionizing radiations, *Blood* **7**, 417–428 (1952).

29. S. MACPHERSON, The stunting of growth in young rabbits injected with Sr^{90}, *International J. Radiation Biol* (1961) in press.

30. J. VAUGHAN, L. F. LAMERTON and H. LISCO, The relation of Radiation Damage to Radiation Dose in Bone, Report of Conference in Oxford sponsored by International Atomic Energy Agency, Vienna, 7–20 (April, 1960).

31. F, G. J. HAYHOE, *Leukaemia: Research and Clinical Practice*, J. & A. Churchill Itd., London 32 (1960).

PART IV

DOSIMETRY OF INTERNALLY DEPOSITED RADIONUCLIDES

INTERACTIONS OF α AND β PARTICLES WITH MATTER

R. D. EVANS

Massachusetts Institute of Technology, Cambridge 39, Mass.

IN THE University of Utah project on the toxicity of radionuclides deposited internally in beagle dogs, we are concerned with the interactions of α rays and β rays from more than 20 different radionuclides. The α-ray energies extend from 4·78 MeV (Ra) to 8·78 MeV (ThC'). The β-ray energies extend from 0·05 MeV (MsTh$_1$) to 3·26 MeV (RaC) with special emphasis on the 0·54 MeV (Sr^{90}) and 2·26 MeV (Y^{90}) domain. The following introductory remarks refer especially to α rays and β rays in these energy domains.

A. ALPHA RAYS

Velocity. The α rays are, of course, He^4 nuclei expelled from the nucleus of the parent with a velocity β, relative to the velocity of light, of β ∼ 0·06. Thus $\beta^2 \sim 0.004$, and nonrelativistic collision theory is applicable.

Line spectra. From a given radionuclide, α rays are emitted in one or more monoenergetic groups, usually closely spaced in energy. For example, Pu^{239} emits 5·147 MeV α rays in 72 per cent of the disintegrations, and also 5·134 MeV α rays (17 per cent), and 5·096 MeV α rays (11 per cent).

Scattering. Because of its large mass, the α ray passes through absorbing materials such as water, soft tissue, or bone salts in a straight path, with negligible deflections due to nuclear elastic scattering and negligible bremsstrahlung production. Substantially the entire energy dissipation is due to coulomb interactions with individual atomic electrons, and results in ionization and excitation of atoms in the material traversed.

Mean linear energy transfer. An α ray of velocity $V = \beta c$ loses, on the average, kinetic energy dE while traversing a distance dr in an elementary absorber containing N atoms/cm³. If each atom has Z electrons there are NZ electrons/cm³ and the energy loss, or linear energy transfer, is

$$\frac{\mathrm{d}E}{\mathrm{d}r} = \frac{4\pi z^2 e^4}{m_0 V^2} NZ \ln \frac{2m_0 V^2}{I} \tag{1}$$

where $ze = 2e$ is the initial charge on the α particle, $-e$ is the charge of the struck electron, I is the geometric mean of all the ionization and excitation potentials of the atoms in the absorber, and nonparticipation of K electrons is neglected. To a good approximation $I = 13 \cdot 5\, Z$ eV for solid absorbers.

Mixtures and compounds. Chemical binding energies between individual atoms in a molecule are so small that from the standpoint of energy transfer all atoms behave independently. Absorbers comprising mixtures of elements produce total linear energy transfers which are the sum of the separate effects of each type of atom, each with its individual value of N, Z, and I. Often these can be lumped into effective values, as in the invaluable tables calculated by Douglas Lea[1] whose standard wet tissue contains $NZ = 3 \cdot 307 \times 10^{23}$ electrons/g and has an effective mean excitation and ionization potential of $I = 66$ eV.

Specific ionization curve. The ratio of ionization to excitation is roughly 1-to-1 (except for the noble gases) and the mean energy, w, required to form one ion pair is commonly about twice the first ionization potential. For air w is about 35 eV and this value is commonly used, but without experimental justification, for water, wet tissue, and bone. From Eq.(1) the linear energy transfer dE/dr, and hence the ionization per unit path length, varies *roughly* as $1/\beta^2$ hence inversely with the kinetic energy. Thus as an α ray slows down, its ionization per unit path length increases

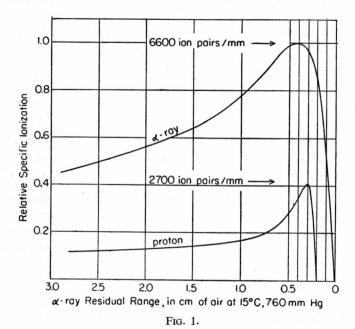

FIG. 1.

Specific ionization of a single α ray in air. (*From* Evans[2].)

(Fig. 1). This specific ionization reaches a maximum value when the α ray slows down to a velocity of about 0.6×10^9 cm/sec ($\beta \sim 1/50$), hence an energy of about 0·75 MeV, because the more slowly moving helium nucleus repeatedly captures and loses electrons, and reduces its effective charge and its ionizing ability. Typical values of the linear energy transfer dE/dr are 66 keV/micron of water or tissue for an 8 MeV α ray, 94 keV/μ for 5 MeV, 176 keV/μ for 2 Mev, and 264 keV/μ for a 1 MeV α ray (p. 25 of ref. 1). Each micron of path in tissue is equivalent in energy loss to about 1·03 mm of air at 15°C and 760 mm Hg.

Delta rays. Equation (1) represents an integration over the size and frequency of the energy transfers in individual collisions. The classical cross-section for an energy transfer Q in the interval dQ varies as dQ/Q^2. Therefore small energy transfers Q are greatly favored in individual collisions. However there are a few "hard" collisions in which the struck electron receives a large energy transfer Q. The maximum possible energy transfer in a single collision is

$$Q_{max} = 2m_0 V^2 = (4m_0/M_\alpha)E = 0.00055E \qquad (2)$$

or about 2·7 keV from a 5 MeV α ray and only 550 eV from a 1 MeV α ray.

Secondary electrons which receive a kinetic energy Q greater than about 100 eV, and which are therefore able to produce about 3 or more ion pairs along their own path in the medium are called δ rays. Typically there are about 100 such δ rays per micron of path in tissue of any 5 MeV α ray, and the number of δ rays per micron increases as the α ray slows down (Figs. 2, 3). About one-half of the total ionization produced by an α ray (or by a β ray) is secondary ionization produced along the paths of these δ rays.

"Radius" of α ray path. In tissue, the path length is about 0·053 micron for a 1 keV δ ray electron, about 0·020 micron for a 0·5 keV δ ray, and about 0·003 μ for a 100 eV δ ray. Thus the radius of the column of ions along the path of an α ray in soft tissue is in the domain of 0·01 micron or 100 angstroms.

Straggling. Statistical fluctuations in the number and size of the individual energy transfers give rise to slight differences in the total path length, or range, of initially monoenergetic individual α rays. This "straggling" results in a normal-law distribution of ranges with a standard deviation σ about the mean range R. To a good approximation, $\sigma/R \simeq 0.011$ for the α rays considered here. Thus some 32 per cent of an initially mono-

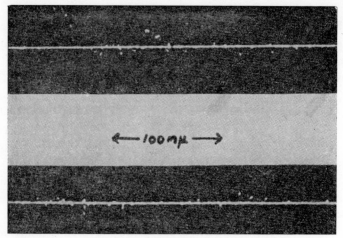

FIG. 2.

Cloud chamber photograph at high magnification of an α ray in air. Note the clearly-defined O rays. The scale is for equivalent millimicrons in tissue. (*From* Gray[3].)

FIG. 3.

The same α ray track superimposed to scale on an electron micrograph of tobacco-necrosis virus. (*From* Gray[3].)

energetic group of α rays will have individual ranges which are longer or shorter than the mean range by more than 1·1 per cent.

Mean range. The mean range R increases with the initial energy E and is well approximated in the 4 to 8 MeV domain by Geiger's (and Briggs') rule

$$R \int E^{1.63} \qquad (3)$$

Because Eq. (1) may be integrated over range elements dr only in the high velocity domain, $2m_0V^2/I \gg 1$, all range-energy relationships rest on measured values for low energy α rays (Fig. 4). The mean range of a 5 MeV α ray is 3·5 cm of air at 15°C and 760 mm Hg, or about 35 microns of wet tissue or water.

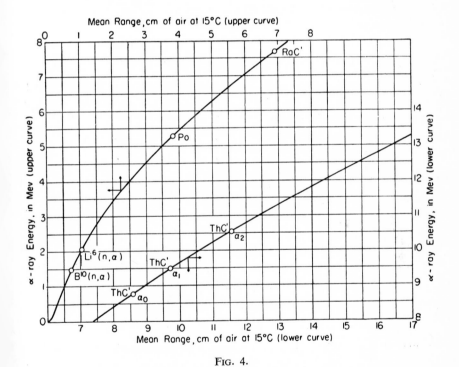

FIG. 4.

Range–energy relationship for α rays in dry air. (*From* Evans[2].)

Relative stopping power. For equal energy loss dE, the ratio of the distance dr_0 traveled in a standard reference material (often air) to the distance

dr_1 traveled in another medium is called the relative *linear* stopping power S_l of the medium. Then

$$S_l = \frac{(dE/dr_1)}{(dE/dr_0)} = \frac{dr_0}{dr_1} = \frac{N_1 Z_1 \ln (2m_0 V^2/I_1)}{N_0 Z_0 \ln (2m_0 V^2/I_0)} =$$
$$= \frac{N_1 Z_1}{N_0 Z_0} \left[1 - \frac{\ln (I_1/I_0)}{\ln (2m_0 V^2/I_0)} \right] \qquad (4)$$

Note that the linear stopping power depends on the number of electrons per cm³, NZ, which is

$$NZ = G\varrho \frac{Z}{A} \frac{\text{electrons}}{\text{cm}^3} \qquad (5)$$

where G is Avogadro's number, ϱ is the density, and A is the atomic weight. For most light elements $Z/A \simeq 0.5$, and hence the number of electrons per cm³ is closely proportional to the density.

Then the relative linear stopping power becomes

$$S_l = \frac{\varrho_1 (Z/A)_1}{\varrho_0 (Z/A)_0} \left[1 - \frac{\ln (I_1/I_0)}{\ln (2m_0 V^2/I_0)} \right] \qquad (6)$$

in which the predominant term often is the density ratio ϱ_1/ϱ_0. For this reason the relative *mass stopping power* S_m is often a convenient quantity (especially for β rays), where

$$S_m = \frac{(\varrho\, dr)_0}{(\varrho\, dr)_1} = \frac{\varrho_0}{\varrho_1} S_l = \frac{(Z/A)_1}{(Z/A)_0} \left[1 - \frac{\ln (I_1/I_0)}{\ln (2m_0 V^2/I_0)} \right] \qquad (7)$$

Hydrogen, for which $Z/A = 1$, has twice as many electrons per gram as most other light elements, and hence about twice the mass stopping power.

The terms in square brackets in Eqs. (6) or (7) show that the stopping power depends on the velocity, and if $Z_1/Z_0 \simeq I_1/I_0 > 1$, the relative stopping power decreases with decreasing velocity.

The relative range of a particular α ray in medium 1 is then dependent on an integral which involves S_l and is of the form

$$\frac{R_1}{R_0} = \frac{\int dr_1}{\int dr_0} = \frac{1}{R_0} \int \frac{dr_0}{S_l} \qquad (8)$$

Because S_l varies with velocity, it cannot be taken outside the integral as a factor, and the relative range R_1/R_0 for two particular media is actually a function of the initial velocity and hence of R_0.

In some cases it is useful to define an effective or average stopping power $\overline{S_l}$ for the entire range, thus

$$R_1 = \frac{R_0}{\overline{S_l}} \qquad (9)$$

Bragg and Kleeman noted experimentally that the effective relative stopping power per *atom* S_a is approximately proportional to $\sqrt{A}$ for α rays in the 5 MeV domain, and hence that

$$\frac{R_1}{R_0} = \frac{1}{\overline{S_l}} = \frac{N_0}{N_1}\,\frac{1}{\overline{S_a}} \simeq \frac{(\varrho/A)_0}{(\varrho/A)_1}\cdot\frac{\sqrt{A_0}}{\sqrt{A_1}} = \frac{\varrho_0}{\varrho_1}\frac{\sqrt{A_1}}{\sqrt{A_0}} \qquad (10)$$

Thus $R_\varrho/\sqrt{A}$ is approximately independent of the medium. This so-called *Bragg–Kleeman rule* is usually good to within ±15 per cent in the 1 to 10 MeV domain, and functions because $Z\,\ln(2m_0V^2/I)$ is roughly proportional to $\sqrt{A}$. For mixtures the effective value of $\sqrt{A}$ is

$$\sqrt{A} = \frac{N_1A_1 + N_2A_2 + N_3A_3 + \cdots}{N_1\sqrt{A_1} + N_2\sqrt{A_2} + N_3\sqrt{A_3} + \cdots} \qquad (11)$$

where N_1, N_2, ... are the number of atoms per cm³ which have atomic weights A_1, A_2, ... For example $\sqrt{A_0} = 3\cdot82$ for air.

Using the Bragg–Kleeman rule, Mays[1] has calculated the range of the 5·14 MeV α rays of Pu^{239} to be 35·4 μ in water, 25·0 μ in compact bone, and 21·1 μ in Ilford emulsion compared with 3·68 cm of air at 15°C and 760 mm Hg.

Recoil daughter atom. The momentum of the residual atom equals the momentum of the emitted α ray. Hence the kinetic energy of the recoiling atom is

$$E_{\mathrm{recoil}} = E_\alpha\,\frac{M_\alpha}{M_{\mathrm{recoil}}} \simeq 0\cdot019E_\alpha \qquad (12)$$

or about 0·1 MeV for a 5 MeV α ray. Because of its large mass and small velocity the recoil atom has a path of only about 0·12 mm in air, or about 0·15 μ in tissue. The ionization along this path is intense. The recoil atom also may produce intensely ionizing knock-on atoms in the absorber (Fig. 5). Any living cell from which an α ray is emitted surely must suffer severe injury or destruction.

Distribution of LET. The total linear energy transfer varies along the primary path in accord with Eq. (1), which includes energy transfers to all δ rays. Some types of radiobiological damage can be correlated with the distribution of linear energy transfer (LET). For α rays the distribution of LET along the "core" of the path, excluding δ rays of more than 100 eV, extends from about 40 keV/μ tissue to about 170 keV/μ tissue. Approximately one-half of the total energy dissipated is along this core. The other one-half is in δ rays for which the distribution of LET extends

FIG. 5.

Very low pressure cloud chamber photograph of recoil atoms in the sequential α
decay of An and AcA. (*From* Joliot[5].)

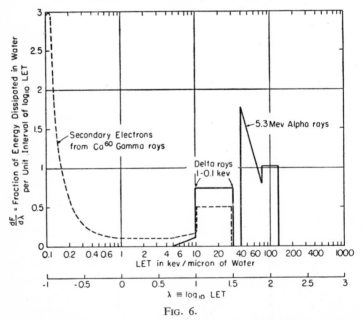

FIG. 6.

Energy-dissipation distribution of linear energy transfer. The distribution of
LET for the secondary electrons from Co⁶⁰ γ rays would be roughly similar (7)
to that for the Y⁹⁰ β rays. (*From* Howard-Flanders[6].)

from about 6 keV/μ tissue for 2·7 keV δ rays to about 33 keV/μ tissue for 100 eV δ rays (p. 24 of ref. 1).

LET for β rays. The LET values for α rays are very large compared with those for β rays and their associated δ rays, which can have energies up to one-half that of the β ray. For the β rays of Y^{90}, for example, the distribution of LET will be concentrated near the minimum possible value of primary ionization which is about 0·1 keV/μ tissue, and will extend in a long-tailed distribution up to the same δ ray domain as for α rays (Fig. 6).

B. BETA RAYS

Beta rays are electrons (either megatrons or positrons) ejected with a companion neutrino from nuclei during the transformation of a nucleon. Because the β decay is a 3-body disintegration (β ray, neutrino, and residual nucleus), the β ray spectrum is continuous below a maximum energy E_{max}, and has mean and modal energies which are in the vicinity of $E_{max}/3$.

The small rest mass m_0 of the β ray and the continuous spectrum account for the differences between the interaction of β rays and α rays with matter. Nuclear elastic scattering and bremsstrahlung are important modes of interaction for β rays, in addition to the ionization and excitation interactions.

All β rays have initial velocities which are comparable with the velocity of light ($\beta=0·4$ for 0·05 MeV β ray, $\beta=0·94$ for 1·0 MeV β ray) hence "all β rays are relativistic". The relationship between the velocity index $\beta=V/c$ and the kinetic energy E is

$$\beta^2 = 1 - \left(\frac{m_0 c^2}{E + m_0 c^2} \right)^2 \tag{13}$$

where $m_0 c^2 = 0·511$ MeV is the rest energy of the electron.

Mean linear energy transfer. The ionization and excitation losses now become (p. 582 of ref. 2), in place of Eq. (1),

$$\frac{dE}{dr} = \frac{2\pi e^4}{m_0 V^2} NZ \left\{ \ln \left[\frac{m_0 V^2 E}{I^2 (1-\beta^2)} \right] - \beta^2 \right\} \tag{14}$$

There appears again the variation with $1/V^2$ at low velocities, but as β approaches unity the logarithmic terms give rise to a minimum in dE/dr at about 1 MeV followed by a gradual rise as the energy increases.

The LET and specific ionization are very much less than for α rays because the β ray velocity is much greater (Figs. 7, 8). A convenient rule of thumb is that the specific ionization in air at 0°C and 760 mm Hg is

$$\frac{dE}{dr} = \frac{45}{\beta^2} \frac{\text{ion pairs}}{\text{cm of air}} \tag{15}$$

As Z increases, $NZ/\varrho(=GZ/A)$ decreases, but I increases. Therefore the mass energy transfer $dE/\varrho\,dr$ decreases slightly with increasing Z (Fig. 9).

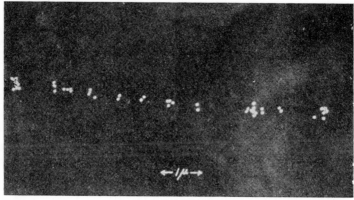

FIG. 7.

Cloud chamber photograph of the path of a 1 MeV β ray. The scale is for equivalent microns in tissue. (*From* Gray[3].)

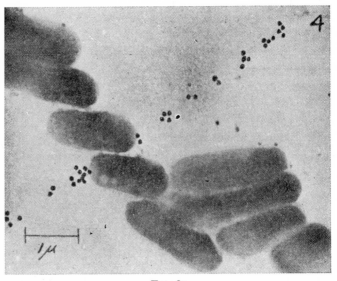

FIG. 8.

The β ray track of Fig. 7 superimposed to scale on an electron micrograph of *Escherichia coli* and bacteriophage. (*From* Gray[3].)

Delta rays. Because the β ray has the same rest mass as an electron, the maximum energy transfer in a single collision with an electron is the entire energy E. However, the maximum energy transfer considered in collision theory is $E/2$, because the convention has been adopted that, after a collision, the higher energy electron is identified as the continuing primary electron. Then δ rays from a 1 MeV β ray may have any energy up to 0·5 MeV, and the distribution of LET for β rays is peaked at low values, as remarked earlier.

Straggling. Because large energy losses are possible in individual collisions, the straggling of energy losses, path lengths, and ranges of electrons are very much greater than for α rays.

Elastic nuclear scattering. Because of its small rest mass, the cross-section for elastic scattering of a β ray by a nucleus in the absorber is large. For example, the cross-section for scattering through more than 90°, i.e., backscattering, of a 0·5 MeV β ray is $Z^2/9$ barns per nucleus (p. 593 of ref. 2).

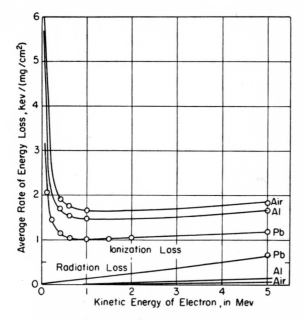

FIG. 9.

Mass-absorption energy losses along the path of electrons in air, Al, and Pb.
(*From* Evans[2].)

The result is that each β ray experiences many nuclear elastic scattering events, and its path through any absorber is not straight, but highly tortuous (Fig. 10).

Range. The "range" is the thickness of absorber which stops essentially all of the incident β rays (Fig. 11). Because of their tortuous path, the range always is less than the total path length measured along the actual path of the β ray. The ratio of path length to range varies from about 1·2 to 4, being greatest for low-energy β rays in high Z materials.

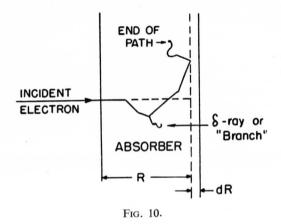

FIG. 10.

Schematic diagram of the path and range R of an electron in an absorber. (*From* Evans[2].)

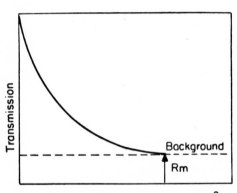

Absorber Thickness in gm/cm²

FIG. 11.

Exponential absorption and the definition of range (or maximum range R_m) of a β ray spectrum. (*From* Evans[2].)

Range vs. energy. The range energy–relationship for β rays is wholly empirical (Fig. 12). To a good approximation for energies between $E \sim 0.01$ MeV and $E \sim 3$ MeV.

$$\rho R \left(\frac{\text{mg}}{\text{cm}^2} \right) = 412 E^n$$

$$n = 1\cdot265 - 0\cdot0954 \ln E \qquad (16)$$

Relative stopping power. The relative stopping power follows basically the same definitions and principles as for α rays, Eqs. (4) to (7), except that the logarithmic terms are more complicated. However, in principle, V is large ($\beta \sim 1$) in Eq. (7) and the square bracket is nearly unity. Hence, for electrons the mass stopping power is closely proportional to Z/A. As Z increases, the increase in path length due to the decrease in Z/A is nearly exactly compensated by increased nuclear elastic scattering and a decreased ratio of range to path length. Then to a good approximation the mass range, in grams/cm², is substantially independent of the chemical nature of the absorber.

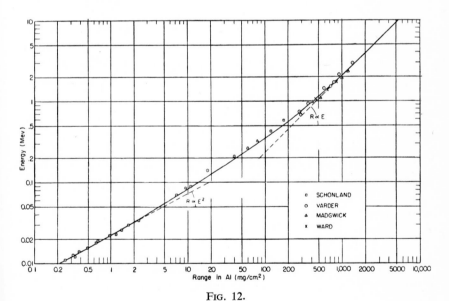

FIG. 12.

Range–energy relationship for β ray spectra. (*From* Evans[2].)

Exponential absorption. Because of the initially continuous character of the β ray spectrum, its transmission through absorbers is fortuitously approximately exponential. The effective mass-absorption coefficient in aluminum and other light elements is (p. 628 of ref. 2).

$$\frac{\mu}{\varrho} = \frac{17}{E_{\max}^{1\cdot14}} \frac{\text{cm}^2}{\text{g}} \qquad (17)$$

Comparison with Eq. (16) shows that the half-value thickness $D_{1/2}$ is approximately one-tenth of the range,

$$D_{1/2} \simeq 0 \cdot 1 \ R \qquad (18)$$

Within about this thickness multiple scattering produces directional randomicity, and approximately the same shape of spectrum is then maintained throughout the absorption, as Dudley and Brownell have shown (p. 305 of ref. 8).

Bremsstrahlung. Most of the collisions of a β ray with atomic nuclei in the absorber are elastic. But about 1 per cent of the collisions with nuclei are inelastic and result in the emission of a photon. This is a 3-body interaction, hence the photon spectrum is continuous and extends for an electron of initial kinetic energy E from $h\nu=0$ to $h\nu_{max}=E$, with most of the bremsstrahlung energy emitted in the domain of low-energy photons. The shape of the spectrum is independent of Z.

The bremsstrahlung yield is proportional to Z^2 per atom traversed. But the number of atoms encountered along the path length, which is controlled by ionization and excitation losses, is proportional to $1/NZ$. Hence the bremsstrahlung yield in an absorber which is thick enough to stop the electron is proportional to Z.

For any continuous β ray spectrum, the bremsstrahlung spectrum is then "doubly" continuous, and is heavily loaded in the low-energy photon domain. Theory and experiment are now in reasonable agreement[9] on the shape and intensity of the spectrum (Fig. 13). A useful rule of thumb, derived from an approximate theory (p. 619 of ref. 2) is that the total energy I_{brems} MeV emitted as bremsstrahlung is

$$I_{brems} \simeq \frac{Z}{7000} E_{max}{}^{2} \qquad (19)$$

where E_{max} MeV is the maximum energy of the β ray spectrum being totally absorbed in material having atomic number Z. For mixtures and compounds

$$Z_{effective} \simeq \frac{N_1 Z_1^2 + N_2 Z_2^2 + N_3 Z_3^2 + \ldots}{N_1 Z_1 + N_2 Z_2 + N_3 Z_3 + \ldots} \qquad (20)$$

where N_1, N_2, ... are the number of atoms per cm³ which have atomic numbers Z_1, Z_2, ... Then, for example in the absorption of the β rays of Y^{90} by bone, roughly 0·7 per cent of the average β ray energy is converted to bremsstrahlung if $Z_{eff} = 9$ for bone. This furnishes one of the routine methods for *in vivo* estimates of the internal burden of Sr^{90} Y^{90}.

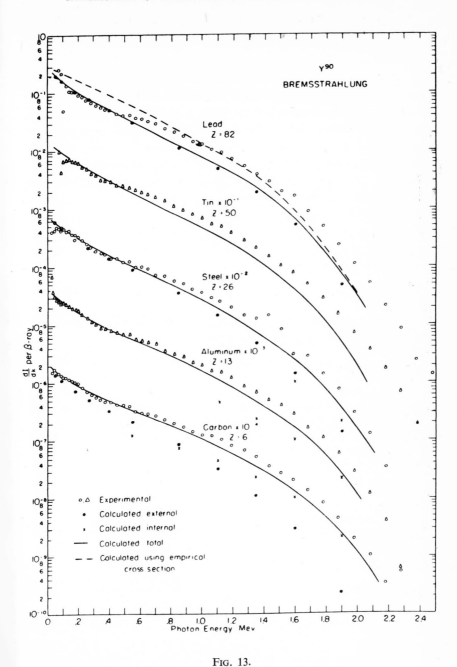

FIG. 13.

Absolute differential bremsstrahlung yield from the total absorption of the β rays from Y^{90}. (*From* Bear[9].)

The bremsstrahlung just discussed is the "external" bremsstrahlung produced by the interaction of β rays with absorbing materials. In addition, there is a weak "internal" bremsstrahlung spectrum which originates within the emitting atoms and is independent of the absorber.

Positron annihilation. In the case of positron β rays each positron, after losing substantially all of its kinetic energy, can capture an electron into a K orbit of positronium, following which the positron and megatron annihilate each other. In the usual (parapositronium) case, two oppositely directed photons are emitted, each having the quantum energy $hv = m_0 c^2 = 0 \cdot 511$ MeV. Coincidence counting of positron annihilation radiation has proved a useful tool in the localization of radionuclides, for example as in the use of As^{74} and Cu^{64} in the localization of brain tumors.[10]

REFERENCES

1. D. E. LEA, *Actions of Radiations on Living Cells*, Cambridge University Press (1947).
2. R. D. EVANS, *The Atomic Nucleus*, McGraw-Hill, New York (1955).
3. L. H. GRAY, Chap. XV in *Biophysical Research Methods*, ed. F. M. UBER, Interscience Pub. (1950).
4. C. W. MAYS, p. 164 of University of Utah Radiobiology Laboratory Progress Report, COO-217, (1958), as amended in personal communication, May 1961.
5. F. JOLIOT, Etude des rayons de recul radioactifs par la méthode des détentes de Wilson, *J. Phys. Radium* **5**, 129 (1934).
6. P. HOWARD-FLANDERS, in *Advances in Biol. and Med. Physics*. eds. C. A. TOBIAS and J. H. LAWRENCE, Academic Press, New York, **6**, 553–603 (1958).
7. M. DANZKER, N. D. KESSARIS, and J. S. LAUGHLIN, Absorbed dose and linear energy transfer in radiation experiments, *Radiology* **72**, 51–61 (1959).
8. R. A. DUDLEY, Chap. 7 in *Radiation Dosimetry*, eds. G. J. HINE and G. L. BROWNELL, Academic Press, New York (1956).
9. J. L. BEAR, The bremsstruhlung produced by continuous beta-ray emitters, Ph. D. Thesis, Massachusetts Institute of Technology (1960).
10. W. H. SWEET, J. MEALEY Jr, G. L. BROWNELL and S. ARNOW, Coincidence scanning with positron-emitting arsenic or copper in the diagnosis of focal intracranial disease, in *Medical Radioisotope Scanning*, International Atomic Energy Agency, Vienna, Austria, 163–188 (1959).

THE RELATIONSHIP BETWEEN ALPHA AND BETA DOSIMETRY

L. F. LAMERTON

Physics Department, Institute of Cancer Research, Royal Cancer Hospital, Fulham Road, London, S.W.3.

INTRODUCTION

THE title of this paper may be somewhat misleading. Although I shall be referring to problems of the relationship between α and β dosimetry, the main question I would like to consider is the extent to which detailed investigations of radiation dose distribution are practicable and worthwhile in studies with bone-seeking radioactive isotopes. In a short paper it is possible to discuss the subject only in very general terms and much of what I have to say will, I am afraid, be very obvious. However, it may provide a basis for discussion.

One's view of the importance of dose distribution data will depend on the ultimate purpose of the work being done. Most of those whose interest in bone-seekers lies in obtaining comparative toxicity data for the better assessment of maximum permissible levels will probably not regard detailed investigation of radiation dose distribution as being of great importance, although it is clear that many of the problems of extrapolation of experimental results to man and to low dosage levels must involve some consideration of the dose distribution.

However, for those whose interest in the bone-seekers lies in the study of mechanisms of tumour production the question of detailed radiation dose distribution is a very important one, with the recognition that the problem is not only that of measuring the dose distribution but of correlating it with histological findings.

It is important not to underestimate the magnitude of the problems involved. Bone is a very complex tissue and the distribution of radiation dose produced by the bone-seekers can be very non-uniform indeed, both in space and in time. In fact, from some points of view bone is a very unsatisfactory material for studies of carcinogenesis. On the other hand, the use of the bone-seekers has two very great advantages in tumour work. Firstly, a high radiation dose can be given to the bone with a relatively small dose to the rest of the body and, secondly, the sites where the tumours are likely to arise are generally known.

The main problems that are involved in studying radiation dose distribution in bone from the bone-seeking isotopes can be grouped under three main headings:

(i) the technical problems of measurement,
(ii) the problem of the type or types of cell to be considered,
(iii) the problem of the time over which the dose should be integrated and the allowance to be made for dose rate.

In addition there are certain special problems when considering low levels of radiation dose and these will also be discussed.

Technical Problems of Measurement

The only techniques available at the present time for the detailed study of radiation dose distribution in bone are based on autoradiography and they are very laborious. Anything approaching a complete distribution of dose in a given bone at any one time is a considerable undertaking even for the longer-range β emitters. For α emitters and the shorter range β emitters a full dose distribution is generally quite an impracticable aim. It must also be recognised that a single dose distribution at one point in time is of little value. For any interpretation of the biological results it is necessary to have information on the change of dose distribution with time, often over a long period.

Significant Cell Type

When considering the particular type of cells for which one is to measure the radiation dose, one becomes very aware of the distinction between what can be done and what should be done. In the past the osteocyte has been one of the favourite cell types for measurement and calculation of dose in the bone, mainly because it is a well-defined cell nicely positioned in the mineral part of bone, but there is no experimental evidence and little theoretical reason for believing that it plays an important part in bone tumour production. There is now evidence from a number of laboratories that tumours tend to arise from the osteogenic tissue at bone surfaces and it is not unreasonable to assume that it is the more primitive cell types which are the most critical. However, to measure the dose received by the primitive osteogenic cells in bone requires not only a detailed knowledge of the radiation dosage distribution in bone, but also a knowledge of the distribution of the cells themselves, with a precision which must increase with the degree of non-uniformity of the dose distribution. There are also severe problems of identification of such cells and, as Kember[1] has shown, they can migrate within the bone. An estimate of the dose received by these cells is a difficult project for the longer-range β emitters. For α emitters and short-range β emitters any useful estimate may be impossible.

With high levels of radiation dose the problem becomes even more complex if generalised tissue damage influences the production of tumours, since the occurrence of a tumour in a given site may be partly the result of radiation damage, for instance to blood vessels, in a different part of bone. At the present time we have not the evidence to express in any quantitative terms the significance of radiation damage to tissues and structures outside those in which the tumours appear.

Although generalized tissue damage may still be an important factor in determining the rate of tumour incidence at a given dose level it is, I believe, becoming increasingly difficult to hold to the view that gross tissue damage is a *necessary* prelude to bone tumour production by radiation, defining 'gross' damage as an obvious and maintained histological change. Reports such as those of Møller[2] suggest that bone tumours have been produced with relatively low doses of radiation, although the experimental data available are by no means extensive. In our own laboratory, using localised external irradiation to the hind limb of rats, we have obtained bone tumours with doses of a few hundred roentgens. At such doses we find it very difficult to observe any appreciable late histological damage in the bones. The definition of 'gross' damage depends, of course, on the detection methods used, and with more subtle methods of detection it may be found that there are forms of generalised damage that play an essential part in bone tumour production.

However, if a generalized tissue damage plays any part at all in bone tumour production then it is likely that the relative importance of irradiation of the more distant parts of bone will be greater for high than for low doses, so that the significance for tumour production of a given dose distribution in bone will depend on the level of dose considered. At low levels of dose the irradiation should be most efficient in tumour production if confined to those cells from which tumours will arise. At high dose levels a wider distribution in bone of the radiation dose might be more efficient, not only because of possible generalised tissue effects, but also because there will be less death in the population of cells from which tumours will arise.

Period Over which Radiation Dose Should be Integrated

In attempting to compare different bone-seekers or different patterns of administration of the same bone-seeker, one often takes as the significant dose parameter the accumulated radiation dose up to the time of first observation of the tumour. This is generally the only dose parameter which can be employed, but it must be recognised that its use would imply large assumptions concerning the biological mechanisms involved even if the dose were averaged over the cells at risk. In particular, it implies that tumour production is a dose rate independent process and also that the time between the production of the malignant cell and the first demonstration of the tumour is short compared with the total period of exposure.

If the tumour production is affected by general tissue disorganisation, or if it is the result of an induced cytological abnormality such as a chromosome exchange the first assumption at least, that of dose rate independence, will not apply.

Scope of Dosage Distribution Studies

In spite of the magnitude of the problems involved it must be accepted that studies of radiation dosage distribution in bone, allied to data on tumour incidence, offer one of the few ways of gaining information on mechanisms of bone tumour production by radiation. However, without some fairly clear lead, which we do not possess at the present time, as to the nature of the important biological processes involved, much detailed radiation dosimetry work may be of little value. The conclusion to be drawn is that, in the present state of knowledge, there are definite limits to the precision with which one should pursue detailed dose distribution studies. At the moment dose distribution studies would appear to be most valuable in investigations of comparative carcinogenic effectiveness, where the number of dosage variables is small, for instance, in studies of differences in tumour incidence following different patterns of administration of the same isotope. When two isotopes of widely different characteristics are being compared the interpretation of detailed dose distribution studies may be very difficult.

Dosimetry Problems at Low Dose Levels

When one is considering problems of radiation dose distribution at low levels of dose certain special problems arise out of the statistical nature of the interaction between radiation and matter. The main problem here is not so much that of the discontinuity of energy transfer *within* cells, which has been studied a great deal, but that of the discontinuity *between* cells.

It is not difficult, knowing the mean energy and range of the radiation, to calculate very approximately the chance of a given cell being traversed by an ionising particle, for a given mean dose in rads to the tissue. The calculations in Table 1 (intended only to represent orders of magnitude) have been carried out for dose rates of 300 m rad/week (corresponding to the ICRP maximum permissible dose rate for β radiation) and for 30 m rad/week (corresponding to the ICRP value for α radiation). For these calculations it has been assumed that the tissue is composed of cells of diameter 10 μ, with nuclei of diameter 5 μ.

TABLE 1

Average Interval between Successive Passages of Ionizing Particles through a 10 micron diameter cell for Uniform Tissue Concentrations giving 30 millirad/week for the α emitter, Pu^{239}, and 300 millirad/week for the β emitters P^{32} and C^{14}

The Values are Very Approximate

Radionuclide	Average energy (MeV)	Average range (microns)	Av. interval between passages		Mean dose per nucleus per passage
			cell	nucleus	
Pu^{239}	5·3	~ 40	~14 yr	~56 yr	~100 rad
P^{32}	0·69	~ 2000	~ 1 day	~ 4 day	~ 0·25 rad
C^{14}	0·045	~ 40	~ 4 day	~16 day	~ 1 rad

It can be seen that with Pu^{239}, an α emitter, at a mean tissue dose rate equivalent to the maximum permissible value, the passage of an α particle through any part of a cell is a very rare event—occurring about once every 56 years for a given nucleus. When, however, a cell is traversed, the energy deposited in it will be large. Considering a cell nucleus of diameter 5 μ the average energy per gram deposited per passage will be equivalent to about 100 rad. It is evident that for α emitters, at these dose levels, 'mean' radiation dose in a tissue can be, biologically, a misleading concept, since the effect of a change in dose level is not to alter the amount of radiation energy delivered to individual cells, which remains large, but to alter the number of cells so affected.

With β emitters at low dose rates, this 'quantisation' of energy transfer to cells is much less severe than for α emitters. Considering P^{32} at the maximum permissible dose rate of 300 m rad/week, any given cell nucleus will be traversed by a β particle about once every 4 days and the mean energy deposited in a nucleus per passage will be equivalent to a dose of only about 0·25 rads. As can be seen from the values for C^{14}, reduction in β ray energy and range leads to some increase in the energy deposited per passage through a nucleus, but is still far less than in the case of α emitters.

The main biological significance of this quantisation of energy transfer between cells is that, for α emitters at low dose levels, any effects that occur must be the result of specific radiation induced changes in individual cells and that effects arising from generalised tissue damage, which may be of importance at higher dose levels, will not occur. Probably the same conclusion can be drawn for β emitters although the possibility cannot be entirely discounted that the more widespread distribution of ionisation can produce some general changes of importance. However, it is reasonable to assume that, if tumours can be produced at these low dose levels, the comparative carcinogenic effectiveness of α and β radiation will be determined entirely by the nature of the significant cytological change. If this change corresponds to a "one-track" event in a critical structure the RBE of α to β radiation will be independent of dose level and dose rate. The actual value of the RBE will depend on the necessary energy requirements, but will be less than unity for a pure one ion-pair event.

However, if the significant cytological change is one corresponding mainly to a multi-track event for β radiation and to a one-track event for α radiation, which appears to be the case for certain types of chromosomal exchange, the carcinogenic effectiveness of β relative to α radiation will decrease as the level of mean radiation dose is reduced, to a value which will depend on the probability of the effect being "one-track" for the β radiation. Such a change in RBE with dose level must greatly complicate the comparison of α and β emitters on a radiation dosimetric basis.

These are very simple radiobiological considerations but they have an important bearing on the concept of RBE at low dose levels. Also they suggest that perhaps the most direct way of obtaining the necessary basic biological information on bone tumour production, of the relative importance of local and generalised damage and of the nature of the significant cytological change, is through studies of the comparative carcinogenicity of an α and a β emitter, extended down to really low dose levels. It would be necessary to use large numbers of animals and there is the difficulty that the lifespan of the experimental animal may be too short compared with the latent period of tumour production at low doses for meaningful results to be obtained. However, if these experiments can be done they might give sufficient information to allow a more useful attack than is possible at present in a number of directions, including the relationship between radiation dose distribution and biological effect of the bone-seeking isotopes.

CONCLUSION

In this paper the difficulties of detailed dose distribution work have been discussed. I hope that I have not given the impression that dose distribution studies may be ignored. The problems encountered are, in fact, only a reflection of the essential complexity of the action of bone-seekers. Without some knowledge of the distribution of radiation dose in any given case it is only too easy to make false deductions or to miss an important conclusion. On the other hand dose distribution studies lacking a close correlation with histological factors are of little use, and herein lie the major problems facing us in this field.

REFERENCES

1. N. F. KEMBER, Cell division in endochondral ossification, *J. Bone and Joint Surg.* **42B**, 824-839 (1960).
2. B. MØLLER, Development of osteogenic sarcomas in ST/EN mice after radio-phosphorous administered in quantities similar to therapeutic doses, *Acta Path. et Microbiol. Scand.* **35**, 549-558 (1954).

DISCUSSION

MAYS: Was your calculated average of 14 years between alpha-particle hits on the same cell for a uniform distribution of Pu^{239}?

LAMERTON: Yes, such that the average dose rate was 30 millirads per week, the cells being 10 microns in diameter and touching each other.

MAYS: It may also be of interest to consider the hit frequency resulting from the actual distribution of Pu^{239} on the bone surfaces of our 5-level Pu^{239} dogs. These dogs were injected with about 2·8 μc of Pu^{239} per kg body weight. Roughly 0·03 disintegrations per day per square micron of endosteal surface in the lumbar vertebrae of these dogs has been measured (J. A. Twente *et al.*, *Research in Radiobiology* COO-220, p. 168, March 1960). A circle 10 microns in diameter next to this surface would therefore be crossed by an average of about

$$\left[0\cdot03 \ \frac{\text{dis/day}}{\text{micron}^2}\right]\left[\frac{1 \ \text{alpha forward}}{2 \ \text{disintegrations}}\right]\left[\pi \ (5 \ \text{micron})^2\right] \simeq 1 \ \frac{\text{alpha}}{\text{day}}$$

LAMERTON: This is a high dose rate, isn't it?

MAYS: It is tremendously high!

LAMERTON: My calculation referred to the maximum permissible average dose rate of 30 millirads per week.

CHAIRMAN EVANS: The problems are similar and you probably agree with each other.

MAYS: The *retained* 5-level Pu^{239} activity per kg body weight is about 3650 times the maximum permissible body burden of 0·04 μc Pu^{239} per 70 kg man. Thus, 1 hit per day at the 5-level scales down to about 1 hit per 10 years at the maximum permissible body burden of Pu^{239}.

SPIERS: Could you say how many cells in the body are hit each day by alpha particles when the average dose rate is 30 millirads per week? This is perhaps the other way one should look at the problem. This number must be quite large.

LAMERTON: Indeed it is. The body contains in the order of 10^{14} cells. If 10^{14} cells are hit each 5000 days (about 14 yr) then roughly 2×10^{10} cells are hit per day.

But the point I was trying to make was that over a limited period of time the cells along each track are going to be separated from the cells along other tracks by considerable distances. At these levels it is probably correct to consider any resulting gross effects as arising from specific events in individual cells rather than from the interaction of different groups of damaged cells. This does not, of course, preclude the possible occurrence of severe late effects.

MOLE: If roughly 10^{10} cells are hit per day, isn't there a certain finite probability that a small group of cells will be irradiated by a large number of alpha particles all in a short period of time?

LAMERTON: This is an important point. In fact, the more non-uniform the distribution of an alpha emitter, the larger the number of multiple hits in a short time.

NORRIS: I have heard some estimates of the amount of heat generated by the traversal of an alpha particle due to the relatively tremendous energy transfers in a very limited volume. Could any cell survive the traversal of an alpha particle through its nucleus?

MAYS: In Dr. Evans' introductory talk he pointed out that the cylinder traced out by an alpha particle was approximately 0·01 microns in radius. We can very easily calculate both the average "micro" dose within this cylinder and the corresponding temperature rise for a 5·14 MeV α particle from Pu^{239} which has a range of about 35·4 microns in soft tissue of density 1 gram/cm³.

$$\text{Micro Dose} \simeq \frac{(5 \cdot 14 \text{ Mev}) (1 \cdot 6 \times 10^{-8} \text{ gram rad/MeV})}{\pi (0 \cdot 01 \times 10^{-4} \text{ cm})^2 (35 \cdot 4 \times 10^{-4} \text{cm})(1 \text{ gram/ cm}^3)} \simeq 7,400,000 \text{ rad}$$

If all the energy is converted into heat, each rad produces a temperature increase of $2 \cdot 39 \times 10^{-6}$ °C in material whose specific heat capacity is 1 cal per gram °C. Thus,

$$\text{Temperature Rise} \simeq (7 \cdot 4 \times 10^6 \text{ rad}) (2 \cdot 39 \times 10^{-6} \text{ °C/rad}) \simeq 18 \text{ °C}.$$

Both of these calculations are very approximate chiefly because of the uncertainty of the "radius" of the cylinder. The local dose and temperature rise along the core of the cylinder are very much higher. Of course we all realize that our conventional concepts of "dose" and "temperature" are somewhat inadequate when applied to these "micro-micro" dimensions.

KEMBER: With reference to the question by Norris as to the possibility of cell survival, I heard Haynes from Raymond Zirkle's laboratory (Abstract, Biophysics Society, Feb. 1961) say that they had to have about 15 alpha rays through the nucleus of amblystoma fibroblasts in tissue culture before they could guarantee detection of some chromosome abnormalities in the cell. So you may have to shoot quite a few alphas through a cell before you can insure a definite change.

SPIERS: The chemistry along the alpha track must be very different from the chemistry along the beta track in terms of OH and H_2O_2 formed. It was a long time ago that Dale, Gray and Meredith showed that for the inactivation of an enzyme, the alpha particle dose was only about $\frac{1}{5}$ as effective as an X-ray dose and in fact, that you could account for practically all of the chemical effect, not in terms of the main alpha particle energy, but simply in terms of the delta-ray energy distributed in the medium.

LAMERTON: You have to be careful about what Bill Spiers just said. That was a very special case. For alpha particles we suspect that most of the biological effects result from the radicals produced along the core of the alpha track. I think this brings up a fundamental point, in that it is surprising that thus far the observed biological effects of alpha rays seem very similar to those of beta rays. Unless the cell can respond in only a very limited number of ways to a great variety of insults, we might expect something very different. When we go down to very low dose rates, as for example at the maximum permissible levels, it is conceivable that we shall find very great differences in types of effects caused by alphas versus betas. One has to recognize that alpha rays may have some effects which are very different from beta rays, particularly over long times.

SPIERS: You could go back to another example. Take the inactivation of one of the very small viruses, in which again alpha particles are only $\frac{1}{5}$ as effective as gamma rays on a rad basis. I am only giving you these two examples because you have to be careful about talking about alpha dose in rads.

MOLE: Is it ever sensible to talk about an alpha dose in rads?

CHAIRMAN EVANS: Surely. That is one of the things for which the rad was invented.

KEMBER: I think when you are talking about alpha rays at the cellular level it is better to express the dose in terms of alpha rays per unit volume. As long as you talk about "alpha" rads in the same terms as "beta" rads it can be very misleading, unless you keep in mind the statistical distributions of alpha ray energy in space and in time.

DURBIN: How else can we compare, for example, the dose or the biological end results from half a microcurie of astatine per gram body weight with 400 r of cobalt γ rays?

VAUGHAN: I should like to register my anxiety at the use of average or mean dose to the skeleton as a satisfactory measure of radiation dose when we all know that there may be considerable variation in radiation dose due to uneven distribution of the isotope. I realize that it is the only measure we can have when we are dependent upon retention figures but it is important to recognize that it may be unsatisfactory.

CHAIRMAN EVANS: I don't know whether this is the place to make the comment, but there is a tendency to oversimplify things. I am sure all physicists would agree that it is not possible to completely specify dosage simply in rads. One must say a lot more about what kind of radiation is involved, and the many other factors which are present.

For example, a serious-minded radiotherapist doesn't stop at saying how many roentgens he delivered to a patient's elbow to try to cure his bursitis. If he is conscientious, he also gives the tube voltage, milliamperes, filtration, target to skin distance and exposure time. You just can't wrap up all this physics in a single number.

It may be putting it in the extreme, but physicists have tried to over-simplify this business in order to explain it to pathologists, hematologists, and internists.

MARINELLI: HARALD Rossi (*Rad. Res.* **10**, 5, 522–532, 1959) is now describing the energy distribution occurring within small volumes. This is very pertinent to biological structures because of their inhomogeneous make up and their very small size.

SNYDER: It seems to me that the reason that energy came into the picture was simply that the physicist has a certain faith that you don't produce changes in the arrangements of matter without the utilization of energy, and in some sense this measures the work that is done.

I grant that not all the energy of that alpha track, or of the betas either, is used for precisely the work or the rearrangements that produce the biological effect, but here I think we have to wait until the biologists or the physicists or the two jointly are prepared to tell us what portion of energy that is. I gather from the sense of this meeting that no one is prepared now to say what portion of that energy or what rearrangements of molecules, and so on, is the one that produces the effect. In the absence of that data, about all one can measure is the total that is absorbed and then hope to work toward the more precise interpretation.

It seems to me that there is still something to be said for the empirical view which Dr. Lamerton paid lip service to in his opening sentence or two and then left completely, and I think it should be left completely as soon as you begin to talk about the cause of the cancer. In the interim, until you have decided the question of what is producing the biological effect, you need some yardstick with which to work for radiation protection. I would advocate the point of view that you can just as meaningfully use any concept of dose—average dose, peak dose, mean square dose, or whatever you want to use—as an empirical means of extrapolating on a biological effect. That is all we are trying to do in the matter of radiation protection while we wait for the biologists to come up with the perfect answer of what really is producing the biological effects.

So, when we try to measure or make a comparison of toxicity of radium and strontium, it matters little whether you make it on the basis of mean dose in the bone or maximum dose in the bone, or any other measure of dose you choose in bone. It is an empirical approach to the question. For neither radionuclide do we know what portion of the energy, at what dose level, is significant, and presumably any measure of dose we use will be proportional to this average dose in bone as long as we don't go so far that we change the metabolic picture.

LAMERTON: Dr. Snyder, you are assuming that the toxicity ratio between radium and strontium in mice at high doses applies to man at low doses. I would suggest that perhaps the toxicity ratio of alphas to betas may be different at low doses.

SR^{90} DOSIMETRY IN RABBITS

MAUREEN OWEN

Medical Research Council, Bone-Seeking Isotopes Research Unit, The Churchill Hospital, Headington, Oxford, England

INTRODUCTION

As PART of a programme of work designed to study the relation of dose to damage in the rabbit's skeleton following the uptake of Sr^{90}, the pattern of radiation dose-rate and accumulated dose in bone and marrow has been determined in rabbits of different ages. This paper will describe the dosimetry results in different parts of the skeleton of young and adult rabbits which were given a single intravenous injection of a solution of Sr^{90}+Y^{90} in equilibrium and killed at different times. The results are briefly compared with the pattern of tumour incidence and radiation damage. An autoradiographic method for measuring the radiation dose-rate is briefly described.

EXPERIMENTAL METHODS

Materials

Dutch rabbits aged 5 to 8 weeks (i.e. young actively growing weanling rabbits) and adult rabbits, with ages varying from 21 to 47 months were given a single intravenous injection of Sr^{90} and killed at varying times after injection. Dosimetric measurements have been made on the proximal portion of the tibia, the vertebra and part of the lower mandible including the molar and premolar teeth.

Method of Measuring Radiation Dose-rate

The method used is an autoradiographic one and has previously been described in detail.[8] Autoradiographs of thick sections of the material were obtained and the dose-rate at any point was calculated by comparing the density of the autoradiographs with that from a known Sr^{90} standard. All bones were embedded in methyl methacrylate. In the case of the upper half of the tibia and of the vertebra the bones were cut in half longitudinally, and in the case of the lower jaw, the jaw was cut in half through the middle of the teeth in a direction along the longitudinal axis of the teeth. The smoothed cut surfaces of the bone halves were exposed on a photographic plate and the density of the autoradiograph over a square $50\mu \times 50\mu$ was determined using a microdensitometer. The total contribution to the dose-rate was obtained by adding the contributions from both halves.

RESULTS

Young Rabbits Given a Single Injection of Sr[90] *at the Age of* 5–8 *Weeks*

The pattern of uptake and retention of Sr[90] in the case of young actively growing rabbits is well known. In the tibia and vertebra the region of maximum uptake and maximum dose-rate is the calcifying cartilage and bone just below the epiphyseal plate at the time of injection. In the teeth and lower jaw there are heavy deposits of Sr[90] in the dentine and enamel surrounding the teeth pulp and in alveolar bone. Thick section autoradiographs of these three regions illustrating the radiation dose-rate picture twenty-four hours after injection are shown in Fig. 1. As the tibiae and

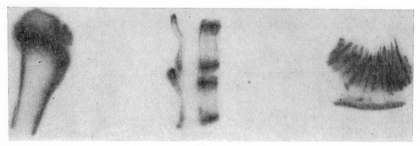

FIG. 1.

Autoradiograph of a thick section (i. e. half) of the upper part of the tibia, two vertebra and part of the lower jaw of a rabbit given 600 μc of Sr[90]/kg at the age of 5–8 weeks, killed 24 hours later. There is a heavy deposit of Sr[90] below the epiphyseal plate in the tibia and vertebra, in the alveolar bone of the jaw and in calcifying dentine and enamel surrounding the pulp chamber of the tooth.

vertebrae grow in length much of the region below the plate is resorbed and the maximum dose-rate falls.[8,9] In the case of the teeth the deposit in the dentine and enamel moves towards the occlusal surfaces and in the process of normal growth the dentine and enamel containing this deposit will have been worn away by a time between 90 and 180 days after injection.[2]

The rate at which the Sr[90] is removed by the normal processes of metabolism depends on the level of the injected dose. It has been found that 100 μc Sr[90]/kg or less given to weanling rabbits does not produce any gross interference with the normal growth pattern of the bones and teeth. In the case, however, of an injected dose of 600 μc/kg, interference does occur and we know that in the tibia, for example, growth is slowed down and proportionally greater amounts of Sr^{90} are retained because resorption is inhibited. The normal eruption of the teeth is interfered with and Sr^{90} which has been taken up in dentine and enamel travels more slowly to the occlusal surfaces and at 180 days it has not yet been worn away but is still retained in the teeth.

The measurements which will be described in some detail are for rabbits which were given 600 μc of Sr^{90} per kg. For this injected amount, in the case of the tibia the maximum dose-rates up to 180 days after injection were found in the posterior wall of the bone at the level at which the epiphyseal plate was at the time of injection. In the vertebra the maximum dose-rates were also at this level. In the jaws the maximum dose-rates were in the heavy deposits in the calcifying tissues of dentine and enamel, and comparable dose-rates were also nearly always found in alveolar bone. A graph of the maximum dose-rates in tibia, vertebra and jaws is shown in Fig. 2.

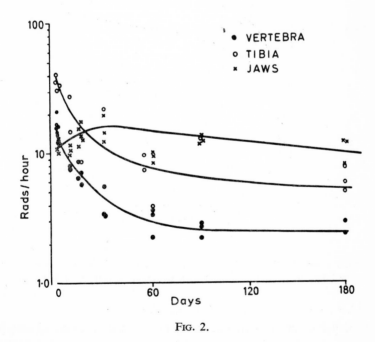

FIG. 2.

Maximum dose-rates in the tibia, vertebra and jaws at different times after injection in rabbits aged 5 to 8 weeks given 600 μc of Sr^{90}/kg.

It can be seen that the highest dose-rates are encountered in the tibia at short times after injection. In this bone dose-rates of 40 rads/hour are being received within the first day and they have fallen off to about 6 rads/hour at 180 days after injection. The shape of the curve for the vertebra is similar to that for the tibia, the highest dose-rates in this case are about 15 rads/hour within the first day after injection falling to $2\frac{1}{2}$ rads/hour at 180 days after injection. In the case of the teeth the maximum dose-rate of 15 rads/hour is not reached until about 30 days after injection, the dose-rate then falling off more gradually to about 10 rads/hour at 180 days.

The maximum value of the accumulated dose at different times after injection is calculated using the curves in Fig. 2 and the results are shown in Fig. 3. The maximum accumulated dose in the jaws and tibia is of the

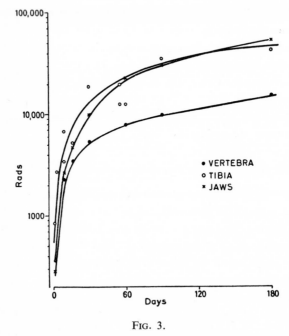

FIG. 3.

Maximum accumulated doses in the tibia, vertebra and jaws at different times after injection in rabbits aged 5 to 8 weeks given 600 μc of Sr^{90}/kg.

same order, about 50,000 rads, and about three to four times the maximum accumulated dose in the vertebra. In the case of the tibia and vertebra the maximum accumulated dose is received by a region at the level at which the epiphyseal plate was at the time of injection, in the case of the jaws by the calcifying dentine and enamel and some parts of alveolar bone. Consequently some soft tissues in conjunction with the alveolar bone receive almost the maximum accumulated dose.

Because of the long range of the beta particles from Sr^{90} and its daughter product Y^{90} (maximum range 1·1 cm in soft tissue) and the widespread uptake of Sr^{90}, it was found that all regions of the bone and marrow of the tibia, vertebra and jaws were receiving a significant radiation dose-rate. The minimum dose-rates in the tibia and vertebra were found in the middle of the marrow in the shaft and in the case of the teeth in the region of soft tissues which fill the spaces at the base of the teeth. The accumulated minimum doses in these regions at 6 months after injection are about 10,000, 3,000 and 11,000 rads in the tibia, vertebra and jaws respectively. In the case of the tibia the variation in the accumulated dose throughout the period of the experiment, i.e. the ratio of $\dfrac{\text{maximum accumulated dose}}{\text{minimum accumulated dose}}$, has a range of values from 5 to 16, being high for a short time after injection, in the vertebra the range is from 3 to 5 and in the jaws from 2 to 5. Thus, except for a short period after injection in the tibia, the variation in accumulated dose throughout the bone and marrow is not greater than a factor of 5 for any one bone. The accumulated doses in the tibia and jaws are, however, about three to four times the accumulated doses in the vertebra. As will be seen, this is of significance in a comparison of sites of tumour origin with radiation dose.

Adult Rabbits Given a Single Injection at the Age of 21 Months or More

The uptake and retention of Sr^{90} by the tibia and vertebra of adult rabbits does not follow any well defined pattern. There is a widespread patchy distribution throughout cortical and trabecular bone. Rabbit teeth, however, continue to grow throughout life, and the pattern of uptake in the teeth of the adult rabbit 24 hours after injection is similar to that in the young animals, though uptake in the alveolar bone of the jaw is much less in the old animals than in the young animals. Fig. 4 shows thick section autoradiographs of these three regions 24 hours after a single injection.

In the case of the tibia and vertebra the maximum dose-rate was nearly always found in trabecular bone at the ends of the bones, though occasionally it was in a deposit on the periosteal or endosteal surface. In the teeth the maximum dose-rates were in the Sr^{90} deposits in dentine and enamel. A graph of the maximum dose-rates in the old animals is shown in Fig. 5.

The most important feature of the results was the very high dose-rates found in the teeth compared with those found in the tibia and vertebra.

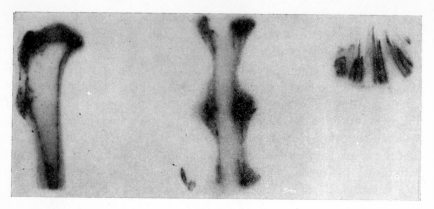

FIG. 4.

Autoradiograph of a thick section of the upper part of the tibia, two vertebra and part of the lower jaw of an adult rabbit given 600 μc of Sr⁹⁰/kg and killed 24 hours later. Sr⁹⁰ deposits are found throughout cortical and trabecular bone in the tibia and vertebra and in calcifying dentine and enamel surrounding the pulp chamber of the teeth.

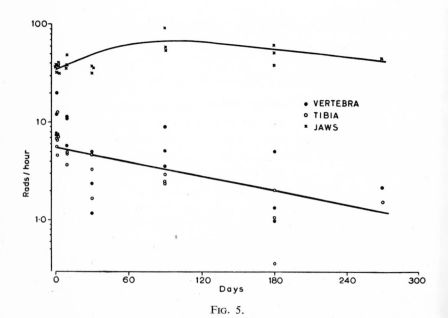

FIG. 5.

Maximum dose-rates in the tibia, vertebra and jaws at different times after injection in adult rabbits given 600 μc of Sr⁹⁰/kg.

The dose-rates found in the tibia and vertebra were very similar, about 7 rads/hour immediately after injection falling to about 2 rads/hour 6 months later. The maximum dose-rates in the teeth were about 35 rads/hour immediately after injection possibly rising to a small maximum at 90 days and then falling off slightly. On the average the maximum dose-rates in the teeth were about 16 times those in the tibia and vertebra.

The accumulated doses are shown in Fig. 6. The top curve is the maximum accumulated dose in the heavy Sr⁹⁰ deposits in the dentine and enamel and reaches a value of about 200,000 rads at 6 months. The more significant dose, however, is probably that received by the soft tissues which fill the spaces between the alveolar bone and the base of the teeth. In the

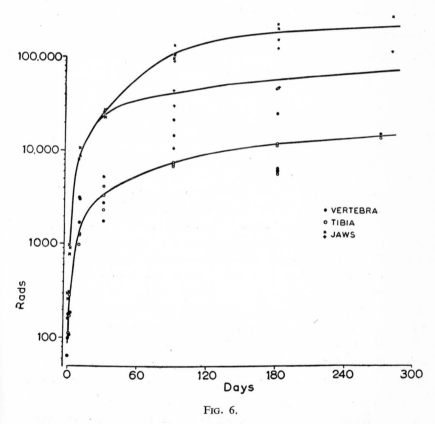

Fig. 6.

Maximum accumulated doses in the tibia, vertebra and jaws at different times after injection in adult rabbits given 600 μc of Sr⁹⁰/kg. The maximum dose received in the heavy deposits in dentine and enamel is indicated by X whereas + indicates the maximum dose received in the soft tissue region between the alveolar bone and the teeth.

case of these old animals the uptake in alveolar bone is much less than in dentine and enamel and consequently the maximum dose received in this region is less. It is shown by the lower curve for the jaws in Fig. 6, about 60,000 rads have been received in this region by 6 months. In the case of the tibia and vertebra the maximum accumulated dose was about 12,000 rads at 6 months.

The distribution of Sr^{90} is also very widespread in these old animals and consequently all the bone and marrow tissue in the three parts of the skeleton studied, received a considerable irradiation dose. In the case of the jaws, tibia and vertebra the minimum accumulated dose was received in similar regions of marrow as in the weanling rabbits and by six months after injection was about 12,000, 5000 and 2000 rads respectively. Throughout the period of the experiment the ratio $\frac{\text{maximum accumulated dose}}{\text{minimum accumulated dose}}$ had a greatest value of about 20 in the case of the jaws, and about 10 in the case of the tibia and vertebra.

Comparison of the Results for Young and Old Rabbits

A comparison of the maximum dose-rates and accumulated doses in the young and old animals showed the following. In the vertebra they were closely similar. In the tibia they were considerably greater in the young animals than in the old animals. In the teeth the opposite was the case, they were greater in the old animals then in the young animals. The occurrence of high dose-rates in the growing end of the long bone of a young rabbit is not surprising considering the very active bone accretion which is taking place in this region. Consequently there is a large volume of bone containing numerous Sr^{90} deposits, the combined cross-fire of beta particles from many closely adjacent deposits resulting in a high dose-rate. The reason for the much higher dose-rates in the teeth of old animals compared with that in young animals is perhaps not so obvious. A simple explanation may be that in old animals the skeleton as a whole takes up less Sr^{90} than in young growing animals, relatively more Sr^{90} is therefore available for the actively growing teeth in the old animals.

Within the two groups of animals the important results from a dosimetric point of view were as follows. In the rabbits injected as weanlings the maximum accumulated dose was received in the jaws and tibia and was about three to four times that received in the vertebra. In the old animals the maximum dose was received in the jaws and was about nine times that received in the tibia and vertebra.

The radiation damage found in young and old rabbits following an injection of about 600 μc of Sr^{90}/kg will not be given in detail here as it has already been or will be described fully in other publications.[4,5,7,9,10] Some general features of the damage, however, and its relation to radiation dose will be commented upon.

Table 1 shows the distribution of tumours in a small group of young rabbits given varying injected doses of Sr^{90} and allowed to survive until they died. There was 100% mortality at about 6 months after injection for those given 500 μc of Sr^{90}/kg or more. Out of the ten rabbits which were examined in all three regions of the skeleton (long bones, spine and jaws), nine had osteogenic sarcoma in their long bones and eight in their jaws. There were no tumours in the vertebra. Rabbits given 100 μc/kg or less were still alive and healthy over two years later.

Table 2 shows the distribution of tumours in a small group of adult rabbits. There was 100% mortality within 28 months for those given 400 μc of Sr^{90}/kg or more. Out of eleven rabbits examined in the three regions of the skeleton, six had tumours in their jaws, there was one tumour in

TABLE 1

Tumour Sites in Rabbits Aged 5–8 Weeks Injected With Sr^{90}

Number of rabbits	Average survival time	μc/kg of Sr^{90} injected	Rabbits with tumours		
			Long bones	Spine	Jaws
2	5½ months	1000	2	Not	examined
8	7 months	600	7	0	8
2	6 months	500	2	0	0
2	Alive at 2 yrs. 3 months	100			
2	Alive at 2 yrs. 3 months	50			

TABLE 2

Tumour Sites in Adult Rabbits Injected With Sr^{90}

Number of rabbits	Average survival time	μc/kg of Sr^{90} injected	Rabbits with tumours		
			Long bones	Spine	Jaws
4	7 months	1000	0	0	2
1	15 months	600	0	0	1
3	22 months	500	0	1	2
3	28 months	400	0	0	1
3	30 months	300	0	0	0
3	38 months	200	0	0	0

the spine and none in the long bones. Admittedly the number of animals in both groups is small, nevertheless in both cases there appears to be some correlation between the sites of tumour incidence and the sites of maximum accumulated dose.

DISCUSSION

Following a single injection of Sr^{90} we find that the maximum dose-rates in different parts of the animal varied from one bone to another and with the age of the animal. This feature resulted in a variation in the maximum accumulated dose in different bones. When the maximum accumulated dose was compared with the distribution of osteogenic sarcomas it was found that there was a correlation between sites of maximum accumulated dose and sites of tumours. We are well aware, however, that accumulated dose is not the only parameter important from the point of view of tumour production.

Indeed the usefulness of this particular value of accumulated dose (integrated up to the time of appearance of the tumour) is doubtful, since it is likely that some of the radiation given in the later stages may be "wasted" in so far as tumour production is concerned. Histological examination of the long bones and jaws of the young animals at earlier time intervals before gross lesions have developed (about 3 months) have revealed small foci of proliferative tissue which have all the features of a presarcomatous lesion. The accumulated dose in these areas was estimated to be between 9000 and 15,000 rad.[5,10] It is therefore more than likely that it is a dose of this order of magnitude which will give 100% incidence of osteogenic sarcoma in young rabbits injected with 600 μc of Sr^{90}/kg.

There is also good evidence from the work of other authors that the maximum accumulated dose is not the only important parameter. Bensted, Blackett and Lamerton[1] in a study of tumour production and dose distribution following uptake of P^{32} found, that for the same total amount of P^{32} injected, repeated injections were much more carcinogenic than a single injection. The maximum accumulated dose in the case of the repeated injections was in fact slightly less than for a single injection. They pointed out, however, that the volume of bone irradiated was much greater in the case of the repeated than the single injection and they also indicated that their results could possibly be better interpreted in relation to the dose received just below the epiphyseal plate, i.e. the region of greatest proliferative activity of the tissue. On the question of the volume of tissue irradiated the results of Jowsey and Rowland[3] are of considerable interest. In their experiments the irradiation was limited to a relatively small volume of bone by the insertion of Sr^{90} pegs at various points in the bone. Two out of nine adult rabbits which survived for more than 140 days produced what were suspected as bone tumours near the site of the peg. The estimated dose in one case was 25,000 rad at a time when abnormal bone proliferation was first visible by X-ray.

Furthermore, Marshall and Finkel[6] have found from a comparison o dose-distribution and tumor data following injections of Ca^{45} or Sr^{90} that their results can best be interpreted in terms of the absorbed dose received by the bone surfaces, in the case of Sr^{90} this is about the maximum accumulated dose but not so in the case of Ca^{45}. They conclude that this is evidence that the tissues on the bone surfaces are the sensitive site, a conclusion we had previously reached from histological studies.[7] Thus, here are three other parameters which are certainly important from the point of view of tumour production. (a) The volume of tissue irradiated (b) the proliferative capacity of the tissue and (c) the particular region irradiated.

Perhaps there is good reason why there is a simple correlation between the sites of maximum accumulated dose and the sites of osteogenic sarcomas in the case of the Sr^{90} rabbits. In our experiments the sites of maximum accumulated dose are the sites where the greatest volume of tissue receives a sizeable dose-rate, they are also the sites where there is maximum proliferative activity of the tissue and because of the long range of the beta ray from Sr^{90} and Y^{90} the osteogenic tissues covering the bone surfaces in these regions receive the maximum accumulated dose. However it must be emphasized that the problem is very complicated and it is likely that there are factors other than those mentioned which are also important.

One of the most interesting features of our results was the relatively greater resistance of the old animals compared with the young animals. In the case of the young animals 100% developed tumours within an average period of 6 months, in the case of the adult animals about 50% developed tumours the average period of induction being about 20 months. The maximum accumulated dose at the site of tumour was, if anything, slightly greater in the case of the adult animals than the young.

As shown above it clearly emerged from this dosimetric study that the uptake of Sr^{90} in rabbits results in generalized irradiation of all bone and marrow and associated soft tissues. Consequently at death the animals were generally in a poor condition and had suffered considerable weight loss. Their blood picture at death was nearly always abnormal. It is important to remember that in all experiments where the marrow tissue receives considerable irradiation the production of bone tumour is only possible in animals that have survived longer than the period in which haemopoietic failure appears to occur. Detailed studies on the nature of the blood lesions following Sr^{90} uptake are currently being made[11] and indicate that this is a period up to about 60 days after injection for rabbits given 600 μc of Sr^{90}/kg, the majority of haemopoietic deaths occurring about 20 days after injection.

ACKNOWLEDGEMENTS

The author would like to thank Dr. Janet Vaughan for her interest and help throughout this work and Mrs. Jeanne Hampton for her expert technical assistance.

REFERENCES

1. J. P. M. BENSTED, N. M. BLACKETT and L. F. LAMERTON, Histological and dosimetric considerations of bone tumour production with radioactive phosphorous, *Brit. J. Rad.* **34**, 399, 160–175 (1961).

2. W. HOLGATE, The incorporation and retention of Sr^{90} in the teeth, *Brit. Dent. J.* **107**, 6, 131–140 (1959).

3. J. JOWSEY and R. E. ROWLAND, Point-source beta irradiation of bone, Argonne National Laboratory Report 6199, 21–35 (1960).

4. SHEILA MACPHERSON, The stunting of growth in young rabbits injected with Sr^{90}, *Internat ional Journal of Radiation Biology* **3**, 515 (1961).

5. SHEILA MACPHERSON, MAUREEN OWEN and JANET VAUGHAN, The relation of radiation dose to radiation damage in the tibia of weanling rabbits, *Brit. J. Rad.* **35**, 221 (1962).

6. J. H. MARSHALL and M. P. FINKEL, The sensitive region in the induction of osteogenic sarcomas, Argonne National Laboratory Report 6199, 44–54 (1960).

7. MAUREEN OWEN, H. A. SISSONS and JANET VAUGHAN, The effect of a single injection of high dose of Sr^{90} (500–1000 μc/kg) in rabbits, *British J. of Cancer* **11**, 229–248 (1957).

8. MAUREEN OWEN and JANET VAUGHAN, Dose-rate measurements in the rabbit tibia following uptake of Sr^{90}, *Brit. J. Rad.* **32**, 383, 714–724 (1959).

9. MAUREEN OWEN and JANET VAUGHAN, Radiation dose and its relation to damage in the rabbit tibia following a single injection and daily feeding of Sr^{90}, *British J. of Cancer* **13**, 424–438 (1959).

10. M. RUSHTON, MAUREEN OWEN, W. HOLGATE and JANET VAUGHAN, The relation of radiation dose to radiation damage in the mandible of weanling rabbits. *Arch. Oral Biology* **3**, 235–246 (1961).

11. JANET VAUGHAN, Preliminary study of the effect of internal irradiation from Sr^{90} on the bone marrow and peripheral blood picture of young rabbits (this vol., p. 361),

DISCUSSION

GOLDMAN: You said there was a difference in fractional retention between the 600 μc/kg rabbits and those receiving 100 μc/kg. What was it?

OWEN: We haven't measured the difference in total body retention. I have just measured the differences in localized dose rates.

For example, the maximum accumulated dose at six months after injection was 50,000 rad in the 600 μc/kg rabbits but only about 4000 rads in the 100 μc/kg rabbits. That is more than a factor of 6.

Immediately after injection the ratio of the measured dose rates are more or less proportional to the injected activity per kilogram, but in the 600 μc/kg animals the dose rate does not fall off as rapidly. Of course there is lots of damage in these animals with failure of resorption and a lot of other things.

CHAIRMAN EVANS: I think your data on the ratio of the maximum to minimum dose are very interesting.

OWEN: The ratio within each bone listed was approximately as follows at the indicated times after the injection of 600 μc of Sr⁹⁰/kg.

Bone	Weanlings		Adults	
	1 day	6 mo	1 day	6 mo
Jaw	5	2	10	20
Tibia	16	5	10	10
Vertebra	5	3	7	10

CHAIRMAN EVANS: Dr. Rowland has some data on the human that would be useful for comparison.

ROWLAND: In the human who acquired radium as an adult, the ratio of the activity in the hot spots to the activity in the diffuse component ranges from 250 to 1, when acquired over an 8-week period, to less than 20 to 1, when acquired over a several-year period. In contrast, in a dog given radium over an 8-week period, this ratio was found to be 25 to 1. The difference is due to the much greater uptake of radium in the diffuse component in the dog.

CHAIRMAN EVANS: A basic difference between alpha rays and beta rays is their range and the character of their paths. With beta rays, due to their longer range and their tortuous paths, you get more uniform irradiation of the whole tissue, don't you? It is as easy as that.

VAUGHAN: As a biologist I would like to interject one remark, and that is that the measurements at the 6-month interval must not be taken as the tumor-producing dose. The earliest lesion that might be considered sarcomatous in the bone was found histologically about three months after injection when the accumulated dose in those regions was of the order of 20,000 rads in rabbits injected with 600 μc of Sr⁹⁰.

So it is important for those of you who have seen these charts not to think of the tumor-producing dose as the terminal dose that we measured. The tumor-producing dose was probably very much lower. There is a great deal of what one might call wasted radiation.

THEORETICAL AND EXPERIMENTAL DOSIMETRY BASED ON MODELS OF BONE STRUCTURE

F. W. Spiers and M. Susan Chesters

Department of Medical Physics, The University of Leeds, Leeds, England

Radiation dosimetry in bone is a problem of peculiar difficulty because of the complex nature of the bone structure itself. The juxtaposition of mineral salts and soft tissues on a microscopic scale present an extremely heterogeneous system in which the dosimetry is dominated, on the physical side, by considerations of particle range and, on the biological side, by the difficulty of defining the significant tissue. Frequently the tissue of interest has linear dimensions of about the same magnitude as the range of the ionizing particle and recourse has to be made to approximate mathematical methods in order to determine the distribution of dose. Until recently there has been little direct physical measurement of relevance to dosimetry in bone, other than a few experiments and observations made with X-rays. Considerations by Spiers[1] of some of the early experimental data by Gray[2] and Paterson[3] showed, however, that the calculations led to approximately the correct magnitudes in these cases and indicated a need to take account of the complete distribution of particle ranges involved. A new approach to α-ray dosimetry in bone containing radium was provided by the work of Hoecker and Roofe[4] on α-track counting and, in recent years, photographic dosimetry of both α- and β-radiation in animal bone has been brought to considerable precision by Dudley,[5] Owen[6] and by Marshall and Finkel.[7] Data presented in this paper will show that scintillation dosimetry on models of bone containing Sr^{90} provides experimental evidence to support mathematical methods, and adds measured data on models of trabecular bone where hitherto only an analytical method has been reported by Engström et al.[8]

Theoretical Dosimetry of α and β Particles in Bone

In general, the dose rate in energy per unit time per unit volume in a small volume of soft tissue situated within range of ionizing particles emitted from bone can be written as:

$$D = \frac{n \delta R}{\varrho} G = \frac{nE.}{\varrho} G \qquad (1)$$

where n = number of particles, of energy E and range R in soft tissue, emitted per unit volume of bone per unit time.

δ = mean energy loss per unit length of track in soft tissue, assumed to be at a uniform rate E/R.

ϱ = ratio of the range of the particle in soft tissue to that in bone.

G = dimensionless factor for any given source geometry.

Apart from the assumption of a uniform rate of energy loss along the particle track, other simplifying assumptions are necessary in order to make even an approximate calculation of the geometrical factor G. It is assumed that the ionizing particles are emitted isotropically and that the particle tracks are straight without any scattering. Clearly these assumptions are less extreme in the case of α-particle tracks than they are for β particles but, in the latter case, the use of experimental extrapolated ranges tend to reduce what might otherwise be large errors. By using these approximations G has been calculated for a number of simplified geometrical models of isotope depositions in bone by Spiers,[9] Kononenko,[10] Hindmarsh et al.[10] and Mays.[11] The main features and limitations of these methods are reviewed briefly in the following paragraphs.

Equilibrium dose-rate. For a point surrounded in all directions by a deposition of extent greater than the range R of the emitted particles, $G = 1$, and equation (1) can be shown to be identical with the Bragg–Gray relationship for the energy deposited in a very small volume by ionizing particles arising in the surrounding medium. If the point is at the surface of a semi-infinite plane medium, the value of G, on simple theory, is 0·5 and the dose rate is half the equilibrium dose rate in a medium of "infinite" extent.

Plane slab. The dose rate at a point in soft tissue at a distance less than the particle range, R, from a plane slab of bone has been calculated by Spiers[9] and Kononenko[10] for slabs having dimensions greater than R. The calculations have been extended to cases where the deposition of the isotope is less than the particle range by Hindmarsh et al.[11] In applying equation (1) to the β-ray case it is necessary to summate over the β-ray energy spectrum. If the approximation is made that ϱ is independent of the β-particle energy the required summation can be expressed as:

$$D = \frac{N\overline{E}}{\varrho}\,(a_1 G_1 + a_2 G_2 + ...) \tag{2}$$

where N is now the number of β particles of all energies emitted per unit volume per unit time, $\overline{E}$ is the mean β-particle energy for the given spectrum and a_1 is the fraction of the total β-particle energy spectrum associated with particles of energy E_1 for which the geometrical factor is G_1, etc.

Cavities—cylinders and spheres. Approximate calculations of the average dose-rate in a cylinder of soft tissue, surrounded by an "infinite" deposition of an α emitter in bone, were made by Spiers[9] by assuming the distribution of dose-rate across the diameter to be the same as that in a slab of tissue of the same thickness as the cylinder diameter, situated between two slabs of bone. An average dose-rate over the cylinder area was then obtained by weighting this radial distribution of dose-rate by the radial distribution of mass in a cylinder. On the basis of the same physical assumptions, Kononenko[10] derived analytical expressions for dose-rates averaged over the particle range near plane and spherical boundaries. In the case of the plane boundary, they reduce to the same value for G as given by Spiers.[9] Kononenko[10] showed, however, that an approximation to the cylindrical case can be obtained from the results for the spherical boundary and his results indicated that the earlier approximations for the average dose-rates in cylinders were too low. Kononenko[10] also gave results of ionization measurements in cylindrical chambers having an α emitter incorporated in the wall; he was able to show that the mean ionization current varied with gas pressure in accord with his calculations. Some measurements with β particles will be reported in this paper.

Analytical expressions have been given by Hindmarsh *et al.*[11] for the dose-rate on the axis of a cylinder for any value of the cylinder radius and any value of the thickness of the cylindrical deposit of isotope around it. An analytical expression has also been given by Kononenko[10] for the radial dose distribution within a sphere; only approximate data are available for the radial dose distribution in a cylinder.

Trabecular bone. Engström *et al.*[8] have given an analysis of the case of a sandwich model of trabecular bone in which the thickness of the bone trabecular has been taken as 70μ together with various sizes of marrow space up to 900μ. Numerical values are given for different β-particle energies and for the β-particle spectrum of $Sr^{90} + Y^{90}$.

Experimental β-Particle Dosimetry with Plastic Scintillators

Plastic scintillators are now commercially available with characteristics which make them very suitable as soft tissue dosimeters. They are composed of light elements, have nearly unit density and, over a considerable range of energy their light output is proportional to the energy dissipated in them by an ionizing particle. They are obtainable in the form of thin sheet so that the dose can be measured in a medium which can have dimensions of the same order as some of the soft tissue structures within bone. With thin pieces of scintillator, and with the weak radioactive sources incorporated in our models of bone and bone marrow, the dose is determined by measuring the number and size of the light pulses, as a pulse-height spectrum, and then by summation:

$$D = \sum_{E=0}^{E=E_{max}} \left(\frac{\Delta N}{\Delta E} \right) E(\Delta E) \tag{3}$$

where $\Delta N/\Delta E$ is the average count rate per unit energy between energies $E - \dfrac{\Delta E}{2}$ and $E + \dfrac{\Delta E}{2}$.

Slab model. The model and the dosimeter are illustrated in Fig. 1. A "bone" slab was made of any desired thickness by compressing salts, having the atomic composition of mineral bone, to a density of approxi-

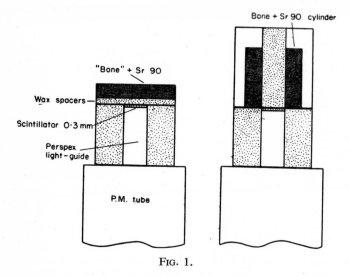

FIG. 1.

Models of bone slab and bone cylinder.

mately 1·5 g/cm³. A little sucrose was included to make the salts adhere and prevent crumbling. This artificial bone contained no water so that its β-particle stopping power per gram was slightly less than that for natural bone. Before making into slabs the stock of "bone" powder was uniformly contaminated with $Sr^{90}+Y^{90}$ solution to a level of 0·1 µc/g. A thin disc of plastic scintillator NE102* (0·3 mm thickness), painted with white

* Made by Nuclear Enterprises (G.B.) Ltd., Edinburgh.

lacquer on its upper surface, was sealed with silicone oil to a short light guide leading to a photomultiplier. The output pulses of the photomultiplier were passed to a linear amplifier and thence to a single-channel analyser and scaler. The diameter of the slab was 3·8 cm, this dimension being sufficient to ensure that the scintillator discs were surrounded by the slab to a distance at least equal to the maximum range of the $Sr^{90}+Y^{90}$ β particles. Thin spacers of tissue-equivalent wax (Jones and Raines[13]) could be interposed between the scintillator and the slab so that the variation of dose with distance from a plane surface could be measured.

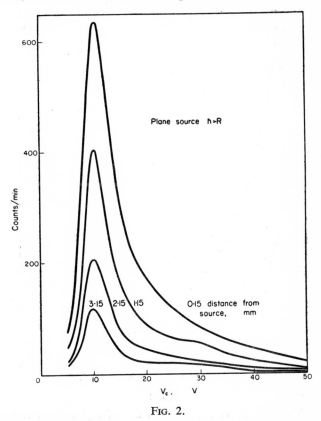

FIG. 2.

β-particle pulse-height spectra for bone slab loaded with $Sr^{90} + Y^{90}$.

Typical pulse-height spectra for different scintillator-slab distances are shown in Fig. 2 and these when integrated as in equation (3) gave the results shown for the 0·6 g/cm² slab in Fig. 3. This slab was sufficiently thick to approximate the semi-infinite source condition and the continuous curve in Fig. 3 represents the theoretical variation of G with distance from such a source. G is also the value of D/D_β, the ratio of the dose at a point in soft tissue to the equilibrium dose at the centre of an "infinite" source. At its nearest point the centre of the scintillator was 0·15 mm from the surface of the slab and hence the pulse-height integral for this

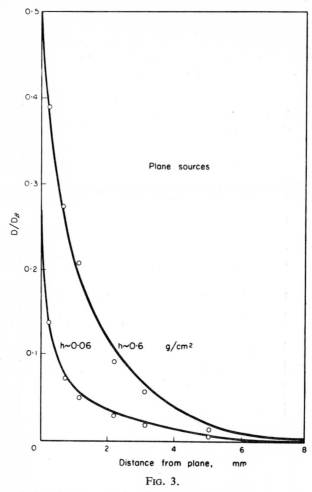

FIG. 3.

Theoretical and experimental values of D/D_β for plane slabs of bone.

point is set at the value $G=0·39$. This point then normalizes all the other experimental points on both curves in Fig. 3 and also in Fig. 5. Results are also shown in Fig. 3 for a slab of only one-tenth the equilibrium thickness, together with the corresponding theoretical curve. For both slabs the experimental results accord reasonably well with the theoretical calculations.

Cylindrical models. A thin disc of scintillator (0·3 mm thickness) was also used to record the mean dose rate inside a cylinder. For reasons of symmetry the scintillator disc could be placed at one end of a cylinder to record a dose-rate equal to one half of that at the centre of an "infinitely long" cylinder. The arrangement is shown in the second diagram in Fig. 1 where the relationship of the scintillator to the photomultiplier tube is the same as in the slab model. The "bone" wall of the cylinder has a thickness greater than the maximum β-particle range in bone and a length greater than the maximum range in soft tissue. Three models were made with internal diameters of 5, 10 and 18 mm to simulate marrow cavities in the shafts of long bones. Tissue-equivalent wax was used to fill the cylinders above the scintillator.

In the measurements on each model, pulse-height integrals were determined (a) with the bone cylinder in position and (b) with the scintillator exposed in contact with the thick "bone" slab. All the measurements

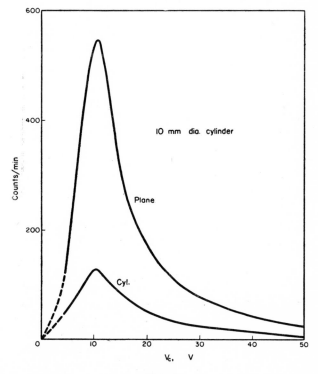

FIG. 4.

β-particle pulse-height spectra for bone slab and 10 mm diameter bone cylinder
loaded with Sr^{90} + Y^{90}.

on the cylinders were related, therefore, to the point at 0·15 mm from the surface of the semi-infinite plane source. Pulse-height spectra are shown in Fig. 4 for the plane and the 10 mm diameter cylinder and the values of $\overline{G}$, or $\overline{D}/D_\beta$, for the three cylinders are shown in Fig. 5. together with theoretical curves (a) calculated by the approximate method of Spiers by Hindmarsh *et al.*[11] and (b) calculated by applying Kononenko's results[10] to the β-particle spectrum of $Sr^{90}+Y^{90}$. The measured values are in better agreement with the Kononenko calculations, although there is a suggestion that the D/D_β ratio falls more steeply with cylinder diameter than the theory indicates.

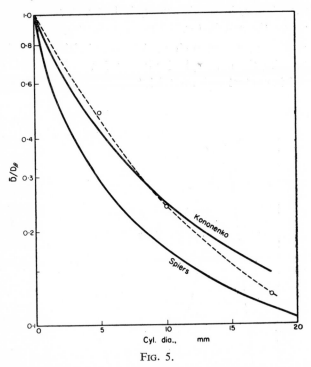

FIG. 5.

Comparison of theoretical and experimental values of $\overline{D}/D_\beta$ for cylinders of bone.

Models of trabecular bone. A first approximation to the structure of trabecular bone is a layer model in which thin layers of "bone" containing $Sr^{90}+Y^{90}$ alternate with layers of a tissue-like material. It was found to be impossible to produce sufficiently thin and uniform layers of compressed salts and so a dense liquid was used to simulate the bone. An aqueous solution containing 50 per cent by weight of $CaBr_2$ and density 1·53 g/cm³ was finally chosen. The stopping power of this solution, calculated from elemental stopping powers given by Spencer,[14] is 1·57 MeV cm²/g for electrons of 1 MeV energy. This compares with similarly calculated stopping powers of 1·65 and 1·58 MeV cm²/g based on a composition of bone salts quoted by Wilson[15] together with a water content of, respectively, 40 and 20 per cent. The composition of the "dry" artificial bone used for the slab and cylinder models gave a corresponding stopping power of 1·51 MeV cm²/g. The $CaBr_2$ solution was activated with 0·1 μc $Sr^{90}+Y^{90}$ per gram and small amounts of Sr and Y carrier were added to prevent adsorption on plastic and other surfaces. The marrow spaces were simulated by polythene sheet which was available in 125μ and 250μ thicknesses.

Details of the model on which the present measurements have been made are shown in Fig. 6. The left-hand diagram shows the relationship of the model, contained in a cylindrical plastic box, to the light guide and

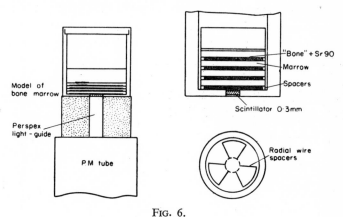

FIG. 6.

Model of trabecular bone structure.

photomultiplier tube and the enlarged diagrams on the right-hand side of Fig. 6 illustrate the construction of the model. Basically, "marrow" spaces of 500μ thickness (2 polythene discs) were separated by annular spacer rings of 125μ thickness which provided the space for the 125μ layer of bone-equivalent solution—the "trabeculum". In order to maintain a uniform thickness of solution, three pairs of radial stainless steel wire spacers, 125μ diameter, were placed inside the annular polythene ring. These extended inwards only as far as the edge of the scintillator and had a negligible effect on the mass and stopping power of the enclosed liquid layer. Before assembly, the surfaces of the polythene discs adjacent to the solution were rubbed with a smear of glycerine to make the solution spread evenly over the area of the layer. In the formation of each layer, a spacer-ring was sealed to a polythene disc and the wire spacers put in position. An amount of bone-equivalent solution just sufficient to fill the layer was then weighed on to the disc and a second disc pressed gently into position. The first layer was formed in the bottom of the cylindrical box and subsequent pairs added to increase the total thickness of trabecular bone. A disc of plastic 1 cm thick was placed on top of the discs to keep them in position and simulate tissue beyond the trabecular bone.

The base of the cylindrical box was 500μ thick and the scintillator disc, 0·3 mm thick, was located centrally in it so that, in effect, it was situated in the middle of a "marrow" space. The scintillator response was then a reasonably good approximation to the mean marrow dose; if exactly centred it would give a mean dose only 1·6 per cent less than that for the whole 0·5 mm marrow space; if allowance is made for the thickness of the lacquer on the upper surface of the scintillator, this error could be as high as −6 per cent. As in the measurements with slabs and cylinders the scintillator response was standardised with reference to a semi-infinite "bone" layer by making measurements with the cell filled to the appropriate depth with bone-equivalent solution. The ratio of the response for a model of given thickness to that for the semi-infinite layer of solution then gave the required value D_c/D_β.

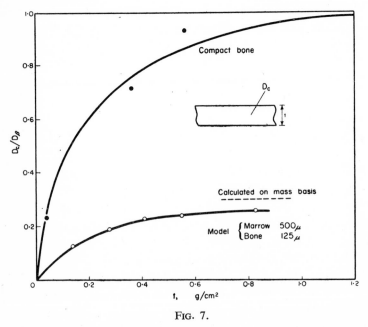

FIG. 7.

Build-up of the ratio D_c/D_β with thickness of trabecular bone model.

The results for models comprising 1 to 6 layers are given in Fig. 7 where D_c/D_β is plotted against the total thickness of the "trabecular" bone expressed in g/cm². The theoretical build-up of D_c/D_β with thickness of the bone-equivalent solution ("compact" bone) is also given in Fig. 7, together with measured points for three layers of solution having depths less than the maximum β-particle range. These latter measurements and that on the equilibrium layer were corrected by theoretical factors to allow for the fact that the scintillator was not in the surface of the layer of solution.

It is evident that the dose in the centre of this particular model of trabecular bone has reached an equilibrium value at a total thickness of about 0·8 to 1·0 g/cm² at which D_c/D_β as measured is 0·26. This value could be increased to 0·28 if allowance is made for the small displacement of the scintillator from the centre of the marrow space. This equilibrium value of D_c/D_β is somewhat less than the value 0·31 calculated simply on the mean $Sr^{90}+Y^{90}$ content of the trabecular structure, obtained by regarding the isotope content diluted in the ratio of the mass of trabecular bone to the total mass of trabeculae and marrow.

It is difficult to make a precise comparison of this experimental result with the calculations by Engström et al.[8] who used a model with a bone layer of 70μ. For this thickness and a 500μ marrow space their value of D_c/D_β would appear to be about 0·29 but for a model having the same mass ratio (0·31) as that used in the present experiment, i.e. a marrow space of about 300μ the D_c/D_β ratio would be about 0·4.

DISCUSSION

It would appear from the results reviewed and the measurements reported in this paper that there is reasonable experimental justification for the use of formulae developed for the calculation of α- and β-particle doses near plane slabs of bone, of both equilibrium dimensions and less, and for Kononenko's calculations of the mean dose inside cylinders of equilibrium dimensions. By inference it may be expected that the calculations of the axial dose in cylinders of less-than-equilibrium dimensions and in spheres also give reasonably accurate results.

In the case of bone marrow the equilibrium dose measured for the one model investigated was only about 10 per cent less than that deduced on the basis of a mean isotope concentration. The experimental results, however, enable the dose to be deduced for over-all trabecular bone dimensions which are less than the particle range. Measurements on other models, having different bone marrow ratios, are in progress and these should yield a relationship between the equilibrium value of D_c/D_β and the fraction of bone mass present in the whole structure. The knowledge of the mean trabecular thickness and mean marrow space in any given bone would then enable a realistic value of D_c/D_β to be determined for any over-all size of the trabecular bone structure. Combination of this value with an estimation of the contribution to the dose from the isotope in the approximately cylindrical or spherical shell of cortical bone would then determine the dose in the trabecular marrow. This method could be expected to apply at least to isotopes emitting β particles of 1 MeV energy or more where the effects of non-uniform concentration of the isotope are considerably smoothed out by the relatively long β- particle ranges.

REFERENCES

1. F. W. SPIERS, The influence of energy absorption and electron range on dosage in irradiated bone, *Brit. J. Radiol.* **22**, 521–533 (1949).
2. L. H. GRAY, Physical investigation of the contribution of the photo-electrons from sulphur to X-ray ionization, *Brit. J. Radiol.* **13**, 25–30 (1940).
3. E. PATERSON, A comparison of the action of x- and gamma- radiation on fibroblasts, *Brit. J. Radiol.* **15**, 302–306 (1942).
4. F. E. HOECKER and P. G. ROOFE, Studies of radium in human bone, *Radiol.* **56**, 89–98 (1951).
5. R. A. DUDLEY, Photographic film dosimetry, in *Radiation Dosimetry*, ed. by G. J. HINE and G. L. BROWNELL, Academic Press, New York, p. 299 (1956).
6. M. OWEN and J. VAUGHAN, Dose-rate measurements in the rabbit tibia following uptake of strontium-90, *Brit. J. Radiol.* **32**, 714–724 (1959).
7. J. H. MARSHALL and M. P. FINKEL, Comparison of microdosimetry and tumor production by Ca^{45}, Sr^{90} and Ra^{226} in mice, Argonne National Laboratory report **6199**, 44 (Jan.–June, 1960).
8. A. ENGSTROM, R. BJORNERSTEDT, C. J. CLEMEDSON and A. NELSON, *Bone and Radio-strontium*, John Wiley & Sons, New York, p. 100 (1958).
9. F. W. SPIERS, Alpha-ray dose in bone containing radium, *Brit. J. Radiol.* **26**, 296–301 (1953).
10. A. M. KONONENKO, Calculation of the dose-rate created by alpha radiation when a radioactive substance spreads inside the organism, *Biofizika* **2**, 98–117 (1957).
11. M. HINDMARSH, M. OWEN, J. VAUGHAN, L. F. LAMERTON and F. W. SPERS, The relative hazards of strontium-90 and radium-226, *Brit. J. Radiol.* **31**, 518–533 (1958).
12. C. W. MAYS, Determination of localized alpha dose, Radiobiology Laboratory, University of Utah Report COO-217, p. 161 (Sept. 1958) and *ibid.* COO-220, p. 200 (March 1960).
13. D. E. A. JONES and H. C. RAINE, A tissue-equivalent wax, *Brit. J. Radiol.* **22**, 549–550 (1949).
14. L. V. SPENCER, Energy dissipation by fast electrons, National Bureau of Standards, Monograph 1, (1959).
15. C. W. WILSON, The quantity and quality of the radiations scattered within a medium irradiated by high voltage radiation, *Brit. J. Radiol.* **18**, 345–355 (1945).

DISCUSSION

BJORNERSTEDT: I would like to ask a question. What would be the comparative sensitivity of your scintillation dosimetry compared with autoradiographic dosimetry?

SPIERS: The sensitivity of the scintillation dosimetry is fairly good, although of course, much lower levels of activity can be measured autoradiographically. In my model I never used more than 0·1 µc per gram, which is relatively small. In other words, you can experiment with these models at a very low specific activity. By models such as these the mean marrow dose from environmental Sr^{90} could be determined.

DUDLEY: The main technique in localized dosimetry has been autoradiography, and thus the chief instrument has been film. It is my impression that at least for beta rays and probably also equally for alpha rays, the accuracy one can get with film is very good.

The difficulties come in, not because of the instrument, but because of the nature of the biological problem. Assessing what region of the skeleton to examine in most detail is a very severe problem, but the present physical techniques are quite good.

KEMBER: I agree that there are methods available to measure the alpha or beta dose to any region within the skeleton except in the case of very non-uniform distributions of alpha emitters. The real problem is to determine which are the important cells and where are they located.

KORNBERG: Have comparisons been made between this physical model and an actual cylinder of bone?

SPIERS: Not using an actual piece of bone. This might be possible to do if you had a bone shaft which was sufficiently radioactive. It would be a bit difficult, but it could be done. I think you might even do it with trabecular bone too, if you cut it up into slices and put it on the scintillator.

My first aim was to try to test against theory and secondly, to try to work out the dose near a mass of trabecular bone.

NORRIS: Just as a practical point, how do you calibrate the response of your detector?

SPIERS: My absolute calibration is the response obtained near to what is, in effect, the plane surface of an infinite medium. Every other geometry is referred back to this one.

STOVER: Since trabecular bone is more like a honeycomb than a sandwich, what might we expect if we had a honeycomb rather than a multilayer sandwich? How would this fit into the whole picture of this model and method?

SPIERS: I could drill holes in my plastic and in fact make up a model which is much more like trabecular bone. I think this is quite possible to do. I could then determine the resulting curves and see whether in fact the equilibrium levels follow the mass ratio. If they follow the mass ratio in this as well as in the sandwich then I shall not be too badly off. I think it would be a fairly good point.

CHAIRMAN EVANS: When one learns how to make a calculation and can verify it experimentally, one can feel more comfortable in calculating the honeycomb or anything else that Betsy Stover or others might want.

Closely related to this is the question of the spectral distribution and the number of beta rays which escape from an intact boundary. I think this is a very important problem not only from the point emphasized in the next manuscript but also from the standpoint of Bremsstrahlung production which is used in this and some other laboratories for *in vivo* dosimetry of Sr^{90} in the intact animal, where the beta rays of Sr^{90} and particularly Y^{90} produce continuous X-rays which are measured external to the body.

SKELETAL SELF-ABSORPTION OF BETA-PARTICLE ENERGY*

W. W. PARMLEY, J. B. JENSEN AND C. W. MAYS

Radiobiology Division, Department of Anatomy, University of Utah, Salt Lake City, Utah

INTRODUCTION

WHEN beta-particles are emitted in bone, only part of their energy is absorbed in the skeleton.† The remaining energy is either absorbed in the surrounding soft tissue or may even escape from the body of the animal. In the small-boned mouse only about 32 per cent of the total energy resulting from the decay of Sr^{90} plus its energetic daughter, Y^{90}, is absorbed by the skeleton, whereas in man the corresponding skeletal absorption is about 88%. In the past, this information was not available to persons desiring to extrapolate the biological effects of Sr^{90} with respect to Ra^{226} from mouse to man.[1] Knowledge of the absorbed energy is needed for meaningful comparison of the effects of (a) alpha vs beta emitters, (b) high energy vs low energy beta emitters, and (c) the same beta emitter in animals of different size.

Several years ago a method was developed for calculating the skeletal self-absorption of energy from beta-particles emitted within bone.[2] At that time the desirability of experimentally verifying this procedure was indicated. This has now been done and the theoretical and experimental results will be jointly presented in this paper.

THEORETICAL

Loevinger[3] has developed an empirical equation which gives the dose at any distance from a point source of beta-particles with a fair degree of accuracy. From this equation he has calculated the dose inside a tablet‡ and inside a sphere in which the density and radioactive concentration are uniform throughout. From reference[3] the fraction of the beta-particle energy absorbed in a tablet may be obtained from Figs. 16 and 19, and the fraction absorbed in a sphere from Figs. 23 and 25. Most bones, however, are neither spherical nor tabular in configuration but are more

---

* This work was supported by the U.S. Atomic Energy Commission.
† Throughout this article the term, skeleton, refers to bone plus marrow plus attached cartilage. The brain and spinal cord are not included with skeletal tissues.
‡ Tablet is defined as an infinite plane source of thickness x.

nearly cylindrical. Although it is clear that the energy absorption in a cylinder of diameter (x) is intermediate between that in a sphere of diameter (x) and a tablet of thickness (x), the equations for the cylindrical case have not yet been developed.

In an analogous problem, theoretical equations have been derived for the diffusion of radon from spheres, cylinders and tablets.[4] The radon retention in a cylinder of diameter (x) is about 43% of the way between the retentions in a sphere of diameter (x) and a tablet of thickness (x). A similar relationship for the absorption of beta-particle energy has been assumed. The error thus introduced is believed to be small.

The beta-particle absorptions in spheres, cylinders and tablets of uniform density and uniform radioactive concentration are plotted versus the product of "linear absorption coefficient" and the diameter (or thickness) in Fig. 1.

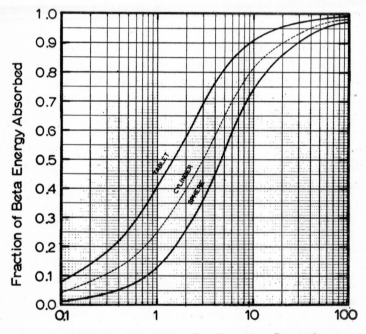

Fig. 1.

Absorption of beta-energy by spheres, cylinders and tablets uniform in density and uniform in radioactive concentration. The horizontal scale is the dimensionless product of linear absorption coefficient and diameter (or thickness). These curves apply particularly to high-energy beta-emitters (1·5 to 3·0 MeV in maximum energy), but are also approximately correct for lower energy beta-emitters.

The linear absorption coefficient (ν) is a measure of the ease with which various beta-particles can be stopped. For an allowed beta transition of maximum energy (E) MeV in a soft tissue medium of density (ϱ) gm/cc, Loevinger[3] gives

$$\nu = \frac{18 \cdot 6 \; \varrho \; \mathrm{cm}^{-1}}{(E - 0 \cdot 036)^{1 \cdot 37}} \tag{1}$$

This equation has also been applied to bone because there is no better equation available. As shown in Equation 1, the linear absorption coefficient decreases as the beta-particle energy increases.

The physical properties of several common bone-seeking beta emitters are listed in Table 1.

TABLE 1

Physical Properties of Several Bone-Seeking Beta Emitters

Emitter	Physical half-period	Beta energy		Soft tissue range		Linear abs. coef.** cm^{-1}
		maximum MeV	average MeV	maximum cm	average* cm	
Y^{90}	64 hr	2·24	0·93	1·07	0·21	6·2 ϱ
P^{32}	14·3 d	1·70	0·69	0·79	0·14	9·3 ϱ
Sr^{89}	51 d	1·46	0·56	0·66	0·11	11·5 ϱ
Sr^{90}	28 yr	0·536	0·20	0·18	0·033	40·0 ϱ
Ca^{45}	164 d	0·254	0·076	0·061	0·0087	150·0 ϱ

* The radial distance from a point β-source in unit density material in which half of the β-energy is absorbed.

** The density of the absorbing material is (ϱ) gm/cc.

It may be observed that the average beta energy is about $\frac{1}{3}$ of the maximum energy and that the distance in which half of the beta energy is absorbed is about $\frac{1}{6}$ of the maximum range. Because the decay of Sr^{90} is a forbidden transition, its linear absorption coefficient of $40\varrho\mathrm{cm}^{-1}$ is slightly different than that of an allowed transition of 0·536 MeV maximum energy.

The average density of six fresh whole dog humeri including marrow spaces has been found to equal 1·42 gm/cc.[5] This density has been assumed to equal that of wet defleshed skeletons.

An example will illustrate how energy absorption was calculated. A rat was injected with Sr^{90}. Later it was sacrificed and the effective diameter of its defleshed femur was measured with calipers and found to be 0·31 cm. The product of linear absorption coefficient and diameter is ($40 \times 1 \cdot 42$ cm^{-1})

$(0.31 \text{ cm}) = 18$ for Sr^{90} and $(6.2 \times 1.42 \text{ cm}^{-1})$ $(0.31 \text{ cm}) = 2.7$ for Y^{90}, the daughter of Sr^{90}. From Fig. 1 the corresponding absorptions for a cylinder are 89% for Sr^{90} and 47% for Y^{90}. Weighing these values by their respective average disintegration energies, the total $Sr^{90} + Y^{90}$ energy absorbed in the femur is calculated to be

$$\frac{(89\%)(0.20 \text{ MeV}) + (47\%)(0.93 \text{ MeV})}{0.20 \text{ MeV} + 0.93 \text{ MeV}} = 54\%$$

EXPERIMENTAL

A. *Animals*

The animals listed in Table 2 were each injected subcutaneously with $0.2 \mu C$ of Sr^{90} in 0.2 ml of 0.01 N NaCl solution. Subsequent measurements would have been facilitated if more Sr^{90} had been used. After several days, the animals were sacrificed. The bones were carefully defleshed with a scalpel, rehydrated,* blotted dry, immediately weighed, placed in stoppered vials and kept frozen until shortly before radioactive counting. At the time of counting the Y^{90} was in equilibrium with its parent, Sr^{90}.

TABLE 2

Experimental Animals

Animal	Age		Weight at death		Skeletal absorption of $Sr^{90} + Y^{90}$ energy	
	at inj.	at death	whole body	wet skel.	calc.	meas.
Mouse (CBA, male)	70 d	91 d	23 gm	1.9 gm	31%	32%
Rat (Sprague–Dawley, male)	23	29	125	8.4	41	—
Rat (Sprague–Dawley, male)	40	58	228	19.7	46	51
Rat (Sprague–Dawley, male)	264	288	385	33.8	49	—
Rabbit (N.Z. White, female)	25	38	600	72.7	58	61
Rabbit (N.Z. White, female)	400	411	3450	262.0	65	—

* The bones were placed under water. Air was removed from the bones with a vacuum pump. When the vacuum was released, water refilled the former air spaces.

The effective bone dimensions were measured with calipers* and the theoretical energy absorptions were calculated by the method previously desctibed.

After beta spectra were obtained, the bones were ashed, dissolved in nitric acid solution and assayed for Sr^{90} in a well-type plastic beta-particle scintillation counter using the method described by Stover and Atherton.[6]

B. *Beta-Particle Spectroscopy*

The beta-particle spectrometer, constructed by D. H. Taysum of this laboratory, is shown in Fig. 2.

Samples were suspended inside the spectrometer with thin linen thread. The chamber was not evacuated because (a) the beta-absorption in the air space was very small and (b) the effects on the spectra of the standard

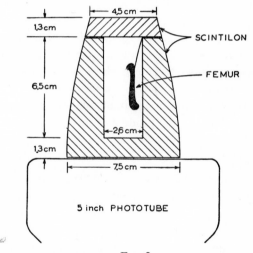

FIG. 2.

Beta-particle spectrometer drawn to scale. The spectrometer was machined from "Scintilon", a scintillation plastic, obtained from National Radiac Inc., 479 Washington Street, Newark 2, New Jersey. The top and sides of the spectrometer were covered with reflecting aluminium foil and its base was optically coupled with Dow Corning QC2-0057 media to a five inch Du Mont K 1438 multiplier phototube. The walls were curved so as to make the light collection efficiency nearly independent of the source position. A beta particle emitted from the source produces a light pulse proportional to its remaining energy from about 0·1 MeV to at least 3·6 MeV.[10]

---

* The effective bone dimension is the diameter (or thickness) of a cylinder (or tablet) of skeletal density whose self-absorption equals that in the bone. Effective dimensions are difficult to measure because of the irregular configurations of bones.

and the bones were similar. The high voltage to the phototube was turned off by a switch actuated when the light-tight cover to the system was raised to change samples. Pulses from the phototube passed through a linear amplifier to a single channel pulse-height analyzer, the output of which was recorded on a decade scaler. By keeping a fixed window width and increasing the base line in serial steps,* the energy spectrum escaping from the sample was measured.

Some of the light produced in the spectrometer was absorbed by the sample.† The magnitude of this effect was measured by comparing the apparent total energy output of the standard when enclosed (a) in a black paper cylinder and (b) in a transparent plastic cylinder of the same height, diameter and mass per unit area. All of the light reaching the black cylinder was assumed to be absorbed whereas 10% light absorption was assumed for the clear plastic cylinder. Results on other cylinder pairs of various diameters showed the effect on apparent total energy output to be roughly proportional to the area of light-absorbing surface. The area of each bone was measured and its light absorptivity estimated visually on a scale in which the light absorptivity of white paper was taken as 0·3 and that of black paper, 1·0. The light absorptivity values estimated for bones ranged from 0·5 to 0·7. The reduction in apparent total energy escape from bone was assumed proportional to the product of surface area and light absorptivity. For example, this reduction amounted to 5% for a pair of rat femurs indicating that the fraction of light not absorbed by these bones was 0·95.

The beta-particle standard consisted of 0·0205 μC of Sr^{90} evaporated on a thin mylar film‡ which was rolled into a hollow cylinder 0·21 cm in diameter, 0·99 cm in height, with a measured mass per unit area of 0·00566 gm/cm². ** The self-absorption of the standard was assumed equivalent to that in a tablet whose mass per unit area was 0·0113 gm/cm². The self-absorption in such a tablet was calculated to be 8·4% for $Sr^{90}+Y^{90}$. A self-absorption of 6·5% was obtained by surrounding the standard with 0·00566 gm/cm² of mylar and measuring the decrease in escaping beta energy it produced. The calculated absorption value of 8·4% was used to give

----

* A multi-channel pulse height analyzer would have been most valuable for these measurements.

† In retrospect, this effect could have been eliminated by silvering the inside of spectrometer or covering it with thin metal foil to prevent the light produced in the plastic scintillator from reaching the sample.

‡ A polyester resin manufactured by Du Pont Co., Wilmington, Delaware.

** If the standard had been thinner, its self-absorption would have been less.

a fractional energy escape of 0·916 for the standard. The light absorptivity of the mylar standard was negligible.

The uncorrected spectra obtained from the mylar standard and from a rat femur are shown in Fig. 3.

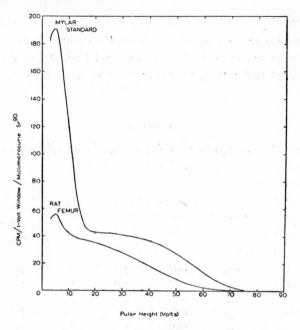

FIG. 3.

Beta spectra of $Sr^{90}+Y^{90}$ (a) evaporated on a thin mylar film, or (b) deposited in a rat femur. The high peak on the left is due to Sr^{90} whereas the broad shoulder on the right is due to the more energetic Y^{90}. For the rat femur note the large reduction of the Sr^{90} peak.

The fraction of energy escaping from a bone or the standard was determined by multiplying each stepwise count rate by its corresponding pulse height and summing over the entire spectrum. The escaping fraction of energy (E_b) is then

$$E_b = \frac{S_b}{S_s} \frac{E_s}{L_b} \tag{2}$$

where (S_b) is the sum of the products of count rate x pulse height for the bone, (S_s) is the sum of the products of count rate x pulse height for the standard, (E_s) is the fraction of beta energy escaping from the standard, and (L_b) is the fraction of light in the plastic scintillator not absorbed

444 W. W. PARMLEY *et al.*

by the bone. The fraction of beta energy absorbed on the bone (A_b) equals
1·0 minus the escaping fraction.

$$A_b = 1 - E_b \tag{3}$$

C. *Experimental Results*

The calculated and measured fractional absorptions of $Sr^{90}+Y^{90}$ beta-particle energies are listed in Tables 3, 4, and 5 for the individual bones in a mouse, rat and rabbit. Information about these animals is listed in Table 2.

TABLE 3

$Sr^{90}+Y^{90}$ *Energy Absorption in the Bones of a Mouse*
(*wet skeleton* = 1·9 gm)

Bones	Geometry	Effective diameter (cm)	% Wet skeletal weight	% skeletal Sr^{90}	Calculate $Sr^{90}+Y^{90}$ % energy abs.	Measured $Sr^{90}+Y^{90}$ % energy abs.
Femurs	Cyl	0·15	5·8	7·3	38	35
Tibiae+fibulae	,,	0·12	5·0	5·9	35	29
Humeri	,,	0·12	2·9	3·6	35	35
Radii + ulnae	,,	0·07	2·1	2·2	24	25
Hind feet	,,	0·05	4·8	3·3	20	19
Fore feet	,,	0·03	1·2	0·5	15	—*
Cervical vert.	,,	0·10	3·6	2·3	31	20
Thoracic vert.	,,	0·12	10·0	6·1	35	40
Lumbar vert.	,,	0·13	6·9	5·2	35	36
Sacrum	,,	0·10	2·4	2·0	31	27
Tail	,,	0·10	13·9	13·0	31	35
Ribs	,,	0·03	6·0	5·8	15	41*
Sternum	,,	0·07	1·1	0·5	24	3*
Pelvis	Tab	0·04	5·2	6·2	27	21
Scapulae	,,	0·02	2·0	2·3	18	18
Maxillae	,,	0·07	12·3	15·2	38	36
Mandible	,,	0·06	5·1	9·4	35	28
Skull	,,	0·04	9·7	9·2	27	34
Totals and weighted averages			100·0	100·0	31	32

* The measured absorptions in the forefeet, ribs and sternum appear to be grossly in error.

TABLE 4

$Sr^{90}+Y^{90}$ *Energy Absorption in the Bones of A Rat*
(*wet skeleton = 19·7 gm*)

Bones	Geometry	Effective diameter (cm)	% Wet skeletal weight	% skeletal Sr^{90}	Calculated $Sr^{90}+Y^{90}$ % energy abs.	Measured $Sr^{90}+Y^{90}$ % energy abs.
Femurs	Cyl	0·31	7·1	8·2	54	56
Tibiae + fibulae	,,	0·27	6·1	7·1	52	51
Humeri	,,	0·23	3·1	2·8	48	48
Radii + ulnae	,,	0·16	2·4	2·8	40	44
Hind feet	,,	0·18	6·5	8·5	43	46
Fore feet	,,	0·11	2·1	2·1	33	34
Cervical vert.	,,	0·19	3·6	3·2	44	60
Thoracic vert.	,,	0·29	8·9	6·4	53	64
Lumbar vert.	,,	0·24	9·8	8·4	49	65
Sacrum	,,	0·24	2·1	1·7	49	42
Tail	,,	0·25	15·5	10·9	50	60
Ribs	,,	0·08	5·4	5·4	27	28
Sternum	,,	0·16	1·5	0·7	40	45
Pelvis	Tab	0·13	5·6	6·3	51	44
Scapulae	,,	0·05	1·7	1·8	31	24
Maxillae	,	0·08	7·5	9·0	40	53
Mandible	,,	0·12	4·2	6·9	51	49
Skull	,,	0·06	6·9	7·8	35	45
Totals and weighted averages			100·0	100·0	46	51

Differences between calculated and measured energy absorptions were primarily due to (a) the difficulty in accurately estimating effective bone diameters due to their irregular configurations and (b) the low counting rates in some samples, especially in the mouse. The Sr^{90} activities contained in the total skeletons were; 0·0273 μC (mouse), 0·122 μC (rat) and 0·141 μC (rabbit). Other factors influencing the differences between computed and measured values were the non-uniform deposition of Sr^{90}, the inability to measure energy escaping from the skeleton into such places as the spinal cord, uncertainties in the correction for light absorption in bones with large exposed surface areas, and inadequacies in the theory.

Calculated energy absorption values were weighted by wet bone weights whereas measured values were weighted by Sr^{90} retentions to obtain weighted skeletal energy absorption values. The weighted averages should be considerably more reliable than most individual values due to the fact that much of the error in individual values was random. All factors considered, the agreement between calculated and measured energy absorption values was fairly good.

TABLE 5

$Sr^{90}+Y^{90}$ *Energy Absorption in the Bones of a Rabbit*
(*wet skeleton* $= 72 \cdot 2$ gm)

Bones	Geometry	Effective diameter (cm)	% Wet skeletal weight	% skeletal Sr^{90}	Calculated $Sr^{90}+Y^{90}$ % energy abs.	Measured $Sr^{90}+Y^{90}$ % energy abs.
Femurs	Cyl	0·56	9·8	11·4	69	61
Tibiae and fibulae	,,	0·49	7·4	7·6	67	62
Humeri	,,	0·43	5·4	4·4	63	54
Radii + ulnae	,,	0·36	4·2	3·5	59	54
Hind feet	,,	0·45	11·0	9·0	64	66
Fore feet	,,	0·28	3·4	2·9	53	56
Cervical vert.	,,	0·31	5·1	4·5	54	69
Thoracic vert.	,,	0·27	7·0	4·4	52	74
Lumbar vert.	,,	0·29	9·3	7·2	53	69
Sacrum	,,	0·32	1·4	1·1	55	67
Tail	,,	0·27	1·5	0·8	52	46
Ribs	,,	0·18	5·4	4·9	43	51
Sternum	,,	0·27	0·9	0·3	52	51
Pelvis	Tab	0·22	4·8	5·5	63	54
Scapulae	,,	0·10	2·6	2·2	46	43
Maxillae	,,	0·14	9·3	12·0	53	64
Mandible	,,	0·23	4·6	9·6	64	60
Skull	,,	0·14	6·9	8·7	53	55
Totals and weighted averages			100·0	100·0	58	61

INTERSPECIES CORRELATIONS

The calculated and measured $Sr^{90}+Y^{90}$ beta-particle energy absorption values for the animals listed in Table 2 are plotted in Fig. 4.

Energy absorption increases with skeletal weight. Empirically we found the data agreed well with the assumption* that in terms of beta-energy absorption, a skeleton of (W) gm is equivalent to a uniform cylinder 1·42 gm/cc in density whose diameter (d) is approximately

$$d = 0·086 \text{ cm} \sqrt[3]{\overline{W}} \qquad (4)$$

For example, a 2 gm mouse skeleton is approximately equivalent in beta-energy absorption to a cylinder whose diameter is $0·086 \text{ cm} \sqrt[3]{2} = 0·11$ cm.

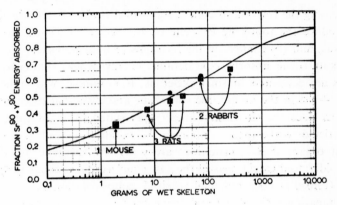

FIG. 4.

Approximate absorption of $Sr^{90} + Y^{90}$ beta energy in skeletons of various wet weights. If wet skeletal weight is unknown it may be estimated for many mammals as being between 7% and 13% of their whole body weight. Calculated skeletal energy absorption values are shown as open squares, whereas measured values are shown as solid circles. The curve was computed from Eq. 4 and Fig. 1.

TABLE 6

Calculated Absorption of Beta-Energy in the Skeleton

Animal	Wet skeletal weight	Equivalent bone diameter	Fraction of energy absorbed in the skeleton			
			$Sr^{90}+Y^{90}$	P^{32}	Sr^{89}	Ca^{45}
Human	7000 gm	1·64 cm	88%	90%	92%	100%
Dog	1000	0·86	79	84	86	99
Rabbit	200	0·50	67	73	78	98
Rat	20	0·23	48	51	57	96
Mouse	2	0·11	32	32	37	91

* The factor $\sqrt[3]{W}$ is derived from the assumptions that (a) bone volume isproportional to bone weight, (b) that bone length is much greater than bone diameter, (c) that bone length is proportional to bone diameter, and (d) therefore that bone diameter increases as the cube root bone weight.

Representative wet skeletal weights for several species are listed in Table 6. Equivalent bone diameters were computed using Equation 4. Skeletal absorptions of beta energy from $Sr^{90}+Y^{90}$, P^{32}, Sr^{89} and Ca^{45} were calculated using Table 1 and Fig. 1.

These calculated absorption values are slightly higher and probably more nearly correct than those previously computed.[2]

DISCUSSION

Decreasing the fraction of beta energy which is absorbed in the skeleton may produce the following two effects: (a) increased damage to nearby soft tissue, and (b) changes in the locations of bone damage.

The soft tissue absorbs considerable energy when high-energy beta emitters are deposited in small skeletons. For example, with bone-deposited $Sr^{90}+Y^{90}$ in the mouse, the soft tissue absorbs about twice as much energy as does the skeleton. Finkel[7] has stated, "Tumor formation is not restricted to the tissue containing the radioisotope but may occur in adjacent organs if the emanations are γ-rays or energetic β-rays. Thus many epidermoid carcinomas of the nasopharynx and oral cavity appeared in our (Finkel's) mice that had received radiostrontium..."

In comparing high-energy and low-energy beta emitters which deposit similarly in the skeleton, one might expect a tendency for the ratio of osteosarcoma incidences in a given bone to increase with the ratio of energy absorptions therein. Thus, data of Finkel[8] on the bone by bone distri-

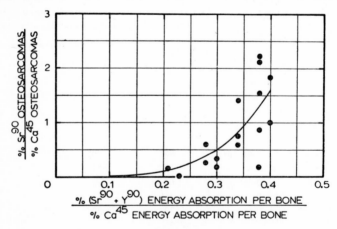

Fig. 5.

Sr^{90}/Ca^{45} osteosarcoma ratios in individual bones of mice vs their beta-absorption ratios. Osteosarcomas were identified by Finkel[8]. Energy absorptions were calculated by us. The equation of the plotted curve is $y = 62 \cdot 5\, x^4$.

bution of osteosarcomas induced in mice by $Sr^{90}+Y^{90}$ and by Ca^{45} is of great interest. These osteosarcoma locations and our computed energy absorption values are listed in Table 7.

The ratio of Sr^{90}/Ca^{45} osteosarcomas is plotted with respect to the ratio of $(Sr^{90}+Y^{90})/Ca^{45}$ energy absorptions in Fig. 5.

TABLE 7

Location of Osteogenic Sarcomas in Radioactive Mice

Bones	Sr^{90} Tumours[8] (% of 352)	Ca^{45} Tumours[8] (% of 182)	% Sr^{90} Tumors / % Ca^{45} Tumors	$Sr^{90}+Y^{90}$ % Energy Abs.*	Ca^{45} % Energy Abs.*	% $Sr^{90}+Y^{90}$ Abs. / % Ca^{45} Abs.
Femurs	35·4	19·2	1·84	38	94	·40
Tibiae & Fibulae	19·6	8·8	2·23	35	92	·38
Humeri	3·4	1·6	2·12	35	92	·38
Radii & Ulnae	0·3	0·5	0·60	24	87	·28
Hind Feet	0·0	0·0	—	20	83	·24
Fore Feet	0·0	0·0	—	15	72	·21
Cervical Vert.	0·3	0·5	0·60	31	90	·34
Thoracic Vert.	1·7	8·8	0·19	35	92	·38
Lumbar Vert.	19·3	22·0	0·88	35	93	·38
Sacrum	7·9	10·4	0·76	31	90	·34
Tail	3·1	2·2	1·41	31	90	·34
Ribs	0·9	5·5	0·16	15	72	·21
Sternum	0·3	1·1	0·27	24	87	·28
Pelvis	4·8	14·3	0·34	27	89	·30
Scapulae	0·0	1·1	0·00	18	78	·23
Maxillae	1·1	1·1	1·00	38	94	·40
Mandible	1·7	1·1	1·55	35	93	·38
Skull	0·3	1·6	0·19	27	89	·30

* Computed skeletal energy absorptions are tabulated.

In spite of considerable scatter, Fig. 5 indicates a tendency for the osteosarcoma ratio to increase with the absorption ratio. Curves of the form $y = a x^n$ were fit to the data by the method of least squares, where y is the osteosarcoma ratio and x is the absorption ratio. There are, of course, other equations which would represent this data as well or perhaps slightly better. For each curve a coefficient of correlation was calculated. The greater the coefficient of correlation the more closely the curve fits the data. The curve, $y = 62.5\ x^4$ had the greatest correlation coefficient (0.71). While this fourth power curve gave the best correlation it must be pointed out that there was little difference in the coefficients of correlation among the second through seventh power curves. The following factors probably contributed to the scatter in data:

(a) Different biologic responses among different bones.

(b) Small numbers of osteosarcomas in some bones.

(c) Errors in the calculated values of energy absorption.

(d) Lumping all injection levels for each radionuclide.

Actually, since the frequency of radiation-induced cancer in a given region is the integrated biological response to all of the localized absorptions of radiation energy, a perfect correlation should not be expected between something as complex as osteosarcoma induction and something as simple as the average beta energy absorption by a whole bone. Excellent progress in mapping out the localized distribution of beta dose has been made by Marshall in mice[8] and Owen in rabbits.[9]

SUMMARY AND CONCLUSIONS

(1) Calculated self-absorptions of beta energy in the skeleton have been experimentally confirmed for $Sr^{90} + Y^{90}$.

(2) Skeletal absorption decreases with increasing beta-particle energy.

(3) Skeletal absorption increases with bone size.

(4) A mammalian skeleton of (W) gm wet weight is roughly equivalent in beta absorption to a cylinder 1.42 gm/cc in density and 0.086 cm $\sqrt[3]{\ }$ W in diameter.

(5) Beta energy escaping from the skeleton may cause damage to the soft tissue in which it is absorbed.

(6) Although two beta emitters may be deposited similarly, differences in their energy absorption ratios may change the ratio of the localized response.

ACKNOWLEDGEMENTS

The helpful discussion with R. D. Evans, J. H. Marshall, and L. D. Marinelli in planning this experiment were sincerely appreciated. Thanks is extended to D. H. Taysum for construction of the beta-particle spectrometer and to L. R. Jackson and G. D. Westenskow for construction and maintenance of the electronic equipment. We are grateful to D. R. Atherton and F. W. Bruenger for preparation of the injection solutions and help in Sr^{90} assay of the ashed bones. Detailed suggestions from R. Loevinger were very helpful in preparing the final manuscript.

REFERENCES

1. M. P. FINKEL, Men, mice and fallout, *Science* **128**, 3325, 637–641 (1958).
2. C. W. MAYS, Escape of beta-energy from the skeleton, Radiobiology Laboratory U. of Utah Report COO-218, 113–120 (March 1959).
3. R. LOEVINGER, E. M. JAPHA and G. L. BROWNELL, Discrete radioisotope sources, I. Beta-radiation, in *Radiation Dosimetry*, ed. by G. J. HINE and G. L. BROWNELL, Academic Press, New York 694–753 (1956).
4. C. W. MAYS, Escape of radon and thoron when produced in bone, Radiobiology Laboratory U. of Utah Report COO-216, 1–51 (1958).
5. B. J. STOVER and T. F. DOUGHERTY, Calcium ion exchange in bone, USPHS Research Grant A-1058 First Progress Report, p. 22 (Sept. 1958).
6. B. J. STOVER and D. R. ATHERTON, Metabolism of Sr^{90} in adult beagle dogs, *Proc. Soc. Exp. Biol. & Med.* **99**, 201–205 (1958).
7. MIRIAM P. FINKEL, Internal emitters and tumor induction, *Peaceful Uses of Atomic Energy*, United Nations, New York, **2**, 160–164 (1956).
8. J. H. MARSHALL and M. P. FINKEL, Autoradiographic dosimetry of mouse bones containing Ca^{45}, Sr^{90} and Ra^{226}, Argonne National Laboratory Radiological Physics Division Report ANL-6104, 48–65 (July–Dec. 1959).
9. MAUREEN OWEN, Sr^{90} dosimetry in rabbits, this vol., p. 409.
10. D. G. GARDNER and W. W. MEINKE, β-ray spectroscopy using a hollow plastic scintillator, *International Journal of Applied Radiation and Isotopes* **3**, 232–239 (1958).

DISCUSSION

KORNBERG: Is there a possibility of different back-scatter from soft tissue into bone as compared to the back-scatter from your chamber walls?

MAYS: Yes. We decided to neglect this effect because we felt it was very small compared with the other errors.

When we planned this experiment our first idea (COO-218, p. 113, March 1959) was to dip the bone in liquid scintillator to duplicate the back-scattering from the soft tissue surrounding the bone.

But this involves real problems, the chief of which is how to prevent the bone from stopping a large fraction of the light formed in the layers of scintillator next to the bone surface. We thought the best approach was to separate the bone and scintillator by a distance so as to minimize the fraction of light intercepted by the bone.

MARINELLI: We have been thinking about that problem for quite a while, but some of my physicists have turned biologists and that was the end of it. That can happen, you know!

As a matter of fact I think the experiment should be done in a liquid scintillator, and corrections developed to account for the light absorbed by the bone surfaces.

Your measurements are very close to unpublished calculations I made back in 1956. You measured 35% $Sr^{90}+Y^{90}$ energy absorption in the mouse femur whereas my calculated value was 36%.

These figures indicate that in terms of energy absorbed in the skeleton, Ca^{45} and Sr^{90} are about equally effective in producing osteogenic sarcomas in mice. But I couldn't convince anybody because this experiment had not been made. I am certainly glad to see that it has been done.

MAYS: A very large share of credit for the success of this experiment we owe to Leo Marinelli, John Marshall and Robley Evans for their helpful advice in planning this study.

NORRIS: One of the things that has puzzled me in making comparisons between species in terms of the toxicity of internal emitters is that the smaller the animal, the more resistant, generally speaking, it tends to be.

I have generally tended to believe (and I think I am not alone) that the soft tissues surrounding bone and perhaps soft tissue in general is more vulnerable to radiation than is bone, which we tend to consider as being relatively resistant. So, I think if you have done anything for me, Chuck, you have compounded the problem of interspecies comparisons rather than enabling me to see any way of simplifying it.

MAYS: Bill, you have stated this problem very nicely. It is complicated. Just telling you how much energy goes into the soft tissue does not tell you what that energy is going to produce.

CHAIRMAN EVANS: Just to take a shot at one of the physical points, I was struck by the pulse-height distributions (Fig. 3) that Chuck Mays showed us. In both the mylar standard and the rat femur, the Sr^{90} spectra are seen riding on top of the Y^{90} spectra. In the rat femur, absorption has almost completely suppressed the Sr^{90} spectrum although it is clearly still there. In spite of large absorptions, the spectral shapes of the Sr^{90} and Y^{90} have remained quite similar to their unabsorbed shapes, as far as this apparatus recorded it.

This looks like another illustration of the handy rule of thumb that absorption does not greatly alter the shape of a beta-ray spectrum (G. L. Brownell, *Nucleonics*

10, 6, p. 30, 1952), and that the fractional transmission (I/I_0) thorugh an absorber of thickness (x) and density (ϱ) gram/cm³ of a beta spectrum of maximum energy (E) MeV is approximately

$$\frac{I}{I_0} \simeq e^{-\mu x} \quad \text{where} \quad \mu = \frac{17\,\varrho}{E^{1.14}}\ \text{cm}^{-1}$$

Loevinger's expression (see Eq. 1 in Parmley's paper) is substantially the same.

MARINELLI: I wonder whether this audience is acquainted with the National Bureau of Standards' theoretical program on the so-called slowing down of electrons in matter (N.B.S. Circular No. 597). As a first approximation you (Evans) are not far off, but there is a shift into the lower energies at greater depths.

Of definite interest is the suggestion of Odeblad (*Acta Radiol.* **43**, 310, 1955) that the beta-ray point-source function be of the form

$$J(x) = \frac{n}{R_0}\left(1 - \frac{x}{R_0}\right)^{n-1}$$

where n is an exponent varying with the maximum energy and shape of the beta spectrum. This simple expression offers the advantages of vanishing at distances $x = R_0$ and of giving to $\dfrac{n}{R_0}$ the meaning of an "average" stopping power. In later work Odeblad (*Acta Radiologica* **48**, 289, 1957) shows a very intriguing relationship between the exponent n and some fundamental parameters related to rate of electron energy loss $\dfrac{dE}{dx}$. and to the spectral shape and maximum β-ray energy; he has also suggested (E. Odeblad, *Acta Radiologica* **51**, 128, 1959) some modifications to account for multiple scattering within the medium. Despite the simplifications involved, this formula seems to agree, within practical limits, with transmission experiments performed with metal foils. It is unfortunate, however, that no effort has been made to test its applicability to the point-source dose function in tissue-like materials foi which ample experimental data are available.

SKELETAL RETENTION OF THE ALKALINE
EARTH RADIOISOTOPES AND BONE DOSIMETRY*

R. E. ROWLAND

Radiological Physics Division, Argonne National Laboratory, Argonne, Illinois

INTRODUCTION

IN ORDER to evaluate the dose delivered to bone tissue by internally deposited radioisotopes of the alkaline earth family, it is necessary to understand the mechanisms that release these isotopes from bone. It has been postulated that processes other than direct resorption of bone mineral must be of importance in the overall removal of these isotopes from bone, particularly in the adult animal.[1,2] The purpose of this report is to describe the experimental studies that have shown the validity of this assumption, and to indicate how the results may be applied to the problems of dosimetry.

In order to avoid semantic difficulties, it is necessary to define a few of the terms that will be employed. The first of these is *resorption*. By resorption is meant the process by which a distinct volume of bone mineral and matrix is removed from bone. Often, but not necessarily, this process is followed by the *apposition* of new bone; the process of new bone formation which results in an increase of mineral volume. It is these two processes that are referred to when the general term, *bone turnover*, is employed. In contrast to the above terms, *exchange* processes are those which do not involve changes in mineral volume. By exchange is meant any process involving equal and opposite rates of transfer of atoms to and from a single microscopic volume of bone mineral.

When we consider the dosimetry of the alkaline earth isotopes in bone, the nuclear characteristics of each, such as the physical half-life, type of decay, and the energy of the emitted radiation, are of paramount importance. However, there exist basic similarities between the members of this chemical family when they are deposited in bone. The work of the Radiobiological Laboratory at the University of Utah has demonstrated the similarity of the retention of Sr^{90} and Ra^{226} in beagles,[3,4,5] while other

---

* Work performed under the auspices of the United States Atomic Energy Commission.

455

laboratories have shown that in this species Ca^{45} and Ba^{133} are also retained in a similar manner.[6] The retention of all, in the adult beagle, can be described by a power function of the form

$$R_t = at^b,$$

where R_t is the fractional retention at any time t (in days) after an intravenous injection of one of these isotopes, a is the fractional retention at one day, and b has a value close to $-0\cdot2$. While the emphasis hereafter will be on the similarities of these radioisotopes in bone, and as a consequence they will all be considered together, it must not be forgotten that the actual dosimetric patterns that result from these isotopes are vastly different. When the term isotope is subsequently used, it will refer to a radioisotope of one of the above-mentioned elements, and will indicate an application where apparently identical results would be obtained with any of the above-mentioned tracers.

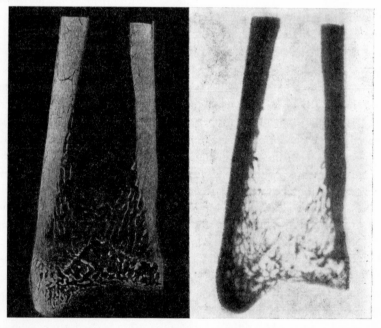

Fig. 1.

A microradiograph and an autoradiograph of a longitudinal section cut through the distal end of the tibia of a dog which had been fed a constant ratio of Sr^{90} per g Ca. Feeding of the isotope started *in utero* and continued until the dog was 450 days old; the animal was sacrificed 21 days after Sr^{90} was removed from the diet.

In Fig. 1 is illustrated a practical problem in dosimetry. Here is an autoradiograph, with an accompanying microradiograph, of the distal end of the tibia of a 16-month-old beagle.* The isotope is Sr^{90}, acquired orally; feeding started *in utero* and continued to 450 days of age, at a constant rate of Sr^{90} per gram of calcium. The dog was sacrificed 21 days after the Sr^{90} was discontinued.

If this animal had lived for several years after the Sr^{90} feeding had been stopped, the total accumulated dose or the dose rate at a given time to a specific volume of tissue might well represent a problem for the radiobiologist to solve. Before such a calculation can be made, the mechanism of removal of the isotopes from bone must be known.

If resorption were the only process that could release an isotope from bone, then, with the passage of time, autoradiographs of bones such as this one would be identical in photographic density, but lighter patches would be present, corresponding to locations in which resorption had occurred. The important point is that, wherever original bone remained, the specific activity of the isotope in the bone mineral would be unchanged.

On the other hand, if exchange alone was responsible for the loss of the isotope, then subsequent autoradiographs would be identical to this one, but they would require longer exposures to produce the same autoradiographic darkening. That is, the specific activity of the isotope in the bone mineral would have decreased with the passage of time.

The concept that isotopes may be lost from bone by exchange processes is not new; indeed, most workers have realized that the diffuse uptake of an isotope into pre-existing bone could not indicate a net transfer of mineral into these regions. This distribution itself, and in particular, the quantitative studies of its magnitude which indicated that it represents about one half of the total skeletal content of a deposited isotope,[7,8] have given a clear indication of the significance of exchange processes in the deposition and retention of isotopes in the skeleton.

Less is known regarding the retention of these isotopes after they have been fixed in the skeleton by the process of new mineral formation. Turning our attention again to Fig. 1, it should be noted that, while this autoradiograph illustrates a uniform distribution of the isotope throughout the bone mineral, much like a diffuse distribution produced in bone by exchange, actually the isotope was originally incorporated everywhere by the process of new mineral formation. Thus, for the case in question, we need to know how isotopes deposited by growth processes are removed from bone.

* Dog 5S3, from AEC Project No. 6, School of Veterinary Medicine, University of California, Davis, California.

EXPERIMENTAL RESULTS

A study has been made to determine the processes by which isotopes, deposited in bone by either exchange or growth, are removed with the passage of time. Since this work has been reported in full elsewhere,[9] it will simply be briefly summarized here.

An adult dog was given equal injections of Ra^{226} once a week for a period of eight weeks; a total of 101 μc Ra^{226} was administered. Four weeks after the last injection a front limb was removed by amputation; one year later the dog was sacrificed. Quantitative autoradiographs were made from the bone sections, in order to compare the Ra^{226} content at amputation to that existing at time of sacrifice. This study was designed so that a comparison of the specific activity of the tracer (Ra^{226}) in two distributions, the regions of exchange and the regions of growth, could be made at two different times. The results indicated that, over the one-year interval, the specific activity decreased in both distributions.

The amount of the decrease is quite significant, and can best be compared with the decrease in the total skeletal burden of the dog. The actual content of the dog was not determined, but the power law retention formula indicated that the Ra^{226} content at sacrifice (including the missing limb) would have been 66% of the content at the time of amputation. However, a comparison between two bones (the radii) was made, which indicated that the one removed at sacrifice contained $74\pm5\%$ as much Ra^{226} per gram as the one removed a year before by amputation. The autoradiographic study showed that the hot spots (which correspond to areas of appositional bone growth) decreased over this time interval to $66\pm12\%$ of their original level, and that the diffuse (exchange labeled bone) decreased to $75\pm15\%$ of the original level.

The fact that the diffuse distribution did not lose as much activity as the hot spots does not imply that the exchange rate is lower for this distribution. The explanation lies in the magnitude of the blood specific activity. At the time of amputation the specific activity (Ra^{226}/g Ca) in the diffuse distribution was less than the specific activity (Ra^{226}/g Ca) of the blood, so that exchange between blood and bone would still be increasing the diffuse concentration. Exchange would not be expected to decrease the diffuse level until the activity in the blood had dropped below the level in the bone; this did not occur until two months after the amputation. Thus, even with equal exchange rates, we would expect to find less loss from the diffuse distribution in this particular study.

Perhaps the most significant finding from this work has been, not simply that both distributions lost activity by exchange processes, but rather, the magnitude of the losses. These observed losses were large enough to account for almost all of the loss of activity from this dog, thus implying that bone resorption must play only a small role in the removal of these isotopes from the skeleton.

Yet, on further consideration, this is not a surprising result, for studies on the distribution of isotopes in bone at long times after injection have indicated that no great amount of resorption has taken place. Consider the autoradiograph shown in Fig. 2; this is from a 100-μ thick section from

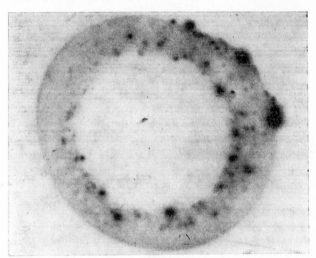

FIG. 2.

An autoradiograph of a 100-μ-thick section cut from the femur of a dog which had received a single injection of mixed Sr^{90} and Sr^{89} as an adult 10½ years before death.

the femur of a dog that carried Sr^{90} for 10½ years after receiving, as an adult, a single injection of mixed Sr^{89} and Sr^{90}.* It can be seen, from the uniformity of the autoradiograph, that little bone turnover has taken place after the isotope was deposited.

From the studies on the radium dial painters we are familiar with the fact that autoradiographs of bone sections from these individuals show little evidence of bone turnover. Figure 3 illustrates the maximum turnover, as indicated by autoradiographic analysis, that has been seen in our studies on human cases at Argonne. This autoradiograph is from a 100-μ -thick bone section from the humerus of a 57-year-old dial painter. Considerable

---

* Bone from dog QA142 was kindly supplied by Dr. M. Finkel. This animal was given mixed Sr^{89} and Sr^{90} on 2/22/1946, as part of a program of toxicity studies carried on by the Biological and Medical Division of Argonne National Laboratory.

non-uniformity is visible in this autoradiograph, indicating regions where turnover has occurred, yet the turnover rate could not have been more than about 2 or 3% per year to leave as much unaltered bone as is visible here.

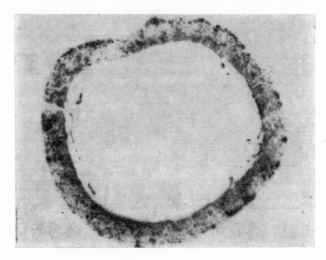

FIG. 3.

An autoradiograph of a 100-μ-thick section cut from the humerus of a radium dial painter (code No. 01–008), who had acquired mixed Ra^{226} and Ra^{228} as the result of a two year exposure 41 years before death. The diffuse distribution here indicates that extensive bone turnover has taken place. The section is not markedly osteoporotic; i.e., bone exists in all of the locations where little autoradiographic darkening is seen.

THEORETICAL STUDIES

Let us now turn our attention to the dosimetric implication of these results. Both distributions, exchange and appositional growth, have been shown to lose activity with time, but can we characterize the time rate of loss? A clue is given by the observations that have indicated that the magnitude of the diffuse distribution is related to the total skeletal content of an isotope. Such observations have been made in dogs, from a few weeks to several years after the isotope was acquired, and in human radium cases, at observation times of twenty to forty years.[8] Hence it is suggested that the loss of activity from this distribution can be described by a function of the same form that describes the total retention, which in the case of beagles is a power function with an exponent of about −0·2. Although it is not conclusively proven by our data, it seems reasonable to assign

a similar rate of loss to the hot spots, i.e., the regions in which the isotope
has been deposited by growth.

Thus, from a terminal autoradiograph from which the quantity of an
isotope per unit mass of bone in specific regions has been determined, it
is possible to calculate the concentration of the isotope that existed in
that location at any previous time. While the ability to make such a
calculation is not necessary for studies in which the isotope has been in bone
for only a short time, it does become important for those cases in which
the isotope has been in bone for many years. Consider for example the
autoradiograph of Fig. 2; the concentration of isotope per gram of bone
that must have existed one month after the injection would have been 2·7
times as great as observed terminally. The case illustrated in Fig. 3, one
year after painting started, would have contained about 6·4 times as much
radium per unit volume of bone than is indicated by its autoradiograph
if the loss of radium from humans is described by the function[10]

$$R_t = 0.54t^{-0.52}$$

The dose delivered to a volume of tissue from a concentration of an
isotope in a microscopic volume of bone is described by a function of the
form

$$\frac{dD}{dt} = Kq_t$$

Here the dose rate, dD/dt, is in rads per day; K is an appropriate constant,
depending on the energy, range, and geometric distribution of the radioisotope with respect to the volume in which the dose is to be computed,
and q_t is the observed concentration ($\mu c/g$ bone) in the bone mineral at
the time of observation. The total accumulated dose to the tissue in question
over the entire time interval the isotope has been in the bone is then

$$D = \int_0^{t_s} Kq_t \, dt$$

where t_s (in days) is the time interval between the acquisition of the isotope
and the observation of the bone section.

If this expression is evaluated on the basis that exchange losses do not
occur, so that the concentration (q_t) of the isotope in bone decreases only
as the result of radioactive decay, then

$$D = \int_0^{t_s} Kq_0 \, e^{-\lambda t} \, dt$$

Here q_0 is the original concentration of the isotope in bone, and λ is the decay constant of the isotope in question. Integration of this expression yields

$$D = Kq_0 \frac{1 - e^{-\lambda t_s}}{\lambda}$$

If the half-life is so long that decay need not be considered, this reduces to

$$D = Kq_0 \, t_s$$

When we allow the original concentration of the isotope in bone to decrease by both decay and exchange losses, and if exchange losses are postulated to follow a power law, such that

$$q_t = q_0 \, t^b \, e^{-\lambda t}$$

then

$$D = \int_0^{t_s} Kq_0 \, t^b \, e^{-\lambda t} \, \mathrm{d}t$$

This integration yields

$$D = Kq_0 \frac{\Gamma \lambda t \, (b + 1)}{\lambda^{b+1}}$$

where $\Gamma \lambda t \, (b+1)$ is the incomplete gamma function. For the case when the half-life is very long, this expression becomes

$$D = Kq_0 \frac{t_s^{(b+1)}}{b + 1}$$

Since, when evaluating bone tissue dose, the actual concentration seen is a terminal one, these equations are most logically compared with each other in terms of the terminal concentration, q_t, of the isotope.

Case I: No loss by decay or exchange;

$$D = Kq_t \, t_s$$

Case II: Loss by decay but not by exchange;

$$D = Kq_t \frac{1 - e^{-\lambda t_s}}{\lambda e^{-\lambda t_s}}$$

Case III: Loss by exchange but not by decay;

$$D = Kq_t \frac{t_s}{b + 1}$$

Case IV: Loss by both exchange and decay;

$$D = Kq_t \frac{\Gamma\lambda t\,(b+1)}{t_s^b \cdot e^{-\lambda t_s} \cdot \lambda^{b+1}}$$

From a comparison of cases I and III it can be seen that for a long lived isotope, such as Ra^{226}, the accumulated dose, calculated from a terminal distribution, will be greater by a factor of $1/b+1$ when loss by exchange is considered than when it is ignored, independent of the time of observation. If $b = -0.5$, as appears to be the case for Ra^{226} in human beings,[10] the accumulated dose is a factor of two greater than the product of the terminal dose rate times the number of days the isotope was carried.*

In Table 1 the values of the incomplete gamma function have been tabulated for use with Sr^{90}.[11] Five different values of the exponent b have been included in the calculations, to bracket the values obtained for this element in man and dog, and six different observation times.

TABLE 1

Values of the Incomplete Gamma Function

b	t_s (years)	$\Gamma\lambda t\,(b+1)$
−0·2	1	0·06413
	2	0·1105
	5	0·2230
	10	0·3701
	20	0·5767
	30	0·7248
−0·25	1	0·08234
	2	0·1371
	5	0·2645
	10	0·4249
	20	0·6425
	30	0·7940
−0·3	1	0·1062
	2	0·1708
	5	0·3152
	10	0·4900
	20	0·7196
	30	0·8748
−0·35	1	0·1376
	2	0·2139
	5	0·3777

* This statement assumes that the radon retention remains constant over the time interval in question. Since it actually does not, a correction for the change in parent to daughter ratio must be included to obtain the correct value of accumulated dose.

Table 1 (cont.)

b	t_s (years)	$\Gamma\lambda t\,(b+1)$
	10	0·5682
	20	0·8097
	30	0·9689
−0·4	1	0·1795
	2	0·2696
	5	0·4552
	10	0·6628
	20	0·9166
	30	1·0801

To demonstrate the magnitude of the errors introduced as a consequence of the failure to consider loss of Sr^{90} (28 year half-life) from bone by exchange, a series of calculations are listed in Table 2. Case IV results are assigned a value of unity in the table, and the values obtained from Case I (no decay or exchange) and Case II (decay but no exchange) are expressed in terms of the values obtained by the Case IV method.

This compilation of values serves two purposes. First, it demonstrates, for Sr^{90}, the magnitude of the error introduced by failure to consider loss by exchange processes. Second, it provides a method for the rapid calculation of total accumulated dose. For example, consider an observation of the terminal concentration of Sr^{90} in a dog which had carried the isotope for ten years. A Case I calculation, which is simply the product of the terminal concentration and the number of days the isotope was carried, ignores both kinds of loss, decay and exchange. However, it is very easy to perform and if the appropriate exponent for exchange loss is assumed to be $b = -0\cdot2$ the value obtained is seen to be 68% of the value that would have been obtained by the rigorous approach of Case IV. Since the calculations involving the incomplete gamma function are quite involved, this comparative approach to the accumulative dose calculations is to be preferred.

While the purpose of this presentation is to relate the problems of skeletal dosimetry to the mechanisms of isotope release from bone, a comment about total body retention appears to be in order. Obviously, the loss by exchange of these isotopes from the skeleton must have a bearing on the manner in which the total body loses activity with time. Empirically it has been observed that the change in retention with time is well described by a power function. Perhaps it had better be stated that exchange losses from the skeleton are described by a power function, and that as long as this is the predominant removal process, the total retention can also be

TABLE 2

Comparison of the Values of Accumulated Dose

b	t_s	Case I	Case II	Case IV
-0.2	1	0·78	0·80	1·0
	2	0·77	0·79	1·0
	5	0·73	0·78	1·0
	10	0·68	0·78	1·0
	20	0·60	0·77	1·0
	30	0·52	0·77	1·0
-0.25	1	0·73	0·75	1·0
	2	0·72	0·74	1.0
	5	0·69	0·73	1·0
	10	0·64	0·72	1·0
	20	0·55	0·72	1·0
	30	0·48	0·71	1·0
-0.3	1	0·69	0·70	1·0
	2	0·68	0·70	1·0
	5	0·65	0·69	1·0
	10	0·60	0·68	1·0
	20	0·52	0·67	1·0
	30	0·44	0·66	1·0
-0.35	1	0·63	0·65	1·0
	2	0·62	0·64	1·0
	5	0·59	0·63	1·0
	10	0·55	0·62	1·0
	20	0·47	0·61	1·0
	30	0·40	0·59	1·0
-0.4	1	0·59	0·60	1·0
	2	0·58	0·60	1·0
	5	0·55	0·59	1·0
	10	0·51	0·58	1·0
	20	·44	0·57	1·0
	30	0·37	0·55	1·0

described by such a function. However, when losses by resorption become comparable in magnitude to losses by exchange, then the total retention should be expected to deviate from the power law.

When will this occur? Unfortunately, very few data on the rate of resorption are available. Our radium studies have indicated that resorption rates of the order of 1% per year were required to explain the uniformity of the autoradiographs of human bone sections.[12] Since, after resorption releases activity from bone, a certain fraction of this activity is redeposited, it is evident that the total release of an isotope by resorption will be less than the rate of resorption. It is of interest to note that, after a burden time of 30 years, the release of Ra^{226} from the skeleton is predicted to be of the order of 1·5% per year; at this time loss by resorption has become greater in magnitude than loss by exchange. The total body radium retention of such cases should be followed with the expectation of observing deviations from the power law.

CONCLUSIONS

Alkaline earth isotopes are incorporated into bone by two processes, bone growth and exchange, and lost therefrom by two similar processes, bone resorption and exchange. In the adult animal (dog and man have been specifically studied), exchange processes are the predominant mechanism for the release of these isotopes.

Since these concepts imply that the concentration of an isotope everywhere in bone is decreasing in magnitude with time, the terminal concentration of activity does not characterize the concentration that was present in the identical location at previous times. It is suggested that these changes in concentration may be described by a power function. Calculations have been performed, based on this hypothesis, to indicate how the dose rate at any previous time, and also the total accumulated dose over the entire exposure, can be determined from a terminal observation of the dose to a particular volume of tissue.

REFERENCES

1. R. E. ROWLAND, J. JOWSEY, and J. H. MARSHALL, Structural changes in human bone containing Ra^{226}, Proc. Geneva Conf. on Peaceful Uses of Atomic Energy 22, 242–246, (1958).
2. J. H. MARSHALL, R. E. ROWLAND, and J. JOWSEY, Microscopic metabolism of calcium in bone. V. The paradox of diffuse activity and long term exchange, Radiation Research 10, 258–270 (1959).
3. C. W. MAYS, D. H. TAYSUM, and B. W. GLAD, Bremestrahlung counting of Sr^{90} injected dogs, Health Physic 1, 282–287 (1958).
4. M. A. VAN DILLA, B. J. STOVER, R. L. FLOYD, D. R. ATHERTON, and D. H. TAYSUM, Radium (Ra^{226}) and Radon (Rn^{222}) metabolism in dogs, Radiation Research 8, 417–437 (1958).
5. B. W. GLAD, C. W. MAYS, and W. FISHER, Strontium studies in beagles, Radiation Research 12, 672–681 (1960).
6. R. E. ROWLAND, Argonne National Laboratory Radiological Physic Division Semiannual Report, ANL-6104: 34–47 (July-December, 1959).
7. J. S. ARNOLD, W. S. S. JEE, and K. JOHNSON, Observations and quantitative radioautographic studies of calcium^{45} deposited in vivo in forming Haversian systems and old bone of rabbit, Am. J. Anat. 99, 291–313, (1956).
8. R. E. ROWLAND and J. H. MARSHALL, Radium in human bone: the dose in microscopic volumes of bone, Radiation Research 11, 299–313 (1959).

9. R. E. ROWLAND, Microscopic metabolism of Ra²²⁶ in canine bone and its bearing upon the radiation dosimetry of internally deposited alkaline earths, *Radiation Research* **15**, 126–137 (1961).
10. W. P. NORRIS, T. W. SPECKMAN, and P. F. GUSTAFSON, Studies of the metabolism of radium in man, *Am. J. Roentgenol. Radium Therapy Nuclear Med.* **73**, 785–802 (1955).
11. K. PEARSON, *Tables of the Incomplete Γ-function.* Cambridge University Press, London (1946).
12. R. E. ROWLAND, Late observations of the distribution of radium in the human skeleton, in *Radioisotopes in the Biosphere*, R. S. CALDECOTT and L. S. SNYDER (Eds.) University of Minnesota, Minneapolis (1960).

30*

DISCUSSION

VAUGHAN: It is rather terrifying as a biologist to be discussing dosimetry among all these physicists. Resorption must play a very large part in the bones of the young due to continual remodelling. I just wanted to emphasize this.

Also, I think the question of exchange has only been discussed in relation to the shafts of the long bones. I would very much like to see the same sort of experiments done on the vertebrae, because I think there is a certain amount of physiological evidence that even more exchange takes place there. It appears clinically, that when the body needs calcium, far more is taken from the trabecular bone in the vertebrae than from cortical bone. It would be extremely interesting to see the same studies of long-term exchange applied to vertebral bone. I hope it will be possible to have this done.

ROWLAND: I think this illustrates a very important point which I deliberately by-passed. I have assumed that the rate of exchange was constant everywhere. This is perhaps unjustified. Exchange takes place everywhere, but we certainly haven't measured the rate of exchange at all bone locations. I don't want to promise that we will do it, but it certainly should be done. I think Marv Goldman has some information right here.

GOLDMAN: We have fed a diet with a constant Sr^{90}/Ca ratio to several beagles from the onset of fetal ossification until 18 months of age, at which time the survivors were placed on a non-radioactive diet. Comparison of the Sr^{90}/Ca ratio in sections of the humerus of a dog which had been on the non-radioactive diet for 2 years with the uniformly labelled bones of dogs which had died during the Sr^{90} feeding period showed practically no loss in the humerus shaft (cortical bone) but about 50% loss in a cross-section of the humerus proximal metaphysis (mainly trabecular bone) (M. Goldman et al., Rad. Res. 14, 4, p. 469, 1961). These results indicated that the rate of loss from trabecular bone was much greater than that from cortical bone. However, we can't tell how much of this difference was due to resorption, secondary mineralization, or exchange, and it is quite possible that the high average dose-rate to the skeleton of about 10 rads per day may have influenced these results.

MAYS: We have looked for, but not yet found, a dose-level effect on the total body retention of Sr^{90} out to at least 1000 days after the injection of up to 100 $\mu c/kg$ with the corresponding mean skeletal dose rates at this time (1000 days) of up to about 6 rads per day (C. W. Mays et al., COO-215, see graph on p. 141, March 1958).*

This does not preclude the possibility that radiation accelerates radionuclide removal in some areas while slowing it down in others. In fact we have recent evidence that the biological retention of our alpha emitters is highest in the highest dose-levels. This is particularly true for radium.

The data from the Davis project on their dogs uniformly labelled with Sr^{90} shows a decidedly slower rate of Sr^{90} removal than occurs in Utah dogs of the same age which were given single injections of Sr^{90} as adults.

In view of what Marv has just said, this really makes sense because, when we inject adult animals, the alkaline earth elements go chiefly into regions of new bone for-

---

* Present measurements (C. W. Mays et al., COO-224, Sept. 1961) extending out to 2300 days after injection suggest fractional retention may be very slightly higher in the higher Sr^{90} dose levels. However, this effect, if present, is very small.

mation which means you get more Sr^{90} per gram of trabecular bone than per gram of cortical bone. If the trabecular bone turns over more rapidly, you are going to lose an adult injection at a more rapid rate than you would a uniform label.

STOVER: Is everyone in the group aware of the contrasting pictures that are being compared? When a dog is about 18 month old we put Sr^{90} in it. When a Davis dog is about 18 months old they stop putting the Sr^{90} in it. So, as Marv Goldman has indicated, his dogs begin making cold spots at roughly the same age our dogs form hot spots. So we and the Davis laboratory have approximately mirror-image beagles.

DURBIN: I would like to reinforce what Marv and Chuck have said. We have found that the elimination rate in a monkey which was fed Sr^{90} from 6 weeks of age to 18 months is very much slower than the elimination rate of adolescent monkeys fed Sr^{90} daily for 6 months. Radiation effects can pretty much be ruled out in our feeding experiments because the retained body burden is only about 0·4 μc.

GOLDMAN: I might add, as a postscript here, that our beagles climb Chuck's totem pole. They start as mice and end as dogs.

PART V

THOROTRAST IN MAN

THOROTRAST IN MAN—THE CARRIER STATE
AND THE SEQUELAE

Mogens Faber

Finsenlaboratory Copenhagen, Denmark

A KNOWLEDGE of the natural history of internally deposited radioactive materials in man is a prerequisite for an evaluation of possible health hazards of chronic irradiation. Patients with a body burden of radium have been studied in detail and we have witnessed an increasing understanding of the processes leading to pathological changes.[37,58]

While radium patients are relatively scarce, this is not the case of persons who carry a body burden of thorium. Compared with the knowledge of the radiation history of radium patients there still are, however, important gaps in our understanding of the behaviour of a body burden of thorium in the state of colloidal thorium dioxide, as it was used in diagnostic medicine between 1930 and 1945. The colloid thorium dioxide behaves quite differently from soluble thorium compounds and has some rather complicated redistribution and self-absorption problems which make dosimetry difficult. It may in itself be noxious due to its colloidal nature. Lastly, all persons carrying thorium dioxide in this form have previously been patients, and the mark of the disease for which the thorium was given is on the late pathological findings.

The idea of using the heavy metal thorium as a contrast medium for X-rays goes back to the German ophtalmologist V. Szily,[72,73] who used a suspension of thorium dioxide for X-ray studies of the lacrymal duct in 1914. The great era of thorium came in the thirties when a preparation, thorotrast, became available which could be used intravenously. I shall just mention that the preparation was used for practically all the diagnostic procedures where a soluble contrast medium was needed. Injection into the blood stream could be used to visualize the vascular system, and after deposition of the material, X-ray studies could be made of liver and spleen.

During the last 12 years a group of patients injected with thorotrast has constantly been under observation at the Finsen laboratory. These clinical studies have been supplemented by animal experiments and physical measurements in an attempt to obtain an understanding of the carrier state itself.

The study was initiated by the late Dr. O. M. Henriques and has since been pursued in collaboration with Drs. Charles Johansen, H. H. Zimsen and O. G. Backer on the medical aspects, Mr. C. Trolle as biologist, and Mr. P. G. Jensen, Dr. A. H. Ward and Dr. J. Rundo as physicists. You may be familiar with some of their published works and I shall draw heavily on their experiences. I shall discuss the movements of the thorotrast granules after injection and try to evaluate the carcinogenic risk connected with a body burden. The patients who form the basis of this discussion were neurosurgical patients injected between 1934 and 1946 in Denmark. A total of 834 patients are known to us. Some of these patients have been seen at the laboratory, others are only known by name but we have taken care that information of death in the group will reach us relatively rapidly. It is, however, impossible to assure that we will be notified early enough to be called in for autopsy. It must be remembered that most of the patients are ignorant of their body burden.

The general fate of the group is given in Table 1. In 233 cases the neurosurgical disease has been the cause of death, whereas 481 are living and 120 have died from other diseases. The period of observation and time of death can be seen from Table 2.

TABLE 1

Thorotrast Cases Studied

Dead from neurosurgical diseases	233
Dead from other diseases	120
Living	481
Total	834

The dose of thorotrast given is listed in Table 3. There appears to be no correlation between gross mortality and dosage.

To illustrate some of the disadvantages in the use of thorotrast which are of importance for the delayed effects, I shall give a survey of what might happen when thorotrast is used in direct canalicular pyelography. This type of diagnostic procedure was introduced by Weiser[77] but after a short and extensive use it fell into disrepute. The procedure was best tolerated in the normal kidney. When there was a delay in emptying the renal pelvis, the colloid nature of the contrast solution could be manifest by a precipitation of thorium dioxide, which showed as horizontal surfaces on the X-ray photographs. The precipitated thorotrast made the emptying of the renal pelvis even more difficult. The precipitated contrast

TABLE 2

Length of Observation

Months after thorotrast inj.	Number of patients	
	Living	Dead
0– 20		7
20– 40		4
40– 60		8
60– 80		17
80–100		15
100–120		13
120–140		15
140–160		14
160–180	64	15
180–200	116	3
200–220	78	5
220–240	93	1
240–260	65	2
260–280	50	1
280–300	14	1
300–320	1	

TABLE 3

Dose Distribution

Thorotrast (ml inj.)	Living patients	Dead patients	Cancer&Leuk deaths	Total cases	Dead Total	Cancer Dead
5	5	3	0	8	38%	0%
10	200	51	8	251	20%	16%
20	156	37	6	193	19%	16%
30	36	12	2	48	25%	17%
40	27	4	0	31	13%	0%
over 50	16	5	3	21	24%	60%
unknown	41	8	2	49	16%	25%

medium would generally stick to the surface of the renal pelvis and stay there for years. Of greater importance was the common demonstration of a reflux into the renal tubules or even a break through the epithelium into the vascular system recognizable by a shadow in the veins from the kidney. Passage of the contrast solution to the outside of the kidney was also common, visualized either as a sheet under the capsule or as streaks in the connective tissue around the psoas muscle.

These signs of a disruption of tissue would only be of significance as an acute event if the contrast medium was removable but this was not the case with thorotrast. The bulk of the substance remained at the place of injection and only small amounts were shifted by the lymphatics to the regional lymph glands. The fate of the part that penetrated into the vascular system shall be discussed later.

This pattern of unintentional deposition of thorotrast is known for all the procedures involving an intracanalicular use and the same pattern will be seen when the solution is injected perivenously by accident.

When thorotrast is brought directly into the interstitial tissues it will be taken up rapidly by macrophages and surrounded by fibroblasts which later will produce the dense sclerotic tissues, the so-called thorotrastomas, in which the thorotrast remains. Clinical experiences give the impression that the sclerosis grows to a certain size and then tends to remain relatively constant. Complications such as nerve compression will appear after a few years and will remain unchanged once established. When the sclerotic tissue is studied years after the injection, the thorotrast granules are mostly found intracellularly in phagocytotic cells and are easily recognized from their yellow granules. When the amount is large a part may be found free in the tissue and the same is the case if there is necrosis in the deposits.

An important question raised by these thorotrastomas is the mechanism of their development. Three types of toxic effects can be envisaged from thorotrast. One is due to the presence of the heavy metal in the granules, another is the physical influence of the thorium dioxide granules themselves, and thirdly, the radiation from the thorium and its daughters. I will not be able to go into detail with a discussion of the relative importance of these three aspects of thorotrast. Only one important point should be mentioned. The daughter products of thorium have a tendency to leave the colloid and a wash out by the blood stream can be demonstrated in many tissues. Measurements performed by Rundo[61] on a piece of thorotrastoma surgically removed from the neck showed, however, no buildup. This demonstrated that the decay products stayed close to the granules in this type of tissue, probably due to avascularity.

When the colloid is left in contact with tissue in this way there may be a risk for the development of malignant tumors, where one or more of the three above-mentioned toxic effects may be active.

Table 4 gives a list of the published cases where a malignant tumor was found in the tissues surrounding a thorotrast deposit. From such a series of clinical observations it is difficult to evaluate the importance

TABLE 4

Cancers Occuring after the Interstitial Deposition of Thorotrast (as reported in the literature)

Type of thorotrast study	Sex	Age at injection (years)	Latent period (years)	Cancer Recognition		Type of tumor	Reference
				Age (years)	Date		
Maxillary Sinus	F	53	11	64	1951	Squamous cell carcinoma	(30)
,,	M	36	15	51	1955	Spindle cell carcinoma	(25)
,,	F	14	18	32	1955	Adeno carcinoma	(35)
,,	M	18	21	39	1956	Squamous cell carcinoma	(35)
,,	M	57	13	70	1958	Mucoepidermoid carcinoma	(35)
Lacrymal duct	M	16	35	51	1948	Squamous cell carcinoma	(59 & 60)
Mammography	F	26	17	43	1954	Scirrhous cancer	(9 & 11)
,,	F	21	19	40	1957	Cancer	(6)
Direct pyelography	M	48	16	64	1949	Spindle cell carcinoma	(82)
,,	F	—	—	60	1955	Hypernephroma	(48)
,,	M	—	—	75	1956	Cancer	(10)
Bronchography	M	—	18	—	1950	Bronchogenic carcinoma	(76)
Ureterography	M	52	15	67	1955	Cancer of seminal vesicles	(21)
Salpingography	F	22	23	45	1955	Cancer of ovary	(68)
Fistulography (coecum)	F	44	16	60	1955	Sarcoma	(65)
,, (lung)	M	24	12	36	1956	Bronchogenic carcinoma	(78 & 55)
,, (liver)	M	22	15	37	1959	Bile duct carcinoma	(4)
A-graphy. Neck deposit.	F	49	5	54	1952	Fibrosarcoma	(50)

of interstitial thorotrast as a carcinogenic agent. The location of the tumors, however, in places where carcinomas are rare, such as the lacrymal duct or maxillary sinus, supports the carcinogenity of thorotrast. In our own series with carotic angiography[3] we found that about 10% had perivascular deposits which agrees with other findings.[34] We have seen no malignancies in cases of carotid angiography and the literature reports only one case, a sarcoma, in this location.[50] If the thorotrast after canalicular injection was deposited in connective tissue, sarcomas would be the type of tumor to be expected; but these injections have mostly given rise to carcinomas, an interesting finding for which no detailed analysis can be given so far.

In a very large group of patients the thorotrast has been given intravascularly and this mode of entrance into the organism gives rise to completely new questions.

According to the studies of Ch. Johansen,[32, 33] the thorium dioxide granules lose their protective dextran immediately after injection and are then treated by a mechanism related to the one described by Knisely[36] with the result that they are rapidly deposited in phagocytizing cells. The initial deposition is complete in less than 24 hours and most of the thorium is found in liver, spleen and bone marrow. However, the lungs, kidneys, intestines, adrenals and lymph nodes take up a considerable amount of thorotrast. This primary deposition is, however, only of short duration. Histological studies show that some of the tissues like the kidneys lose their thorotrast granules quite rapidly. In other tissues like the liver there is a rearrangement inside the organ. Thorotrast moves from a diffuse pattern towards the central vein, and at the same time an increasing deposition takes place around the portal veins. This redistribution in the liver and also in the spleen is easily seen on X-ray pictures of these organs. Due to the redistribution the homogeneous X-ray picture becomes increasingly spotty and in some cases all of the thorium has collected in a small part of the organ. After 15 months, chemical analysis by Ch. Johansen[32] has shown signs of further redistribution among organs with an increase in the liver and a decrease in spleen. In human measurements, Rundo[62] has drawn attention to the difference between his cases measured some 10–15 years after injection with 17% of the thorium in the spleen against results of Looney et al.[31, 38] who found 7% in 4 cases of which 2 were studied less than 2 months after injection. The external radiation measurements of Rundo have the advantage that they will be relatively uninfluenced by local inequalities in distribution. If thorium is determined chemically care must be taken to assure that the sample is representative. We have ourselves met with such difficulties and Looney et al.[31, 38] must have had the same problems with the small samples available. We feel that the differences in the two spleen studies so far must be considered inconclusive.

In the following we should like to discuss the mechanism of this redistribution, the place where the thorium must end and some implications on dosimetry and pathology. The details of the redistribution have been studied experimentally only during the first month, but a reasonable picture of the long-term changes can be inferred from what is seen histologically in thorotrast injected animals and in patients carrying thorotrast.

There is reason to consider that two partly separate mechanisms must be active in the redistribution.

The first is the intracellular transport where phagocytic cells containing large amounts of thorotrast move via the blood stream from one place inside an organ to another inside the same organ or from organ to organ. Histological studies quite often show these cells free in the vessels of liver and spleen or in the sinusoids of the spleen. The previously mentioned early redistribution from the liver lobules to the central vein and then to the portal vein would fit this type of movement. This is, however, not a type of transport to be found only in the early stages of redistribution. In a spleen removed surgically 10 years after injection, free cells were found abundantly in vessels and sinusoids.

This intracellular transport must, however, be supplemented by another route of movements. The number and volume of granules collected in one phagocytic cell is quite large. If we calculate the chances of hitting the nucleus of the phagocytic cell with an α-particle from Th^{232} in the granules and consider this event fatal for the cell, the mean lifespan for the cell is 1 month or less. In tissue like the liver where the phagocytic cells mostly are placed in relation to the blood stream it must be envisaged that the dead cells will lose at least part of their granules into the blood stream. After circulation with the blood the granules will be rephagocytized by new cells in liver or elsewhere. Easton[15] has seen these dying Kupffer cells losing the granules but did not see the emptying into the blood stream.

That the granules may move freely even late after injection can be supported by microscopic studies of tumors in patients carrying thorotrast. The presence of thorotrast in interstitial macrophages is not uncommon. Of greater interest is the presence of granules in the tumor cells themselves. This has been described in tumors connected with local depositions by Schwaiger[67] and Schwenzer and Federlin[68] and in an hemangioendothelioma by Da Silva Horta[70] after previous intravenous thorotrast injection. If artefacts can be excluded this supports the particulate transport.

In Fig. 1 I have tried to give an impression of these two mechanisms in the left half of the figure. If the redeposition continues as described the thorotrast will continuously be moving but will histologically appear as if it remained passive in the deposits. As we shall see, this is not the complete description.

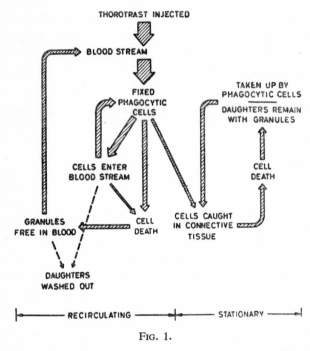

Fig. 1.

A schematic representation of the redistribution of thorotrast after its initial deposition has been completed.

If the cells containing thorium or the thorium granules in the blood are taken up by phagocytic cells in a relative avascular tissue like the connective tissue bands in liver they may be trapped. This localization of thorotrast is seen macroscopically in many cases in human liver and when the deposits are large there is a tendency for the connective tissue to proliferate moderately. The thorium will be present in phagocytic cells, and free granules will also be encountered.

The spleen represents an interesting example of this fixation of thorotrast. With time there is a steady decrease in the cells in the pulp and finally the thorium granules will be trapped in an organ consisting only of connective tissue from the trabecular structure. When the organ is studied early in this process it is difficult to accept that an increase in connective tissue has taken place but no acceptable quantitative estimation is available.

As mentioned earlier there is a wash out of daughter products from the dep osits into the blood. This wash out can most easily be demonstrated by the buildup of radioactivity after removal of an organ from the body (Rundo[61,62]). The daughter which is of greatest interest is Ra^{228} (MsTh I) with a half-life of about 5·8 years. This decay product tends to leave the thorium dioxide granules and may be found in large quantities on the walls of old ampules of thorotrast. The perpetual redistribution of the granules would facilitate the exchange of the daughters from the granules to blood and then to other tissues.

The steady but slow deposition of thorotrast into relatively avascular tissue must influence both the radioactivity of the deposits and the wash out. This effect could be measured as a decrease in wash out of daughter products and in an increase in local γ-activity.

If we calculate from Rundo[62] the relation between thorotrast body burden calculated on the basis of thoron in breath as an expression for free decay products and on the basis of γ–activity of liver and spleen as an expression of the retention we find that this factor decreases with time (Fig. 2) as would be expected from the model suggested.

The behaviour of thorotrast in the liver is dominated by two quite different pathogenic mechanisms. From the clinical literature it is evident that a fibrosis containing thorotrast is a common occurrence, that this fibrosis may be in the form of classical cirrhosis but more frequently is a more discrete process in the larger periportal spaces and especially in the connective tissue bands in the anterior edge of the liver. A mechanism for the appearance of thorium in these perhaps increased fibrous bands in the normal liver has been discussed.

It would, however, be interesting to study what happens when connective tissue is produced from reasons unconnected with thorotrast. Roholm et al.[52] has shown by liver biopsy studies that some cases of cirrhosis start with a widespread cellular necrosis. From the surviving tissue new liver cells will then be produced. The thorium present should under these circumstances be trapped in the scar tissue following the necrosis and should stay here. Animal experiments to study this suggestion are under way in our laboratory. This course of events gives an acceptable explanation for the well known fact that when cirrhosis and

31

thorotrast are found in the same liver, most of the thorium will be visible in the sclerotic bands.

Case histories with this coincidence are relatively common and a pathogenic dependency can not be excluded offhand. It must, however, be remembered that some of these patients were injected with thorotrast to visualize the liver because of clinical symptoms, of which some may

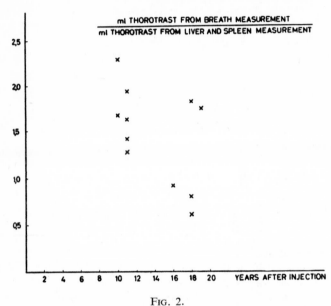

Fig. 2.

When thorotrast is deposited in fibrous tissue the decay products will stay with the granules. This should give a decrease in the factor plotted.

have been early [signs of cirrhosis. The coincidence of a disease which required thorotrast injection with a hepatic disease may not be too rare in places and at times where chronic hepatic damage is common. The material published by Fruhling[18] illustrates this. Eight of his cases have clinical or histological signs of cirrhosis but at least three had ample reason for the cirrhosis without taking thorotrast into account, and we have only very meager clinical information on which to judge. The single case of cirrhosis in the Danish material is a 45 year old woman who appears to belong in the post-war group of subacute hepatitis where the mortality without thorotrast was close to 100%. Taking the yearly mortality of cirrhosis of liver in France to be 32·5/100,000 persons[2] against a Danish mortality of 8·4/100,000 persons, the increase in the number of cirrhotic cases in French material is not unexpected.

TABLE 5

Hepatic and Bile Duct Carcinomas in Thorotrast Patients

Reason for thorotrast injection	Dose (ml)	Sex	Age at injection (years)	Latent period (years)	Cancer recognition		Cirrhosis	Type of tumor	Reference
					Age (years)	Date			
Hepatogram	80	F	33	20	53	1950		Primary liver cell C.	(42)
,,	—	F	29	20	40	1951	+	Bile duct C.	(49)
,,	70	F	31	23	52	1954	+	Cholangioma	(43)
,,	—	F	24	24	48	1956		Primary liver cell C.	(45)
,,	75	—	—	9	—	—		Bile duct C.	(75)
A-graphy	—	M	45	12	58	1953	+	Hepatoma	(5)
,,	—	M	30	24	54	1954	+	Hepatoma	(26)
,,	—	M	24	13	37	1955		Primary liver cell C.	(16)
,,	—	F	23	24	47	1957	+	Bile duct C.	(22)
,,	—	—	42	19	61	1957		Bile duct C.	(6)
,,	—	F	26	17	43	1958		Primary hepatic neoplasm	(37)
,,	20	F	47	22	69	1960		Bile duct C.	Own Ser.

31*

484 M. FABER

Whether thorotrast will augment the sclerosis in a liver with a cirrhotic process is probable but unconfirmed.

With this interpretation of the cirrhotic changes in thorotrast patients it is of interest to study the published cases of carcinoma of the liver, either of hepatic or of bile duct origin. The published 9 cases have been collected in Table 5 together with a single case from the Danish series. Excluded from this table is 1 case where the thorotrast was used to visualize an abscess in the liver and 2 cases where a cancer was found in the extrahepatic bile ducts. The number is insignificant compared to the number of persons injected intravenously with thorotrast and must be considered too small to demonstrate a carcinogenic effect of thorotrast on the cells of liver or bile ducts. That some of these patients also were suffering from a cirrhosis of the liver must make the significance of thorotrast even smaller.

The opposite result is the case if we take a classical thorotrast tumor, the hemangioendothelioma of the liver (Table 6). This tumor, a rarity in human clinical experience, was first described in a thorotrast case by MacMahon et al.[41] The Danish material does not contain any case of this tumor. The descriptions are quite identical from case to case. The tumor has also been produced experimentally by intravenous injection in mice. The connection between thorotrast and this neoplasm is well established.

TABLE 6

Hemangioendotheliomas in Thorotrast Patients

(as reported in the literature)

Dose (ml.)	Sex	Age at injection (years)	Latent period (years)	Cancer recognition		Reference
				Age (yr)	Date	
75	F	58	12	70	1946	(41)
20	F	—	3	—	1949	(70)
—	M	37	12	49	1952	(19)
24	F	—	15	—	1953	(40)
—	M	24	22	46	1954	(69)
72	—	29	23	52	1955	(39)
—	M	40	14	54	1955	(74)
75	M	37	24	61	1956	(23)
—	M	38	20	58	1956	(12)
80	M	37	24	49	1956	(53)

As always there are a number of possibilities in the interpretation of available data. The origin of the tumor is generally accepted to be the endothelial cells including the Kupffer cells. These are the cells where the thorotrast is deposited, and accordingly both the radioactivity and the physical–chemical influence of the colloid can be taken into account. The chemical or particulate influence of intracellularly deposited thorotrast appears to be relatively insignificant according to experience in other deposits. In support of the chemical interpretation we mention that chronic arsenic poisoning as described by Roth[56] has given rise to tumors of the same type. It must be mentioned that his patients came from a population with a high cancer frequency and an especially high incidence of pulmonary and skin cancer, and that all three of his patients had a complicating cirrhosis of the liver.

That the radioactivity is of significance for the genesis of these tumors is more broadly supported. The tumor is known to occur after neutron irradiation in mice as described by Neary et al.[46] and a single case of a complex radium poisoning complicated by this tumor has been described by Ross.[54] The evidence thus favours an irradiation genesis.

Unfortunately we do not know anything of the incidence or dose dependence of this tumor. In only 6 cases was the dosage reported, and this varied from 20 to 80 ml. The latent period is interesting in being short in one of the cases but otherwise varying from 12 to 24 years. In the Danish material of close on 800 cases and in the Swedish material of about 1200 cases no such tumor has been seen. Thus the relative incidence of this type of tumor in the population of thorotrast carrying persons is probably small.

We shall end this part of the review with a discussion of the probability of getting cancer at any other unspecified place. The list from the literature is ridiculously small, consisting of only 10 cases. This is smaller than the comparable list from the Danish cases (see Table 7). Other cases probably have not appeared in the literature because they were considered as being without interest.

In other cases the presence of thorotrast has been unrecognized. It will be evident from the tables that 1955 was the critical year when most of the thorotrast tumors appeared. In our evaluation we therefore only use the systematic surveys. So far four surveys are available with a rather different approach to the problem and accordingly different results.

The survey by Thomas, Henry and Kaplan[75] where radiologists were asked to give information on known sequelae to the use of thorium is interesting because of the small number of late pathological findings rec-

TABLE 7

Internal Tumors Outside the Liver after Intravenous Injection of Thorotrast
(as reported in the literature)

Type of study	Dose (ml.)	Sex	Age at injection (years)	Latent period (years)	Cancer recognition		Type of tumor	Reference
					Age (years)	Date		
Hepatography	75	F	42	16	58	1948	Alveolar cell carcinoma	(1)
"	—	M	19	20	39	1952	Cancer of duct. choledocus	(28)
A-graphy	—	M	52	15	67	1953	Cancer recti	(16)
"	—	M	64	16	75	1954	Bronchogenic carcinoma	(27)
"	—	M	56	13	69	1955	Pancreatic and renal cancer	(81)
Hepatography	—	M	19	24	43	1955	Bronchogenic carcinoma	(48)
A-graphy	—	F	28	17	45	1955	Cancer duct. hepatis	(51)
?	—	F	—	—	65	1956	Cancer coli	(11)
A-graphy	—	M	38	19	57	1957	Bronchogenic carcinoma	(79)
"	—	F	50	15	65	1957	Giant follicular lymphoma	(22)
"	—	—	34	15	49	—	Laryngeal cancer	(20)
"	—	—	—	—	—	—	Gastric cancer	(7)
"	—	—	—	—	—	—	Cancer of oral cavity	"
"	—	—	—	—	—	—	Bronchogenic carcinoma	"

orded. The long lapse in time between injection and induced disease is a perfect reason for this discrepancy.

The series studied by Looney[39] was selected to give other information. Interesting is the study by Berrett and McRae.[7] Among 136 patients with previous arteriography they found 3 malignant tumors; one in the oral cavity, one gastric cancer and one pulmonary cancer. All were considered as unconnected with thorotrast.

The causes of death in the 120 patients of the Danish series who died from causes not directly connected with the neurosurgical disease for which they were injected can be separated into non-malignant and malignant types. The non-malignant are listed in Table 8. Apart from the high incidence of suicide, which probably was indirectly dependent on the cause for the arteriography, the diseases listed are the ones to be expected in any comparable group of patients.

TABLE 8

Non-Malignant Deaths* Apart from Neurosurgical Diseases

Arteriosclerotic heart diseases	30
Other heart diseases	3
Suicide	22
Cerebral hemorrhage	15
Gastro intestinal diseases	8
Accidents	6
Renal diseases	3
Infections	4
Cirrhosis	1
Thorotrastoma of neck	1
Hemolytic anemia (sideroblastosis)	1
Other causes	5
Total	99

* These deaths were not connected with the conditions for which thorotrast was injected.

The cancers are listed in Table 9 by organ system and again the distribution would correspond to expectancy in a general population of the same age and sex. In 1953, at the time of writing a report on the thorotrast problem as seen from the Finsen Institute, Dr. O. M. Henriques made a calculation on the expected total number of cancers in the years to come in the group then under study. The result can be seen in Fig. 3 compared with the total number of cancers found during these years.

TABLE 9

Death from Cancer or Leukemia

Cancer	intestinal tract	3
	gen. int. fem.	2
	mammary	1
	pulm. + pleura	4
	bile ducts	1
	kidneys*	1
	metastatic	4
	thymoma	1
Leukemia	chronic myeloid	1
	acute	3
	Total	21

* Accidental finding at autopsy in patient who died from "neurosurgical" disease.

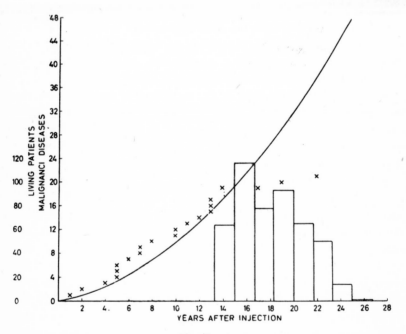

FIG. 3.

Cumulative number of cancer cases versus years after thorotrast injection in the Danish thorotrast patients as of 1961. The observed totals are shown by crosses, whereas the predicted totals expected in a normal Danish population of the same size and age distribution are shown by the smooth curve. The numbers of living thorotrast patients at various times after injection are shown in histogram form. All patients have been at risk for at least 14 years, and up to this time (14 years) the observed numbers of cancer cases agrees well with those predicted.

So much time has passed that we now are able to calculate the status for the first 14 years. As you will see this does not look very dangerous. The calculated total number of cancers expected in the group should be 17·2 cases and the finding is somewhere around 18 cases.

In this group of mixed cases there are two types worth mentioning. An increase of pulmonary carcinomas above the expected could appear reasonable according to the studies of Chamberlain[13] and the dose calculation of Rundo et al.[63] In the Danish material there is, however, only the number to be expected according to a rough estimation taking age and sex and time of observation into consideration.

The other problem which we shall hear more about later this evening from Dr. Marinelli is the effect thorotrast might have on the production of bone cancer. I can only point out that the literature does not so far contain one single case of osseous or periosteal tumor in a patient injected with thorotrast and no such case has been met within the Danish material. The gradual way in which the Ra^{228} is produced would according to my expectations, preclude the production of bone cancer. Furthermore the proposed model for deposition of granules would result in a decrease in the availability to bone of Ra^{228} with increasing time.

We still have the problem of the occurrence of bone marrow diseases as a last field for discussion. I shall start with some words on the leukemias proper as they occur in the literature and as we have seen them in our series and then give a short review of the problems of the other hematological diseases registered as being due to thorotrast.

If we use the published case histories, the leukemias behave as most of the previously mentioned malignancies in thorotrast patients. They are most remarkable for their low incidence. The literature on thorotrast contains only 10 cases of leukemia and out of these, 4 belong in our own series. To give you an impression of the problems connected with the evaluation of these cases, I shall discuss them at some detail. They are listed in Table 10 and you will see that out of the four, only one, a case of chronic myeloid leukemia, is completely straightforward. When we turn to the three cases of acute leukemia the interpretation of the data becomes increasingly difficult. In case No. 242 the patient was treated with therapeutic doses of X-rays years before the leukemia appeared. He was an epileptic and received for this reason different antiepileptic drugs such as mesantion and dimedione. The significance of this medication can best be illustrated by the fact that his case history was published as a case of leukemia induced by these drugs. Of the two last cases one received X-ray treatment at a relatively early time before leukemia, and the other received the

TABLE 10

Leukemia in Thorotrast Patients

Type of injection	Dose ml	Sex	Age at injection (years)	Latent period (years)	Leukemia recognition		Type of leukemia	X-ray treatment	Epilepsia	Reference
					Age (years)	Date				
Hepatography	—	—	—	7	—	—	Acute			(80)
A-graphy	—	M	43	—	51	1950	Acute		+	(16 and 24)
,,	—	—	—	11	—	1952	Acute			(29)
,,	—	F	—	15	—	1954	Acute			(16)
	50	—	52	23	75	1954	Chron. myeloid.			(47)
Hepatography	48	M	38	14	52	1953	Acute	1944–1946	+	Own Series
A-graphy	—	F	11	8	19	1954	Acute		+	,,
	20	M	54	10	64	1954	Chron. myeloid.	1938	+	,,
	50	F	34	18	51	1955	Acute		+	,,

above-mentioned antiepileptic drugs. Accordingly these last three cases are of questionable value to demonstrate a connection between the thorotrast and leukemia.

To study this relationship we have to have recourse to patients who were injected for reasons where these interfering events were avoided. The best choice will probably be a series of cases injected for peripheral vascular diseases.

In the literature there are a number of publications on hematologic disorders, often related to leukemias where thorotrast has been suggested as the provoking agent.[8, 14, 42, 44, 64, 66, 71] In our series we have three such cases. A man with an aplastic anemia who died after many blood transfusions, a woman with myelosclerosis and a man with agranulocytosis, who died from an empyema.

It is difficult to correlate these disorders with the leukemias on one hand, and even more difficult to find the connection to the presence of thorotrast. They may simply represent a coincidence where perhaps the presence of thorotrast has accelerated the disease.

If we shall end by giving a recapitulation of this survey it becomes clear that out of the five groups of malignant diseases seen in patients injected with thorotrast only in two can we claim support for a pathogenic connection. The hemangioendotheliomas are undoubtedly due to thorotrast. It might be suggested that the proliferation of Kupffer cells sometimes seen histologically and which is to be expected from the continuous recirculation can represent part of the carcinogenic mechanism.

The local deposits resulting from canalicular injection are often followed by tumors. This would also fit with the permanency of the deposits and with a probability for higher radioactivity due to low wash out of daughter activity, as is known for the neck deposits.

The deposits in liver, spleen and bone marrow appear quite peaceful as far as carcinogenesis is concerned. This could be expected when the transitory character of the deposits is taken into account. The cells will only be irradiated for a short time, that is with a low dose, and this dose is decreased by the continuous wash out of daughter products at least during recirculation.

It is of interest to study the latent period between thorotrast injection and development of cancer. Only few have a latent period below 10 years and as can be seen from Fig. 4, there is no difference in the latent period for the different locations of malignant tumors.

If we look into the future the picture may be less comforting. The tendency for the thorotrast granules to find a permanent deposit and one where the decay products have a restricted chance for leaving must change the outlook for tumor induction. We must, however, envisage that these tumors will appear at a later time because the latent period will be lengthened by the time it will take for the deposits to be collected.

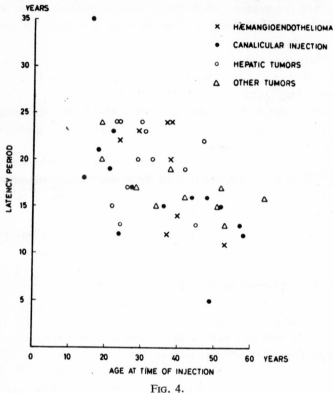

The latent period from the injection of thorotrast to the recognition of cancer according to published cases.

Only the leukemias should behave otherwise. If the Danish experiences are representative, the relative number of new cases should decline with time if an X-ray exposure early during the deposition was the most important leukemogenic factor in the cases which have occurred.

SUMMARY

Colloidal thorium dioxide has under the trade name, thorotrast, been used as a contrast medium for X-ray studies requiring intracanalicular or intravascular injection. After intracanalicular injection, the thorotrast stays at the place of injection and appears to be carcinogenic there. Injected into the blood stream thorotrast will be deposited in phagocytic cells. Immediately a redistribution is started and this will continue for years while an increasing amount of thorotrast will collect in connective tissue. The complicated mechanism of this redistribution has been discussed and the influence on release of thorium daughter products to the blood stream and on carcinogenesis is described on the basis of histological studies and the experiences from a group of 842 patients injected with thorotrast and followed for more than 14 years.

REFERENCES

1. L. ABRAHAMSON, M. H. O'CONNOR and M. L. ABRAHAMSON, Bilateral alveolar lung carcinoma associated with the injection of thorotrast, *Irish J. Med. Sci.* **294**, 229 (1950).

2. ANONYMOUS, Cirrhosis of the liver in France, *W.H.O. Chronicle* **14**, 470 (1960).

3. O. G. BACKER, M. FABER and H. RASMUSSEN, Local sequelae to carotid angiography with colloid thorium dioxide, *Acta Clin. Scand.* **115**, 417 (1958).

4. R. BASERGA, H. YOKOO and G. C. HENEGAR, Thorotrast induced cancer in man, *Can. er* **13**, 1021 (1960).

5. A. BATZENSCHLAGER and E. WILHELM, Cancer primitif de la travée hépatique sur cirrhose thorotrastique, *Ann. Anatomie pathol.* **2**, 39 (1957).

6. K. H. BAUER, Aktuelle Krebsfragen, *Arch. Klin. Chir.* **287**, 19 (1957).

7. A. BERRETT and D. L. McRAE, A follow-up study after thorotrast carotid arteriography, *Can. Med. Ass. J.* **78**, 916 (1958).

8. R. BIRKNER, Die Spätschaden des Thorotrasts beurteilt nach dem ältesten bishier bekannten Thorotrastschadenfall, *Strahlentherapie* **78**, 587 (1949).

9. H. BRODY and M. CULLEN, Carcinoma of the breast seventeen years after mammography with thorotrast, *Surgery* **42**, 600 (1957).

10. FR. BOEMKE, Thorotrastschaden der Nieren, *Zblt. Allg. Path. u. Path. Anat.* **95**, 464 (1956).

11. E. BUDIN and J. GERSHON-COHEN, The danger of cancer from thorotrast as a diagnostic medium, *Am. J. Roentgenol.* **75**, 1188 (1956).

12. J. CAROLI, J. ETEVE, R. PLATTEBORSE and P. FALLOT, Thorotrast et hemangioreticulom malin du foie, *Revue médico-chirurgiale des maladies du foie de la rate* **31**, 53 (1956).

13. A. C. CHAMBERLAIN and E. D. DYSEN, The dose to the trachea and bronchi from the decay products of radon and thoron, *Brit. J. Radiol.* **29**, 317 (1956).

14. G. W. DUANE, Aplastic anemia fourteen years following administration of thorotrast, *Am. J. Med.* **23**, 499 (1957).

15. T. W. EASTON, The role of macrophage movements in the transport and elimination of intravenous thorium in mice, *Am. J. Anat.* **90**, 1 (1952).

16. K. FEDERLIN and H. SCIOR, Spätschaden und Tumorentwicklung nach Thorotrast, *Frankf. Z. Pathol.* **68**, 225 (1957).

17. R. FONTAINE and C. M. GROS, Contribution à l'étude des dangers de la thorotrasto-artériographie à l'occasion d'un cas de cirrhose hépatique tardive, *Presse Med.* **62**, 970 (1954).

494   M. FABER

18. L. FRUHLING, C. M. GROS, A. BATZENSCHLAGER and M. DORNER, La maladie du thorotrast, *Ann. de Médecine* **57**, 409 (1956).

19. L. FRUHLING, C. M. GROS and A. BATZENSCHLAGER, Sacome endothelial angioplastique généralisé chez un malade ayant subi 12 ans auparavant d'une injection intra-artérielle et para-artérielle de thorotrast, *Bull. du Cancer* **42**, 559 (1955).

20. F. FUGAZZOLA, A proposito di donni tardivi da thorotrast, *Arch. Radiol.* (Naples) **28**, 504 (1954). Zit. *Exerpta Medica; Radiology* **9**, 205 (1955).

21. J. GELZER and S. SCHEIDEGGER, Samenblasenkarzinom, *Oncologia* **12**, 27 (1959).

22. D. L. GARDNER and R. F. OGILVIE, The late results of injection of thorotrast. Two cases of neoplastic disease following contrast angiography, *J. Path. a. Bact.* **78**, 133 (1959).

23. G. GRAMPS and A. T. DEGNA, Hemangioendothelioma of the liver following intravenous injection of thorotrast, *Acta gen. et stat, medic.* **8**, 65–78 (1958).

24. S. F. GREBE, Beitrag zur Frage der Thorotrastspätschädigung. Eine myeloische Leukamie nach diagnostischer Thorotrastapplication, *Strachlentherapie* **94**, 311 (1954).

25. C. M. GROS, L. FRUHLING and R. KEILING, Injection de thorotrast dans le sinus maxillaire 15 ans après: Apparition d'un épithéliome malin, *Bull. Ass. franç. du Cancer* **42**, 556 (1955).

26. A. GROSSIORD, J. C. ROUCAYROL, B. DUPERRAT, P. F. CECCALDI and L. MEEUS-BITH, Adenocancer du foie avec cirrhose 21 ans après un artériographie au thorotrast, *Bull. et Mém. Soc. Hôp. Paris* **72**, 49 (1956).

27. P. HACKENTHAL, Beitrag zu den morphologischen Veränderungen durch Thorotrastablagerungen, *Zblt. Allg. Path. u. Path. Anat.* **94**, 352 (1955).

28. W. HEITMANN, Carcinom des Gallengangs und der Leber nach Thorotrastinjection, *Chirurg.* **25**, 223 (1954).

29. G. HIERONYMI and S. SANDKUHLER, Knochenmarkinsuffizienz 11 Jahre nach Thorotrastapplication, *Deutsch. Arch. klin. Med.* **200**, 561 (1953).

30. O. HOFER, Kieferhohlen-karzinom durch radiumhaltiges Kontrastimittel hervorgerufen, *Deutsch. Zahnärztliche Zeitschr.* **7**, 736 (1952).

31. J. B. HURSH, L. T. STEADMAN, W. B. LOONEY and M. COLODZIN, The excretion of thorium and thorium daughters after thorotrast administration, *Acta Radiol.* **47**, 481 (1957).

32. CH. JOHANSEN, The fate of thorotrast in blood, *Finsen Laboratory Report*, 1953.

33. CH. JOHANSEN, Histological changes in man and rabbits after parenteral thorium administration. BACQ and ALEXANDER, Ed., Butterworth Sci. Pub., London, 1955, p. 358.

34. H. KARCHER, Über Thorotrastschaden, *Arch. klin. Chir.* **261**, 459 (1949).

35. M. KLIGERMAN, R. LATTES and R. RANKOW, Carcinoma of the maxillary sinus following thorotrast installation, *Cancer* **13**, 967 (1960).

36. M. H. KNISELY, Annotated bibliography on sludged blood, *Postgrad. Med.* **10**, 15. a. 80 (1951).

37. W. B. LOONEY, R. J. HASTERLIK, A. M. BRUES and E. SKIRMONT, A clinical investigation of the chronic effects of radium salts administered therapeutically (1915–1931), *Am. J. Roentgenol.* **73**, 1006 (1955).

38. W. B. LOONEY, J. B. HURSH, V. E. ARCHER, L. T. STEADMAN and M. COLODZIN, A summary of radium and thorium excretion in humans, *Proc. Internal. Conf. Peaceful Use Atom. Energy*, Vol. 11, p. 55 (1956).

39. W. B. Looney, An investigation of the late clinical findings following thorotrast (thorium dioxide) administration, *Am. J. Roentgenol.* **83**, 163 (1960).

40. M. Ludin, Hämangio-endotheliomatose von Leber und Miltz bei Thorotrastspeicherung, *Schw. Z. Allg. Path. u. Bact.* **16**, 987 (1953). ¡

41. H. E. MacMahon, A. S. Murphy and M. I. Bates, Endothelial cell sarcoma of liver following thorotrast injections, *Am. J. Path.* **23**, 585 (1947).

42. T. Matthes, Thorotrastschaden und Krebsgefahr, *Arch. Geschwulst. Forsch.* **6**, 162 (1954).

43. T. Matthes, Zur Frage der Entstehung eines Carcinoms auf dem Boden einer Thorotrast-Narbenleber, *Strahlentherapie* **99**, 94 (1956).

44. S. Moeschlin, H. R. Marti and W. Germann, Totliche Panmyelopathie durch Thorotrast (thorium dioxide), *Schweiz. Med. Wochschr.* **83**, 1061 (1953).

45. A. D. Morgan, W. H. W. Jayne and D. Marrack, Primary liver cell carcinoma 24 years after intravenous injection of thorotrast, *J. Clin. Path.* **11**, 7 (1958).

46. G. J. Neary, R. J. Munson and R. H. Mole, *Chronic radiation hazards.* Pergamon Press London, 1957.

47. M. Netousek, J. Bores and K. Dvorak, Chronic myelosis following the use of Thorotrast, *Blood* **12**, 391 (1957).

48. G. Nielsen and J. Kracht, Zur Cancerogenese nach diagnostischer Thorotrastanwendung, *Frankf. Z. Pathologie* **68**, 661 (1958).

49. S. Okinaka, K. Nakao, H. Ibayashi, M. Nakaidzumi, H. Kakehi and T. Sugimura, A case report on the development of biliary tract cancer eleven years after the injection of thorotrast, *Am. J. Roentgen.* **78**, 812 (1957).

50. K. Plenge and K. Kruckemeyer, Über ein Sarcom am Ort der Thorotrastinjection, *Zblt. Allg. Path. u. Path. Anat.* **92**, 255 (1954).

51. J. C. Roberts and K. E. Carlson, Hepatic duct carcinoma seventeen years after injection of thorium dioxide, *A.M.A. Arch. Path.* **62**, 1 (1956).

52. K. Roholm, N. B. Krarup and P. Iversen, Aspirationsbiopsie der Leber, *Ergebn. inn. Med.* **61**, 635 (1942).

53. F. J. Rosenbaum, Lebersarcom nach Thorotrast, *Deutsch. Med. Wschr.* **84**, 428 (1959).

54. I. M. Ross, A case illustrating the effects of prolonged action of radium, *J. Path. a. Bact.* **35**, 899 (1932).

55. Roth, Thorotrastkarzinom der Bronchien, *Zblt. Allg. Path. u. Path. Anat.* **96**, 417 (1957).

56. F. Roth, Über die chronische Arsenvergiftung der Moselwinzer unter besonderer Berücksichtigung des Arsenkrebses, *Zschr. für Krebsforsch.* **61**, 287 (1956).

57. W. Rotter, Über Gewebsschaden durch Thorotrast. Unter besonderer Berücksichtigung der Gefassveränderungen und aplastischer Knochenmarksreactionen, *Beitr. Path. Anat. u. Allg. Path.* **111**, 144 (1951).

58. R. W. Rowland, J. Jowsey and J. H. Marshall, Structural changes in human bone containing Ra^{226}, *2nd U.N. Conf. Peaceful Uses of Atomic Energy* **22**, 242 (1958).

59. H. Rudolphi, Spätentwicklung eines Unterlid Karzinoma nach Thoriumoxydinjection, *Beitr. Path. Anat. u. Allg. Path.* **111**, 158 (1958).

60. F. Ruf and K. Philipp, Zur Radioactivität des Thorotrast. Ein Beitrag zur Frage eventueller Spätschädigungen bei seiner Vervendung als Kontrastmittel, *Arch. klin. Chir.* **263**, 573 (1950).

61. J. RUNDO, The determination of the distribution of internally deposited thorium by means of studies with a realistic phantom, *Acta Radiol.* **47**, 65 (1957).

62. J. RUNDO, Measurements and dosimetry of radioactive isotopes deposited within the human body. Ph. D. Thesis, University of London, 1958.

63. J. RUNDO, A. H. Ward and P. G. JENSEN, Measurements of thoron in the breath, *Phys. Med. Biol.* **3**, 101 (1958).

64. ROSSLE and BIRKNER, Spätschaden durch Thorotrast, *Z. Allg. Path. u. Path. Anat.* **85**, 227 (1949).

65. G. SCHEIBE, Malignes intraperitoneales Thorotrastom beim Menschen, *Zblt. Chirurgie* **80**, 588 (1955).

66. W. SCHMIDT, A. A. SCULTE and C. H. LAPP, Klinischen und Pathologisch-anatomischer Beitrag zur Frage der Schädigung durch Thorotrast (Panmyelopathie nach Thorotrastinjection vor 10 Jahren), *Strahlentherapie* **81**, 93 (1950).

67. M. SCHWAIGER, Intracavitare Thorotrastschaden, *Arch. klin. Chir.* **265**, 356 (1950).

68. A. W. SCHWENZER and FEDERLIN, Salpingographie mit Thorotrast vor 23 Jahren und Entstehung eines Ovarialkarzinoms, *Geburtshilfe und Frauenheilkunde* **17**, 225 (1957).

69. J. DA SILVA HORTA, Late lesions in man caused by colloidal thorium dioxide (thorotrast), *A.M.A. Arch. Path.* **62**, 403 (1956).

70. J. DA SILVA HORTA, Lebersarcom einer Frau, 3 Jahre und 2 Monate nach Thorotrastinjection, *Chirurg.* **24**, 218 (1953).

71. J. SPIER, L. E. CLUFF and W. D. URRY, Aplastic anemia following administration of thorotrast, *J. Lab. Clin. Med.* **32**, 147 (1947).

72. A. v. SZILY, Die Pathologie des Tranensacks und des ductus naso-lacrymalis im Röntgenbild, *Klin. Monatsbl. Augenheilk.* **1**, 847 (1914).

73. A. v. SZILY, Die Pathologie der Tranenwege im Röntgenbild, *Berichte 40 Versamml. ophtal. Ges.* p. 410 (1916).

74. H. TESLUK and W. A. NORDIN, Hemangioendothelioma of liver following thorium dioxide administration, *A.M.A. Arch. Path.* **60**, 493 (1959).

75. S. F. THOMAS, G. W. HENRY and H. S. KAPLAN, Hepatolienography: Past, present, and future, *Radiology* **57**, 669 (1951).

76. J. VOGTLIN and W. MINDER, Ueber Thorotrastschaden nach Bronchographie, retrograder Pyelographie, Salpingographie und Arteriographie, *Radiol. clinica acta* **21**, 96 (1952).

77. A. WEISER, Die Verwendung von Thoriumverbindungen zur Urographie, *Wien med. Wschr.* II, 1427 (1930).

78. M. WEISER, Strahlentod durch Thorotrast, *Röntgenbl.* **10**, 270 (1957).

79. A. WERTHEMANN, Über Spatschaden verschiedener Organe durch Thorotrast und autoradiografischer Nachweiss derselben, *Schw. Z. Allg. Path.* **22**, 350 (1959).

80. F. WOHLWILL, Untersuchungen über die Gewebsreaction auf Thorotrast bei Anwendung dieser Substanz zu diagnostischen Zwecken am Menschen, *Schw. Z. Path.* **5**, 21 (1942).

81. S. WUKETICH and T. MARK, Doppelkarcinom nach Thorotrast-Arteriographie, *Z. Krebsforsch.* **62**, 95 (1957).

82. H. U. ZOLLINGER, Ein Spindelzell Sarcom der Niere. 16 Jahre nach Thorotrastpyelographie, *Schw. Med. Wschr.* **79**, 1266 (1949).

DISCUSSION

CHAIRMAN MARINELLI: Dr. Baserga has a comment.

BASERGA: The intravascular injection of thorotrast gives a preponderance of liver tumors, whereas local administration results in specific tumors at the site of injection.

HURSH: Are the tumors at neck sites malignant?

FABER: These thorotrastomas are benign. They grow to a certain size and give a lot of trouble in the way of nerve compression, but so far only one has become malignant.

MOLE: Since the range of alpha particles in tissue is in tens of microns, why does the fibrosis in the neck continue to progress and extend?

FABER: The fibrosis in the neck does not progress. It becomes stable after a time and behaves as any ordinary fibrosis does so that symptoms begin after four or five years.

MOLE: Why does thorotrast outside a vein in the neck lead to dense fibrosis whereas thorotrast in the liver does not?

FABER: I do not know for certain but the material outside the vein will have dextran in it. What the liver takes up will be different. It is certainly true that production of connective tissue is a minor problem in all other tissues.

HURSH: I have another question for Dr. Faber: If I am given 15 ml of thorotrast, what is the probability that I will get a malignant tumor in 20 years?

FABER: Your question is most impoitant. Of course what you want to know is the increased risk due to thorotrast apart from natural tumor incidence. I think that the added tumor incidence caused by thorotrast is extremely small.

Nobody really knows how many patients have been injected with thorotrast. In Denmark we have over 800 cases and we could probably find 100 to 200 more. In Sweden they think they know of some 1200 cases. We know for certain that the Wehrmacht used thorotrast as a primary contrast medium during the war. Also there are many large clinics in which thorotrast was used. Thus, my guess is that there are between 10,000 and 100,000 cases of thorotrast, probably closer to 100,000. Roughly 28 hemangioendotheliomas and local site tumors have been identified in thorotrast patients in the last 15 to 20 years.

HURSH: But these 28 cases would not have occurred in the normal course of events and thus were clearly due to thorotrast.

WARREN: Hemangioendotheliomas are seen practically only in thorotrast cases. I have studied perhaps 8000 to 10,000 vascular tumors, and there is virtually no similarity between these vascular tumors and the hemangioendotheliomas that one sees with thorotrast.

HASTERLIK: Wouldn't you say the peripheral bile duct carcinomas are especially interesting because this carcinoma is otherwise so rare?

FABER: It is very difficult to evaluate these tumors at this stage of the study. Careful histology is necessary to avoid confusion with metastatic liver tumors. This special interest is not present ordinarily and the result is that the reported incidence of these tumors in the normal population is not comparable with that in the thorotrast group.

I would like to add there is a possibility that chronic phagocytosis of the particles of thorotrast and not its radiation might cause cancer. Of course this would be extremely difficult to prove because of the lack of a non-radioactive thorotrast.

LAMERTON: Dr. Faber mentioned that it might be the other properties of the colloid which were responsible for some of these effects. We have now done an experiment, unfortunately not very conclusive, comparing thorotrast and colloidal zirconium dioxide which we have called "zirconotrast". Zirconotrast is non-radioactive and can be produced to be very similar to thorotrast chemically and in particle size. Using mice we have observed no very marked difference in the response to the I.V. injection of thorotrast or zirconotrast, but unfortunately the incidence of lung adenomas and the incidence of hepatomas was high in the control group and the experiment needs to be repeated.

DUDLEY: It seems to me that altering the radioactivity in thorotrast would be more promising than using an imitation thorotrast (such as zirconotrast). Thorotrast activity can be greatly increased by adding the thorium isotopes, Th^{230} (ionium) or Th^{228} (radiothorium). On the other hand, since $\frac{7}{8}$ of the alpha energy associated with Th^{238} at equilibrium is due to its daughters, thorotrast of significantly lower specific activity could be made of Th^{232} from which the radium daughters had been serially removed during several prior years to permit Th^{228} to decay to a low value. More animal work is needed to distinguish possible physical and chemical effects of thorotrast particles from the radiation effects.

TRANSLOCATION OF THORIUM DAUGHTERS
TO BONE*

L. D. MARINELLI and H. F. LUCAS, JR.

Radiological Physics Division, Argonne National Laboratory, Argonne, Illinois

INTRODUCTION

ALTHOUGH evidence that thorium daughters separate from thorotrast deposits in humans has been sought before, it remained for Stenstrom[1] to establish in 1941 "that some elements of the thorium series were eliminated to a considerable extent from the tissues". In the postwar period both Rotblat *et al.*[2] and Rundo[3,4,5] reported results of more precise measurements on the radioactive equilibrium status of the thorium chain in liver, spleen and a few other tissues. Hursh *et al.*[6] in 1955 published detailed analysis of Th^{232} contents in several tissues, with some indications as to Th^{228} contents, and measured the excretion rate of the radium isotopes up to several months after injection. From these studies and various types of measurements at our laboratory,[7,8] sporadically described in our semiannual reports,[9,10,11] has emerged a rough picture of the physical and metabolic problems involved. The very attempt to a description of the phenomenon is hampered by the conflict entailed by the desirability of emphasizing simultaneously both the kinetics of metabolism and the relation between the volume of thorotrast injected and the absorbed radiation dose in various sites.

THE RADIOACTIVITY OF THE SKELETON

In this paper we shall concern ourselves principally with the radioactivity in the skeleton, referring only occasionally to the radioactivity of the active bone marrow which, potentially, may lead to greater tangible damage. We have gathered in Tables 1 and 2 all the known measurements of Th^{232}, Ra^{228} and Th^{228} made on human bone. Unfortunately, values for all three elements exist on only a few specimens. Hence, reference to contents at time of autopsy (*in vivo*) is strictly lacking in those instances in which considerable time elapsed between autopsy and analysis. The values shown have been obtained by extrapolating the radioactive content

---

* Work performed under the auspices of the U.S. Atomic Energy Commission.

of a given specimen to the whole skeleton* and by dividing this value by the radioactivity of the thorotrast injected, a ml of which contains 0·2 g or 0·022 μc of Th^{232}. The latter is not excreted by the human body in significant quantities,[6] and having a long half-life, it is essentially constant during the life of an individual.

The bone data have been separated into two tables to emphasize the necessity of distinguishing bone (*per se*) from bone not cleaned of marrow. The radioactive content of raw trabecular bone, as shown in Table 1, is conspicuously high and occasionally leads to absurd values. The only tenable explanation is that the bone enclosed marrow accumulates from the very beginning considerable thorotrast, and that the daughters Ra^{228} and Th^{228}, two decades after injection, are still present therein in quantities lower than expected from undisturbed radioactive growth, but considerably higher than expected from translocation (*vide infra*). In the two samples from which the values of three long-lived elements are available, there is sharp variation in the apparent equilibrium status of the chain. Sternum bone (Table 1, item 4), 20 years post injection, shows a much greater loss of daughters ($\sim$ 80%) than rib bone ($\sim$ 20%) one week after injection.† The values of Rotblat et al.[2] for the only two ratios of Th^{228} and Th^{232} reported in human marrow (12 years post injection) show losses of the order of 50%. We cannot say whether these values indicate that a slow change in "washout" takes place in the marrow. It is obvious, however, that to evaluate accurately the marrow dose, it is necessary to establish this trend carefully in as many patients as possible.

As far as bone is concerned, this time dependent increase in translocation of daughters from marrow will lead to increase in skeletal activity; however, if one considers that the marrow contains only about 10%[5] of the total Th^{232}, this increase should be small and negligible, to a first approximation at least.

---

* By assuming a weight of 7 kg for the skeleton and 2·8 kg for its ash. For patient 04-105 (Table 1), the body weight was known and the fresh skeleton weight was assumed to be 10% of it.

† As for the rib, R. E. Rowland of our laboratory has obtained positive chemical and autoradiographic evidence that the radioactivity was limited entirely to marrow. Hence, the absolute values obtained by extending the activity via the skeletal weight are not unexpectedly absurd in magnitude. The relative values of Th^{232}, Ra^{228} and Th^{228}, however, can be taken as representative of the marrow and deemed trustworthy because their actual proportions, both as actually injected and *in vivo*, were accurately measured, and extrapolation to full equilibrium in the injection was a matter of simple proportionality, involving no questionable assumptions.

TABLE 1

The Computed Activity of Th^{232}, Ra^{228} and Th^{228} in the Entire Skeleton as Obtained from Measurements of Samples of Fresh Trabecular Bone Containing Marrow. Activity of Injected $Th^{232} = 100$

Item	Patient code	Duration of burden	Specimen and weight	Time between biopsy analysis	Total skeletal activity as % of injected Th^{232}			Thorotrast injected cc	Method of analysis	Ref.
					Th^{232}	Ra^{228}	Th^{228}			
(1)	M.H.	17 d	Cancellous bone 97 mg ashed	—	6·0	—	—	75	Radiochemical	(6)
(2)	04-105*	9 d	Ribs 46 g fresh	3–300 d	(118)	(81)	(80)	48	γ-ray spectroscopy radioautograph	(9)
(3)	No. 2 (a)	15–20 y	Body of vertebra 12 g fresh	15 d	—	7·5	8·4	20	Radiochemical	(13)
	(b)		Head of femur 2·7 g fresh	180 d	—	2·9	2·6			
(4)	No.1 (a)	20 y	Sternum bone 1·41 g fresh	200 d	34	6·7	5·9	60	Radiochemical	(13)
	(b)		1·35 g fresh	1·7 y	—	5·7	6·7			
(5)	A.D.	19 y	Cancellous bone 25 mg ash	—	26·4	—	—	75	Radiochemical	(6)

* Extrapolation to Th^{232} in equilibrium at injection (skeletal weight equals 10% body weight).

TABLE 2

The Computed Activity of Th232, Ra228 and Th228 in the Entire Skeleton as Obtained from Measurements of *Clean* Trabecular or Cortical Bone. Activity of Injected Th232 = 100

Item	Patient code (age)	Duration of burden	Specimen and weight	Time between biopsy analysis	Total skeletal activity as % of injected Th232			Thorotrast injected cc	Method of analysis	Ref.
					Th232	Ra228	Th228			
(A)	04-101 (53)	18 y	Molar tooth 0.9 g ashed	350 d	0·50	—	1·68	10	Radiochemistry α-ray spectrometry	(10)
(B)	A.D. (a) (85) (b)	19 y	Compact bone 830 mg ash	—	0·56	—	—	75	Spectrochemistry	(6)
			Trabecular bone 4·2 µg fresh	1 y	—	—	1·74		Autoradiography	(17)
(C)	M.H. (58)	17 d	Compact bone 20 mg ashed	—	0·56	—	—	75	Spectrochemistry	(6)
(D)	04-102 (a) (32) (b)	16 y	Vertebral bone 1·9 g ash	60-90 d	—	5·5	4·2	(75)*	Radiochemistry	(10) (7)
			0·2 mg fresh		—	—	3·7		Radioautography	(18)
(E)	04-104 (75)	26·5 y	Trabecular epiphysis tibia 4·9 g ash (B-3)	zero	0·7	1·15	1·11	10·	Radiochem. and α-spectrometry	(7) (8)
			Trabecular femur epiphysis 6·07 g ash (B-5)	zero	(0·7)*	0·76	1·04			(AA)
			Cortical femur 3·04 g ash (B-6)	zero	0·40	(063)*	0·80			
			Cortical femur 4·4 g ash (B-1a)	zero	(0·40)*	0·63	0·76			
(F)	04-103 (a) (37) (c)	15 y	Cortical femur 7·6 g fresh	2·3 y	—	1·5	1·8	50	γ-ray spectrometry:	(AA)
			5·4 g fresh	2·0 y	—	2·3	3·4		high energy γ's	(14)
			vertebrae**	2·0 y	—	6·7	4·3		low energy γ's	

* Assumed values.
** Contaminated in jar by very active samples of liver and spleen.

TABLE 3

Retention of Th^{232} Daughters in R.E.S. after Correction for Radioactive Growth

For significance of L'_1, L_2, L'_3 and L_3, see text

Item	Patient code	Tissue (weight)	Duration of burden	Retention factors in vivo			Method of analysis	Ref.
				Ra^{228} L_1 or L'_1	Th^{228} L_2	Ra^{224} L_3 or L'_3		
(A)	No. 1	Liver (whole)	13·5 y	0·625	0·50	0·33	Growth of γ-activity	(3)
(B)	No. 2	Liver (whole)	14·5 y	0·62	0·45	0·30		
(C)	No. —	Spleen (whole)	13 y	0·69	0·57	0·43		
(D)	No. 1	Spleen (1.1g)	20 y	0·48	0·46	—	Radiochemistry and α-analysis	(13)
(E)	No. 2	Liver (43 g)	20 y	—	0·9 L_1	—	Radiochemistry and α-analysis	(13)
(F)	04-105 (a)	Liver (472 g)	9 d	0.56	0·78	—	γ-ray crystal spectrometry and growth of γ-activity	(9)
	04-105 (b)	Rib (46·2 g)	9 d	0·73	0·67	—		
(G)	04-103 (a)	Liver (24 g)	15 y	0·41	0·36	—	α- and γ-spectrometry, activity growth	(AA) (15)(14)
	04-103 (b)	Whole body	15 y	—	—	0·83 L_1	Crystal spectrometry	(14)
(H)	04-101	Whole body	18 y	0·63	$=L_1$	0·88 L_1	Crystal spectrometry	(11)
(I)	A.T.	Whole body	70-236 d	—	$=L_1$	0·88 L_1	Injection and excretion measurements	(6)
(L)	average 9 patients	Whole body	not specified	—	$=L_1$	0·78 L_1	Liquid scintillation counting	(16)
(M)	A.D.	Ten different tissues	19 y	—	0·46-0·75	—	Radiochemistry	(6)

Th^{232} Activity = 1·0 in Tissue of Column 3

The data concerning the radioactivity of specimen of trabecular bone cleaned with ethylenediamine or examined by radioautography to avoid the activity in the marrow, and of cortical bone (devoid of marrow) appear much more consistent (Table 2), despite the variety of methods of analysis employed.

Surprising, in a way, is the relatively small variation of the fraction of the Th^{232} in the skeleton. A question raised by item E in Table 2 is whether the difference in the Th^{232} contents of trabecular and cortical bone of a single subject (2-E) is due to normal anatomical factors or whether it is really a consequence of the atherosclerosis which led to the amputation of the limb. For the same reason, it is also impossible to show what relative values of Th^{232}, Ra^{228} and Th^{228} predominate in normal trabecular and compact bone. The higher values of Ra^{228} (and Th^{228}) in the younger patients, (2-D and 2-F), are in keeping with the greater avidity of the young skeleton for radium; they cannot be considered representative, however, inasmuch as values of washout from the R.E.S.* are not available for the first patient, and the washout in the second patient is greater than normal (*vide infra* and Table 3).

Worthy of note is the fact that Th^{228} is not always higher than Ra^{228}, and then by not much more than 30% (experimental error?) suggesting that translocated Th^{228} does not migrate *en masse* to the skeleton. It is more likely instead that this element is born in bone mineral from the decay of its parent Ra^{228}.

It is unfortunate that no data are now available about the presence of Ra^{224} and its short-lived daughters in the living skeleton of the thorotrast patient, for this element should be responsible for most of the dose in bone. To be reliable, this information will require proper handling of the specimen to avoid cross-contamination, and prompt analysis immediately after biopsy to establish the status of the shorter-lived daughters.

THE RADIOACTIVITY IN SOFT TISSUE

Although the contents of Th^{232} in a variety of tissues have been reported by Hursh,[6] and its retention in large fractions in the liver (70%) and spleen (7–20%) is well established,[5] the levels of its daughter products throughout the body is not clear.[12] Rundo [5] has measured the radioactivity of the blood (Pb^{212}, Ra^{224}) and the exhalation of thoron from the breath and has come to the conclusion that some thoron from the liver and spleen must reach the lung directly.

* R.E.S. = reticulo-endothelial system.

Fortunately, the data on the equilibrium of the main repositories of $Th^{232} O_2$ are more complete, though not abundant. In Table 3 we have gathered the pertinent results of Rundo,[3] Hursh[6,13] and those of our laboratory. In the table the letters L_1, L_2 and L_3 denote the fractions obtained by dividing the activities $\lambda_1 Ra^{228}$, $\lambda_2 Th^{228}$ and $\lambda_3 Ra^{224}$ in a given tissue (*in vivo*) by the corresponding activities that would obtain in a solution of Th^{232} (equal to that present in the tissue and initially devoid of all daughters) if it were sealed *in vitro* for an interval of time equal to the duration of the patient's burden. (See Eq. 3 below.) In what follows the factors pertaining to the body as a whole will be primed, i.e., L_1', L_3', etc.

The *in vitro* relative activities, t years after separation are computed as follows:

$$Th^{232} = 1 \cdot 0$$
$$Ra^{228} = (1 - e^{-\lambda_1 t}) = X \qquad (1)$$
$$Th^{228} = (1 - 1 \cdot 48\, e^{-\lambda_1 t} + 0 \cdot 48\, e^{-\lambda_2 t}) = Y$$

Ra^{224} may be considered in equilibrium with Th^{228} throughout the interval for which the patient is at risk.

In our calculations we have assumed:

$$\lambda_1(Ra^{228}) = 3 \cdot 25 \times 10^{-4}\, day^{-1}{}^{(19)}$$
$$\lambda_2(Th^{228}) = 1 \cdot 0 \times 10^{-3}\, day^{-1} \qquad (2)$$
$$\lambda_3(Ra^{224}) = 0 \cdot 190\, day^{-1}.$$

In Table 3 are included some miscellaneous values obtained from analysis of tissue specimens which may not be wholly representative of the entire organs from which they originated. Data obtained soon after injection (3-F), extrapolated to an injection in full radioactive equilibrium, confirms the absence of a true ionic fraction of Ra^{228} both in liver and in rib marrow, in agreement with the findings of Hursh *et al.*[6]

The value of L_1' in item 3-H is perhaps the only value available from whole-body measurements. It was obtained by measuring the Ra^{228} (actually Ac^{228}) by means of the intensity of the 900 keV γ-ray and by dividing it by the *known* Th^{232} injected.* The ratio L_1 should be essentially the same as L_1' because the skeleton contains only a few per cent of the Ra^{228} in the body (*vide infra*).

---

* Whole body measurements of patient 3-G did not yield L_1 because the amount of Th^{232} injected was not known. In fact the latter was estimated by the intensity of the 2·62 MeV γ-ray of Tl^{208} and the $Tl^{208}/Th^{232} = 0 \cdot 24$ in liver specimens.

The factor L'_3 represents the ratio of activity of Ra^{224} (no growth correction necessary because of its short life) to that of Th^{232} for the body as a whole. Since whole-body measurements give essentially the $\lambda_3 Ra^{224}/\lambda_1 Ra^{228}$ (and Th^{228} is not excreted) it is evident that the latter ratio represents the ratio L'_3/L_1, when duly corrected for radioactive growth (see below). The assumption herein involved is that no daughters of Ra^{224} are lost from the body; experiments in humans[5] and animals[20] have shown that this can be considered true to a first approximation ($\sim 10\%$).

THEORETICAL CONSIDERATIONS ON TRANSLOCATIONS

A. The Growth of Activity in Thorium-bearing Tissues

Before entering into a comparison between the radioactivity of the various elements of the chain in liver and spleen (as repository of most of the thorium parent) and the activity found in bone samples and of the body as a whole on the basis of what is known about retention of soluble Ra^{226}, it is well to look into the "metabolic" meaning of the factors L as previously defined.

It is apparent that if we assume L_1, L_2 as constants and equal to:

$$L_1 = \frac{\lambda_1 Ra^{228} \; (in \; vivo)}{X \times \lambda_0 Th^{232} \; (injected)}$$

$$L_2 = \frac{\lambda_2 Th^{228} \; (in \; vivo)}{Y \times \lambda_0 Th^{232} \; (injected)}$$

$$(3)$$

we are really assuming that in the R.E.S. the following differential equations hold:

$$\frac{d \, (Ra^{228})}{dt} = L_1 \lambda_0 Th^{232} - \lambda_1 Ra^{228}$$

$$\frac{d \, (Th^{228})}{dt} = \frac{L_2}{L_1} \lambda_1 Ra^{228} - \lambda_2 Th^{228}.$$

$$(4)$$

These expressions can be interpreted to indicate that a fraction L_1 of the Th^{232} atoms and a fraction $\dfrac{L_2}{L_1}$ of the Ra^{228} atoms disintegrating in the R.E.S. are retained therein, and that the rest are released to the circulation in time short compared to the half lives of the element in question.

The time-dependent behavior of the retentions $R \; (Ra^{228})$ and $R \; (Th^{228})$ in the R.E.S. system is easily evaluated by solving Eq. 4. If one assumes that only Th^{232} was injected, one obtains the following activities in the R.E.S.:

$$R(Ra^{228}) = L_1(1 - e^{-\lambda_1 t}) = L_1 X$$

and

$$R (Th^{228}) = L_2(1 - 1 \cdot 48\, e^{-\lambda_1 t} + 0 \cdot 48\, e^{-\lambda_2 t}) = L_2 Y \tag{5}$$

when the Th^{232} activity—namely $\lambda_0\, Th^{232}$—is taken as unity and X and Y are as stated in Eq. 1.

The case of Ra^{224} needs special attention because its parent, Th^{228}, is translocated from the R.E.S. but it is not excreted from the body. This means that for the body as a whole the retention R' (Th^{228}) is given by:

$$R' (Th^{228}) = L_1 Y. \tag{6}$$

The question arises as to whether the retained fraction of the Th^{228} atoms disintegrating in the body is the same everywhere, irrespective of the site of disintegration. If this is the case, the differential equation for Ra^{224} retained by the whole body can be written as:

$$\frac{d\,(Ra^{224})}{dt} = \frac{L'_3}{L'_1} \lambda_2 Th^{228} - \lambda_3\, Ra^{224} \tag{7}$$

which means that a fraction L'_3/L'_1 of the atoms of Ra^{224} born is retained *in situ*. This leads to the following value for the Ra^{224} retained by the body:

$$R' (Ra^{224}) \simeq L'_3 Y. \tag{8}$$

The value of L'_3 can be calculated from the value of $L' = Ra^{224}/Ra^{228}$, observable by whole body counting. Obviously from Eq. (5) and (8)

$$L' = \frac{L'_3 Y}{L_1 X},$$

and therefore:

$$L'_3 = \frac{L' X}{Y} \cdot L_1. \tag{9}$$

The values of L'_3 entered in Table 3 have been calculated as per Eq. (9) whenever the burden time was known; otherwise X/Y was taken as unity.

B. *The Growth of Activity in the Skeleton*

The elimination and skeletal retention of a radium daughter released into the general circulation by an internally deposited thorium isotope has been the object of several studies which have led to the calculation of the skeletal retention function $A_n(t)$ and the elimination function $E_n(t)$

($n = 1$ for Ra²²⁸, $n = 2$ for Th²²⁸ and $n = 3$ for Ra²²⁴) for a number of radium daughters.[21,22]

For our purposes the retained fraction $R_c(t)$ of radium released is assumed to be:

$$R_c(0) = 1 \qquad (10)$$
$$R_c(t) = (1-b)\,t^{-b} \text{ for } t > 1.$$

Under these conditions the activity ratio $A(t)$ of the radium retained by the skeleton to the *effective* thorium releasing the daughter is given by:

$$A(t) = \frac{\lambda_R R(t)}{\lambda_T e^{-\lambda_T t}} = \lambda_r \int_o^t R_c(u) \cdot e^{-(\lambda_R - \lambda_T)}\mu du$$

and the elimination function, $E(t)$, namely, the daily rate of radium elimination divided by the effective thorium deposit, is given by:

$$E(t) = \lambda_r \left[e^{-(\lambda_R - \lambda_T)} + R_c(t) - 1 + \frac{\lambda_R - \lambda_T}{\lambda_R} A(t) \right].$$

Values of $A_1(t)$ for the Ra²²⁸–Th²³² combination have been plotted in Fig. 1 as a function of time for various values of b,* values $A_3(t = \infty)$ and $E_3(\infty)$ for the Ra²²⁴ and $E_1(\infty)$ for Ra²²⁸ are tabulated in Table 4.

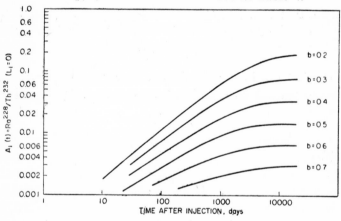

FIG. 1.

Activity ratio $A_1(t)$ describing the accumulation of Ra²²⁸ in the skeleton per unit activity of Th²³² in the R.E.S. It is assumed that no Ra²²⁸ is retained in the R.E.S., that is $L_1 = 0$. Coefficient b refers to skeletal retention function $R_c(t) = (1-b)t^{-b}$. From Reynolds et al.[21]

* The reader should be reminded that in Reynolds et al. tables, the half-life of Ra²²⁸ was assumed to be 6·7 y instead of 5·8 y.[19] The values $A_1(t)$ for this isotope are, therefore, up to about 15% too low. This error is negligible for our purposes.

With these premises it is possible to proceed to some sort of comparison by summarizing in Table 5 some of the potentially observable quantities, such as skeletal retention and elimination rate, as functions of the "metabolic parameters" L and $A(t)$ of colloidal thorium and radium respectively. Before proceeding further it is necessary to consider the fate of Ra^{228} and Th^{228} injected with Th^{232}. The experimental evidence[6, 2, 9, 5] indicates that the Ra^{228} injected with a thorotrast solution does not behave like "ionic" radium, since it is not excreted rapidly (only 20% of amount injected in about 8 days)[6] and it is found in the R.E.S. at 56% of the proportion

TABLE 4*

Activity Ratio $A_3(\infty)$ and Elimination Rates $E_3(\infty)$ and $E_1(\infty)$ for Various Values of the Exponent b

b	Ra^{224} $A_3(\infty)$	Ra^{224} $E_3(\infty)$	Ra^{228} $E_1(\infty)$
0·1	0·809	0·037	$1·63 \times 10^{-4}$
0·2	0·651	0·067	2·32
0·3	0·524	0·091	2·61
0·4	0·419	0·111	2·74
0·5	0·333	0·127	2·80
0·6	0·261	0·141	2·82
0·7	0·200	0·153	2·82
0·8	0·147	0·163	2·82
0·9	0·101	0·171	2·84

* From Reynolds, *et al.*[21] The subscripts (1) and (3) refer to Ra^{228} and Ra^{224}, respectively. Times sufficiently long for equilibrium.

present in the injected material nine days after injection (item 3-F). The latter findings points to an elimination of 37% of the injected value in 9 days if the exponent in the skeletal $b = 0·5$ (Eq. 10). In anticipation of a value of b less than 0·5, we may assume that Hursh's[6] and our findings are not incompatible in demonstrating that there exists a limited, but definite, amount of early washout of Ra^{228}. We shall assume as a maximum: (a), that the activity B of Ra^{228} in clinically injected thorotrast cannot possibly be greater than 44% of the activity of Th^{232} (thorotrast at most 5 years old), and (b), that 50% is retained in the bottle.[6, 9] Hence, even if Ra^{228} were all ionic, it cannot possibly reach the skeleton in proportion greater than 22%.

If we assume $(1-L_1) = 0·35$ as an average (Table 3), and assume $b = 0·2$ (the lowest value found by Norris *et al.*[23] (for late Ra^{226} retention) we

TABLE 5

Summary of Retention and Kinetics of Th^{232} Daughters in the Body. Activity of Injected Th^{232} = 1·0

Element	R.E.S. retention (R)	Skeletal retention (R)	Total body retention (R')	Daily rate "injected" in the circulation	Rate of formation	Daily elimination rate
Ra^{228}	$L_1 \cdot X$	$(1-L_1)A_1(t)$	$L_1 \cdot X + (1-L_1)A_1(t)$	$\lambda_1 \cdot (1-L_1)$	λ_1	$(1-L_1) \cdot E_1(t)$
Th^{228}	$L_2 \cdot Y$	None	$L_1 \cdot Y + (1-L_1) \cdot A_2(t)$	$\lambda_2(L_1-L_2) \cdot X$	$\lambda_2 \cdot L_1 \cdot X$	0
Ra^{224}	$L_3 \cdot Y$	$[L_1-L_3] \cdot Y \cdot A_3(t)$	$L_3 Y + (L_1-L_3) \cdot Y \cdot A_3(t) + (1-L_1)A_2(t)$	$\lambda_3(L_1-L_3) \cdot Y$	$\lambda_3 \cdot L_1 \cdot Y$	$[L_1-L_3] \cdot Y \cdot E_3(t)$

may calculate with the aid of Fig. 1 and Fig. 2 the maximum value of the Ra^{228} activity in the skeleton as:

Maximum skeletal $Ra^{228} = (1-L_1)A_1(t)+0.22\times(1-0.2)t^{-0.2}e^{-\lambda_1 t}$

if the activity of Th^{232} injected is equal to unity.

This function, shown in Fig. 3, indicates that the value of Ra^{228} in the skeleton could be as high as 6 to 10% of that of the Th^{232} injected as early as 0.1 years and could be fairly constant from there on if $b = 0.2$. However,

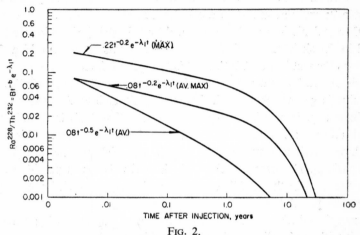

FIG. 2.

The retention of injected Ra^{228} (in units of Th^{232} activity) calculated for initial fractions B equal to 0.22 and 0.08 and for skeletal exponents $b = 0.2$ and $b = 0.5$.

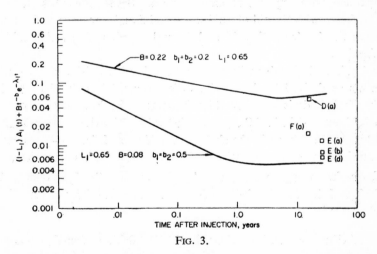

FIG. 3.

Calculated limits of skeletal Ra^{228} activity for average R.E.S. retention fraction $L_1 = 0.65$ and parameters values: $0.2 < b < 0.5$ and $0.08 < B < 0.22$. Experimental points refer to items in Table 2.

a more realistic value from actual experience is $B = 0{\cdot}08$ and, for *externally* injected Ra^{226}, $b = 0{\cdot}5$. Assumption of these values leads to:

$$\text{Average } Ra^{228} \text{ skeletal value} = (1-L_1)\,A_1(t)+0{\cdot}08\times(1-0{\cdot}5)t^{-0{\cdot}5} \quad (11)$$

represented by the lower curve in Fig. 3. The range delineated by these assumptions straddles the values found experimentally at $t > 15$ years, some of which are represented in the figure by the corresponding letters used in Table 2; experimental data are lacking at shorter times.

In these calculations we have assumed that the $0{\cdot}5\%$ of the injected Th^{232} found in the skeleton (Table 2) behaves—as far as retention of Ra^{228} and Th^{228}—as the rest in the R.E.S. That is to say, that its average contribution to skeletal Ra^{228} could not be much more than $0{\cdot}005\times L_1 = 0{\cdot}003$. This is a value large enough to push the lower limit slightly above some of the experimental points (atherosclerotic limb of patient 2-E) but still compatible with a reasonable value of b somewhat different from $0{\cdot}5$. This correction, however, is not sufficient to explain the higher bone values in the other patients. For case 2-F the high skeletal value is in part due to the lower retention in the R.E.S. (see 3-G) and hence a much lower value of b is not required.

As mentioned above, Th^{228} does not seem to migrate to bone mineral, hence it will not be discussed further in this paper.

Since no Ra^{224} measurements are available on bone itself, no direct comparison with experiment can be made. Some inferences, however, can be drawn with the aid of Tables 3, 4 and 5 and some comparison made between the *in vivo* ratios L_3' and L_3 and Hursh's observation of Ra^{224} elimination.

In Table 5 the reader will recognize the local activities of the various elements as derived in the previous discussions. Thus the Ra^{224} activity of the whole body is represented by the sum: (a) of the activity of the fraction L_3Y retained in R.E.S., (b) the skeletal activity due to translocation, and (c) the Ra^{224} born in the skeleton via Th^{232} and $Ra^{228} - Th^{228}$ on the assumption that no translocation of Th^{228} and Ra^{224} takes place therefrom.

If, on the average, we assume that for the R.E.S., $L_1 = 0{\cdot}65$ and $L_3 = 0{\cdot}35$, and that for the skeleton $b = 0{\cdot}5$, then the activity of Ra^{224} in the whole body is:

$$R'\,(Ra^{224}) = (0{\cdot}35)Y+(0{\cdot}3\times Y\times0{\cdot}333)+0{\cdot}008 = 0{\cdot}45Y+0{\cdot}008$$

and the activity of Ra^{228}

$$R'(Ra^{228}) = L_1X = 0{\cdot}65\,X.$$

Hence we calculate for $t \simeq 15$ years (Eq. 9):

$$L_3' = L' \frac{X}{Y} L_1 = \frac{0\cdot45\, Y \times 0\cdot008}{0\cdot65\, X} \cdot \frac{X}{Y} \cdot L_1 \simeq 0\cdot7.$$

This value is somewhat smaller than $L_3' \simeq 0\cdot83\, L_1$ observed experimentally (Table 3). Values of $b < 0\cdot5$ would increase these values of $A_3(t)$ in accord with the results of whole-body measurements, just as it would help explain higher Ra^{228} bone values discussed above.*

We may conclude, therefore, that in view of our scant knowledge concerning Ra retention at early times after injection, the predictions of the power law are satisfactory as a first approximation; these findings sustain the hope that the metabolic pattern in these patients may be found constant enough to justify the undertaking of a large international census[24,25,26] without incurring into too numerous whole-body γ-ray measurements nor into extensive (and expensive) analysis of body tissues and excreta.

SUMMARY

An attempt has been made to correlate the Th^{232}-Ra^{228} and Th^{228} values found in skeletal specimens of patients injected with known amounts of thorotrast with the radioactive equilibrium of the chain in the reticulo-endothelial system (R.E.S.).

The data for Ra^{228} are in accord with the predictions of Reynolds et al.[21] for values of the retention parameter $0\cdot2 < b < 0\cdot5$. No excess of skeletal Th^{228} is found to justify the assumption that "washout" Th^{228} translocates from the R.E.S. to bone mineral.

No data for actual Ra^{224} in bone are available, but whole-body and excreta activity measurements are consistent with the assumption that Ra^{224} is retained in the skeleton to a greater extent than Ra^{228}. Reliable direct measurements of this isotope are needed to establish with greater precision the chronic absorbed dose to the skeleton.

ACKNOWLEDGEMENTS

The authors wish to thank Miss D. E. Wallace and Mr. D. P. Krause for the measurements of many skeletal samples and Mr. R. E. Rowland for communicating to us the results of his autoradiographs. Special thanks are due to Dr. C. E. Miller for whole-body measurements and to Drs.

---

* The activity of Ra^{224} in the skeleton $\simeq 0\cdot1\, Y$ supplies the bulk of the dose in the skeleton, hence it merits direct measurement. Further dosimetric consideration are to be found in ref. (21).

R. J. Hasterlik, R. Baserga, S. F. Thomas, L. W. Brady, D. C. Dahlin and A. J. Finkel for their help and cooperation in obtaining tissues suitable for analysis.

REFERENCES

1. W. STENSTROM, Elimination of radioactive elements by patients and rabbits after injection of thorotrast *Radiology* 37, 6, 698–704 (1941).
2. J. ROTBLAT and G. WARD, The radioactivity from thorotrast and its retention in tissues *Phys. Med. Biol.* 1, 125–137 (1956).
3. J. RUNDO, The radioactivity of thorotrast *Phys. Med. Biol.* 1, 138–146 (1956).
4. J. RUNDO, Radiation dosage from thorotrast *Transactions of IX Internat. Congress of Radiology*, Munich, Germany, July 23–30, 1959, 2, 1258–1265, Georg Thiem. Verlag, Stuttgart (1961).
5. J. RUNDO, Measurements and dosimetry of radioactive isotopes deposited within the human body, with special reference to colloidal thorium dioxide, following intravenous injection, Ph. D. Thesis, Univ., London (1958).
6. J. B. HURSH, L. T. STEADMAN, W. B. LOONEY and M. COLODZIN, The excretion of thorium and thorium daughters after thorotrast administration *Acta Radiol.* 47, 481–498 (1957).
7. D. E. WALLACE, Argonne National Laboratory, Private Communication (1961); ANL-6398 (in press).
8. D. P. KRAUSE, Argonne National Laboratory, Private Communication (1961).
9. C. E. MILLER and L. D. MARINELLI, Preliminary study on the retention of Th^{232} daughters following thorotrast injections, Radiological Physics Division Semiannual Report, Argonne National Laboratory, ANL-5967, pp. 103–104 (July–Dec. 1958).
10. L. D. MARINELLI and A. F. STEHNEY, Radioactivity in bones of patients injected with thorotrast, Radiological Physics Division Semiannual Report, Argonne National Laboratory, ANL-5967, pp. 105–106 (July–Dec. 1958).
11. C. E. MILLER, Study of thorotrast in humans, Radiological Physics Division Semiannual Report, Argonne National Laboratory, ANL-5829, pp. 154–155 (July–Dec. 1957).
12. W. B. LOONEY, An investigation of the late clinical findings following thorotrast (thorium dioxide) administration *Am. J. Roentgenol. & Rad. Therapy* 83, 1, 163–185 (1960).
13. J. B. HURSH, Univ. Rochester, Personal communication (November 1957).
14. C. E. MILLER, Argonne National Laboratory, Personal communication (1961).
15. R. BASERGA, H. YOKOO and G. C. HENEGAR, Thorotrast-induced cancer in man *Cancer* 13: 5, 1021–1031 (1960).
16. H. MUTH and E. OBERHAUSEN, Measurement of radium and thorium burdens, I.A.E.A. Symposium on Whole Body Counting, Vienna, June 12–16 (1961).
17. Private communication; track counting by C. Mays on radioautograph of W.S.S. Jee, Univ. Utah. (1961).
18. R. E. ROWLAND, Argonne National Laboratory, Personal communication (1961).
19. C. W. MAYS, D. R. ATHERTON, F. W. BRUENGER, B. J. STOVER, W. M. HAMMER and W. W. PARMLEY, Redetermination of the half-period of Ra^{228} (Mesothorium), Radiobiology Division Univ. Utah Report COO-222, pp. 27–48 (Sept. 1960).

20. B. J. Stover, On the metabolism of Th[228] (RdTh) and its daughters: Blood studies *Radiation Research* **3**, 3, 352 (1955).
21. J. C. Reynolds, P. F. Gustafson and L. D. Marinelli, Retention and elimination of radium isotopes produced by the decay of thorium parents within the body-calculations and comparison with experimental findings, Argonne National Laboratory Report, ANL-5689, pp. 1–43 (1957).
22. J. C. Reynolds, Calculation of retention and elimination of Ra[228] and Ra[224] from a single injection of Th[232], Radiological Physics Division Semiannual Report, Argonne National Laboratory, ANL-5829, pp. 51–60 (July–Dec. 1957).
23. W. P. Norris, T. W. Speckman and P. F. Gustafson, Studies of the metabolism of radium in man, *Am. J. Roentgenol., Rad. Therapy. & Nuclear Med.* **73**, 785–802 (1955).
24. L. D. Marinelli, The effect of chronic low levels of radiation in man: the contribution of epidemiological studies *Transactions of IX Internat. Congress of Radiology* Munich, Germany, July 23–30, 1959, **2**, 1234–1238, Georg Thieme Verlag, Stuttgart (1961).
25. L. D. Marinelli, Radioactivity and the human skeleton. The Janeway lecture *Am. J. Roentgenol., Rad. Therapy & Nuclear Med.* **80**, 729–739 (1958).
26. L. D. Marinelli, Epidemiological studies on radiation cancerogenesis in the human skeleton, Radiological Physics Division Semiannual Report, Argonne National Laboratory, ANL-6049, pp. 30–42 (Jan.–June 1959).

DISCUSSION

WARREN: Using Dr. Faber's estimate of about 100,000 thorotrast-treated cases, there ought to be at least 1 case of osteogenic sarcoma in this large a population.

CHAIRMAN MARINELLI: We expect to see a few osteogenic sarcomas, in 2 or 3 years anyway.

DUDLEY: Perhaps the most useful practical data that can come out of the thorotrast work concern lung radiation dose rates because these dose rates are quite high. Observations of thorotrast patients may be helpful in evaluating the hazard to uranium miners, who are in fact breathing alpha emitters.

Rundo (*Phys. in Biol. & Med.* 3, 101, 1958) found about 8% Tn^{220} (thoron) exhalation in thorotrast patients and we found the same in several patients measured at the Massachusetts Institute of Technology. Probably at least as much and quite likely more, Tn^{220} decays in the blood thereby giving rise to considerable Pb^{212} (thorium-B) and its subsequent daughters which will distribute in some pattern throughout the body. Who knows where they go? Is there any information as to whether these might localize in the skeleton?

FABER: Pb^{212} (thorium-B) tends to stick to red blood cells in animals breathing thoron. A member in our laboratory is working on this.

HURSH: We have recently injected four patients, each with 20 ml of thorotrast. So far the experiment is only half complete because we have only been able to make *in vivo* and excreta measurements (using a sodium iodide crystal γ-ray spectrometer). We have used Ac^{228} as an indicator for Ra^{228}, and Tl^{208} as an indicator for Ra^{224}. Measurements presently extend out to a year, and at least in some of our patients we will be able to follow them longer. For this early period our whole-body gamma measurements indicate that each day the patients excrete an amount of Ra^{228} equal to 90% of the daily Ra^{228} production and an amount of Ra^{224} equal to 40% of daily Ra^{224} production. In order to calculate these values, measurements of the "steady state" level of Ra^{228} and of Ra^{224} in the body were made. Since the amount injected is known (in one case, $0.614\,\mu c\ Th^{232}$, $0.16\,\mu c\ Ra^{228}$, $0.17\,\mu c\ Th^{228}$ and $0.135\,pc\ Ra^{224}$) and since the measurements on man have shown that thorium is excreted to a negligible extent the rate of production and rate of decay of the nuclides are easily calculated and the rate of excretion arrived at. We will be interested in whether longer residence time in the body alters these excretion rates.

SUBJECT INDEX

Strontium-90, 117, 212, 213, 216, 218, 222, 229
  autoradiograms, 345, 346
  continuous feeding of, 319
  dental changes, 349
  dietary intake, 341
  dog femur, 459
  dose in adult rabbits, 415
  dose in young rabbits, 412
  dosimetric studies, 349, 351, 409
  effect of dose on rate of removal, 410
  effect of high dose on retention, 421
  energy absorbed in mouse bones, 444
  energy absorbed in rabbit bones, 446
  energy absorbed in rat bones, 445
  energy absorbed by skeletons of various sizes, 447
  feeding level, 342
  fractional injections, 230
  gavage, 329
  imbibed, 329, 330
  in utero, 319
  Long-Evans rats, 329
  osteosarcomas, 338
  peripheral blood examinations, 321
  Rhesus monkeys, 329
  skeletal dosage, 320
  spectra of energy escaping a bone, 443
  theoretical and experimental dosimetry, 423

T

Tapetum lucidum, 167
  cataracts, 176
  color changes, 175
  cytological changes, 173
  densely packed osmophilic rods, 173
  microscopic changes in, 173
  site of earliest symptoms in beagle, 168
  visual impairment, 176
Tate Emery load cell, 146
Teeth, 40
  arrested growth, 349
  changes, 74
  dentin, 357
  destructive changes, 65, 68
  growth and eruption, 351, 357
  indicator of bone burden, 359
  irregular resorption, 68
  resorption of, 63, 75
  mesothorium, 39, 63–65, 74–76, 95–97, 109, 111, 114, 158
Tensile,
  forces, 146
  stresses, 145
Testes, 207
Testosterone, 337
Thorium-228, 111, 121–126, 128
  bone, 28
  bone cancer, 50
  blood vessels, 28
  kidney, 28
  translocation of daughters, 499
Thorotrast,
  in man, 473
  specific activity, 498
  thoron exhalation, 516
  thorotrastomas, 476
  translocation of daughters, 499
Thorotrast studies,
  Finsen laboratory, 473
Thrombosis, 114
Thyroid hormone, 337
Tibial compacta, 34, 95
Tissue,
  gross damage, 111
  loose connective, 104
Torsion, 161
Toxicity,
  alpha, 406
  beta, 406
  of bone-seeking isotopes (comparative), 347
  radium, 338
  relative, 27, 266
  quantitative expression, 266
TPNH, 180
Trabeculae, 66
  coarsening of, 63
  sclerotic, 67